PREPARING TO USE ALGEBRA

Fourth Edition

Albert P. Shulte
Director, Mathematics Education
Oakland Schools
Pontiac, Michigan

Robert E. Peterson
Chairman, Mathematics Department
Fraser High School
Fraser, Michigan

Glencoe
Mission Hills, California

Cover Photographer Don Renner / Photo Trends

ISBN 0-8445-1850-6

Send all inquiries to:
Glencoe
15319 Chatsworth Street
Mission Hills, California 91345-9509

Printed in the United States of America

8 9 10 11 12 98 97 96 95 94

CONTENTS

Chapter 1 Symbols and Sentences

Chapter 2 Solving Open Sentences

Chapter 3 Important Properties

Chapter 4 Fractions and Mixed Numbers

Chapter 5 Decimals and Estimating

Chapter 6 Adding and Subtracting Integers

Chapter 7 Multiplying and Dividing Integers

Chapter 8 Graphing

Chapter 9 Ratios, Proportions, and Per Cents

Chapter 10 Indirect Measurement

Chapter 11 Adding and Subtracting Rational Numbers

Chapter 12 Multiplying and Dividing Rational Numbers

Chapter 13 Square Roots

Chapter 14 Using Algebra

Chapter 15 Statistics and Probability

Chapter 16 Geometry

Chapter 17 More Algebra

SPECIAL TOPICS

Career Corner:

Consumer Corner:

Activities:

Other Topics:

Getting Ready for Chapter 1

Compute.

1. $\begin{array}{r} 12 \\ +73 \\ \hline \end{array}$ **2.** $\begin{array}{r} 83 \\ +19 \\ \hline \end{array}$ **3.** $\begin{array}{r} 95 \\ +8 \\ \hline \end{array}$ **4.** $\begin{array}{r} 45 \\ +68 \\ \hline \end{array}$

5. $63 + 9$ **6.** $21 + 46$ **7.** $7 + 27 + 13$ **8.** $700 + 6 + 40$

9. $\begin{array}{r} 87 \\ -35 \\ \hline \end{array}$ **10.** $\begin{array}{r} 24 \\ -3 \\ \hline \end{array}$ **11.** $\begin{array}{r} 56 \\ -37 \\ \hline \end{array}$ **12.** $\begin{array}{r} 846 \\ -578 \\ \hline \end{array}$

13. $40 - 27$ **14.** $20 - 13$ **15.** $100 - 43$ **16.** $60 - 19$

17. $\begin{array}{r} 32 \\ \times 3 \\ \hline \end{array}$ **18.** $\begin{array}{r} 71 \\ \times 4 \\ \hline \end{array}$ **19.** $\begin{array}{r} 52 \\ \times 21 \\ \hline \end{array}$ **20.** $\begin{array}{r} 38 \\ \times 65 \\ \hline \end{array}$

21. 90×3 **22.** 57×10 **23.** 30×100 **24.** $3 \times 15 \times 7$

25. $128 \div 4$ **26.** $96 \div 3$ **27.** $408 \div 24$ **28.** $2500 \div 100$

List the numbers in order from smallest to largest.

29. 19, 7, 9 **30.** $5 + 12$, 9×3, $18 - 4$

Note: The "Getting Ready" page in each chapter reviews material that will be used or extended in the chapter.

Brent Jones

1 SYMBOLS AND SENTENCES

A good worker learns what each tool is used for, when to use it, and how to use it.

A good problem-solver also needs a set of tools. In this chapter you will learn about such mathematical tools as units of measure, operations, variables, and equations. You will see some things these tools are used for. You will also begin to learn when and how to use them.

Metric Units of Measure

1.1

One way to describe something is by stating some of its measurements, such as its height, weight, or temperature. There are several systems of measurement. The one used in most of the world today is the **metric system.** We will use this system often in this book.

The person in the picture at the left is using a *meterstick* (a stick one meter long) to make a measurement. A doorway is usually about two meters high. An outside doorway is a little less than one meter wide.

The **meter** (m) is the basic unit of length in the metric system.

Other metric units of length are named by using a prefix with the word *meter*. The meanings of some metric prefixes are shown in the chart. The prefixes used most often are in color.

prefix	symbol	meaning
kilo-	k	thousand
hecto-	h	hundred
deka-	da	ten
deci-	d	tenth
centi-	c	hundredth
milli-	m	thousandth

In this unit there are this many smaller units.	
1 kilometer (km)	1000 meters
1 hectometer (hm)	100 meters
1 dekameter (dam)	10 meters
1 meter	10 decimeters (dm)
1 meter	100 centimeters (cm)
1 meter	1000 millimeters (mm)

The **gram** (g) is a unit of mass (often called *weight*) in the metric system.

In 1 gram there are 1000 milligrams (mg).

In 1 kilogram (kg) there are 1000 grams.

Ed Hoppe Photography

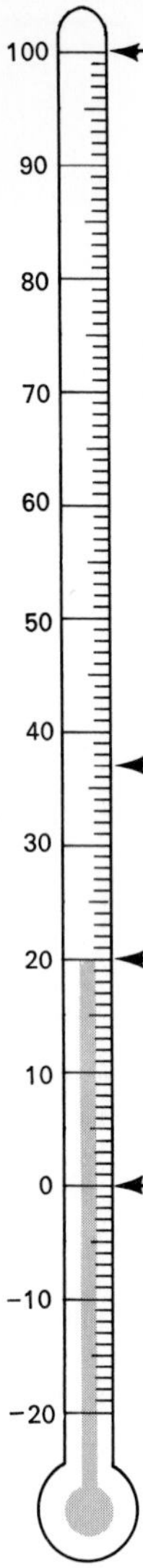

The degree Celsius (°C) is a unit of temperature in the metric system.

The amount a container will hold is its *capacity*.

The **liter** (L) is a unit of capacity in the metric system.

In 1 liter there are 1000 milliliters (mL).
In 1 kiloliter (kL) there are 1000 liters.

Ed Hoppe Photography

Exercises

A

1. *Kilo-* means (*ten, hundred, thousand*).
2. *Centi-* means (*hundred, hundredth, tenth*).
3. Which is shorter, a centimeter or a millimeter?
4. Which is longer, a kilometer or a meter?
5. Which is heavier, a kilogram or a milligram?
6. Which is more, a liter or a milliliter?
7. What is normal body temperature in degrees Celsius?
8. What does each symbol stand for? **a.** m **b.** km **c.** mm **d.** cm
9. What does each symbol stand for? **a.** g **b.** mg **c.** kg **d.** L
10. On the Celsius scale, 0° and 100° are the freezing and boiling points of ____.

B 11. Which are more than 1 meter?

a. a car length **b.** the length of your foot

c. the length of this book **d.** your height

12. Which weigh less than 1 gram?

a. a feather **b.** a car

c. a lettuce seed **d.** you

13. Which hold more than 1 liter?

a. an eye dropper **b.** a cup

c. a car's gas tank **d.** a swimming pool

14. Which hold more than 1 kiloliter?

a. a milk pitcher **b.** an oil tanker

c. a car's gas tank **d.** Lake Erie

15. Which would weigh about 1 gram?

a. a dog **b.** a paper clip **c.** a nickel

16. The temperature of ice is about (*0 °C, 32 °C, 20 °C*).

17. The temperature of a person with a fever might be (*37 °C, 98 °C, 41 °C*).

18. Most people would wear a sweater or a coat if the air temperature was (*50 °C, 30 °C, 10 °C*).

19. How many meters to the next exit?

C 20. There are 1 000 000 grams in a metric ton. How many kilograms are there in a metric ton?

21. One centimeter contains how many millimeters?

1.2 Order of Operations

In mathematics, we write a *phrase* (also called an *expression*) by using numbers and operation symbols like $+$, $-$, $\times$, and $\div$. For example, here are some phrases:

$$3 + 1 \qquad 2 \times 5 \qquad 8 - 4 + 1 \qquad 4 + 5 \times 3$$

For a phrase indicating more than one operation, like $4 + 5 \times 3$, you must decide which operation to do first.

If you add first,

$$4 + 5 \times 3$$
$$9 \times 3$$
$$27$$

If you multiply first,

$$4 + 5 \times 3$$
$$4 + 15$$
$$19$$

To make sure that a phrase has only one value, we use the following rule for the order of operations:

> As indicated from left to right,
> 1. First multiply and divide.
> 2. Then add and subtract.

Example 1: What is the value of each phrase?

a. $4 + 5 \times 3$

$4 + 15$ Multiply first.

19 Then add.

b. $18 \div 3 - 2$

$6 - 2$ Divide first.

4 Then subtract.

c. $8 - 4 + 1$

$4 + 1$ Add and subtract from left to right.

5

d. $5 \times 4 \div 2$

$20 \div 2$ Multiply and divide from left to right.

10

"GOSH! I HOPE THOSE SLIDES WEREN'T IN ANY PARTICULAR ORDER"

If you want to write a phrase that does not follow the rule for order of operations, you can use parentheses. For example,

$4 + 5 \times 3$		$(4 + 5) \times 3$
means to multiply first	BUT	means to add first

> Do the operations within the ( ) first. Then use the rule for the order of operations.

Example 2: What is the value of each phrase?

a. $(4 + 5) \times 3$

9×3

27

b. $18 \div (3 - 2)$

$18 \div 1$

18

c. $15 \div (3 + 2) - 1$

$15 \div 5 - 1$

$3 - 1$

2

d. $(9 + 7) \div 4 + (2 \times 3)$

$16 \div 4 + 6$

$4 + 6$

10

Exercises

A Which operation should you do first?

1. $7 + 5 - 2$ **2.** $7 + (5 - 2)$ **3.** $10 - 3 + 6$

4. $10 - (3 + 6)$ **5.** $4 \times 6 \div 3$ **6.** $4 \times (6 \div 3)$

7. $5 \times 2 + 3$ **8.** $(5 \times 2) + 3$ **9.** $12 \div 2 + 4$

10. $12 \div (2 + 4)$ **11.** $14 \div (2 + 5) - 1$ **12.** $(14 \div 2) + 5 - 1$

B Find each value.

13. $18 - 7 + 5$ **14.** $23 + 4 - 2$

15. $5 \times 4 + 7$ **16.** $3 + 6 \times 4$

17. $6 \times 3 \div 2$ **18.** $12 \div 2 \times 3$

19. $28 \div 4 + 3$ **20.** $20 + 16 \div 2$

21. $7 \times (6 + 5)$ **22.** $12 - (2 + 9)$

23. $(10 + 8) \div 6$ **24.** $42 \div (3 + 4)$

25. $(32 - 12) \div 5$ **26.** $(5 + 7) \times 3$

27. $(9 \times 4) \div (11 - 5)$ **28.** $(17 - 9) \times (2 + 7)$

29. $32 \div (6 + 2) \times 5$ **30.** $14 \times (8 - 5) - 26$

C Find each value. Do the operations in ( ) first. Then do the operations in [ ].

31. $6 + [4 \times (5 - 2)]$ **32.** $[(14 + 6) \div 4] - 2$

33. $[(21 - 5) + 4] \div 5$ **34.** $47 - [3 \times (21 \div 7)]$

35. $9 \times [6 + (5 - 4)]$ **36.** $[(9 + 6) \times 3] + 13$

Insert ( ), or ( ) and [ ], so each phrase has the given value.

	Phrase	*Value*		*Phrase*	*Value*
37.	$48 \div 4 \times 3$	4	**38.**	$16 + 11 \div 3$	9
39.	$4 - 3 - 2 - 1$	2	**40.**	$10 + 6 \times 3 + 12$	60
41.	$4 - 3 - 2 - 1$	0	**42.**	$10 + 6 \times 3 + 12$	240

Variables 1.3

Let h represent the number of hours it takes to tune up your car. Then you can write the following phrase for the cost of the tune-up.

Tune-Up

$12 per hour labor

plus $15 for parts

JIM'S AUTO SERVICE

$$(12 \times h) + 15$$

charge per hour → 12; number of hours → h; cost of parts → 15

M. Wannemacher/Taurus Photos

"Twelve times h" can be written in the following ways.

$12 \times h$ $\qquad$ $12(h)$ $\qquad$ $12h$

For example, the phrase for the cost of the tune-up can be changed to

$$12h + 15.$$

The letter h may be replaced with different numbers. It is an example of a *variable*.

> A **variable** is any symbol, like *h*, *x*, *A*, or □, that may be replaced with numbers.

Example 1: Suppose it takes 2 hours for the tune-up of your car. To find the cost, replace h with 2 and find the value.

$12h + 15$	
$12(2) + 15$	Replace *h* with 2.
$24 + 15$	Multiply.
39	Add.

NOTE: 12*h* means "12 times *h*," but 122 does not mean "12 times 2." So we write 12(2) or 12 × 2.

The cost of the tune-up is $39.

Example 2: Find the value of $7 + (x \div 3)$ if x is replaced with 36.

$7 + (36 \div 3)$	Replace x with 36.
$7 + 12$	Divide.
19	Add.

Example 3: Find the value of $16 + n - 5$ if n is replaced with 9.

$16 + 9 - 5$	Replace n with 9.
$25 - 5$	Add.
20	Subtract.

Exercises

A What is the variable in each phrase?

1. $17 - x$ **2.** $\square + 31$ **3.** $5n + 2$

4. $29 - 3r$ **5.** $3(t + 4)$ **6.** $13b \div 4$

7. $43c$ **8.** $3d + 7$ **9.** $6y - 1$

B Replace the variable with 4. Find the value of each phrase.

10. $12x$ **11.** $9n + 17$ **12.** $21(\triangle - 1)$

13. $8a - 15$ **14.** $35 \div (3 + y)$ **15.** $16 + 5x$

16. $11x - 20$ **17.** $n \times n$ **18.** $3a + 2a$

Replace the variable with 7. Find the value of each phrase.

19. $31 - x + 5$ **20.** $6y \div 3$ **21.** $4(n + 13)$

22. $82 - 5y$ **23.** $9 \div (x - 4)$ **24.** $17 - 2x + 6$

25. $8x - 3x$ **26.** $y \times y$ **27.** $5a + 4a$

Find all the values of each phrase for the given values of x.

28. $7 + 3x$ values of x: 3, 4, 20, 112

29. $9x - 13$ values of x: 6, 2, 10, 27

30. $(x + 6) \div 3$ values of x: 9, 3, 30, 93

31. $75 \div (x - 2)$ values of x: 7, 5, 17, 27

32. $51 + 4x$ values of x: 8, 12, 148, 222

Replace the variable in the phrase $\square \times 10$ with the given number of centimeters to find the length in millimeters.

33. 10 cm 34. 150 cm 35. 230 cm 36. 20 cm

Replace the variable in the phrase $g \div 1000$ with the given number of grams to find the weight in kilograms.

37. 3000 g 38. 1000 g 39. 92 000 g 40. 10 000 g

Note: Metric measurements with 5 or more digits are usually written with space instead of commas.

C Replace x with 2 and y with 5. Find the value of the phrase.

Example: $3x + y$

$3(2) + 5$ Replace x with 2 and y with 5.

$6 + 5$ Multiply.

11 Add.

41. $x + 7y$ 42. $4x + y$ 43. $6x + 3y$

44. $x(y + 8)$ 45. $7(y - x)$ 46. $8y - 6x$

Quick Quiz
Sections 1.1 to 1.3

1. The gram is a unit of ____ in the metric system.

2. The liter is a unit of ____ in the metric system.

3. The meter is the basic unit of ____ in the metric system.

Find each value.

4. $7 + 2 \times 3$ 5. $9 + 6 \div 3$

6. $(8 - 4) \div 2$ 7. $(3 + 7) \div (5 - 3)$

Find the value if the variable is replaced with 3.

8. $3h + 8$ 9. $5(n + 2)$

1.4 Translating Into Symbols

Miller Services Limited

Which symbols on the sign tell you which way to turn to find gasoline? To find a campsite?

Often you must translate words into symbols in order to solve a problem.

Example 1: Translate into symbols.

a. six divided by eleven

$\frac{6}{11}$ or $6 \div 11$ or $11\overline{)6}$

b. eight more than nine

$9 + 8$

Here are some possible translations.

WORDS:	add	subtract	multiply	divide
	plus	minus	times	divided by
	increased by	decreased by	multiplied by	divided into
	added to	subtracted from	twice	quotient
	sum of	difference	product of	
	more than	less than		
SYMBOLS:	$+$	$-$	$\times$ or other symbols	$\div$

A number, some number, and *the number of* can be translated as *n, x,* or any other variable.

You need to be careful that the order of terms is correct.

four *subtracted from* a number *n* → $n - 4$

from four *subtract* a number *n* → $4 - n$

Example 2: Translate into symbols.

a. three times a number r ⟶ $3r$

b. five less than some number n ⟶ $n - 5$

c. the product of two numbers ⟶ xy

d. ten minus twice a number ⟶ $10 - 2n$

Exercises

A Tell what operation is involved in each phrase.

1. $9 + 1$ **2.** $7 - 3$ **3.** 12×3 **4.** $8(4)$

5. $9 \div 1$ **6.** $2\overline{)4}$ **7.** $\frac{8}{4}$ **8.** $3x$

9. $n - 8$ **10.** $8 - n$ **11.** $7(3)$ **12.** ab

B Translate into symbols.

13. fifty-two minus twenty

14. the sum of four and three

15. twelve divided by three

16. eight multiplied by seven

17. nine more than a number x

18. thirty times a number a

19. twice a number B

20. four less than a number s

21. six subtracted from some number r

22. the product of five and a number N

23. a number n increased by two

24. seventeen decreased by three

25. three added to eighty

26. from eight subtract a number x

27. from three times a number c subtract four

28. nine subtracted from the product of five and a number d

29. the sum of eight and twice some number b

30. the product of two numbers a and b, plus seven

C **31.** six divided by the sum of some number s and nine

32. four times the difference when one is subtracted from n

1.5 Sentences

Sentences about numbers are often written entirely in symbols.

Example 1: Use symbols to show that $3 + 1$ and 4 name the same number.

$$3 + 1 = 4$$

This is read *three plus one* **equals** *four* or, sometimes, *three plus one* **is** *four.*

$=$ is used to show that two phrases have the same value.	A sentence using $=$ is called an **equation.**

$<$ and $>$ are used to show that two phrases do not have the same value.	A sentence using $<$ or $>$ is called an **inequality.**

Example 2: Read each sentence.

a. $2 < 5$

Two **is less than** five.

b. $3 + x > 3$

Three plus x **is greater than** three.

Notice that both $<$ and $>$ always point to the name of the smaller number. So any sentence using $<$ or $>$ can be rewritten using the other symbol.

Example 3: Write a sentence using $<$ to show which number is smaller. Then rewrite the sentence using $>$.

a. 3, 4

b. $8 + 3$, 8

smaller number

$3 < 4$ $\qquad$ $8 < 8 + 3$

$4 > 3$ $\qquad$ $8 + 3 > 8$

smaller number

Exercises

A Tell how to read each sentence.

1. $13 = 12 + 1$ **2.** $24 < 30$ **3.** $15 > 7$

4. $9 = 9$ **5.** $2 \times 7 > 13$ **6.** $x + 2 < 10$

7. $6 \div 3 = 2$ **8.** $5 < 3(2)$ **9.** $4x > 8$

B Write a sentence using $<$ to show which number is smaller. Then rewrite the sentence using $>$.

10. 10, 14 **11.** 9, 2 **12.** $4 + 3$, 17

13. 91, $82 + 5$ **14.** 7(5), 32 **15.** $12 \div 4$, 4

16. $9 + 16$, 22 **17.** $13 - 4$, 10 **18.** 37, $40 - 13$

19. 92, 12(8) **20.** 17, $54 \div 3$ **21.** 3(8), 5(5)

22. $17 + 12$, $13 + 15$ **23.** $72 + 10$, $97 - 12$

24. 7(15), $24 + 83$ **25.** $75 \div 15$, $22 - 19$

Replace the ? with $=$, $<$, or $>$ to show that the measures are equal or that one is smaller than the other.

26. 1 cm ? 1 m **27.** 1 m ? 100 cm **28.** 1000 g ? 1 kg

29. 1 g ? 1 mg **30.** 1 mL ? 1 L **31.** 1 km ? 1000 m

Translate into symbols.

32. A number increased by four equals twenty.

33. Twelve subtracted from twice a number is less than thirty.

34. Twenty-five more than a number is one hundred fifty.

35. A number divided by two is more than forty.

C **36.** Ten times the number of centimeters is the number of millimeters.

37. The number of kilograms is the number of grams divided by one thousand.

1.6 Open Sentences

Classify each sentence below as *True, False,* or *Can't decide.*

a. Florida is one of the 50 states in the U.S.A.

b. A meter contains 100 millimeters.

c. Little Orphan Annie is a comic-strip character.

d. He won an Olympic gold medal.

e. She was a famous scientist.

f. It is my worst subject.

Why couldn't you decide on sentences **d, e,** and **f?**

If you replace *She* in sentence **e** with *Marie Sklodowska Curie,* most people would mark the sentence *True.* If you replace *She* with *Susan B. Anthony,* most people would mark the sentence *False.*

Classify each sentence below as *True, False,* or *Can't decide.*

g. $3 + 5 = 8$ **h.** $\square + 6 = 10$

i. $4 + 7 = 9$ **j.** $1111 \times 9 = 9999$

k. $8 - n > 15$ **l.** $3a < 9$

Why couldn't you decide on sentences **h, k,** and **l**?

Sentences **h, k,** and **l** are neither true nor false. They are called *open sentences.* If you replace $\square$ with 4 in $\square + 6 = 10$, the sentence is *True.* If you replace $\square$ with 7, the sentence is *False.*

An **open sentence** contains one or more variables and is neither true nor false.

Exercises

A Classify each sentence *True, False,* or *Can't decide.*

1. Lake Erie is one of the Great Lakes.
2. Football is called the national anthem.
3. It is the smallest state in the U.S.A.
4. Martha Washington invented the light bulb.
5. A meter contains 100 centimeters.
6. He is bigger than you.
7. The kilogram is a unit for measuring length.
8. She is a United States Senator.
9. 20° Celsius is a comfortable room temperature.
10. Chicago is the largest city in Illinois.

Classify each sentence *True, False,* or *Open.*

11. $2 \times 2 \times 2 \times 2 \times 2 = 32$
12. $8 + \square = 14$
13. $7 - n > 3$
14. $7 - 5 > 3$
15. $7 - 5 < 3$
16. $8x = 16$
17. $2x + x = 11 + 7$
18. $39 = 13 + 13 + 13$
19. $81 > 3 \times 20$
20. $26 > 2 \times 7$

B For each sentence, find a replacement that makes it true. Then find a replacement that makes it false.

21. It is the capital of the U.S.A.
22. It is the third letter of the English alphabet.
23. He invented the telephone.
24. She discovered radium.

25. $7 + \square = 19$

26. $4 \times \square + 3 = 11$

27. $14 > 2n$

28. $n \div 5 = 7$

29. $3 \times 2 < a$

30. $x - 6 = 13$

C Find a number that will make each sentence true.

Example: $3a + a = 32$

Replace both a's with the same number.

$3(8) + 8 = 32$

$24 + 8 = 32$ Multiply.

$32 = 32$ Add.

Since $32 = 32$ is true, 8 makes the sentence true.

31. $a + a = 18$

32. $3x + x < 8$

33. $x + 2x = 12$

34. $3a - a > 6$

35. $n + 2 = 2 + n$

36. $4x + 2 = 3x + 4$

Find a pair of numbers that makes each sentence true. Then find a pair of numbers that makes each sentence false.

Example: $x + y = 10$
- Let $x = 6$ and $y = 4$ ▶ $6 + 4 = 10$ True
- Let $x = 7$ and $y = 1$ ▶ $7 + 1 = 10$ False

37. $2x + 3y = 35$

38. $y = 2x + 7$

39. $x + y = y + x$

40. $2x + y > 15$

Quick Quiz

Sections 1.4 to 1.6

1. *Translate into symbols:* a number n increased by one

Replace the ? with < or > to show which number is smaller.

2. $3 + 12$? 14

3. $9(2)$? $24 - 2$

4. $27 \div 3$? $2(5)$

For each sentence, find a replacement that makes it true.

5. $12 + n = 17$

6. $15 > 3x$

7. $16 - r < 13$

Replacement and Solution Sets

1.7

When the variable in an *open sentence* is replaced by a number, a sentence is formed that is either true or false. In different problems, the replacement numbers may come from different sets.

> The set of numbers that can replace a variable is called the **replacement set.**

Suppose the replacement set for the open sentence $n + 7 = 10$ is $\{1, 2, 3, 4\}$. It may help to think of the open sentence in terms of a "pattern frame" as shown here.

Brent Jones

$1 + 7 = 10$	False
$2 + 7 = 10$	False
$3 + 7 = 10$	True
$4 + 7 = 10$	False

The number three made the sentence true. It was the *only* number that did.

> The set of numbers that makes a sentence true is called the **solution set.**

Each number in the solution set is called a *solution.* To *solve* a sentence means to find its solution(s).

$n + 7 = 10$	$\{1, 2, 3, 4\}$	$\{3\}$	$n = 3$
variable	replacement set	solution set	solution

sentence — replacement set

Example 1: Solve $13 = 3x + 4$. Use $\{1, 2, 3, 4\}$.

$13 = 3(1) + 4$

$13 = 7$ False

$13 = 3(3) + 4$

$13 = 13$ True

$13 = 3(2) + 4$

$13 = 10$ False

$13 = 3(4) + 4$

$13 = 16$ False

The solution set is $\{3\}$; $x = 3$.

Example 2: Solve $2n > 7$. Use $\{0, 1, 2, 3, 4, 5\}$.

$2(0) > 7$

$0 > 7$ False

$2(3) > 7$

$6 > 7$ False

$2(1) > 7$

$2 > 7$ False

$2(4) > 7$

$8 > 7$ True

$2(2) > 7$

$4 > 7$ False

$2(5) > 7$

$10 > 7$ True

The solution set is $\{4, 5\}$.

Example 3: Solve $n + 5 = 12$. Use $\{4, 5, 6\}$.

$4 + 5 = 12$ False

$6 + 5 = 12$ False

$5 + 5 = 12$ False

There is no solution in the given replacement set.

When no numbers in the given replacement set make a sentence true, as in Example 3 above, the solution set is said to be the **empty set.** $\{\ \}$ and $\varnothing$ are symbols for the empty set.

Example 4: Solve $3(x + 2) = 3x + 6$. Use $\{4, 6, 8, 10\}$.

$3(4 + 2) = 3(4) + 6$

$3(6) = 12 + 6$

$18 = 18$ True

$3(6 + 2) = 3(6) + 6$

$3(8) = 18 + 6$

$24 = 24$ True

$3(8 + 2) = 3(8) + 6$

$3(10) = 24 + 6$

$30 = 30$ True

$3(10 + 2) = 3(10) + 6$

$3(12) = 30 + 6$

$36 = 36$ True

The replacement set is also the solution set.

Exercises

A For each diagram, state **(a)** the open sentence, **(b)** the replacement set, and **(c)** all sentences that can be formed by replacing the variable.

1.

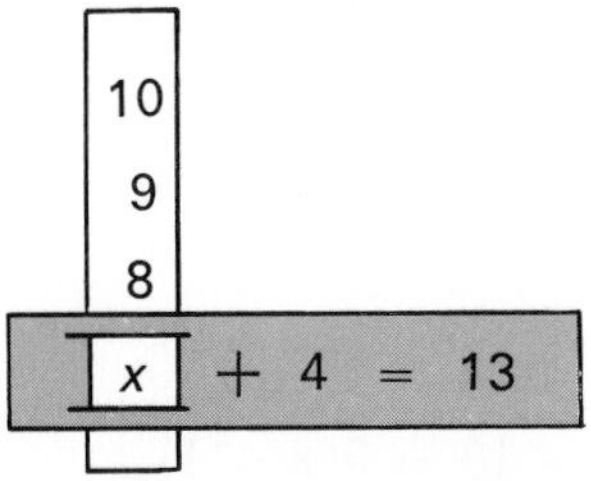

2.

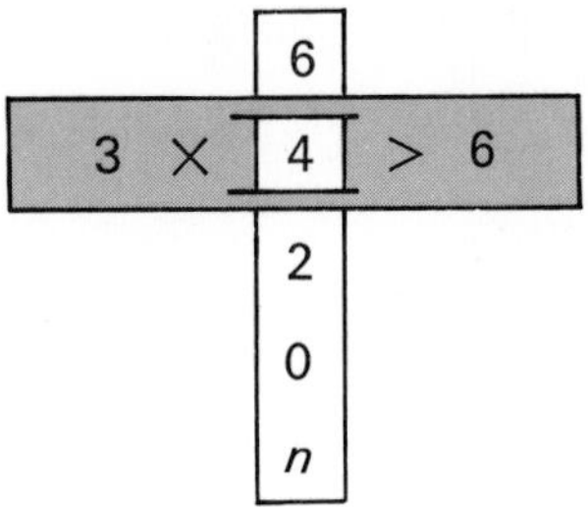

3.

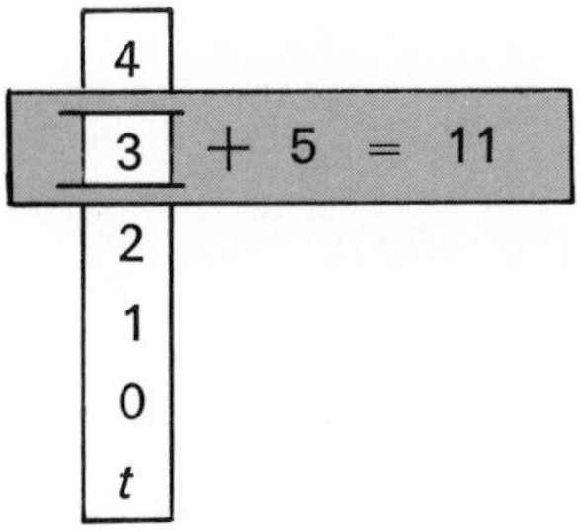

4.

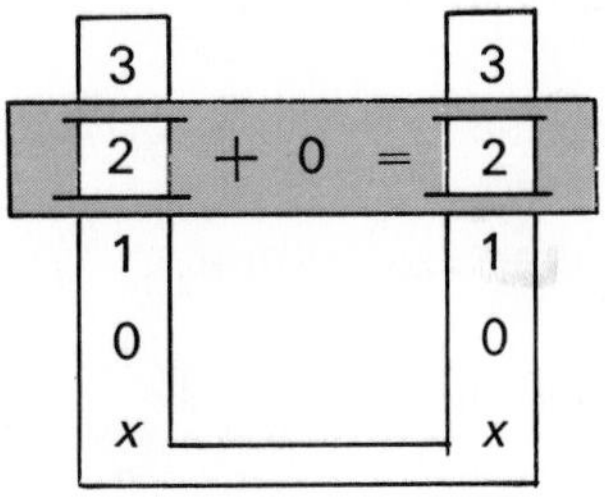

B Use {0, 1, 2, 3, 4, 5} as the replacement set. Solve.

5. $n + 8 = 12$

6. $3n = 15$

7. $4x \div 2 = 2x$

8. $8x + 4 = 5$

9. $n > n + 1$

10. $n + 1 > n$

11. $2(x + 1) = 2x + 1$

12. $2(x + 1) = 2x + 2$

13. $4x + 3 = 11$

14. $6n - 4 = 20$

Solve. Use the given replacement set.

15. $2n - 2 = 12$	$\{5, 7, 9, 13\}$
16. $2n - 3 < 4$	$\{2, 3, 5, 8, 12\}$
17. $17 = 2x + 5$	$\{4, 6, 8, 10\}$
18. $24 - 3y = 15$	$\{2, 3, 4, 5, 6\}$
19. $31 = 7n + 3$	$\{2, 3, 4, 5\}$
20. $4x - 8 = 0$	$\{1, 2, 3, 4\}$
21. $5(x - 4) = 5x - 20$	$\{5, 6, 7, 8\}$
22. $3n + 15 = 3(n + 5)$	$\{0, 1, 2, 3\}$
23. $3n > 2n$	$\{2, 3, 4, 5\}$
24. $4x = 10$	$\{3, 4, 5, 6\}$

The replacement set is {50, 51, 52, 53}. Solve.

25. $2x + 7 = 3x - 44$

26. $4x + 4 = 2(2x + 2)$

27. $3n < 156$

28. $5x - 10 = 5(x - 1)$

29. $2x - 1 > 103$

30. $n + 19 = 19 + n$

C Solve. Use the given replacement set.

31. 4 cm = ____ mm	{4, 40, 400, 4000}
32. 3000 mL = ____ L	{3, 30, 300, 3000}
33. 10 g = ____ mg	{100, 1000, 10 000, 100 000}
34. 1 km = ____ cm	{100, 1000, 10 000, 100 000}
35. 10 kg = ____ g	{10, 100, 1000, 10 000}

Equations on the Balance Beam

Finding solutions by trying all numbers in a replacement set can take a long time. In fact, it is impossible for replacement sets like the *whole numbers*, {0, 1, 2, 3, ⋯}. (The ⋯ means "and so on.") Here is another way to solve equations when the replacement set is the whole numbers.

Example 1: Solve $n + 3 = 5$.

Step 1: You can think of the equation on a balance beam.

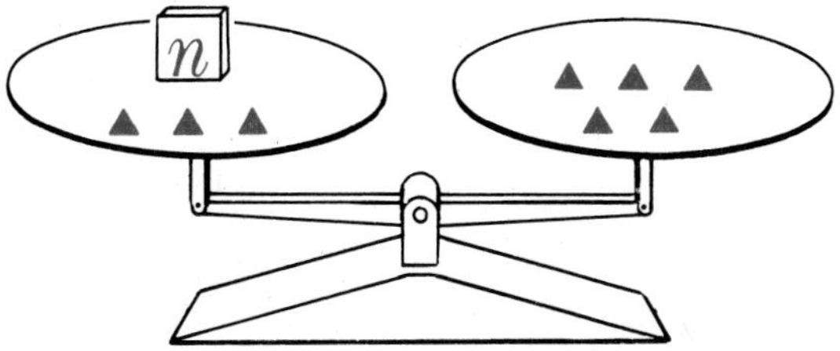

To keep the balance, whatever you do to one side, you must also do to the other side.

Step 2: To get n by itself, take 3 weights off the left side. To keep the balance, also take 3 weights off the right side.

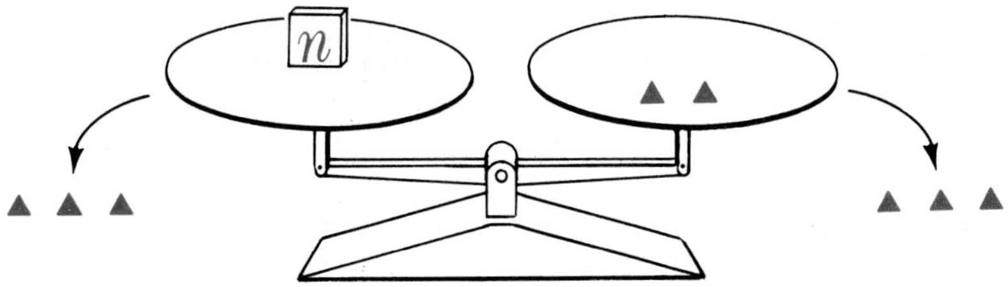

$$\begin{array}{rcrl} n + 3 & = & 5 & \\ -3 & & -3 & \text{Remove 3 from each side.} \\ \hline n & = & 2 & \text{Solution} \end{array}$$

Step 3: Always check the solution.

Check: $n + 3 = 5$ Original equation

$2 + 3 = 5$ Replace n with 2.

$5 = 5$ ✓ It checks!

Example 2: Solve $12 = n + 7$.

Step 1: Think of the equation on a balance beam.

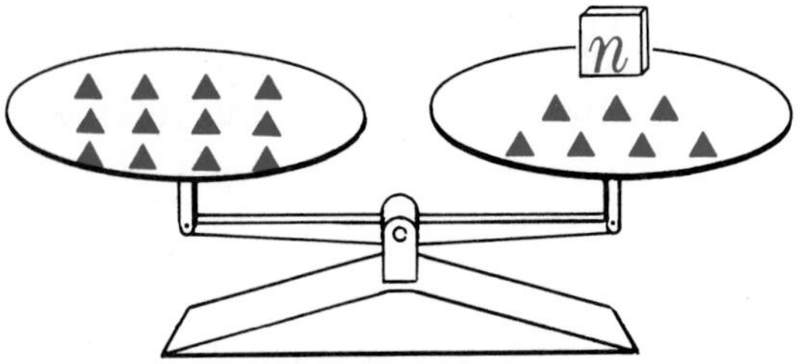

Step 2: Remove 7 weights from each side.

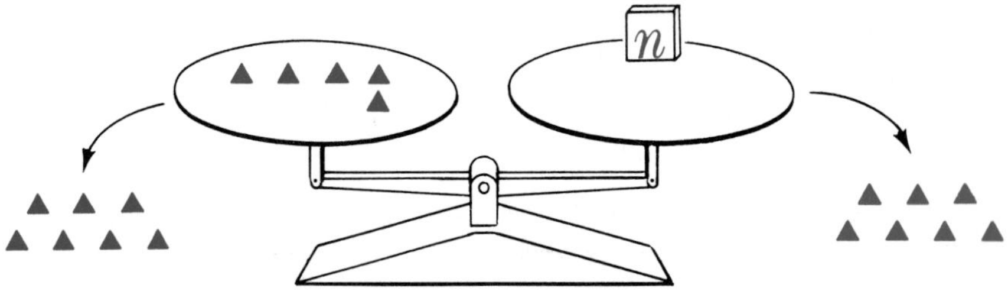

$$\begin{array}{rcl} 12 & = & n + 7 \\ \underline{-7} & & \underline{-\ 7} \\ 5 & = & n \end{array}$$

Remove 7 from each side.

Solution (or you can write $n = 5$)

Step 3: Check: $12 = n + 7$

$12 = 5 + 7$

$12 = 12$ ✓ It checks!

Exercises

[A] Solve the equations shown on the balance beams.

1. 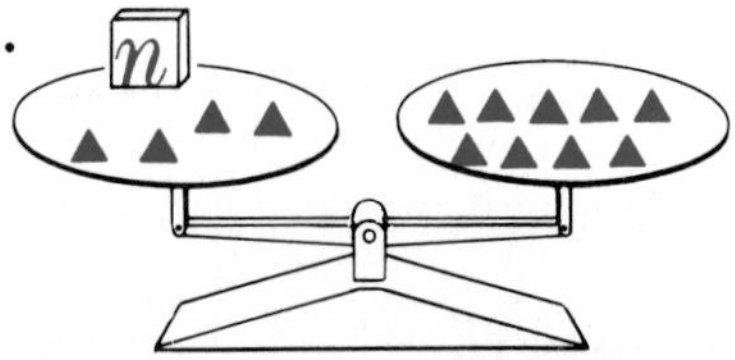

2. 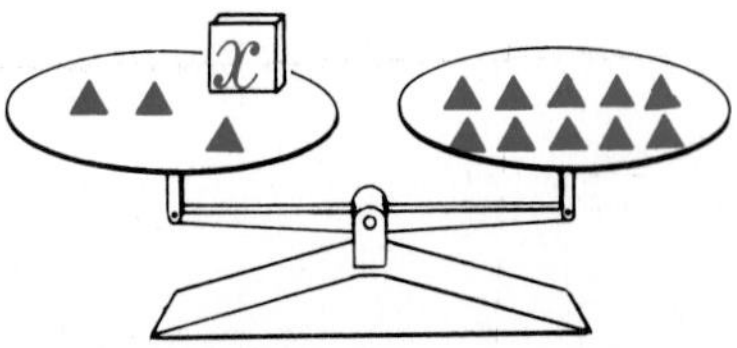

3.

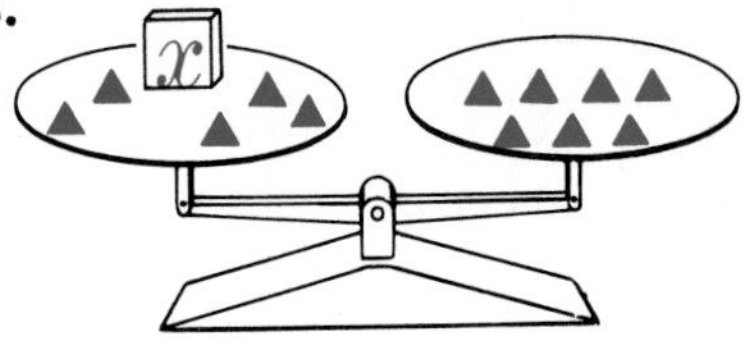

4.

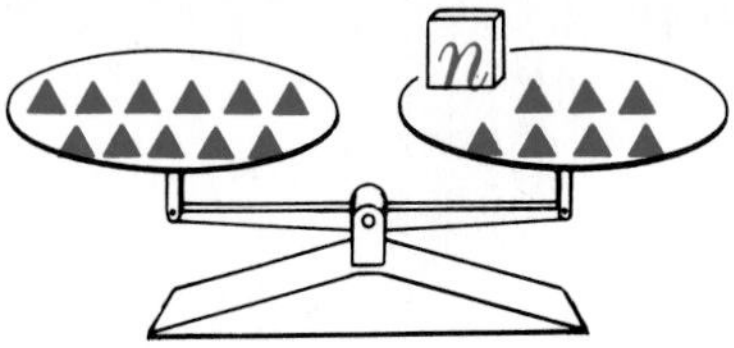

B Solve. Be sure to check your solution.

5. $n + 5 = 13$

6. $x + 4 = 11$

7. $y + 23 = 39$

8. $21 = a + 9$

9. $x + 4 = 14$

10. $26 = n + 15$

11. $c + 2 = 7$

12. $36 = x + 18$

13. $y + 6 = 19$

14. $n + 10 = 43$

15. $33 = x + 11$

16. $a + 2 = 9$

17. $56 = n + 21$

18. $t + 30 = 72$

19. $308 = x + 105$

20. $n + 7 = 10$

21. $y + 46 = 81$

22. $a + 55 = 90$

23. $x + 87 = 90$

24. $n + 240 = 354$

25. $y + 100 = 579$

26. $x + 750 = 1275$

C 27. $8 + y = 17$

28. $64 = 29 + n$

29. $y + (5 + 3) = 39$

30. $x + (26 - 12) = 57$

31. $n + 13 = 4(9 + 2)$

32. $y + 10 = 16 + (18 \div 3)$

Which Way?

Jon was working on an algebra assignment. Being somewhat absent-minded, he forgot whether he was to add or to multiply the three numbers recorded on his paper. So he decided to do it both ways. Much to his surprise, the answers were the same.

The numbers were three different whole numbers. What were they?

1.9 Formulas

A **formula** is a rule or principle written as a mathematical sentence.

The number of meters is the number of centimeters divided by 100.

meters → $m = c \div 100$ ← centimeters

Example 1: How many meters equal 300 centimeters?

Step 1: $m = c \div 100$ **Write the formula.**

Step 2: $m = 300 \div 100$ **Substitute the given value.**

Step 3: $m = 3$ **Divide.**

Step 4: 3 meters **Answer the question. Include the unit of measure if it is needed.**

The distance traveled is the rate of speed multiplied by the time of travel.

$d = rt$ (distance → d, rate → r, time → t)

Example 2: How far will an object travel in 4 hours at 33 kilometers per hour (also written 33 km/h)?

Step 1: $d = rt$ **Write the formula.**

Step 2: $d = 33 \times 4$ **Substitute the given values.**

Step 3: $d = 132$ **Multiply.**

Step 4: 132 kilometers **Answer the question.**

Exercises

A

1. A formula is a rule or principle written as a ____.

2. How many variables did we replace to use the formula $m = c \div 100$?

3. What operation does rt indicate?

4. How many variables did we replace to use the formula $d = rt$?

B Find the number of meters equal to the given number of centimeters.

5. 1200
6. 7800
7. 10 000
8. 13 500

9. 100 000
10. 28 700
11. 1 320 200
12. 3 400 000

Find the distance for the given rate and time. The following are standard abbreviations: min for *minute(s)*, h for *hour(s)*, wk for *week(s)*.

13. 30 km/h; 6 h
14. 360 cm/h; 3 h

15. 23 m/min; 10 min
16. 3 cm/min; 28 min

17. 90 m/wk; 52 wk
18. 3 km/wk; 8 wk

Formulas for the perimeters of some geometric figures are shown.

triangle

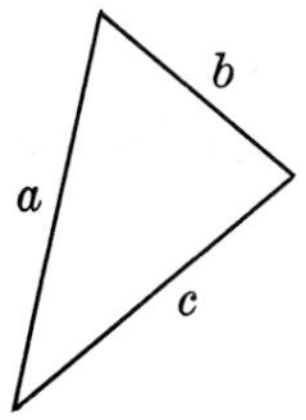

$p = a + b + c$

rectangle

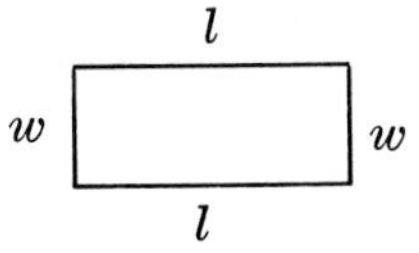

$p = 2(l + w)$

square

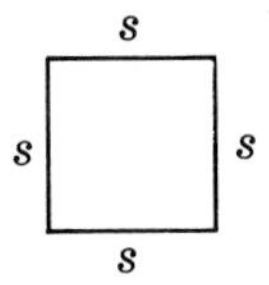

$p = 4s$

regular pentagon

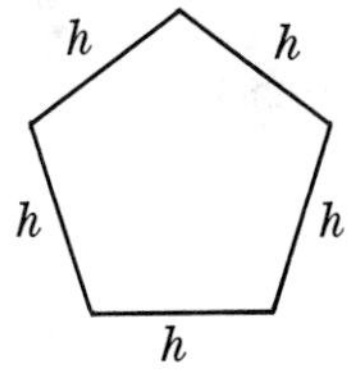

$p = 5h$

Find the perimeter; use one of the formulas above.

19. square; $s = 132$
20. rectangle; $l = 20$, $w = 13$

21. rectangle; $l = 23$, $w = 10$
22. triangle; $a = 3$, $b = 7$, $c = 5$

23. regular pentagon; $h = 15$
24. triangle; $a = 30$, $b = 30$, $c = 30$

C Use a formula from this section to solve each problem.

25. What is the perimeter of a swimming pool 50 m long and 20 m wide?

26. A truck driver stops to rest every three hours. If the driver averages 80 km/h between stops, how far is it between stops?

Terms and Symbols Review

Match each term or symbol with the best description.

1. meter	**a.** find the solution set
2. gram	**b.** all numbers that make a sentence true
3. liter	**c.** metric unit of capacity
4. degree Celsius	**d.** symbol for centimeter(s)
5. kilo-	**e.** prefix meaning "hundredth"
6. centi-	**f.** n in $5n + 4$
7. cm	**g.** shows that phrases have the same value
8. mg	**h.** all numbers that can replace the variable
9. variable	**i.** metric unit of length
10. $=$	**j.** symbol for milligram(s)
11. $<$	**k.** rule written as a mathematical sentence
12. $>$	**l.** means "is greater than"
13. solve	**m.** prefix meaning "thousand"
14. solution set	**n.** metric unit of weight
15. replacement set	**o.** means "is less than"
16. formula	**p.** metric unit of temperature

Chapter 1 Review

1.1 Which is less?

1. your height or 1 meter

2. your weight or 1 kilogram

3. a bathtubful or 1 liter

4. normal body temperature or 50 °C

5. the distance you could throw a ball or 1 kilometer

Find each value. 1.2

6. $7 + 2 \times 4$

7. $(5 \times 6) \div (17 - 7)$

8. $21 \div (5 + 2)$

9. $24 \div (2 + 6) - 3$

Replace the variable with 5. Find the value of each phrase. 1.3

10. $7y - 20$

11. $(n + 7) \times 4$

12. $18 + 2x$

13. $65 \div (a + 8)$

Translate into symbols.

14. one more than twice three

15. four less than a number n 1.4

16. Five increased by nine is the product of two and a number x. 1.5

17. Eight divided by three is less than the sum of one and a number a.

18. Five times seven is greater than fifty minus a number b.

Classify each sentence *True, False,* or *Open*. 1.6

19. $12 = 12$

20. $9 + n = 17$

21. $x - 7 = 8$

22. $87 \div 3 = 26$

23. $6 + 7 = 10$

24. $3 \times 13 < 40$

Solve. Use the given replacement set. 1.7

25. $3x - 4 = 5$ $\{1, 2, 3, 4\}$

26. $6y - 5 < 10$ $\{0, 1, 2, 3\}$

27. $4x + 3 > 23$ $\{5, 6, 7, 8\}$

Solve. 1.8

28. $y + 8 = 13$

29. $x + 19 = 42$

30. Use the formula $d = rt$ to find the distance run by a long-distance runner who runs 13 kilometers per hour for 3 hours. 1.9

Chapter 1 Test

Find each value.

1. $21 - 6 \div 3$

2. $(17 - 8) \div (2 + 1)$

3. $(4 + 5) \times 9$

4. $32 - (6 \times 3) + 7$

Replace the variable with 3. Find the value of each phrase.

5. $14 - 4x$

6. $(a + 6) \times 11$

7. $7y + 8$

8. $72 \div (15 - n)$

Classify each sentence *True, False,* or *Open.*

9. $7 + 2 = 9$

10. $(x - 4) \times 8 < 22$

11. $(3 \times 4) + 5 = 17$

12. $64 \div 8 > 8$

Solve. Use $\{3, 4, 5, 6, 7, 8, 9\}$ as the replacement set.

13. $x + 7 = 13$

14. $7 > n + 2$

15. $y - 5 > 1$

Solve.

16. $n + 8 = 12$

17. $5 = n + 2$

18. *Translate into symbols:* The product of four and some number x is less than nine decreased by three.

What does each stand for?

19. **a.** mg **b.** km **c.** L

20. **a.** centi- **b.** milli- **c.** kilo-

Find the distance for the given rate and time.

21. $r = 22$ km/h, $t = 9$ h

22. $r = 13$ cm/min, $t = 27$ min

RATE YOURSELF

Number Correct	
21–22	Superior
19–20	Excellent
16–18	Good
12–15	Fair
0–11	Poor

CAREER CORNER

SYMBOLS AT WORK

A symbol is usually easier to see and understand than the words for the same idea. And a symbol can have the same meaning to people who read and speak different languages. The skull and crossbones, for example, means **POISON** the world over. And symbols like +, −, ×, and ÷ mean the same thing to mathematicians everywhere.

Special symbols are used in many kinds of work. For example, shippers and freight handlers use the symbols below. Can you figure out what they mean?

Truck drivers in all countries must understand the symbols shown below. (If you drive a car, you should also know them.) What do they mean?

Carpenters, plumbers, and electricians need to be able to read the symbols used on blueprints. Some of these symbols are shown below.

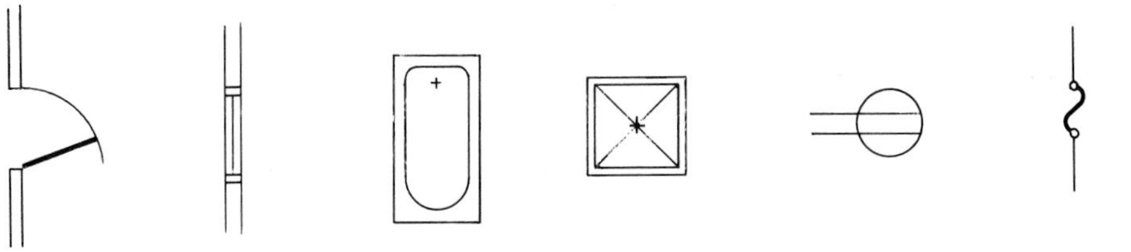

door window tub shower electrical outlet fuse

GET ON THE BEAM

Activity 1

Make a balance beam. You might use two paper cups, a ruler, a round pencil or drinking straw, a paper clamp, and two paper clips as shown. Place the paper-clip hooks at about the 1-inch and 11-inch marks, adjusting the distance to make the beam balance.

Use the balance beam you made to do the following activities:

Activity 2

1. Hang 10 paper clips on each hook.
2. Remove half the paper clips from each hook.
3. Hang 2 more paper clips on each hook.
4. Remove 1 paper clip from each hook.

Did the beam stay balanced at all times?

Activity 3

1. Hang 4 paper clips on the left hook and hang 7 on the right hook.
2. Remove 2 paper clips from each hook.
3. Double the number of paper clips on each hook.
4. Hang 3 more paper clips on each hook.

Did the beam stay tipped in the same direction at all times?

Getting Ready for Chapter 2

Match each item with the best description.

1. liter	**a.** n is greater than three.	1.1
2. cm	**b.** metric unit of temperature	
3. centi-	**c.** three subtracted from some number n	
4. degree Celsius	**d.** some number n divided by three	
5. $3n$	**e.** metric unit of capacity	1.4
6. $3 + n$	**f.** Three is less than n.	
7. $n - 3$	**g.** prefix meaning "hundredth"	
8. $\frac{n}{3}$	**h.** three times some number n	
9. $3 < n$	**i.** three plus some number n	1.5
10. $n > 3$	**j.** symbol for centimeter(s)	

Find each value.

11. $4 \times 2 + 9$ **12.** $(6 + 2) \div 2$ **13.** $6 \div 2 \times 3 - 1$ 1.2

14. $n - 8$ if $n = 19$ **15.** $5a + 6$ if $a = 7$ **16.** $(4n - 3) \div 7$ if $n = 6$ 1.3

Solve. Use the replacement set {0, 1, 2, 3, 4}.

17. $n + 3 = 7$ **18.** $x - 2 < 1$ **19.** $r + 5 > 6$ 1.7

Solve.

20. $5 = x + 3$ **21.** $n + 2 = 8$ **22.** $12 = a + 5$ 1.8

23. If a car is driven at 50 kilometers an hour for 3 hours, how far does it travel? (Use $d = rt$.) 1.9

2

SOLVING OPEN SENTENCES

Letting out a deep breath undoes taking in that deep breath. Climbing down a ladder undoes climbing up the ladder. And unlocking a door undoes locking the door. But, on the other hand, nothing undoes breaking an egg!

In mathematics, an operation by a number can often be undone by another operation by the same number. In this chapter you will learn how to use this fact to solve equations and inequalities.

2.1 Inverse Operations

Addition, subtraction, multiplication, and division are the four basic operations. Each of them can be undone by another of the four.

Example 1: What operations undo each other?

$(13 + 5) - 5 = 13$ 13 and 13: same Subtraction undoes addition.	$(14 - 2) + 2 = 14$ 14 and 14: same Addition undoes subtraction.
$(5 \times 3) \div 3 = 5$ 5 and 5: same Division undoes multiplication.	$(12 \div 4) \times 4 = 12$ 12 and 12: same Multiplication undoes division.

> Operations that undo each other are called **inverse operations.**
> Addition and subtraction are inverse operations.
> Multiplication and division are inverse operations.

Example 2: Use an inverse operation to check each answer.

$$\begin{array}{r} 139 \\ -47 \\ \hline 92 \end{array} \longrightarrow \begin{array}{r} 47 \\ +92 \\ \hline 139 \end{array}$$

Addition is used to check subtraction.

$$14\overline{)3388} = 242 \longrightarrow \begin{array}{r} 242 \\ \times 14 \\ \hline 3388 \end{array}$$

Multiplication is used to check division.

Example 3: Simplify each phrase.

a. $\underbrace{t + 7 - 7}_{t}$ Subtracting 7 undoes adding 7.	**b.** $\underbrace{n - 8 + 8}_{n}$ Adding 8 undoes subtracting 8.
c. $\underbrace{\frac{3x}{3}}_{x}$ Dividing by 3 undoes multiplying by 3.	**d.** $\underbrace{\frac{r}{4} \times 4}_{r}$ Multiplying by 4 undoes dividing by 4.

Exercises

A What is the inverse of each of the following?

1. adding 1

2. subtracting 1

3. multiplying by 10

4. dividing by 1000

5. subtracting 10

6. multiplying by 45

7. adding 7

8. dividing by 3

9. subtracting 16

10. multiplying by 16

B Find each answer. Then use an inverse operation to check.

11. $\begin{array}{r} 78 \\ -26 \\ \hline \end{array}$

12. $25\overline{)625}$

13. $4\overline{)76}$

14. $\begin{array}{r} 65 \\ -32 \\ \hline \end{array}$

15. $15\overline{)930}$

16. $\begin{array}{r} 195 \\ -76 \\ \hline \end{array}$

17. $\begin{array}{r} 352 \\ -48 \\ \hline \end{array}$

18. $12\overline{)312}$

Simplify each phrase.

19. $19 + 5 - 5$

20. $27 - 3 + 3$

21. $n + 7 - 7$

22. $\frac{12 \times 9}{12}$

23. $\frac{15}{4} \times 4$

24. $\frac{8x}{8}$

Which operation by what number would give the variable by itself?

Example: $a - 8$ *Answer:* Adding 8, because $a - 8 + 8 = a$

25. $n + 25$

26. $t - 4$

27. $5m$

28. $\frac{x}{7}$

29. $23y$

30. $\frac{a}{4}$

C Simplify each phrase.

31. $4n - 6 + 6$

32. $\frac{2t \times 3}{3}$

33. $\frac{(w - 3)}{5} \times 5$

34. $\frac{r + 6}{8} \times 8$

35. $(x + 9) - 2 + 2$

36. $\frac{t}{5} + 4 - 4$

Equations With Addition or Subtraction

In Chapter 1, you saw that it helps to think of a balance beam when solving some equations. It can also help to think of inverse operations. Remember that we have to get the variable by itself on one side of the equation.

Example 1: Solve $n + 3 = 5$.

$$n + 3 = 5$$

Notice 3 is added to *n*. To undo this, subtract 3.

$$n + 3 - 3 = 5 - 3$$

To keep the balance, subtract 3 from each side.

$$n = 2$$

Check:

$$n + 3 = 5$$

$$2 + 3 = 5$$

$$5 = 5 \checkmark$$

The check is a required part of solving an equation.

Example 2: Solve $15 = a - 7$.

$$15 = a - 7$$

Notice 7 is subtracted from *a*. To undo this, add 7.

$$15 + 7 = a - 7 + 7$$

Add 7 to each side.

$$22 = a$$

Check:

$$15 = a - 7$$

$$15 = 22 - 7$$

$$15 = 15 \checkmark$$

Exercises

A To solve each equation, what would you do on each side?

1. $s + 5 = 9$ **2.** $x - 10 = 34$ **3.** $13 = n + 7$

4. $8 = x + 8$ **5.** $n - 7 = 16$ **6.** $a + 14 = 23$

7. $n - 8 = 13$

8. $y + 12 = 13$

9. $a - 12 = 50$

10. $y - 1 = 11$

11. $27 = n + 17$

12. $8 = x - 23$

B Solve each equation. (Remember that checking is required.)

13. $x + 7 = 18$

14. $n - 7 = 17$

15. $x - 8 = 18$

16. $8 = y + 8$

17. $c - 4 = 2$

18. $n - 12 = 0$

19. $x + 13 = 27$

20. $n - 21 = 11$

21. $13 = a - 17$

22. $14 = n + 11$

23. $z - 19 = 14$

24. $28 = x - 9$

25. $n - 6 = 10$

26. $t + 52 = 100$

27. $49 = n + 23$

28. $y - 6 = 6$

29. $100 = n + 80$

30. $x + 9 = 31$

31. $x - 7 = 1$

32. $r + 3 = 75$

33. $12 = a + 10$

34. $y - 8 = 5$

35. $213 = x + 121$

36. $x + 14 = 15$

Use one of the given formulas to solve each problem.

Example: Find the "scratch score" for a handicap of 23 and a final score of 138. (See the formula below.)

scratch score ↓ final score ↓

$$s + h = f$$

↑ handicap

$$s + 23 = 138$$

$$s + 23 - 23 = 138 - 23$$

$$s = 115$$ ← Check as required.

The scratch score is 115.

H. Armstrong Roberts

37. Nancy's handicap is 58. Her scratch score was 133. What was her final score?

38. Peg's final score was 147. Her handicap is 42. What was her scratch score?

39. Joe's final score was 221. His handicap is 39. What was his scratch score?

retail price → $p = w + m$ ← markup; wholesale price → w

sale price → $s = p - d$ ← discount; regular price → p

40. Find w if $p = 14$ and $m = 7$.

41. Find p if $s = 128$ and $d = 40$.

42. Find w if $p = 35$ and $m = 15$.

43. Find p if $s = 301$ and $d = 51$.

44. If a storekeeper added \$42 to the wholesale price of an item and charged \$78 for it, what was the wholesale price?

45. If an appliance that sells at wholesale for \$90 has an \$87 markup, what is the retail price?

46. What is the regular price of the bikes?

47. What is the regular price of the dresses?

C Solve for x.

Example:

$$x - a = b$$
$$x - a + a = b + a$$
$$x = b + a$$

Check:

$$x - a = b$$
$$b + a - a = b$$
$$b = b \checkmark$$

48. $1 = x + a$

49. $x + 3 = d$

50. $r = x - 2$

51. $7 = x - p$

52. $x - n = a$

53. $x - r + 5 = 7$

2.3 Equations With Multiplication or Division

Inverse operations can also be used to solve an equation if the variable has been multiplied or divided by a number.

Example 1: Solve $35 = 7x$.

$35 = 7x$ — Notice x is multiplied by 7. To undo this, divide by 7.

$\frac{35}{7} = \frac{7x}{7}$ — Divide each side by 7.

$5 = x$

Check: $35 = 7x$

$35 = 7(5)$ — Remember that we use ( ) because $7x$ means 7 times x, but 75 does not mean 7 times 5.

$35 = 35$ ✓

Example 2: Solve $\frac{n}{4} = 8$.

$\frac{n}{4} = 8$ — Notice n is divided by 4. To undo this, multiply by 4.

$\frac{n}{4} \times 4 = 8 \times 4$ — Multiply each side by 4.

$n = 32$

Check: $\frac{n}{4} = 8$

$\frac{32}{4} = 8$

$8 = 8$ ✓

Exercises

A To solve each equation, what would you do on each side?

1. $3n = 12$ **2.** $140 = 10n$ **3.** $0 = 3n$

4. $7n = 49$ 5. $8 = \frac{n}{5}$ 6. $36 = 12n$

7. $\frac{n}{5} = 1$ 8. $\frac{x}{2} = 13$ 9. $\frac{y}{9} = 2$

10. $\frac{a}{7} = 12$ 11. $\frac{n}{11} = 6$ 12. $\frac{c}{20} = 5$

B Solve each equation. (Remember that checking is required.)

13. $8y = 64$ 14. $8a = 32$ 15. $10n = 350$

16. $7x = 49$ 17. $100 = 20y$ 18. $5c = 75$

19. $15x = 60$ 20. $144 = 12n$ 21. $6y = 72$

22. $50a = 400$ 23. $105 = 35x$ 24. $6x = 42$

25. $10 = \frac{n}{1}$ 26. $10 = \frac{n}{5}$ 27. $11 = \frac{n}{10}$

28. $\frac{n}{4} = 15$ 29. $\frac{n}{15} = 0$ 30. $\frac{n}{8} = 12$

31. $\frac{x}{7} = 30$ 32. $\frac{y}{2} = 34$ 33. $\frac{a}{20} = 4$

34. $9 = \frac{x}{6}$ 35. $\frac{n}{3} = 17$ 36. $\frac{z}{9} = 11$

37. $9y = 81$ 38. $25n = 75$ 39. $30a = 150$

40. $7x = 56$ 41. $84 = 12y$ 42. $50z = 250$

43. $96 = 6t$ 44. $11b = 77$ 45. $15c = 900$

Use one of the given formulas to solve each problem.

46. Maria earns \$32 a day at the rate of \$4 an hour. How many hours does she work a day?

47. Joe earns \$3 an hour. How many hours must he work to earn \$117?

C 48. What is the earned run average of a pitcher who allowed 52 earned runs in 117 innings?

49. A pitcher has an earned run average of 3 for 42 innings. How many earned runs did the pitcher allow?

total wages → w; hourly rate → p; hours worked → t

$$w = pt$$

innings pitched → i; earned run average → e; earned runs allowed → r

$$ie = 9r$$

2.4 Inequalities With One Operation

Like equations, inequalities can be solved by using inverse operations. Get the variable by itself on one side by doing the same operation on each side. (In this section, the replacement set is the whole numbers.) Always check at least one solution.

Example 1: Solve $3x < 12$.

$3x < 12$

> Notice x is multiplied by 3. Undo this by dividing by 3.

$\frac{3x}{3} < \frac{12}{3}$

$x < 4$

Check: $3x < 12$

$3(2) < 12$

$6 < 12$ ✓

Use any whole number less than 4.

A graph can help you "see" the solutions of an open sentence.

Example 2: Graph $3x < 12$.

Step 1: Solve the open sentence. (We solved this open sentence in Example 1. So $x < 4$; the solutions are 0, 1, 2, and 3.)

Step 2: Make a number line. Graph the solutions.

Draw dots at 0, 1, 2, and 3.

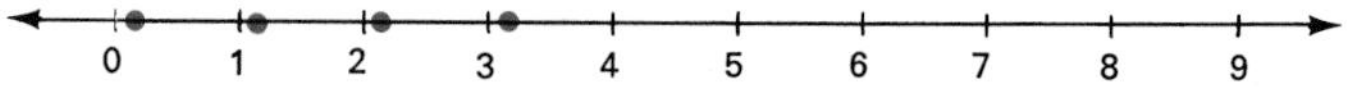

Example 3: Solve and graph $4 > n + 3$.

Step 1: $4 > n + 3$

> Notice 3 is added to n. Undo this by subtracting 3.

$4 - 3 > n + 3 - 3$

$1 > n$

Check: $4 > n + 3$

$4 > 0 + 3$

$4 > 3$ ✓

The only whole number less than 1 is 0.

Step 2:

Draw a dot at 0.

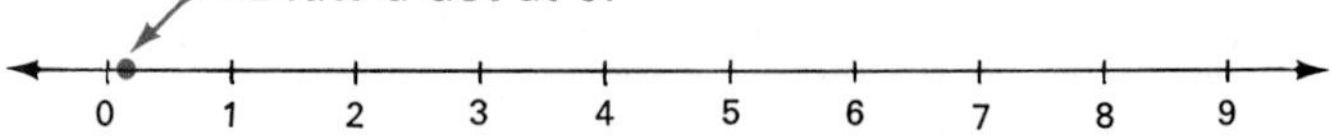

Example 4: Solve and graph $x - 6 > 10$.

Step 1: $x - 6 > 10$

$x - 6 + 6 > 10 + 6$

$x > 16$

Notice 6 is subtracted from x. Undo this by adding 6.

Check: $x - 6 > 10$

$18 - 6 > 10$

$12 > 10$ ✓

Use any whole number greater than 16.

Step 2:

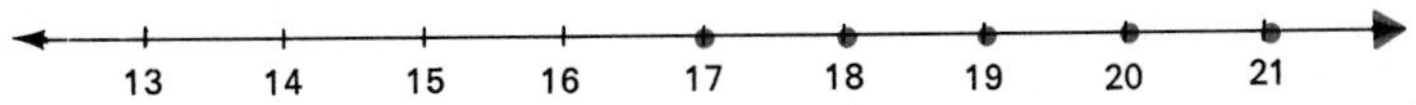

The dots and the ⟶ show that all whole numbers greater than 16 are in the graph.

Exercises

A To solve each inequality, what would you do on each side?

1. $n + 4 < 13$ **2.** $n - 2 > 9$ **3.** $n - 8 > 5$

4. $3 > \frac{n}{6}$ **5.** $7n > 35$ **6.** $\frac{n}{3} < 11$

Tell how you would graph each set on a number line.

7. $\{4, 5, 6\}$ **8.** whole numbers greater than 8

9. $\{3\}$ **10.** whole numbers less than 6

11. $\{\ \}$ **12.** whole numbers greater than 4

13. $\{0, 1, 2, 3, 4, 5\}$ **14.** all whole numbers

B Solve and graph. (Remember that checking is required.)

15. $n - 8 < 18$ **16.** $3 > n - 8$ **17.** $7 > n - 3$

18. $n - 12 < 9$ **19.** $n + 5 < 5$ **20.** $n - 6 < 0$

21. $\frac{n}{10} < 5$ **22.** $\frac{n}{2} > 8$ **23.** $n - 2 > 2$

24. $\frac{n}{7} > 20$ **25.** $\frac{n}{4} < 10$ **26.** $n - 21 < 9$

27. $\frac{n}{12} < 1$ **28.** $\frac{n}{5} < 8$ **29.** $n - 10 < 156$

30. $\frac{n}{7} > 0$ **31.** $n + 3 > 4$ **32.** $5 < \frac{n}{6}$

33. $13 < n - 12$ **34.** $4n > 12$ **35.** $19n > 19$

36. $n + 8 < 12$ **37.** $11n < 44$ **38.** $108 < 6n$

The temperature to which water can be heated in an open kettle depends on altitude. The formula below is based on the temperature at which water turns to vapor (boils).

$$t < 100 - \frac{a}{279}$$

altitude in meters (a)
temperature of water in degrees Celsius (t)

39. How hot could you heat water in an open kettle in each city? (Approximate altitude is given.)

a. Roanoke, Va.; 279 m

b. Grand Junction, Colo.; 1395 m

c. San Angelo, Tex.; 558 m

40. How hot could you heat water in an open kettle at 6138 meters on Mount McKinley in Alaska?

C The formulas shown here describe what happens to rainfall in a desert.

$$100e > 97p$$

$$100r < 3p$$

kg of water that evaporates (e)
kg of rainfall (p)
kg of water that runs off (r)

41. Suppose an afternoon shower in the desert delivers 8 532 000 kilograms of water. According to the formula, about how much of this evaporates? About how much runs off?

42. About how many kilograms of rain must fall in the desert to allow 9 700 000 kilograms of water to evaporate?

Open-Sentence Review

2.5

This section is a review of solving and graphing open sentences. The replacement set is the whole numbers. Remember that checking is required.

Example: Solve and graph.

a.	b.	c.
$x + 5 < 9$	$3x < 12$	$2 > \frac{x}{2}$
$x + 5 - 5 < 9 - 5$	$\frac{3x}{3} < \frac{12}{3}$	$2 \times 2 > \frac{x}{2} \times 2$
$x < 4$	$x < 4$	$4 > x$

Check: Replace each *x* with any whole number less than 4.

$x + 5 < 9$	$3x < 12$	$2 > \frac{x}{2}$
$1 + 5 < 9$	$3(3) < 12$	$2 > \frac{2}{2}$
$6 < 9$ ✓	$9 < 12$ ✓	$2 > 1$ ✓

For each open sentence, the solutions are 0, 1, 2, and 3. The graph of each open sentence is the same.

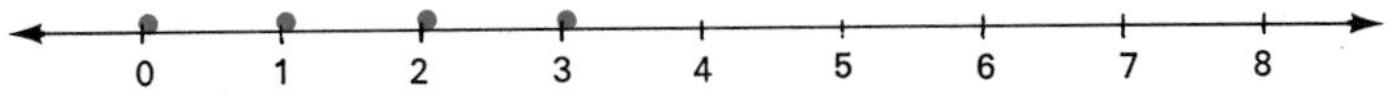

Exercises

A Match each open sentence with its graph.

1. $n > 5$ **2.** $n = 5$ **3.** $5 > n$ **4.** $5 < n$

a.
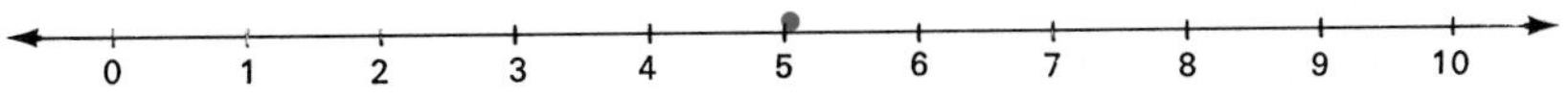

b.
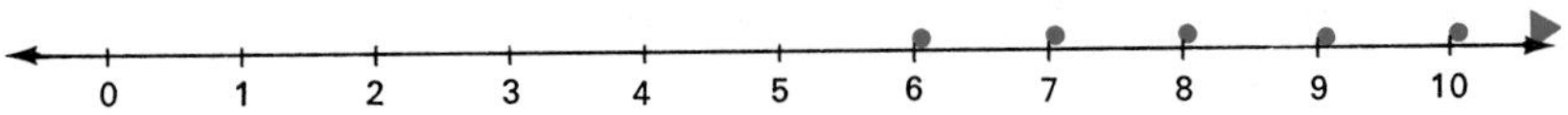

c.
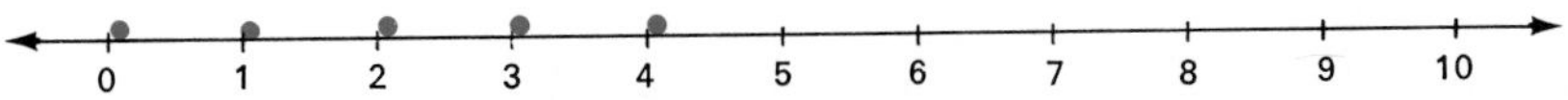

B Solve and graph.

5. $x - 4 = 12$	**6.** $x - 5 > 10$	**7.** $\frac{x}{2} = 15$
8. $x - 8 = 17$	**9.** $\frac{x}{3} > 5$	**10.** $63 = 9x$
11. $\frac{x}{8} = 0$	**12.** $14 < 7x$	**13.** $12x = 48$
14. $x - 11 = 1$	**15.** $9x < 9$	**16.** $\frac{x}{10} = 7$
17. $\frac{x}{4} < 10$	**18.** $\frac{x}{4} = 5$	**19.** $2x > 12$
20. $x + 8 < 12$	**21.** $7x = 21$	**22.** $x + 7 < 8$
23. $\frac{x}{4} < 12$	**24.** $x + 3 = 8$	**25.** $x + 7 > 8$
26. $x - 5 > 1$	**27.** $15x = 15$	**28.** $\frac{x}{1} > 10$

number of millimeters, milliliters, or milligrams ↓

$$n = \frac{m}{1000}$$

↑ number of meters, liters, or grams ↓

$$n = 1000k$$

↑ number of kilometers, kiloliters, or kilograms

C Complete. Use the given formulas.

29. 7 km = ____ m	**30.** 4000 m = ____ km
31. 7000 mm = ____ m	**32.** 147 kg = ____ g
33. 22 000 L = ____ kL	**34.** 24 000 m = ____ km
35. 13 000 mL = ____ L	**36.** 91 m = ____ mm
37. 135 g = ____ mg	**38.** 320 000 g = ____ kg
39. 17 000 km = ____ m	**40.** 3000 kL = ____ L
41. 7 L = ____ mL	**42.** 20 000 mg = ____ g

Quick Quiz

Sections 2.1 to 2.5

1. Subtraction and ____ are inverse operations.

2. Multiplication and ____ are inverse operations.

Solve and graph.

3. $a - 12 = 15$	**4.** $714 = 7n$	**5.** $x + 8 = 10$
6. $n + 3 < 17$	**7.** $12x > 24$	**8.** $a - 6 < 4$
9. $\frac{x}{5} = 10$	**10.** $8 > \frac{n}{4}$	

Equations With Two Operations

You have solved equations by doing the same operation on both sides. But to solve some equations, you must do more than one operation on both sides. First, see what operations have been done to the variable. To solve, undo these operations **in the reverse order.**

Example 1: What operations have been done to the variables?

$\frac{n}{3} + 7$ — First n is divided by 3. Then 7 is added.	$\frac{n+7}{3}$ — First 7 is added to n. Then the sum is divided by 3.
$2x - 3$ — First x is multiplied by 2. Then 3 is subtracted.	$2(x - 3)$ — First 3 is subtracted from x. Then the difference is multiplied by 2.

Example 2: Solve $2x - 3 = 17$.

First x is multiplied by 2.
Then 3 is subtracted.
} Undo these operations in the reverse order.

$$2x - 3 = 17$$

$$2x - 3 + 3 = 17 + 3 \quad \text{Add 3 to each side.}$$

$$2x = 20$$

$$\frac{2x}{2} = \frac{20}{2} \quad \text{Divide each side by 2.}$$

$$x = 10$$

Check:

$$2x - 3 = 17$$

$$2(10) - 3 = 17 \quad \text{Multiply first.}$$

$$20 - 3 = 17 \quad \text{Then subtract.}$$

$$17 = 17 \checkmark$$

} In checking, do the operations in the usual order.

Example 3: Solve $\frac{n+7}{3} = 12$.

$$\frac{n+7}{3} = 12$$

First 7 is added to n.
Then the sum is divided by 3.
Undo these operations in the reverse order.

$$\frac{n+7}{3} \times 3 = 12 \times 3$$ Multiply each side by 3.

$$n + 7 = 36$$

$$n + 7 - 7 = 36 - 7$$ Subtract 7 from each side.

$$n = 29$$

Check: $\frac{n+7}{3} = 12$

$\frac{29+7}{3} = 12$ Add first.

$\frac{36}{3} = 12$ Then divide.

$12 = 12$ ✓

Exercises

A Tell **(a)** what operations have been done to each variable and **(b)** the two steps you would use to solve each equation.

1. $3x - 7 = 8$

2. $4x + 9 = 29$

3. $\frac{n}{2} + 10 = 36$

4. $\frac{n-5}{7} = 4$

5. $12 = \frac{a+10}{5}$

6. $\frac{a}{8} - 11 = 21$

7. $47 = \frac{x}{4} + 7$

8. $5 = \frac{x-18}{6}$

9. $9y - 17 = 19$

10. $83 = 10y + 3$

11. $\frac{n+7}{3} = 11$

12. $\frac{n}{5} - 14 = 6$

B Solve.

13. $6x - 3 = 39$

14. $7(x + 13) = 91$

15. $\frac{x}{3} + 9 = 45$

16. $\frac{x-8}{3} = 11$

17. $\frac{x+1}{9} = 9$

18. $\frac{x}{4} - 14 = 6$

19. $\frac{x}{10} + 17 = 21$

20. $\frac{x-2}{4} = 6$

21. $8x - 9 = 7$

22. $77 = 12x + 5$

23. $\frac{x+25}{4} = 7$

24. $\frac{x}{9} - 3 = 17$

25. $3(x - 2) = 18$

26. $8x + 4 = 76$

27. $\frac{x}{6} + 5 = 10$

28. $\frac{x}{7} - 5 = 11$

29. $28 = 11x - 5$

30. $\frac{x-1}{4} = 5$

31. $\frac{x}{8} + 1 = 4$

32. $4x - 6 = 10$

33. $13x + 3 = 42$

34. $52x - 104 = 364$

This formula can be used when all objects in a container weigh the same amount.

$$w = pn + c$$

total weight (w); weight of each object (p); number of objects (n); weight of container (c)

35. A box that weighs 790 g is filled with pears weighing 180 g each. The full box weighs 7990 g. How many pears are in it?

36. Machine parts that weigh 3 kg each are to be packed in a box that weighs 35 kg empty. If the packed box cannot weigh more than 347 kg, how many machine parts can be put in it?

C 37. A spool wound with wire weighs 386 kg. If the spool weighs 1 kg when empty and the wire weighs 35 g per meter, how many meters of wire are on the spool?

Solve. (Use the same methods as for two-step equations.)

38. $8x - 4 < 12$

39. $4x + 3 < 15$

40. $5x + 4 < 29$

41. $15x - 75 > 0$

42. $121 > 11x + 11$

43. $10x - 90 > 160$

44. $\frac{x}{8} - 5 > 4$

45. $12 > \frac{x}{6} + 3$

46. $\frac{x}{16} + 4 < 4$

47. $\frac{x}{16} - 4 > 4$

48. $\frac{x+5}{8} < 5$

49. $\frac{x-13}{3} < 2$

50. $5 < \frac{x-9}{4}$

51. $\frac{x+12}{7} > 2$

2.7 U.S. Units of Measure

In the United States, the metric system of measurement is now more widely used than it has been in the past. But an older system, now often called the **U.S. system,** is still in use. Some units of this system are shown in the chart below.

To measure	you can use	Common equivalents
Length	inches (in.), feet (ft), yards (yd), miles (mi)	1 ft = 12 in. 1 yd = 3 ft 1 mi = 5280 ft
Weight	ounces (oz) pounds (lb) tons	1 lb = 16 oz 1 ton = 2000 lb
Capacity	cups (c), pints (pt), quarts (qt), gallons (gal.)	1 pt = 2 c 1 qt = 2 pt 1 gal. = 4 qt

To convert from larger units to smaller, multiply.

To convert from smaller units to larger, divide.

Examples:

12 yd = ____ ft

Each yard contains 3 feet.

So multiply 12 by 3.

12 yd = <u>36</u> ft

38 pt = ____ qt

There are 2 pints in each quart.

So divide 38 by 2.

38 pt = <u>19</u> qt

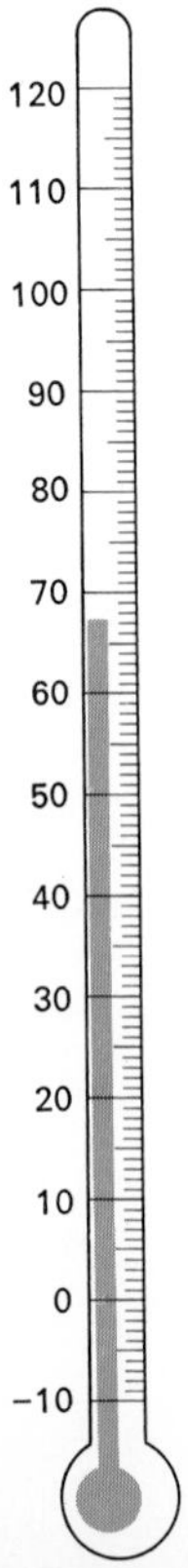

The degree Fahrenheit (°F) is the unit of temperature in the U.S. system.

- Water boils at 212 °F.
- Normal body temperature is between 98 °F and 99 °F.
- Comfortable room temperature is 68 °F.
- Water freezes at 32 °F.

Exercises

A

1. How would you find how many feet are in 3 miles?
2. How would you find how many pounds are in 5 tons?
3. How would you find how many pints are in 8 cups?
4. How would you find how many gallons are in 24 quarts?
5. To convert from a larger to a smaller unit, (*divide, multiply*).
6. To convert from a smaller to a larger unit, (*divide, multiply*).
7. On the Fahrenheit scale, water boils at (*32, 100, 212*) degrees.
8. A feverish person's temperature could be (*37 °F, 102 °F, 212 °F*).

B Complete.

9. 6 pt = ____ c
10. 8 qt = ____ pt
11. 7 gal. = ____ qt
12. 3 tons = ____ lb
13. 15 ft = ____ in.
14. 32 lb = ____ oz
15. 27 yd = ____ ft
16. 33 ft = ____ in.
17. 6 mi = ____ ft
18. 64 lb = ____ oz
19. 4 gal. = ____ qt
20. 320 oz = ____ lb
21. 108 ft = ____ yd
22. 156 in. = ____ ft
23. 360 ft = ____ yd
24. 6 pt = ____ qt
25. 64 oz = ____ lb
26. 15,840 ft = ____ mi
27. 180 in. = ____ ft
28. 82 c = ____ pt
29. 8000 lb = ____ tons
30. 52 qt = ____ gal.
31. 76 qt = ____ gal.
32. 10 yd = ____ ft
33. 30 yd = ____ ft
34. 6 qt = ____ pt

35. 336 c = ____ gal.

36. 3 gal. = ____ c

37. 5 qt = ____ c

38. 4 yd = ____ in.

39. 72 pt = ____ gal.

40. 108 in. = ____ yd

41. 284 c = ____ qt

42. 2 mi = ____ yd

43. The cheetah is the fastest land animal over short distances. A cheetah can run 600 yards in about 20 seconds. How fast is this in yards per second? In feet per second?

Use this formula to convert the given temperatures.

$$F = \frac{9C}{5} + 32$$

(C: degrees Celsius; F: degrees Fahrenheit)

44. 25 °C = ____°F

45. 70 °C = ____°F

46. 0 °C = ____°F

47. 100 °C = ____°F

48. Iron melts at 1535 °C. What is the melting point of iron in degrees Fahrenheit? (Use the formula above.)

C For each pair of measures, write a formula to show how they are related. Check your formula by substituting values.

Example: i inches, f feet

Answer: $i = 12f$ (or $f = \frac{i}{12}$)

Check:

f	1	2	3
i	12	24	36

49. m miles, f feet

50. t tons, p pounds

51. p pints, g gallons

52. g gallons, q quarts

53. f feet, y yards

54. n ounces, p pounds

55. c cups, q quarts

56. p pints, c cups

2.8 Area and Volume

The **area** of a figure is the amount of surface it covers.

Area is measured in *square units*.

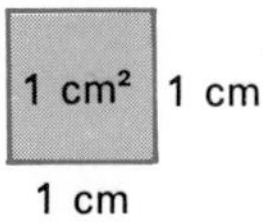

1 square centimeter or 1 cm^2

Example 1: Find the area of the rectangle.

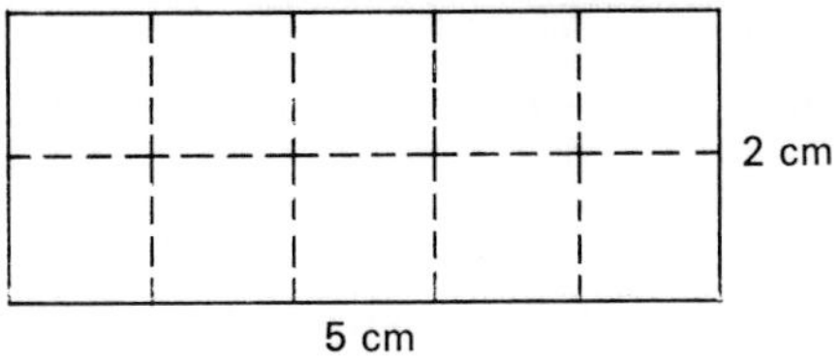

The rectangle covers the same amount of surface as 10 squares of 1 cm^2 each. So its area is 10 cm^2.

Length and width must be in the same units.

$$\begin{array}{ccccc} 5 & \times & 2 & = & 10 \\ \downarrow & & \downarrow & & \downarrow \\ \text{cm} & & \text{cm} & & \text{cm}^2 \end{array}$$

length × width = area

For a rectangle, $A = lw$.

The **volume** of a solid is the amount of space it occupies.

Volume is measured in *cubic units*.

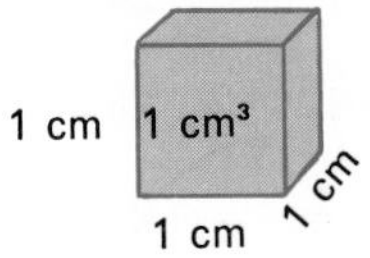

1 cubic centimeter or 1 cm^3

Example 2: Find the volume of the solid. (The faces are rectangles.)

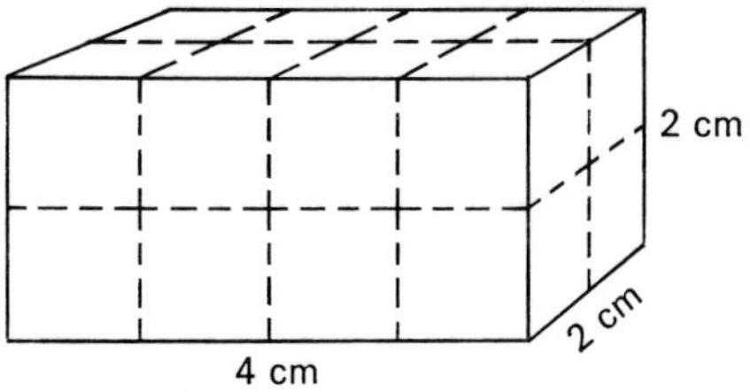

The solid occupies the same amount of space as 16 cubes of 1 cm^3 each. So its volume is 16 cm^3.

Length, width, and height must be in the same units.

$$\begin{array}{ccccccc} 4 & \times & 2 & \times & 2 & = & 16 \\ \downarrow & & \downarrow & & \downarrow & & \downarrow \\ \text{cm} & & \text{cm} & & \text{cm} & & \text{cm}^3 \end{array}$$

length × width × height = volume

For a rectangular solid, $V = lwh$.

Exercises

A What unit of area has all sides of the given length?

1. 1 cm **2.** 1 in. **3.** 1 yd **4.** 1 m

What unit of volume has all edges of the given length?

5. 1 cm **6.** 1 in. **7.** 1 ft **8.** 1 km

What is the length of each side of the given unit of area?

9. 1 sq ft **10.** 1 km^2 **11.** 1 sq mi **12.** 1 mm^2

What is the length of each edge of the given unit of volume?

13. 1 cu yd **14.** 1 mm^3 **15.** 1 cu in. **16.** 1 m^3

B Find each area or volume.

RECTANGLES

	area	length	width
17.		7 in.	3 in.
18.		9 m	6 m
19.		12 yd	4 yd
20.		11 km	9 km
21.		21 ft	13 ft
22.		15 mm	7 mm

RECTANGULAR SOLIDS

	volume	length	width	height
23.		8 m	5 m	3 m
24.		11 ft	6 ft	9 ft
25.		13 mm	8 mm	4 mm
26.		24 in.	17 in.	10 in.
27.		9 km	1 km	9 km
28.		8 yd	3 yd	18 yd

Find each width or height.

Examples:

area: 27 cm^2
length: 9 cm
width: ? cm

$A = lw$

$27 = 9w$

$3 = w$

width: 3 cm

volume: 30 cu in.
length: 5 in.
width: 2 in.
height: ? in.

$V = lwh$

$30 = (5 \times 2)h$

$3 = h$

height: 3 in.

	area	length	width
29.	65 sq yd	13 yd	
30.	48 m^2	12 m	

	volume	length	width	height
31.	90 mm^3	6 mm	3 mm	
32.	140 cu ft	7 ft	5 ft	

Find the area. Use one of the given formulas.

33. parallelogram; $b = 5$ cm, $h = 8$ cm

34. triangle; $b = 43$ m, $h = 24$ m

35. trapezoid; $a = 3$ in., $b = 7$ in., $h = 9$ in.

36. triangle; $h = 22$ mi, $b = 13$ mi

parallelogram

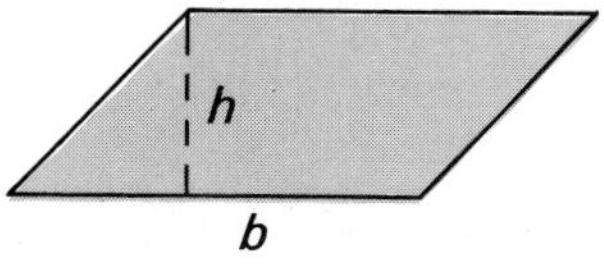

$A = bh$

triangle

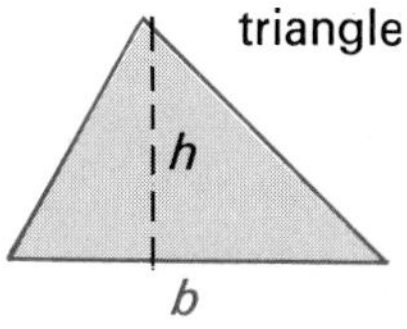

$A = bh \div 2$

Find the volume. Use one of the given formulas.

37. prism; $B = 7\ cm^2$, $h = 11$ cm

38. pyramid; $B = 21\ m^2$, $h = 8$ m

39. prism; $B = 16$ sq yd, $h = 5$ yd

C **40.** pyramid with triangular base; $h = 11$ in., h of base $= 4$ in., b of base $= 3$ in.

prism

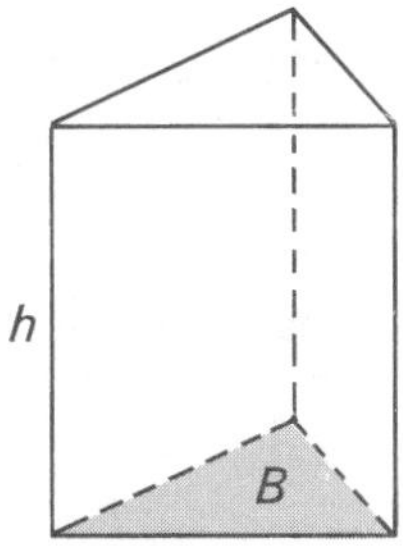

$V = \text{area of base} \times h$
$= Bh$

trapezoid

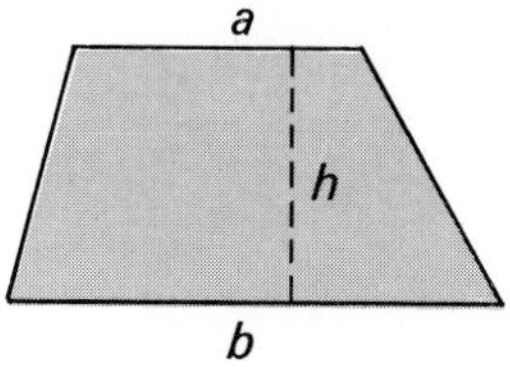

$A = h(a + b) \div 2$

Complete.

41. For a rectangle, if $w = 2$ cm and $l = 30$ mm, then $A =$ ____ cm^2 or $A =$ ____ mm^2.

42. For a rectangular solid, if $l = 2$ m, $w = 100$ cm, and $h = 3000$ mm, then $V =$ ____ m^3 or $V =$ ____ cm^3.

pyramid

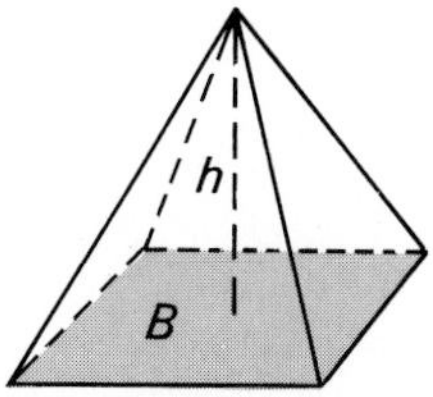

$V = \text{area of base} \times h \div 3$
$= Bh \div 3$

Solve. (1 L $= 1000\ cm^3$)

43. There are about 8543 cubic kilometers of usable fresh water on the earth. How many liters of fresh water is this?

44. There are about 29 200 cubic kilometers of fresh water in ice caps and glaciers. How many liters is this?

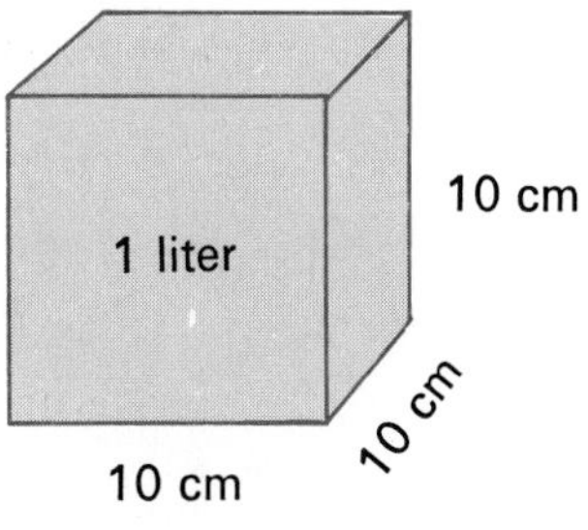

2.9 More Translating Into Symbols

Some English sentences can be translated directly into symbols.

Example 1: Translate into symbols.

Three plus twice a number n is fifteen.

$$3 + 2n = 15$$

If the variable is not given in the problem, you must start by choosing a variable and saying what it represents.

© Photo Graphics/Kreutzig

Example 2: Translate into symbols.

A 48-inch board is cut into two pieces.

One piece is 8 inches longer than the other.

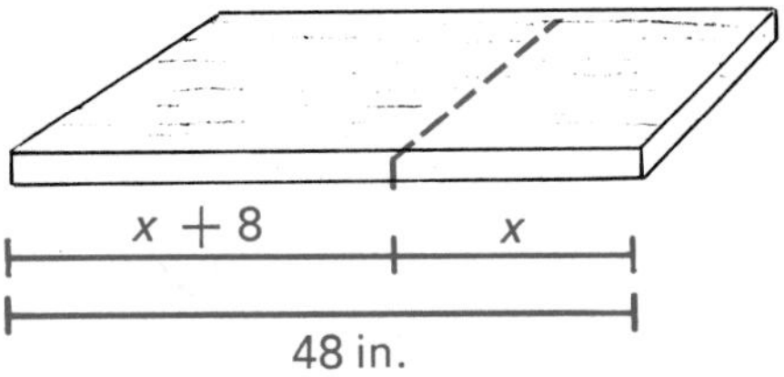

Let x = length of shorter piece.

Then $x + 8$ = length of longer piece.

$x + (x + 8) = 48$ ◀ The sum of the lengths is 48.

Example 3: Translate into symbols.

Bob's age is 6 more than twice Jim's age. Bob is 42.

Let a = Jim's age.

Then $2a + 6$ = Bob's age.

$2a + 6 = 42$ ◀ Bob's age is 42.

Exercises

A Tell how you would represent each quantity.

1. One number is five times a second number.

a. second number **b.** first number

2. One carton weighs 50 pounds less than a second carton.

a. weight of second carton **b.** weight of first carton

3. Arlene is 3 years older than her brother Paul.

a. Paul's age **b.** Arlene's age

4. One number is 2 less than twice a second number.

a. second number **b.** first number

B Translate into symbols.

5. Twenty-one is six more than a number.

6. 15 is subtracted from twice a number. The result is 11.

7. Twelve is twice Mario's age divided by 3.

8. The perimeter of a rectangle is 30 inches. The length is twice the width.

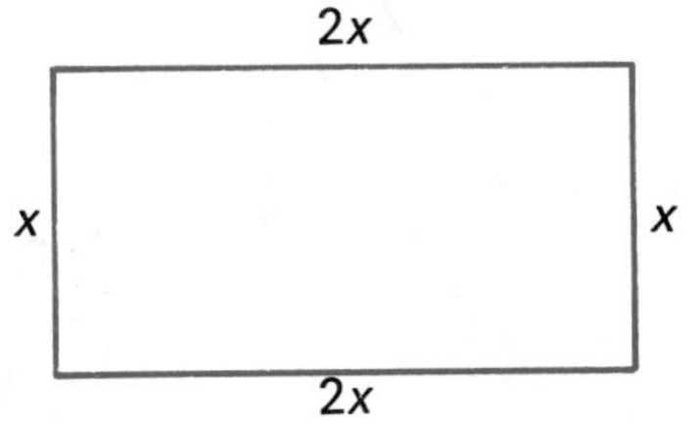

9. One shirt costs two dollars more than a second shirt. The total cost of the two shirts is twenty-four dollars.

10. Jan has saved \$235. This is \$15 less than the amount she needs for her vacation.

11. One number is 3 times a second number. The sum of the two numbers is 20.

12. Ann's father's age is 6 more than twice Ann's age. He is 51.

13. An adult ticket costs \$1 more than a student ticket. The cost of 2 adult and 3 student tickets is \$12.

14. The difference between two numbers is 3. Their sum is 15.

15. Stuart and Evie played 20 games of rummy. Evie won 2 more games than Stuart did.

16. 52 students were placed in two classes. There were 4 more students in Ms. Krol's class than in Mr. Luster's class.

17. The Detroit Pistons beat the Chicago Bulls by 20 points. Their combined score was 210 points.

Courtesy Chicago Bulls

C Translate these sentences into inequalities.

Example: Twice a number is greater than 10.

Let n = number.

$2n > 10$

18. 45 is less than 3 times a number.

19. Rich is older than Karen. Karen is 27.

20. A number divided by 3 is less than 15.

21. The sum of 11 and a number is greater than 36.

22. \$5.00 is more than what Diane wants to spend.

23. Aretha scored more points in the game than Cora. Cora scored 18 points.

24. Mark spent less than \$6.00 on the gift.

Terms and Symbols Review

Match each item with the best description.

1. addition	**a.** inverse of division
2. subtraction	**b.** units of temperature
3. multiplication	**c.** inverse of subtraction
4. division	**d.** units of weight
5. graph of $x < 3$	**e.** inverse of addition
6. ounces and tons	**f.** graph of $\{0, 1, 2\}$
7. degrees Fahrenheit	**g.** units of length
8. cups and gallons	**h.** inverse of multiplication
9. feet and yards	**i.** units of capacity

Chapter 2 Review

Find each answer. Use an inverse operation to check. 2.1

1. $\begin{array}{r} 72 \\ -13 \\ \hline \end{array}$ **2.** $\begin{array}{r} 195 \\ -23 \\ \hline \end{array}$ **3.** $215 \div 5$ **4.** $183 \div 3$

Simplify each phrase.

5. $27 + 4 - 4$ **6.** $9 \times 7 \div 7$

7. $\frac{3}{2} \times 2$ **8.** $14 - 5 + 5$

Solve.

9. $x + 7 = 15$ **10.** $2 = n - 5$ 2.2

11. $y - 32 = 17$ **12.** $x - 11 = 0$

13. $7n = 14$ **14.** $\frac{x}{8} = 10$ 2.3

15. $84 = 12x$ **16.** $31 = \frac{n}{3}$

2.4 Solve.

17. $n + 11 < 16$

18. $x + 7 > 10$

19. $3 > y - 7$

20. $31 < n - 8$

21. $\frac{x}{7} > 1$

22. $5 < \frac{n}{6}$

23. $8x > 24$

24. $120 < 10y$

2.5 Solve and graph.

25. $n - 7 = 2$

26. $\frac{y}{6} = 3$

27. $5x = 20$

28. $3 = y + 3$

29. $\frac{n}{4} < 1$

30. $12 < 4y$

31. $x - 2 > 3$

32. $5 > n - 14$

2.6 Solve.

33. $3x - 4 = 8$

34. $21 = 8x + 5$

35. $\frac{n}{7} + 3 = 5$

36. $7 = \frac{n + 8}{2}$

37. $\frac{x - 6}{9} = 9$

38. $\frac{a}{4} - 3 = 7$

2.7 Complete.

39. 13 ft = ____ in.

40. 6 lb = ____ oz

41. 5 qt = ____ pt

42. 72 in. = ____ ft

43. 96 oz = ____ lb

44. 24 qt = ____ gal.

2.8 Find each area or volume.

RECTANGLES

	area	length	width
45.		13 km	7 km
46.		27 ft	20 ft

RECTANGULAR SOLIDS

	volume	length	width	height
47.		9 in.	6 in.	20 in.
48.		12 cm	7 cm	5 cm

2.9 Translate into symbols.

49. Thirty-five is seven more than a number.

50. The profit is \$100. This is \$6 less than twice the cost.

Solve.

1. $x + 7 = 19$
2. $12 = y - 8$
3. $9n = 72$
4. $96 = \frac{x}{6}$
5. $4n - 5 = 19$
6. $72 = 7y + 2$
7. $\frac{x}{8} + 7 = 10$
8. $\frac{n - 6}{3} = 10$
9. $3x < 39$
10. $\frac{n}{7} > 2$
11. $n - 8 > 2$
12. $6 < y + 5$

Solve and graph.

13. $\frac{x}{2} = 6$
14. $n + 8 = 13$
15. $y + 3 < 7$
16. $6n > 12$

Complete.

17. 240 in. = ____ ft
18. 7 qt = ____ pt
19. 9 lb = ____ oz
20. 24 ft = ____ yd

21. A rectangle with length 15 centimeters and width 4 centimeters has area ______.

22. A rectangular solid with length 7 inches, width 3 inches, and height 10 inches has volume ______.

Translate into symbols.

23. Carolyn Andrews has 3 more strikes than twice the number her daughter Angie has. Carolyn has 7 strikes.

RATE YOURSELF

Number Correct	
22–23	Superior
20–21	Excellent
17–19	Good
12–16	Fair
0–11	Poor

"I LIKE THE WAY THEY SPOT THE PINS HERE!"

UNIVERSAL PRODUCT CODE

Most packages in a food store are now marked with a pattern of bars and spaces like the one shown here. The bars are of three different widths. They are separated by spaces of three widths.

Part of the pattern stands for the manufacturer's code number.

Part of the pattern stands for the code number of the product.

These patterns can be "read" by a scanner connected to a computer. The computer has a matching pattern stored in it, along with the price of the item in the package.

Courtesy NCR Corporation

The check-out system works like this:

1. The shopper brings the packages to the check-out clerk.
2. The clerk runs the pattern on each package past an electronic scanner.
3. The scanner reads the pattern.
4. The computer looks up the pattern in its memory to find today's price on the item.
5. The computer prints the price on the cash-register tape. It also prints the name of the item.
6. The computer totals the bill and adds the tax.
7. The shopper pays the bill!

Getting Ready for Chapter 3

Answer each question.

1. What are the first 10 odd numbers?

2. What are the first 10 even numbers greater than 0?

Compute. 1.2

3. $5 + 6 + 8$

4. $12 + (8 + 9)$

5. $17 - (8 - 3)$

6. $(12 - 9) - 2$

7. $(3 \times 4) \times 3$

8. $10 \times (2 \times 4)$

9. $16 \div 2 \div 2$

10. $12 \div (9 \div 3)$

11. $1 + 7 \times 3$

12. $8 \times 3 + 4$

13. $(1 + 7) \times 3$

14. $8 \times (3 + 4)$

15. $(7 \times 2) + (7 \times 4)$

16. $(2 \times 5) + (3 \times 5)$

Solve.

17. $x + 8 = 20$

18. $22 = n + 16$ 2.2

19. $y - 6 = 6$

20. $6 = z - 13$

21. $63 = 9r$

22. $7y = 56$ 2.3

Solve. 1.9

23. A rectangle has a length of 8 inches and a width of 6 inches. What is its perimeter? ($p = 2l + 2w$)

24. A car is going 55 mph. How long will it take the car to go 165 miles? ($d = rt$)

3

IMPORTANT PROPERTIES

Courtesy American Trucking Association

3

A good driver follows the "rules of the road." Using the rules is an important part of a safe trip.

Some "rules of the road" in mathematics are called *properties*. Others are important facts about whole numbers. In this chapter you will use these rules to solve equations and to learn more about whole numbers.

Commutative Properties

3.1

Walk 5 blocks E and 2 N. *Walk 2 blocks N and 5 E.*

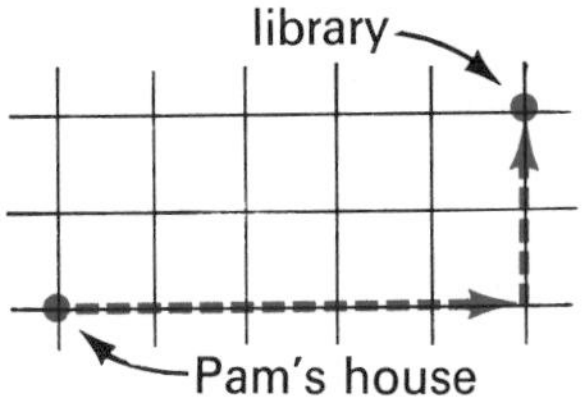

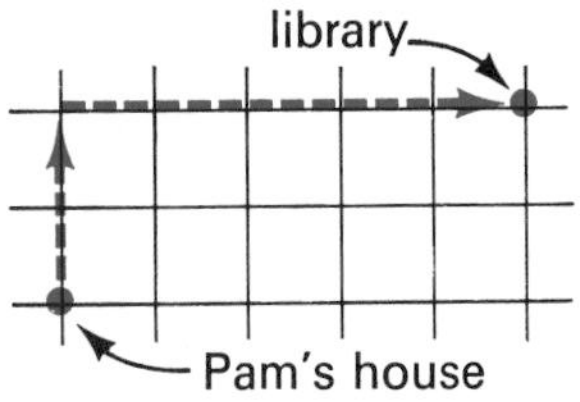

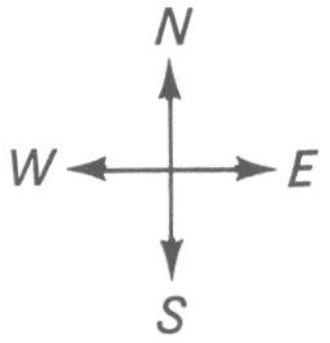

The order in which Pam walks from her house to the library does not change the result. She gets to the library either way.

Changing the order of some activities changes the result.

Go out and close the door. *Close the door and go out.*

In mathematics an operation is **commutative** if you can change the order and still get the same result.

You can change the order of the numbers for some operations but not for others. For example, *addition is commutative.*

change the order

$3 + 4 = 7$ $\qquad$ $4 + 3 = 7$

same sum

so

$$3 + 4 = 4 + 3$$

Commutative Property of Addition

Any two numbers a and b can be added in either order without changing the sum. So

$a + b = b + a$. $\qquad$ *Example:* $2 + 7 = 7 + 2$

Example 1: Is multiplication commutative?

change the order

$6 \times 2 = 12$ $\qquad$ $2 \times 6 = 12$

same product

so

$$6 \times 2 = 2 \times 6$$

Yes, *multiplication is commutative.*

Commutative Property of Multiplication

Any two numbers a and b can be multiplied in either order without changing the product. So

$a \times b = b \times a$. $\qquad$ *Example:* $8 \times 3 = 3 \times 8$

Example 2: Are subtraction and division commutative?

a. change the order

$4 - 3 = 1$ $\qquad$ $3 - 4 = {}^{-}1$

different

b. change the order

$8 \div 2 = 4$ $\qquad$ $2 \div 8 = \frac{1}{4}$

different

No, *subtraction and division are not commutative.*

Example 3: Sometimes changing the order of the factors makes the computation easier.

$$\begin{array}{r} 20 \\ \times 586 \\ \hline 120 \\ 1600 \\ 10000 \\ \hline 11720 \end{array} \qquad \longrightarrow \qquad \begin{array}{r} 586 \\ \times 20 \\ \hline 11720 \end{array}$$

Example 4: For each equation, use the commutative property to write a new equation.

a. $5 + x = 7$

$x + 5 = 7$

b. $d \times 3 = 12$

$3d = 12$

Exercises

A Tell if you can change the order of the following activities without changing the result.

1. putting on your hat; putting on your coat

2. washing a car; waxing a car

3. taking the phone off the hook; dialing your number

4. salting your soup; peppering your soup

5. filling a swimming pool; diving in

6. addressing an envelope; putting a stamp on an envelope

B Compute. Whenever possible, use the commutative property to make the computation easier.

7. $\begin{array}{r} 20 \\ \times 425 \\ \hline \end{array}$ **8.** $\begin{array}{r} 300 \\ \times 625 \\ \hline \end{array}$ **9.** $\begin{array}{r} 428 \\ \times 30 \\ \hline \end{array}$ **10.** $\begin{array}{r} 200 \\ \times 856 \\ \hline \end{array}$

11. $\begin{array}{r} 142 \\ \times 72 \\ \hline \end{array}$ **12.** $\begin{array}{r} 83 \\ \times 524 \\ \hline \end{array}$ **13.** $\begin{array}{r} 40 \\ \times 6295 \\ \hline \end{array}$ **14.** $\begin{array}{r} 300 \\ \times 6675 \\ \hline \end{array}$

For each equation, use the commutative properties to write a new equation. (See Example 4.) Then solve.

15. $5 + x = 9$ **16.** $4 + y = 10$ **17.** $14 = 8 + z$

18. $m \times 3 = 15$ **19.** $49 = t \times 7$ **20.** $r \times 6 = 42$

21. $14 = 6 + t$ **22.** $k \times 9 = 72$ **23.** $11 + m = 69$

24. $96 = z \times 8$ **25.** $13 + n = 81$ **26.** $y \times 7 = 245$

27. $18 + c = 96$ **28.** $r \times 11 = 242$ **29.** $91 = 17 + d$

Use the formulas below to solve the following problems.

distance, rate, time:

$$d = rt$$

retail price, wholesale price, markup:

$$r = w + m$$

30. It took Barb 3 hours to ride her bike 18 miles. What was her rate of speed?

31. A train traveled 345 miles in 5 hours. How fast was the train going?

32. The retail price of a record album is \$7. If the wholesale price is \$5, how much is the markup?

33. The retail price of a tennis racket is \$27, and the wholesale price is \$21. How much is the markup?

total cost, cost per unit, number of units, delivery charge:

$$C = un + a$$

[C] **34.** A fence installer received an order of 54 fence posts. The total cost of the order was \$123, and the delivery charge was \$15. What was the cost of each fence post?

35. The total cost of an order for 13 shrubs was \$77. If the cost of each shrub was \$5, what was the delivery charge?

3.2 Associative Properties

You often have to find the sum of three numbers, such as

$$3 + 5 + 7$$

Should you begin by adding 3 and 5? Or 5 and 7? Or does it matter?

$$3 + 5 + 7$$

$(3 + 5) + 7$ $\qquad$ $3 + (5 + 7)$

$8 + 7$ $\qquad$ $3 + 12$

15 $\qquad$ 15

same

so

$$(3 + 5) + 7 = 3 + (5 + 7)$$

An operation is **associative** if you can group in different ways as above without changing the result.

Associative Property of Addition

Any three numbers a, b, and c can be added by grouping the first two or the last two numbers without changing the sum. So

$(a + b) + c = a + (b + c)$.

Example:
$(1 + 3) + 6 = 1 + (3 + 6)$

Multiplication is also associative.

$$6 \times 8 \times 5$$

$(6 \times 8) \times 5$ $\qquad$ $6 \times (8 \times 5)$

48×5 $\qquad$ 6×40

240 $\qquad$ 240

same

so

$$(6 \times 8) \times 5 = 6 \times (8 \times 5)$$

Associative Property of Multiplication

Any three numbers *a*, *b*, and *c* can be multiplied by grouping the first two or the last two numbers without changing the product. So

$(a \times b) \times c = a \times (b \times c).$

Example:
$(3 \times 5) \times 4 = 3 \times (5 \times 4)$

Example 1: Tell which method of grouping makes the computation easier.

$28 + 96 + 4$

$(28 + 96) + 4$	$28 + (96 + 4)$
$124 \quad + 4$	$28 + \quad 100$
128	128

$28 + (96 + 4)$ enables most people to do the addition mentally.

Example 2: Sometimes the commutative and associative properties are both used to make the computation easier.

Long way		*Short way*
$25 \times 68 \times 4$		$25 \times 68 \times 4$
$(25 \times 68) \times 4$	Associative property	
$(68 \times 25) \times 4$	Commutative property	
$68 \times (25 \times 4)$	Associative property	
68×100		68×100
6800		6800

Example 3: Sometimes the commutative and the associative properties are used in solving equations.

a.

$(x + 5) + 6 = 39$	
$x + (5 + 6) = 39$	Associative property
$x + 11 = 39$	Add.
$x + 11 - 11 = 39 - 11$	Inverse operation
$x = 28$	

b.

$54 = (2t)3$	
$54 = 3(2t)$	Commutative property
$54 = (3 \times 2)t$	Associative property
$54 = 6t$	Multiply.
$\frac{54}{6} = \frac{6t}{6}$	Inverse operation
$9 = t$	

Check as required.

Exercises

A Study the examples. Tell if subtraction and division are associative.

1. $9 - 5 - 2$

$(9 - 5) - 2$ → $4 - 2$ → 2

$9 - (5 - 2)$ → $9 - 3$ → 6

2 ← different → 6

2. $24 \div 6 \div 2$

$(24 \div 6) \div 2$ → $4 \div 2$ → 2

$24 \div (6 \div 2)$ → $24 \div 3$ → 8

2 ← different → 8

Tell how you would group the addends or the factors to make the computation easy.

3. $30 + 60 + 18$ **4.** $72 + 91 + 9$ **5.** $54 + 6 + 27$

6. $5 \times 2 \times 9$ **7.** $12 \times 4 \times 5$ **8.** $25 \times 4 \times 16$

9. $16 + 84 + 99$ **10.** $33 \times 25 \times 8$ **11.** $4 \times 250 \times 172$

B Compute. Use the properties to make the computation as easy as possible.

12. $6 + 4 + 9$ **13.** $5 \times 40 \times 6$ **14.** $19 + 13 + 17$

15. $9 \times 4 \times 25$ **16.** $20 \times 83 \times 50$ **17.** $63 + 59 + 37$

18. $68 + 89 + 11$ **19.** $943 + 68 + 57$ **20.** $8 \times 25 \times 6$

21. $8 \times 250 \times 17$ **22.** $4 \times 63 \times 25$ **23.** $83 + 69 + 31$

24. $16 + 24 + 48$ **25.** $72 + 83 + 17$ **26.** $50 \times 19 \times 20$

Solve. (See Example 3.)

27. $(n + 3) + 7 = 20$

28. $12 + (5 + p) = 34$

29. $(4 + q) + 3 = 21$

30. $40 = 6 + (r + 14)$

31. $(2s + 1) + 3 = 16$

32. $(8 + 3t) + 1 = 27$

33. $48 = (2u)4$

34. $36 = (6v)3$

35. $(5w)2 = 120$

36. $(15x)2 = 90$

37. $12 = 2(y \times 3)$

38. $(z \times 4)5 = 80$

Use the formulas below to find the missing values.

perimeter of a triangle (p); lengths of sides (a, b, c)

$$p = a + b + c$$

volume of a box (v); length (l), width (w), height (h)

$$v = lwh$$

39. The perimeter of a triangle is 16 in. If $a = 4$ in. and $c = 7$ in., find b.

40. The perimeter of a triangle is 43 cm. If $a = 16$ cm and $c = 12$ cm, find b.

41. The volume of a box is 36 cu ft. If $w = 3$ ft and $h = 2$ ft, find l.

42. The volume of a box is 480 m^3. If $l = 8$ m and $h = 12$ m, find w.

total points in football (p); touchdowns (t), conversions (c), field goals (f), safeties (s)

$$p = 6t + 1c + 3f + 2s$$

Camerique

C **43.** Suppose $p = 47$, $t = 5$, $f = 3$, and $s = 2$. Find c.

44. Suppose $p = 36$, $t = 4$, $c = 4$, and $s = 1$. Find f.

Zero and One

You already know that 0 and 1 have special properties. For example, what happens when you add 0 to a number?

$8 + 0 = 8 \qquad 0 + 275 = 275 \qquad y + 0 = y$

$0 + t = t \qquad 0 + 0 = 0$

Identity Property of Addition

0 is the *identity number for addition.* The sum of 0 and any number n is that number. So

$0 + n = n$ and $n + 0 = n$. *Example:* $0 + 4 = 4$
$4 + 0 = 4$

What about multiplying by 1?

$1 \times 5 = 5 \qquad 6 \times 1 = 6 \qquad 1 \times w = w$

$r \times 1 = r \qquad 1 \times 1 = 1$

Identity Property of Multiplication

1 is the *identity number for multiplication.* The product of 1 and any number n is that number. So

$1 \times n = n$ and $n \times 1 = n$. *Example:* $1 \times 7 = 7$
$7 \times 1 = 7$

Can you multiply by 0?

$3 \times 0 = 0$ $\qquad 0 \times 37 = 0$ $\qquad a \times 0 = 0$

$0 \times t = 0$ $\qquad 0 \times 0 = 0$

Multiplication Property of 0

The product of 0 and any number n is 0. So

$0 \times n = 0$ and $n \times 0 = 0$. *Example:* $0 \times 2 = 0$
$2 \times 0 = 0$

What happens when you divide a number by itself?

$4 \div 4 = 1$ $\qquad 24 \div 24 = 1$ $\qquad 142 \div 142 = 1$

But what about $0 \div 0$?

$0 \div 0 = ? \longrightarrow 0\overline{)0}$ with quotient ?

Check: $? \times 0 = 0$

◀ Every number works. So there is no answer for $0 \div 0$.

Any number except 0 divided by itself is 1. That is, for any nonzero number n,

$n \div n = 1$. *Example:* $6 \div 6 = 1$

0 cannot be divided by itself, but 0 can be divided by other numbers.

$0 \div 5 = 0 \longrightarrow 5\overline{)0}$ with quotient 0

Check: $0 \times 5 = 0$ ◀ It checks.

0 divided by any number except 0 is 0. That is, for any nonzero number n,

$0 \div n = 0$. *Example:* $0 \div 16 = 0$

Dividing any number by 0 is meaningless.

$3 \div 0 = ? \longrightarrow 0\overline{)3}$ with quotient ?

Check: $? \times 0 = 3$

◀ No number works. So there is no answer for $3 \div 0$.

Never divide by zero.

Exercises

A Find the value of each phrase.

1. 4×1 **2.** 1×16 **3.** $42 + 0$

4. $0 + 172$ **5.** 19×0 **6.** 0×16

7. $0 \div 16$ **8.** $0 \div 8$ **9.** $3 \div 3$

B Use the properties of 0 and 1 to solve each equation.

10. $1 \times 16 = m$ **11.** $0 \div y = 0$ **12.** $184 + 0 = d$

13. $37 \times 0 = k$ **14.** $36 \div 36 = c$ **15.** $k \times 32 = 32$

16. $14 \div r = 1$ **17.** $84 \times x = 0$ **18.** $0 \times 189 = p$

19. $79 \times 1 = r$ **20.** $596 + m = 596$ **21.** $h \times 0 = 0$

22. $t \div 4 = 0$ **23.** $1 \times t = 89$ **24.** $196 \times c = 196$

25. $f + 0 = 296$ **26.** $26 \div a = 1$ **27.** $b \div 8 = 0$

28. $g \div 31 = 1$ **29.** $0 + n = 197$ **30.** $s \times 597 = 0$

C Find the value of each phrase without doing any written computation.

31. $32 + (9 - 9)$ **32.** $(19 - 18) \times 56$ **33.** $182 - (0 \div 4)$

34. $385 \times (284 - 283)$ **35.** $(14 \div 14) \times 163$ **36.** $24 \div [8 - (4 + 3)]$

3.4 Distributive Property

Suppose you buy 5 tapes and 4 records at the sale price. You can figure the cost in either of these two ways.

cost per item	number of items		cost of tapes	cost of records
3	$\times (5 + 4)$		(3×5)	$+ (3 \times 4)$
3	$\times\ 9$		15	$+\ 12$
27			27	

27 ← same → 27

so

$$3(5 + 4) = (3 \times 5) + (3 \times 4)$$

This relationship is useful in solving problems. It is called the *distributive property of multiplication over addition.*

Distributive Property

For any numbers a, b, and c,

$$a(b + c) = ab + ac$$

and

$$ab + ac = a(b + c).$$

The commutative property allows us to state the distributive property as $ba + ca = (b + c)a$. This pattern is helpful in solving equations.

Example 1: Solve $7x + 9x = 64$.

$$7x + 9x = 64$$

$$(7 + 9)x = 64 \quad \text{Distributive property}$$

$$16x = 64$$

$$\frac{16x}{16} = \frac{64}{16} \quad \text{Inverse operation}$$

$$x = 4$$

Check:

$$7x + 9x = 64$$

$$(7 \times 4) + (9 \times 4) = 64$$

$$28 + 36 = 64$$

$$64 = 64 \checkmark$$

Example 2: Solve $21 = 2x + x$.

$$21 = 2x + x$$

$$21 = 2x + 1x \quad \text{1 is identity number for multiplication.}$$

$$21 = (2 + 1)x \quad \text{Distributive property}$$

$$21 = 3x$$

$$\frac{21}{3} = \frac{3x}{3} \quad \text{Inverse operation}$$

$$7 = x$$

Check:

$$21 = 2x + x$$

$$21 = (2 \times 7) + 7$$

$$21 = 14 + 7$$

$$21 = 21 \checkmark$$

Exercises

A Tell what number or variable should replace each ?.

1. $3(2 + 6) = (3 \times ?) + (3 \times 6)$
2. $4(? + 8) = (4 \times 7) + (4 \times 8)$
3. $(9 \times 6) + (9 \times 5) = 9(6 + ?)$
4. $(8 \times 3) + (? \times 2) = 8(3 + 2)$
5. $x + x = 1x + 1x = (? + 1)x$
6. $4r + r = (4 + ?)r$

7. $5x + 6x = (5 + 6)?$

8. $8y + 16y = (? + 16)y$

9. $10c + 3c = (10 + ?)c$

10. $25d + 7d = (25 + 7)?$

B Compute in two ways: **(a)** Add; then multiply.
(b) Use the distributive property.

Example: **a.** $6(5 + 3)$
$6(8)$
48

b. $6(5 + 3)$
$(6 \times 5) + (6 \times 3)$
$30 + 18$
48

11. $6(8 + 9)$

12. $5(9 + 6)$

13. $14(3 + 10)$

14. $8(17 + 13)$

15. $12(4 + 10)$

16. $9(20 + 8)$

Solve. (See Example 2.)

17. $7t + 2t = 72$

18. $6c + 14c = 180$

19. $198 = g + 8g$

20. $300 = 57m + 43m$

21. $16y + 34y = 2500$

22. $2000 = 19n + n$

23. $348 = 12a + 46a$

24. $b + b = 420$

Solve.

Example:

$$10x - 4x = 36$$
$$(10 - 4)x = 36$$
$$6x = 36$$
$$\frac{6x}{6} = \frac{36}{6}$$
$$x = 6$$

Check:

$$10x - 4x = 36$$
$$(10 \times 6) - (4 \times 6) = 36$$
$$60 - 24 = 36$$
$$36 = 36 \checkmark$$

25. $9a - 6a = 21$

26. $12b - 7b = 25$

27. $10c - c = 18$

28. $30 = 25d - 10d$

29. $18 = 20f - 11f$

30. $17g - 7g = 100$

31. $88 = 38h - 16h$

32. $240 = 25j - j$

C Solve.

Example:

$$
\begin{aligned}
5x + 3 + 2x + 6 &= 23 \\
(5x + 2x) + (3 + 6) &= 23 \\
(5 + 2)x + 9 &= 23 \\
7x + 9 - 9 &= 23 - 9 \\
7x &= 14 \\
\frac{7x}{7} &= \frac{14}{7} \\
x &= 2
\end{aligned}
$$

Check:

$$
\begin{aligned}
5x + 3 + 2x + 6 &= 23 \\
(5 \times 2) + 3 + (2 \times 2) + 6 &= 23 \\
10 + 3 + 4 + 6 &= 23 \\
(10 + 3) + (4 + 6) &= 23 \\
13 + 10 &= 23 \\
23 &= 23 \ \checkmark
\end{aligned}
$$

33. $3a + 7 + 6a + 4 = 92$

34. $9b + 12 + 6b + 8 = 65$

35. $11c + 4 + 2c + 16 = 85$

36. $14d + 18 + 11d + 30 = 148$

37. $14x + 10 + x + 24 = 94$

38. $y + 23 + 7y + 14 = 237$

Quick Quiz
Sections 3.1 to 3.4

Match each example with the property it illustrates.

1. $(3 \times 6) \times 4 = 3 \times (6 \times 4)$

2. $2 \times 5 = 5 \times 2$

3. $9(8 + 7) = (9 \times 8) + (9 \times 7)$

a. commutative property of $\times$

b. distributive property

c. associative property of $\times$

Solve.

4. $3 + a = 12$

5. $30 = (m + 5) + 15$

6. $36 = (6x)3$

7. $22 \times 1 = y$

8. $0 \times 25 = n$

9. $32 + 0 = b$

10. $18 \div 18 = f$

11. $0 \div 17 = s$

12. $5c + c = 60$

13. $12h - 8h = 28$

3.5 Factors and Divisibility

Camp Hiawatha's director has to buy tennis rackets for 48 girls. Each racket is to be shared by the same number of girls.

If the director buys 48 rackets, each girl gets a racket. If she buys 24 rackets, 2 girls share a racket. If she buys 16 rackets, 3 girls share a racket.

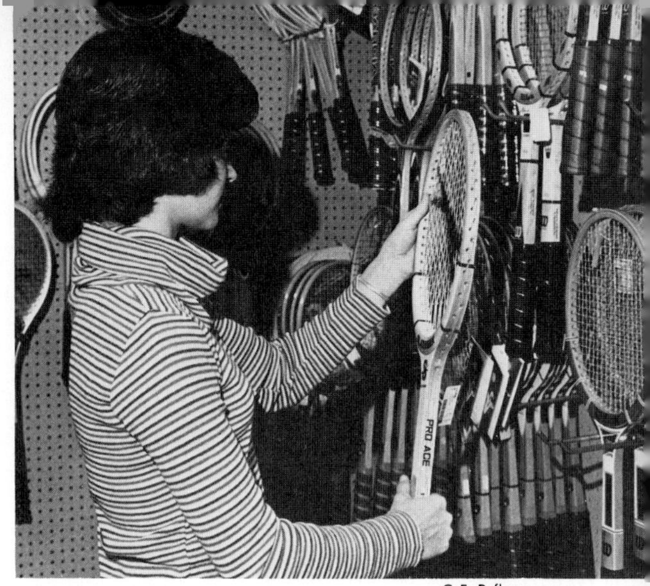

C. E. Pefley

48, 24, and 16 are *factors* of 48.

$48 \times 1 = 48 \qquad 24 \times 2 = 48 \qquad 16 \times 3 = 48$

factors of 48

> If two or more numbers are multiplied, each is a **factor** of the product.

Example 1: The director bought 12 rackets. Is 12 a factor of 48?

Yes, because $12 \times 4 = 48$.

Example 2: Find all the factors of 24.

$$\begin{aligned} 24 &= 1 \times 24 \\ &= 2 \times 12 \\ &= 3 \times 8 \\ &= 4 \times 6 \end{aligned}$$

factors of 24

> Listing all the ways to express a number as a product gives you all the factors of that number.

An easy way to check whether one whole number is a factor of another is by dividing. A number is *divisible* by each of its factors. That is, the quotient should be a whole number, and the remainder should be 0.

Example 3: Is 8 a factor of 96?

$96 \div 8 = 12$ — 96 is divisible by 8.

So 8 is a factor of 96.

Example 4: Is 7 a factor of 96?

$96 \div 7 = 13$ R5 — 96 is not divisible by 7.

So 7 is not a factor of 96.

Exercises

A Find the factors of each number.

1. 6	**2.** 12	**3.** 8	**4.** 15	**5.** 21
6. 10	**7.** 18	**8.** 16	**9.** 20	**10.** 14

11. Is 7 a factor of 63?

12. Is 9 a factor of 54?

13. Is 6 a factor of 25?

14. Is 11 a factor of 11?

B Divide to find whether 3 is a factor of each number.

15. 38	**16.** 117	**17.** 51	**18.** 144	**19.** 82

Divide to find whether 8 is a factor of each number.

20. 105	**21.** 216	**22.** 172	**23.** 87	**24.** 144

Express each number as the product of two factors other than 1.

Examples: $35 = 5 \times 7$ $\quad$ $20 = 2 \times 10$ or 4×5

25. 12	**26.** 16	**27.** 36	**28.** 32	**29.** 28
30. 45	**31.** 30	**32.** 70	**33.** 48	**34.** 26

Find all the factors you can for each number.

35. 26	**36.** 27	**37.** 33	**38.** 35	**39.** 32
40. 28	**41.** 25	**42.** 9	**43.** 13	**44.** 17

C 45. Write 18 as the product of three factors. Use factors other than 1.

46. Write 56 as the product of four factors. Use factors other than 1.

47. Write 72 as the product of five factors. Use factors other than 1.

48. Write 37 as the product of two factors.

49. A number is a perfect number if the sum of its factors (other than the number itself) is that number.

Example: $\underbrace{1 + 2 + 3}_{\text{factors of 6}} = 6$, so 6 is a perfect number.

There is another perfect number under fifty. Try to find it.

50. 496 is a perfect number. Find its factors and prove that it is perfect.

Operation Decode

A spy intercepted this message: 426 7039 9240 91267.

The code below had previously been intercepted. It was known that the letter O is 3 and the letter A is 2. Find the number for each letter. Then decode the message given above.

CODE:

LOT	ANT
× ALL	+ LOT
LOT	OPT
LOT	
ANT	
ASCOT	

3.6 Shortcuts to Divisibility

Since a number is divisible by each of its factors, some rules for divisibility can help you find the factors of a number.

> A number is divisible by 2 if its last digit is even.

Example 1: Which of these numbers are divisible by 2?

285	9864	402	51,790	333,338
odd	even	even	even	even
Not divisible by 2	Divisible by 2			

> A number is divisible by 3 if its digit sum is 3, 6, or 9.

Example 2: Which of these numbers are divisible by 3?

285 9864 402 51,790 333,338

Number	Add the digits.	If needed add again.	
285	$2+8+5=15$	$1+5=6$ (Digit sum)	Divisible by 3
9864	$9+8+6+4=27$	$2+7=9$	Divisible by 3
402	$4+0+2=6$		Divisible by 3
51,790	$5+1+7+9+0=22$	$2+2=4$	Not divisible by 3
333,338	$3+3+3+3+3+8=23$	$2+3=5$	Not divisible by 3

> A number is divisible by 5 if its last digit is 0 or 5.
>
> A number is divisible by 10 if its last digit is 0.

Example 3: Which of these numbers are divisible by 5? By 10?

285 9864 402 51,790 333,338

285 and 51,790 are divisible by 5.
51,790 is divisible by 10.

Exercises

A Which of these numbers are divisible by 2 ? By 3 ? By 5 ? By 10 ?

1. 84 **2.** 205 **3.** 52 **4.** 2310 **5.** 135

6. 77 **7.** 110 **8.** 291 **9.** 450 **10.** 111,111

B Which of these numbers are divisible by 2 ? By 3 ? By 5 ? By 10 ? Use the rules for divisibility to help you.

11. 1560 **12.** 5691 **13.** 2382 **14.** 42,655

15. 12,345 **16.** 711,026 **17.** 880,800 **18.** 2,081,491

Find all the factors you can for each number.

19. 55 **20.** 39 **21.** 30 **22.** 19 **23.** 70

C To be divisible by 6, a number must be divisible by 2 and by 3. Which of these numbers are divisible by 6 ?

24. 32,212 **25.** 2916 **26.** 22,440

27. 48,964 **28.** 54,162 **29.** 36,639

A Shorter Shortcut

When testing if a number is divisible by 3, you don't have to add all the digits. You can throw out all the 3's, 6's, and 9's. Now, a digit sum of 0 will also mean the number is divisible by 3.

Number	Throw out 3, 6, and 9.	Add digits.	If needed, add again.	
9864	~~9~~8~~6~~4	$8 + 4 = 12$	$1 + 2 = 3$	← Divisible by 3
333,338	~~333~~,~~33~~8	←	←	Not divisible by 3
396	~~396~~	←	←	Divisible by 3

Primes and Composites

On TV, prime time is important because the biggest audience is tuned in. In mathematics, *prime numbers* are important because, among other things, they can be a big help when working with fractions.

The first ten prime numbers are

2, 3, 5, 7, 11, 13, 17, 19, 23, 29.

> A whole number greater than 1 that has only 1 and itself as factors is a **prime number.**

The table below shows the ways to express each number from 2 to 9 as a product of its factors.

2	3	4	5	6	7	8	9
1×2	1×3	1×4	1×5	1×6	1×7	1×8	1×9
		2×2		2×3		2×4	3×3
						$2 \times 2 \times 2$	

Notice that each of the numbers 2, 3, 5, and 7 can be expressed as a product only one way—1 times the number. The numbers 2, 3, 5, and 7 are prime numbers. The numbers 4, 6, 8, and 9 are *composite numbers.*

> A whole number greater than 1 that has at least one other factor besides itself and 1 is a **composite number.**

Example 1: Show that 24 can be written as a product of primes.

$24 = 6 \times 4$	$24 = 8 \times 3$	$24 = 12 \times 2$
$= (2 \times 3) \times (2 \times 2)$	$= (2 \times 2 \times 2) \times 3$	$= (3 \times 2 \times 2) \times 2$
$= 2 \times 3 \times 2 \times 2$	$= 2 \times 2 \times 2 \times 3$	$= 3 \times 2 \times 2 \times 2$

Notice that each way yields the same prime factors.

Every composite number can be expressed as a product of prime numbers in only one way. This product of prime numbers is the **prime factorization** of the composite number.

Factor trees aid in finding the prime factorization of a number.

Example 2: Find the prime factorization of 210.

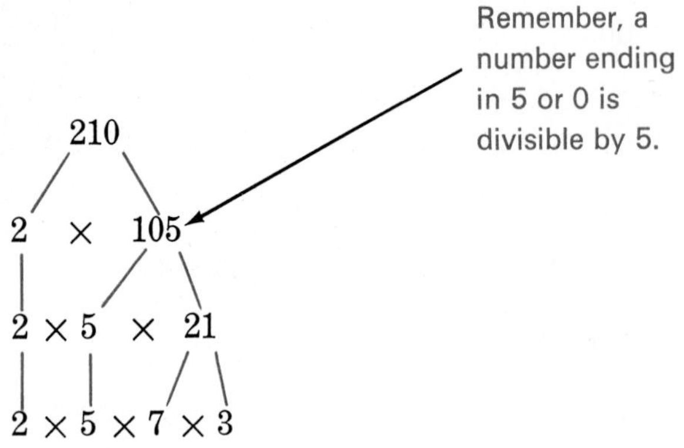

So $210 = 2 \times 5 \times 7 \times 3$.

Example 3: Find the prime factorization of 396.

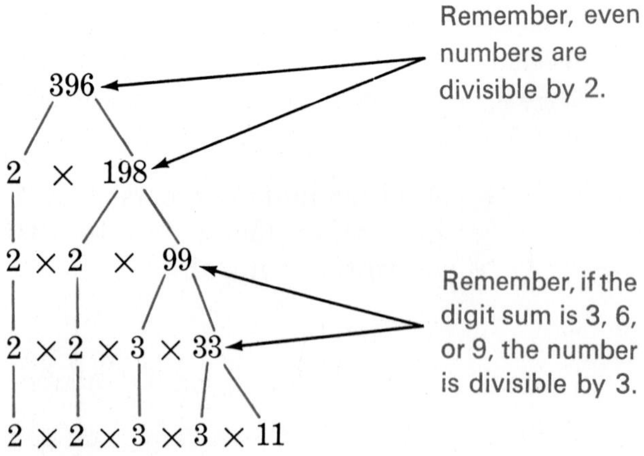

So $396 = 2 \times 2 \times 3 \times 3 \times 11$.

Exercises

A Use the chart below to tell whether each number is prime or composite.

1. 10 **2.** 11 **3.** 12 **4.** 13 **5.** 14 **6.** 15 **7.** 16

10	11	12	13	14	15	16
1 × 10	1 × 11	1 × 12	1 × 13	1 × 14	1 × 15	1 × 16
2 × 5		2 × 6		2 × 7	3 × 5	2 × 8
		3 × 4				4 × 4
		2 × 2 × 3				2 × 2 × 4
						2 × 2 × 2 × 2

B Tell whether each number is prime or composite.

8. 33 **9.** 17 **10.** 52 **11.** 30 **12.** 23 **13.** 19

14. 40 **15.** 45 **16.** 51 **17.** 49 **18.** 29 **19.** 77

Give the prime factorization of each number.

20. 18 **21.** 26 **22.** 20 **23.** 22 **24.** 25 **25.** 35

26. 34 **27.** 27 **28.** 48 **29.** 36 **30.** 39 **31.** 49

32. 40 **33.** 144 **34.** 98 **35.** 225 **36.** 126 **37.** 585

C Here's a way to find all the primes less than 100.

38. Write a list of all whole numbers from 2 to 100.

39. The first prime is 2. So cross off every second number after 2. That is, cross off 4, 6, 8, and so on (because they contain 2 as a factor).

40. The next prime is 3. So cross off every third number after 3. That is, cross off 6, 9, 12, and so on. (Why?)

41. The next prime is 5. So cross off every fifth number after 5.

42. What's the next prime? What numbers do you cross off now?

All numbers left not crossed off are prime numbers.

3.8 Exponents and Powers

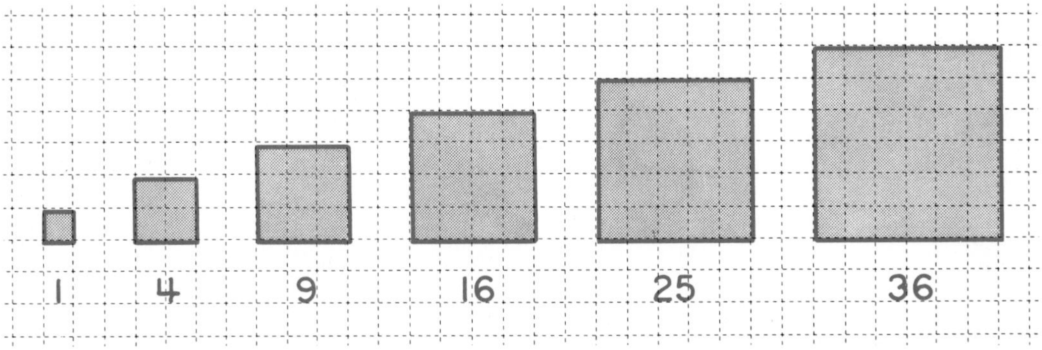

1, 4, 9, 16, 25, and 36 are **square numbers.** Each can be written as the product of two equal factors or as a power.

Number	Equal factors	Power
1	1×1	1^2
4	2×2	2^2
9	3×3	3^2

Number	Equal factors	Power
16	4×4	4^2
25	5×5	5^2
36	6×6	6^2

$2 = 2^1$ *two to the first power*

$2 \times 2 = 2^2$ *two squared* or *two to the second power*

$2 \times 2 \times 2 = 2^3$ *two cubed* or *two to the third power*

$2 \times 2 \times 2 \times 2 = 2^4$ *two to the fourth power*

$2 \times 2 \times 2 \times 2 \times 2 = 2^5$ *two to the fifth power*

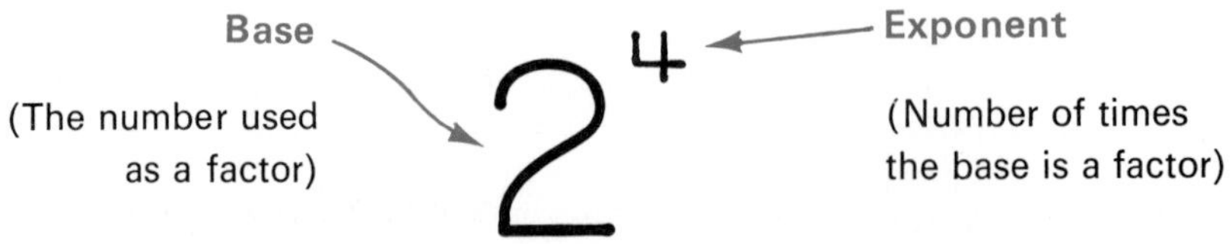

Example 1: Write $n \times n \times n \times n \times n$ using exponents.

Since n is a factor 5 times, $n \times n \times n \times n \times n = n^5$.

Example 2: Express 3^4 as a product of factors. Then find the value of 3^4.

$$3^4 = 3 \times 3 \times 3 \times 3 = 81$$

Example 3: Find the cube of 4.

$$4^3 = 4 \times 4 \times 4 = 64$$

Example 4: Find the prime factorization of 72. Write the answer using exponents.

$$\begin{aligned} 72 &= 8 \times 9 \\ &= (2 \times 2 \times 2) \times (3 \times 3) \\ &= 2^3 \times 3^2 \end{aligned}$$

Example 5: Express the prime factorization of 300 using exponents.

$300 = 3 \times 100$

$= 3 \times (10 \times 10)$

$= 3 \times (5 \times 2) \times (5 \times 2)$

$= 3 \times (5 \times 5) \times (2 \times 2)$ Like factors have been grouped.

$= 3^1 \times 5^2 \times 2^2$ If the exponent is 1, it does not have to be written.

$= 2^2 \times 3 \times 5^2$ Factors have been arranged from least to greatest.

Exercises

A Tell how to read each expression. Then name the base and the exponent.

1. 6^1 **2.** 10^4 **3.** 4^{10} **4.** x^5 **5.** 11^2

Express the following using exponents.

6. $1 \times 1 \times 1 \times 1 \times 1 \times 1$ **7.** $x \times x \times x \times x \times x \times x \times x$

8. $z \times z \times z \times z$ **9.** $5 \times 5 \times 5 \times 5 \times 5$

Find the square of each number.

10. 7 **11.** 8 **12.** 9 **13.** 10 **14.** 12

15. Does 2^3 equal 3^2?

16. Does 3×4 equal 4^3?

B Find the cube of each number.

17. 2 **18.** 3 **19.** 1 **20.** 5 **21.** 6 **22.** 8

Find the value of each expression.

23. 2^4 **24.** 2^5 **25.** 2^1 **26.** 1^8 **27.** 10^6

28. five to the fourth power

Express the prime factorization of each number using exponents. List the factors from least to greatest.

29. 54 **30.** 75 **31.** 88 **32.** 196 **33.** 288

34. 720 **35.** 1250 **36.** 1053 **37.** 1400 **38.** 1575

39. Does $2^2 + 3^2 = (2 + 3)^2$?

C Compute the squares of these numbers.

40. 11 **41.** 111 **42.** 1111 **43.** 11,111

44. Predict the square of 111,111.

Complete these statements.

45. $1^3 + 2^3 = (1 + \_\_\_)^2$

46. $1^3 + 2^3 + 3^3 = (1 + 2 + \_\_\_)^2$

47. $1^3 + 2^3 + 3^3 + 4^3 = (\_\_\_ + \_\_\_ + \_\_\_ + \_\_\_)^2$

Find each exponent. Recall that $2^5 = 32$ and $2^6 = 64$.

48. $2^2 \times 2^3 = 2^?$

49. $(2^3)^2 = 8^2 = 2^?$

50. $(2^2)^3 = 4^3 = 2^?$

3.9 Greatest Common Factor

When you are simplifying fractions, you often need to find the *greatest common factor* (*GCF*) of the numerator and the denominator.

> The **GCF** of two or more numbers is the greatest number that is a factor of each number.

Prime factorization can help you find the GCF of two or more numbers.

Example 1: Find the GCF of 36 and 24.

$$36 = 6 \times 6 = 3 \times 2 \times 3 \times 2 = 2^2 \times 3^2$$

$$24 = 3 \times 8 = 3 \times 2 \times 2 \times 2 = 2^3 \times 3$$

3 is a common factor once.

2 is a common factor twice.

$$2^2 \times 3 = 12 \quad \text{GCF}$$

> To find the GCF of two or more numbers, find the smallest power of each *common* prime factor and multiply these powers.

Example 2: Find the GCF of 16 and 40.

$$16 = 2 \times 8 = 2 \times 2 \times 2 \times 2 = 2^4$$

$$40 = 10 \times 4 = 2 \times 5 \times 2 \times 2 = 2^3 \times 5$$

$$2^3 = 8 \quad \text{GCF}$$

Example 3: Find the GCF of 49 and 30.

$$49 = 7 \times 7$$

$$30 = 5 \times 6 = 5 \times 3 \times 2$$

There are no common prime factors. Since 1 is a factor of every number, 1 is the GCF.

Example 4: Find the GCF of 45, 75, and 120.

$$45 = 5 \times 9 = 5 \times 3 \times 3 = 3^2 \times 5$$

$$75 = 3 \times 25 = 3 \times 5 \times 5 = 3 \times 5^2$$

$$120 = 10 \times 12 = 2 \times 5 \times 3 \times 2 \times 2 = 2^3 \times 3 \times 5$$

$$3 \times 5 = 15 \text{ ◀ GCF}$$

Exercises

A What is the GCF of each pair of numbers?

1. $3 = 3$
$12 = 2^2 \times 3$

2. $6 = 2 \times 3$
$18 = 2 \times 3^2$

3. $3 = 3$
$7 = 7$

4. $4 = 2^2$
$10 = 2 \times 5$

5. $12 = 2^2 \times 3$
$18 = 2 \times 3^2$

6. $66 = 2 \times 3 \times 11$
$77 = 7 \times 11$

7. $27 = 3^3$
$39 = 3 \times 13$

8. $9 = 3^2$
$16 = 2^4$

9. $28 = 2^2 \times 7$
$52 = 2^2 \times 13$

B Find the GCF of each set of numbers.

10. 30 and 50
11. 36 and 45
12. 34 and 85
13. 24 and 66
14. 3 and 19
15. 42 and 116
16. 38 and 57
17. 100 and 625
18. 198 and 396
19. 4, 8, and 24
20. 27, 54, and 108
21. 90 and 126
22. 50, 78, and 112
23. 16, 96, and 108
24. 33, 42, and 90

C **25.** 400, 696, and 1960
26. 128, 256, and 640

27. When is the GCF of two numbers equal to the lesser of the two numbers?

Least Common Multiple

Since 2 × 3 = 6, we say 2 and 3 are factors of 6. We also say 6 is a **multiple** of 2 and 3.

$$2 \times 3 = 6$$

factors (2 and 3)   multiple (6)

	×1	×2	×3	×4	×5	×6	×7	×8	×9	×10 ···
Multiples of 2	2	4	6	8	10	12	14	16	18	20 ···
Multiples of 3	3	6	9	12	15	18	21	24	27	30 ···

Notice that 6, 12, and 18 are *common multiples* of 2 and 3. Later, in working with fractions, it will help to find the *least common multiple* (LCM). The LCM of 2 and 3 is 6.

> The LCM of two or more numbers is the least nonzero number that has each given number as a factor.

Example 1: Find the LCM of 36 and 24.

$$36 = 2 \times 2 \times 3 \times 3 = 2^2 \times 3^2$$

$$24 = 2 \times 2 \times 2 \times 3 = 2^3 \times 3$$

3 must be included twice.

2 must be included three times.

$$2^3 \times 3^2 = 72 \quad \blacktriangleleft \text{LCM}$$

> To find the LCM of two or more numbers, find the largest power of each prime factor and multiply these powers.

Example 2: Find the LCM of 15 and 45.

$$15 = 5 \times 3 = 3 \times 5$$
$$45 = 5 \times 3 \times 3 = 3^2 \times 5$$
$$3^2 \times 5 = 45 \quad \text{◀ LCM}$$

Example 3: Find the LCM of 15 and 8.

$$15 = 5 \times 3 = 3 \times 5$$
$$8 = 2 \times 2 \times 2 = 2^3$$
$$2^3 \times 3 \times 5 = 120 \quad \text{◀ LCM}$$

Example 4: Find the LCM of 18, 27, and 30.

$$18 = 3 \times 3 \times 2 = 2 \times 3^2$$
$$27 = 3 \times 3 \times 3 = 3^3$$
$$30 = 3 \times 2 \times 5 = 2 \times 3 \times 5$$
$$2 \times 3^3 \times 5 = 270 \quad \text{◀ LCM}$$

Exercises

A Find the LCM of each pair of numbers.

1. $4 = 2^2$; $6 = 2 \times 3$

2. $7 = 7$; $21 = 3 \times 7$

3. $4 = 2^2$; $15 = 3 \times 5$

4. $6 = 2 \times 3$; $48 = 2^4 \times 3$

5. $18 = 2 \times 3^2$; $24 = 2^3 \times 3$

6. $20 = 2^2 \times 5$; $35 = 5 \times 7$

7. $8 = 2^3$; $32 = 2^5$

8. $20 = 2^2 \times 5$; $40 = 2^3 \times 5$

9. $3 = 3$; $10 = 2 \times 5$

B Find the LCM of each set of numbers.

10. 9 and 36

11. 5 and 7

12. 35 and 12

13. 16 and 80

14. 18 and 32

15. 25 and 49

16. 18 and 45 **17.** 36 and 72 **18.** 7, 21, and 84

19. 30 and 105 **20.** 39 and 26 **21.** 3, 4, and 6

22. 11, 33, and 44 **23.** 15, 75, and 50 **24.** 3, 5, and 7

C **25.** When is the LCM of a set of numbers equal to the greatest number in the set?

Find the LCM of each set of numbers. You can leave the answer written as a product of powers.

26. 20, 90, and 36 **27.** 30, 40, 48, and 60 **28.** 144, 24, 18, and 72

29. 66, 96, and 54 **30.** 28, 68, 88, and 110 **31.** 38, 42, 57, and 95

32. When is the LCM of two numbers the product of the numbers?

LCM's Around You

1. Cartons 24 inches tall are being stacked next to cartons 36 inches tall. What is the shortest height at which the stacks will be the same height?

2. The 17-year cicada is an insect that spends its preadult life underground. It appears aboveground as an adult only once every 17 years. Another breed of cicada appears every 13 years. If both breeds appear this year, how many years will pass before they again appear in the same year?

3. Susan, George, and Dick have part-time jobs after school. Susan works every other day, George works every third day, and Dick works every fourth day. If all three of them start work on the same day, in how many working days will they again all be working on the same day?

4. Some people think they can tell what kind of day they are going to have by checking their biorhythm cycles. There are three cycles. One is a 23-day physical cycle, another is a 28-day emotional cycle, and the third is a 33-day intellectual cycle. If all three cycles start on the day a person is born, how many days will it take before all three cycles again start on the same day?

Terms and Symbols Review

Complete each sentence. Choose from these words.

associative *commutative* *distributive* *identity*

1. Zero is the ___ number for addition.

2. $7 \times 3 = 3 \times 7$ illustrates that multiplication is ___.

3. $(7 + 5) + 9 = 7 + (5 + 9)$ illustrates that addition is ___.

4. $(9 \times 6) + (9 \times 5) = 9(6 + 5)$ illustrates the ___ property of multiplication over addition.

Choose the best term.

5. 2 is (*a factor of, divisible by, a multiple of*) 10.

6. (3×4, $3 \times 3 \times 2$, $3 \times 2 \times 2$) is the prime factorization of 12.

7. (*13, 14, 15*) is a prime number.

8. In the expression 3^5, 3 is the (*base, exponent*).

9. 6^2 is read (*two to the sixth power, six to the second power*).

10. 8 is the (*LCM, GCF*) of 2 and 8.

11. 2 is the (*LCM, GCF*) of 2 and 8.

Chapter 3 Review

3.1 For each equation, use the commutative property to write a new equation. Then solve.

1. $5 + x = 11$

2. $8 + y = 10$

3. $z \times 6 = 96$

4. $r \times 5 = 85$

Compute. Use the properties to make the computation easy. 3.2

5. $16 + 14 + 39$

6. $29 + 83 + 17$

7. $6 \times 5 \times 7$

8. $69 \times 25 \times 4$

Solve.

9. $(a + 5) + 7 = 25$

10. $78 = (3x)2$

11. $1 \times 16 = x$

12. $16 \div 16 = r$ 3.3

13. $0 \times 48 = y$

14. $8 + 0 = s$

15. $0 \div 96 = r$

16. $32 \times 1 = t$

17. $c = 7(19 + 21)$

18. $q = (9 \times 16) + (9 \times 34)$ 3.4

19. $7r + 2r = 99$

20. $10y - y = 18$

21. $16n + 14n = 300$

22. $19s - 7s = 48$

Find all the factors you can for each number. 3.5

23. 34

24. 4

25. 30

26. 19

Divide to find whether 7 is a factor of each number.

27. 54

28. 98

29. 105

30. 121

Which of these numbers are divisible by 2? By 3? By 5? By 10? 3.6

31. 870

32. 3025

33. 192

34. 61,215

35. 7312

36. 45,100

Tell whether each number is prime or composite. 3.7

37. 23

38. 51

39. 17

40. 39

Find the prime factorization of each number.

41. 46

42. 56

43. 81

44. 65

3.8 Express the following using exponents.

45. $5 \times 5 \times 5 \times 5 \times 5 \times 5$ **46.** $y \times y \times y$

47. $9 \times 9 \times 9 \times 9 \times 2 \times 2$ **48.** the prime factorization of 72

Find the value of each expression.

49. the cube of 9 **50.** the square of 13 **51.** 3^1 **52.** 1^7

3.9 Find the GCF of each set of numbers.

53. 63 and 84 **54.** 32 and 51 **55.** 22, 66, and 33

56. 29 and 75 **57.** 100, 50, and 6 **58.** 68 and 85

59. When is the GCF of two numbers equal to 1?

3.10 Find the LCM of each set of numbers.

60. 23 and 92 **61.** 64 and 96 **62.** 35 and 9

63. 75 and 45 **64.** 6, 50, and 100 **65.** 68 and 85

Chapter 3 Test

Match each example with the property it illustrates.

1. $14 + (6 + 9) = (14 + 6) + 9$ **a.** commutative property of +

2. $126 + 621 = 621 + 126$ **b.** distributive property

3. $(9 \times 7) + (9 \times 4) = 9(7 + 4)$ **c.** associative property of +

Solve.

4. $295 \times 1 = v$ **5.** $1 \times 85 = x$ **6.** $76 \times 0 = t$

7. $85 + 0 = k$ **8.** $0 \div 96 = c$ **9.** $26 \div 26 = b$

10. $(36 + 14) + 39 = r$ **11.** $4(5 \times 9) = s$

12. $(5x)3 = 90$ **13.** $6r + 2r = 96$

14. $16m + m = 34$ **15.** $16n - 11n = 50$

Find all the factors you can for each number.

16. 11 **17.** 20 **18.** 22

19. Is 620 divisible by 2? By 3? By 5? By 10?

Tell whether each number is prime or composite.

20. 39 **21.** 19 **22.** 29

Write the prime factorization of each number using exponents.

23. 60 **24.** 54 **25.** 72

Find the value of each expression.

26. two to the fourth power **27.** the square of 15 **28.** 6^1

Find the GCF of each pair of numbers.

29. 8 and 15 **30.** 24 and 36

Find the LCM of each set of numbers.

31. 28 and 40 **32.** 6, 9, and 18

RATE YOURSELF

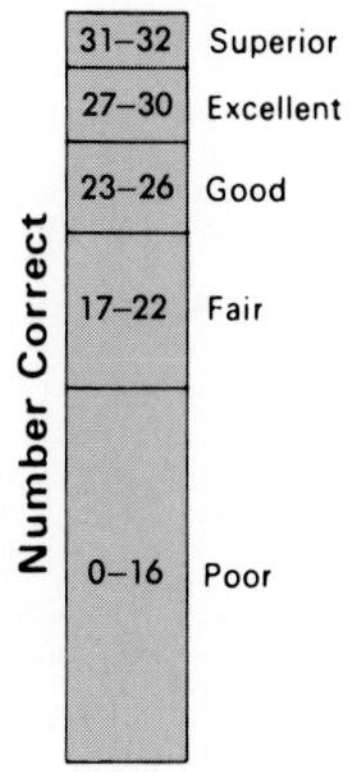

CAREER CORNER

MATH IN LANDSCAPING

Courtesy Illinois Bell Telephone

A tree mover knows it is important to keep as much of the root system as possible when transplanting a tree. However, a large root ball adds weight and expense.

To compute the weight of a balled tree, use the following formula.

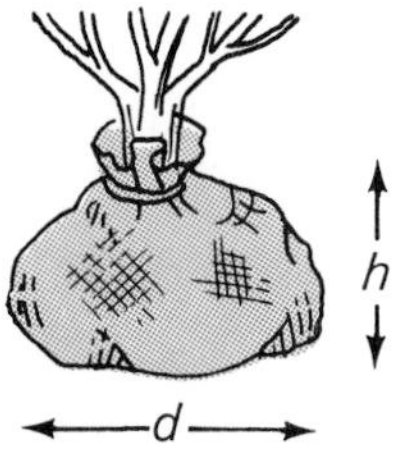

weight (lb) → W; height of ball (in.) → h; diameter of ball (in.) → d

$$W = (d^2 \times h) \div 20$$

You would proceed as follows to compute the weight of a balled tree where the diameter of the ball is $3\frac{1}{3}$ feet (40 inches) and the height of the ball is 3 feet (36 inches).

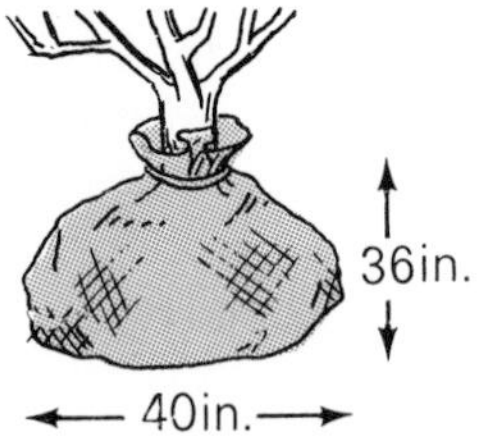

$$\begin{aligned} W &= (d^2 \times h) \div 20 \\ &= (40^2 \times 36) \div 20 \\ &= 2880 \end{aligned}$$

The weight is 2880 pounds.

Compute the weight of each balled tree indicated in the table.

Diameter of ball	*Height of ball*	*Weight of balled tree*
20 in.	18 in.	____
60 in.	48 in.	____
3 ft	$2\frac{1}{2}$ ft	____

TRY A NEW TWIST

Before doing the activities on this page, you will need to do the following.

1. Take a sheet or two of notebook paper and cut along every third line from the bottom until you have 13 strips of paper. Each strip will have 2 lines and 3 spaces on it.

2. Use 10 of the strips to make 5 crosses like the one in fig. 1.

fig. 1

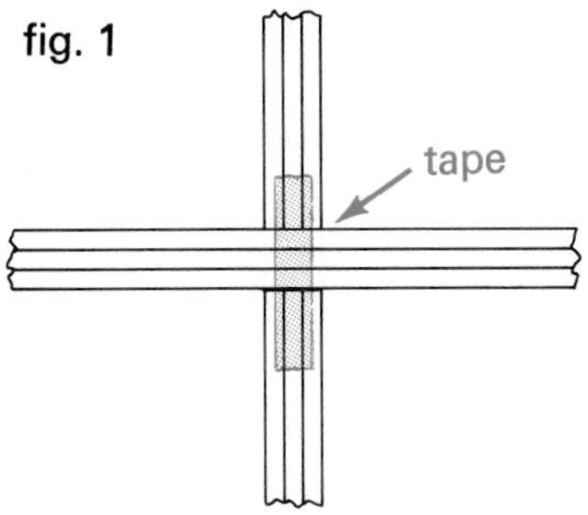

Activity 1

A. Take one of the leftover strips and connect the ends to make a ring. (See fig. 2.) *Bisect* the ring by cutting between the lines on the ring. (See fig. 2.) What happens?

fig. 2

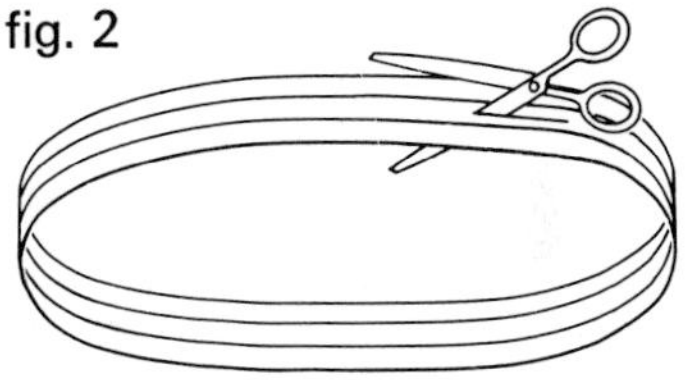

B. Take another of the leftover strips and give it a twist as in fig. 3. Then connect the ends to make a ring with a twist in it. Bisect the ring. What happens?

fig. 3

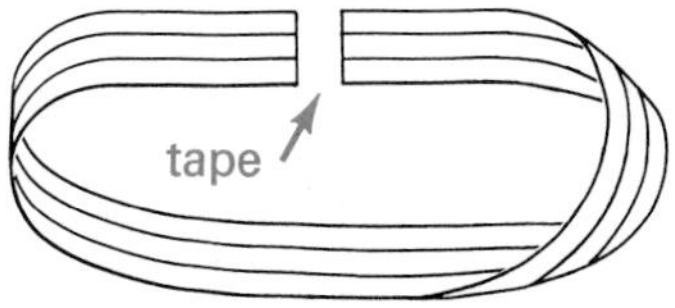

C. Make another ring with a twist in it. *Trisect* the ring by cutting along the lines on the ring. (See fig. 4.) What happens?

fig. 4

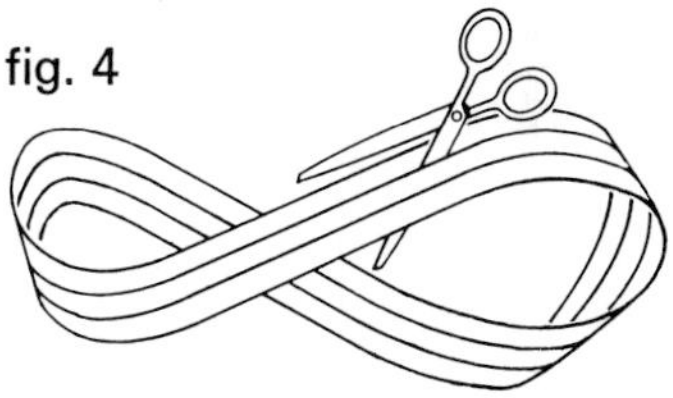

Activity 2

A. Take one of the crosses and make a ring without a twist with each strip. (See fig. 5. You will have two connected rings.) Bisect each ring. What happens?

fig. 5

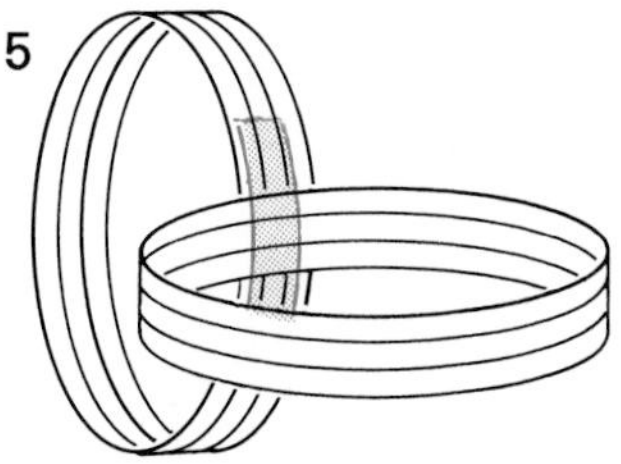

B. Take another of the crosses and make 1 ring without a twist and 1 ring with a twist. (See fig. 6.) Then **(a)** bisect the ring with the twist, and **(b)** bisect the ring without the twist. What happens?

C. Repeat part **B,** but do **(b)** first; then do **(a).** Are activities **(a)** and **(b)** commutative?

fig. 6

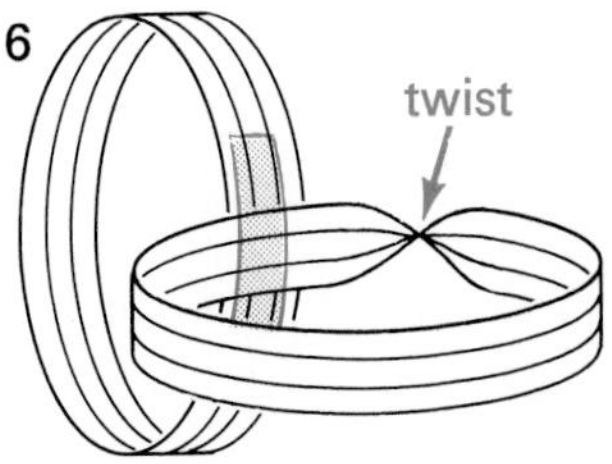

D. Make another figure like the one in fig. 6. Then **(c)** trisect the ring with the twist, and **(b)** bisect the ring without the twist. What happens?

E. Repeat part **D,** but do **(b)** first, then do **(c).** Are activities **(b)** and **(c)** commutative?

Terms and Symbols Review: Chapters 1–3

Ch. 1 Which term or symbol in parentheses is the best choice?

1. The (*liter, meter, gram*) is a metric unit of capacity.
2. The degree Celsius is the metric unit of (*angle measure, length, temperature*).
3. The prefix (*kilo-, centi-, milli-*) means "thousand."
4. The symbol (*m, mm, mg*) stands for a metric unit of weight.
5. The symbol ($<$, $>$, $=$) is read "is greater than."
6. To solve an open sentence means to find the (*replacement set, variable, solution set*).
7. A formula is a rule written as (*an inequality, an equation, a mathematical sentence*).

Ch. 2 What term best completes each statement?

8. Addition and ____ are inverse operations.
9. If the replacement set is the whole numbers, the graph of $x < 5$ contains ____ points.
10. Pounds and ounces are units for measuring ____.
11. The degree Fahrenheit is a unit for measuring ____.
12. Pints and quarts are units for measuring ____.
13. Inches and miles are units for measuring ____.

Ch. 3 Which lettered choice best matches each numbered item?

14. Associative property of $\times$	**a.** $3k + 7k = (3 + 7)k$
15. Commutative property of $\times$	**b.** $4 \times 25 \times 7$
16. Distributive property	**c.** $3(5x) = (3 \times 5)x$
17. A factor of 16	**d.** $2^2 \times 5^2 \times 7$
18. The GCF of 5 and 10	**e.** 5
19. The prime factorization of 700	**f.** 10
20. The exponent in the expression 2^{10}	**g.** $b \times 5 = 5b$
	h. 2

Cumulative Review: Chapters 1–3

Ch. 1

1. Your pencil is (*more*, *less*) than 1 centimeter long.
2. You are (*more*, *less*) than 1 meter tall.

Find each value.

3. $6 + 8 \div 2$
4. $3 + (2 \times 3) \times 2$
5. $(n + 3) \times 6$ if n is replaced with 2
6. $4 + 7x$ if x is replaced with 3

Translate into symbols.

7. seven minus twice x
8. Divide a number n by ten.
9. Nine divided into a number b is less than seventy.
10. The product of five and a number p is sixty.

Classify as *True*, *False*, or *Open*.

11. $48 \div 12 = 4$
12. $9n < 23$
13. $21 \div 7 > 2$

Solve. Use {1, 2, 3, 4} as the replacement set.

14. $2x + 1 > 9$
15. $7n - 5 < 10$
16. $6 < 2n - 1$
17. $a + 5 = 7$
18. $13 = n + 9$
19. $x + 21 = 35$
20. Use the formula $m = c \div 100$ to find how many meters equals 31 300 centimeters.

Ch. 2

Simplify.

21. $13 - 7 + 7$
22. $17 \times 5 \div 5$
23. $42 + 8 - 8$

Solve.

24. $x + 7 = 38$
25. $4 = n - 18$
26. $\frac{r}{4} = 8$
27. $\frac{r}{6} = 15$
28. $5a = 315$
29. $52 = 4z$
30. $6 = n - 3$
31. $2x + 5 = 13$
32. $5 = \frac{n + 4}{3}$

Solve and graph.

33. $9 < y + 4$ **34.** $7n < 35$ **35.** $\frac{r}{2} < 1$

Complete.

36. 6 ft = ____ in. **37.** 48 oz = ____ lb **38.** 8 qt = ____ gal.

39. Find the area of a rectangle with length 21 cm and width 17 cm.

40. Find the volume of a rectangular solid with length 7 ft, width 3 ft, and height 16 ft.

41. Translate into symbols: The sum of a number and twice that same number is twenty-one.

Ch. 3

Solve.

42. $6 + a = 25$ **43.** $b \times 4 = 36$ **44.** $29 = (c + 10) + 15$

45. $(10d)8 = 160$ **46.** $1 \times 25 = e$ **47.** $f = 0 + 19$

48. $g = 0 \div 21$ **49.** $h = 31 \div 31$ **50.** $17 \times 0 = j$

51. $12k + 6k = 54$ **52.** $5m + m = 42$ **53.** $18n - 10n = 96$

54. Find all the factors you can for 36.

55. Is 450 divisible by 2? By 3? By 5? By 10?

56. Tell whether each number is prime or composite.

a. 30 **b.** 17 **c.** 29

57. Write the prime factorization of 72 using exponents.

58. Find the value of each expression.

a. 5^1 **b.** the cube of 3 **c.** two to the fourth power

59. Find the GCF of 24 and 36.

60. Find the LCM of 5, 6, and 10.

Getting Ready for Chapter 4

Find each remainder.

1. $6\overline{)13}$ 2. $32 \div 5$ 3. $52 \div 16$

Find the prime factorization of each number. 3.7

4. 8 5. 9 6. 10 7. 14

8. 16 9. 20 10. 24 11. 25

Find the GCF of each pair of numbers. 3.9

12. $12 = 2^2 \times 3$
    $18 = 2 \times 3^2$

13. $15 = 3 \times 5$
    $30 = 2 \times 3 \times 5$

14. 6 and 9 15. 5 and 10 16. 3 and 7

17. 12 and 15 18. 21 and 28 19. 16 and 24

20. When is the GCF of two numbers equal to 1?

Find the LCM of each pair of numbers. 3.10

21. $6 = 3 \times 2$
    $8 = 2^3$

22. $5 = 5$
    $9 = 3^2$

23. 3 and 4 24. 12 and 18 25. 6 and 10

26. 8 and 24 27. 4 and 5 28. 7 and 35

Arthur Lavine from De Wys

4 FRACTIONS AND MIXED NUMBERS

Many different kinds of workers are in the building trades. There are carpenters, plasterers, tile setters, electricians, plumbers. . . . The list goes on and on. When reading building plans and when making measurements, these workers often use fractions and mixed numbers.

Everyone uses fractions and mixed numbers at one time or another. In this chapter you will learn how and when to use them.

Meaning of Fractions

Fractions are used to indicate amounts.

$\frac{5}{8}$ of the pie and $\frac{3}{2}$ quarts of milk are gone.

Fractions are also used to indicate division. For this reason, *0 is never a denominator.*

numerator → 2

$\frac{2}{3}$ means $2 \div 3$, or $3\overline{)2}$.

denominator → 3

Example 1: Express $7 \div 4$, $3\overline{)1}$, and $6 \div 1$ as fractions.

$$7 \div 4 = \frac{7}{4}$$

$$3\overline{)1} = \frac{1}{3}$$

$$6 \div 1 = \frac{6}{1}$$

> Any whole number n divided by 1 equals itself. So
>
> $\frac{n}{1} = n \div 1 = n.$ *Example:* $\frac{3}{1} = 3 \div 1 = 3$

Example 2: Express 2, 5, and 9 as fractions.

$$2 = \frac{2}{1} \qquad 5 = \frac{5}{1} \qquad 9 = \frac{9}{1}$$

Fractions that express the same amount are **equivalent**. In the diagram, $\frac{1}{2}$, $\frac{2}{4}$, and $\frac{4}{8}$ are equivalent.

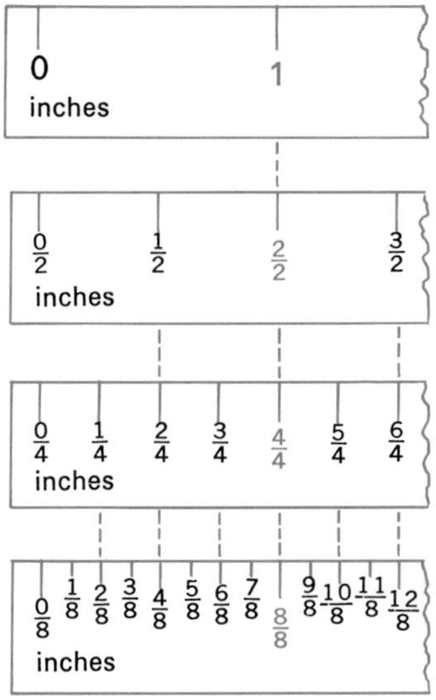

Example 3: Use the rulers at right to find fractions equivalent to $\frac{1}{4}$, $\frac{6}{8}$, 1, $\frac{5}{4}$, and $\frac{6}{4}$.

$$\frac{1}{4} = \frac{2}{8} \qquad \frac{6}{8} = \frac{3}{4}$$

$$1 = \frac{2}{2} = \frac{4}{4} = \frac{8}{8}$$

$$\frac{5}{4} = \frac{10}{8} \qquad \frac{6}{4} = \frac{3}{2} = \frac{12}{8}$$

The diagram below shows how to add two fractions when their denominators are the same number.

$$\frac{3}{8} + \frac{4}{8} = \frac{3+4}{8} = \frac{7}{8}$$

7 ← sum of numerators

8 ← the common denominator

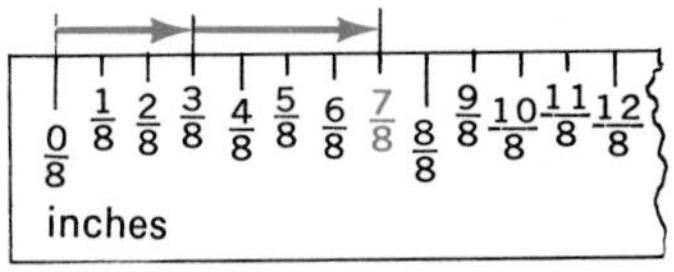

The sum of any two fractions with a common denominator is equal to the sum of their numerators over the common denominator. So

$\frac{a}{c} + \frac{b}{c} = \frac{a+b}{c}$. *Example:* $\frac{2}{7} + \frac{3}{7} = \frac{2+3}{7} = \frac{5}{7}$

Example 4: Add $\frac{3}{5}$ and $\frac{4}{5}$.

$$\frac{3}{5} + \frac{4}{5} = \frac{3 + 4}{5} = \frac{7}{5}$$

Exercises

A **1.** $\frac{2}{3}$ means (*2 ÷ 3, 2 + 3, 3 ÷ 2*).

2. Since fractions are used to indicate division, 0 can never be a (*numerator, denominator, quotient*).

Express as fractions.

3. $1 \div 4$ **4.** $4 \div 3$ **5.** $6\overline{)5}$ **6.** $2\overline{)11}$

7. 3 **8.** 20 **9.** 6 **10.** 1

B Use the rulers to find equivalent fractions.

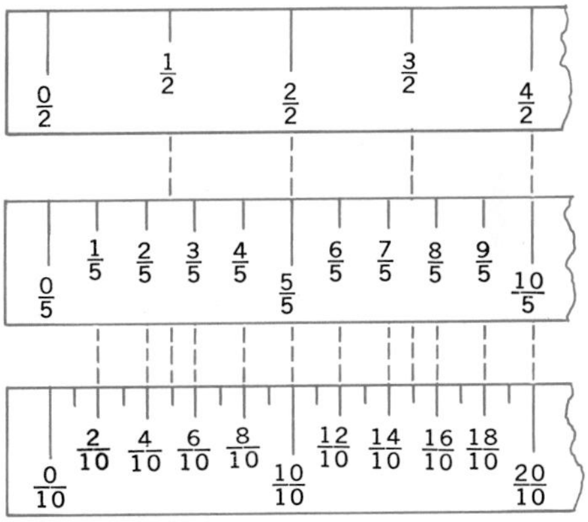

11. $\frac{1}{5} = \frac{\square}{10}$ **12.** $\frac{18}{10} = \frac{\square}{5}$

13. $\frac{8}{10} = \frac{\square}{5}$ **14.** $\frac{3}{2} = \frac{\square}{10}$

15. $\frac{1}{2} = \frac{\square}{10}$ **16.** $\frac{4}{2} = \frac{\square}{5} = \frac{\square}{10}$

Use the rulers to find equivalent fractions.

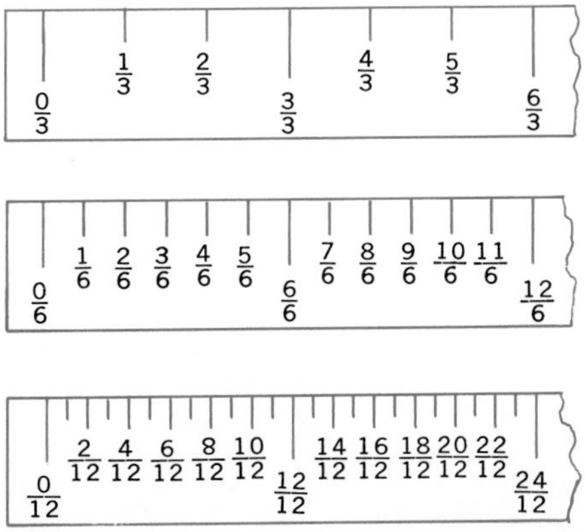

17. $\frac{5}{6} = \frac{\square}{12}$ **18.** $\frac{18}{12} = \frac{\square}{6}$

19. $\frac{4}{6} = \frac{\square}{3} = \frac{\square}{12}$ **20.** $\frac{1}{3} = \frac{\square}{6} = \frac{\square}{12}$

21. $\frac{14}{12} = \frac{\square}{6}$ **22.** $\frac{4}{3} = \frac{\square}{6} = \frac{\square}{12}$

Add.

23. $\frac{1}{2} + \frac{4}{2}$ 24. $\frac{2}{3} + \frac{3}{3}$ 25. $\frac{2}{5} + \frac{2}{5}$ 26. $\frac{3}{10} + \frac{6}{10}$

27. $\frac{5}{6} + \frac{2}{6}$ 28. $\frac{4}{8} + \frac{3}{8}$ 29. $\frac{7}{7} + \frac{2}{7}$ 30. $\frac{6}{4} + \frac{3}{4}$

31. $\frac{1}{9} + \frac{9}{9}$ 32. $\frac{2}{5} + \frac{3}{5}$ 33. $\frac{4}{3} + \frac{4}{3}$ 34. $\frac{5}{11} + \frac{2}{11}$

35. What whole number is equivalent to this sum: $\frac{8}{8} + \frac{8}{8} + \frac{8}{8}$?

36. For what number n is $\frac{n}{1} = \frac{n}{n}$?

C Add.

Example: $\frac{5}{8} + \frac{3}{8} + \frac{7}{8} = \frac{5+3+7}{8} = \frac{15}{8}$

37. $\frac{2}{3} + \frac{4}{3} + \frac{2}{3}$ 38. $\frac{4}{5} + \frac{2}{5} + \frac{3}{5}$ 39. $\frac{1}{10} + \frac{7}{10} + \frac{5}{10}$

40. $\frac{5}{6} + \frac{1}{6} + \frac{5}{6}$ 41. $\frac{3}{2} + \frac{1}{2} + \frac{5}{2}$ 42. $\frac{7}{4} + \frac{3}{4} + \frac{3}{4}$

Example: $\frac{1}{a} + \frac{3}{a} = \frac{1+3}{a} = \frac{4}{a}$

43. $\frac{2}{x} + \frac{5}{x}$ 44. $\frac{7}{y} + \frac{8}{y}$ 45. $\frac{6}{z} + \frac{3}{z}$

In Other Words

The word *fraction* comes from the Latin word meaning "broken." The words for fraction in other languages also come from words meaning "broken." Some are given below. Pronunciation symbols are taken from Webster's *New Collegiate Dictionary,* eighth edition.

Language	Word	Pronunciation
French	fraction	frak-ˈsyəⁿ
German	der bruch	da(ə)r-brək
Polish	ułamki	ü-wäm-kē
Spanish	fracción	fräk-sē-ˈōn
Swedish	bråk	brōk

4.2 Multiplying Fractions

$\frac{4}{5}$ of Jill's backyard is covered with grass. She wants to dig up $\frac{2}{3}$ of the grass to plant a garden. How much of the whole yard will the garden cover?

The first rectangle shows $\frac{4}{5}$ of the yard covered with grass.

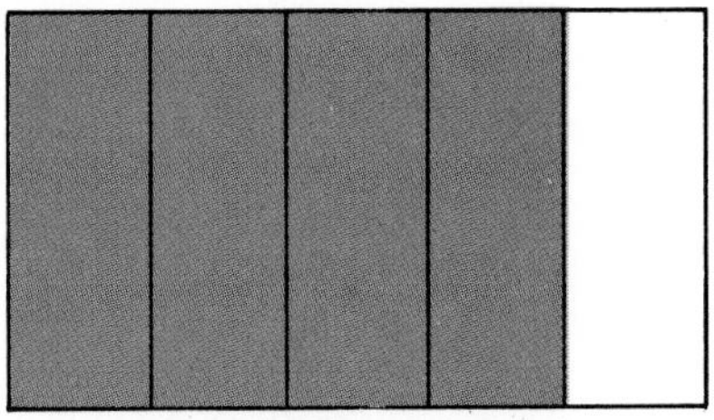

$\frac{4}{5}$

The second rectangle shows $\frac{2}{3}$ of the grass covered by the garden.

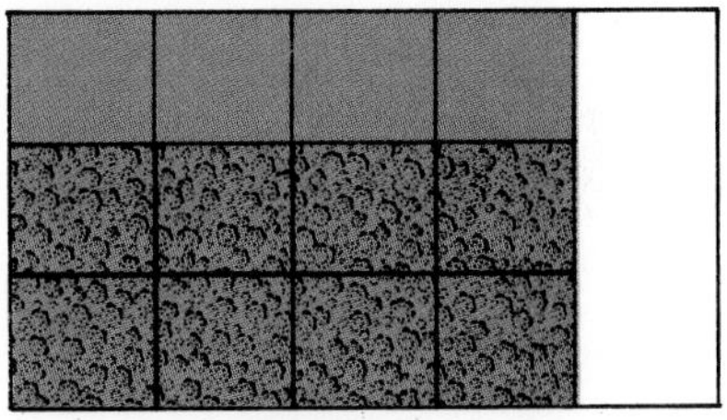

$\frac{2}{3}$ of $\frac{4}{5}$

The third rectangle shows the yard separated into 15 equal parts. The garden will be 8 of the parts. So the garden will cover $\frac{8}{15}$ of the whole yard.

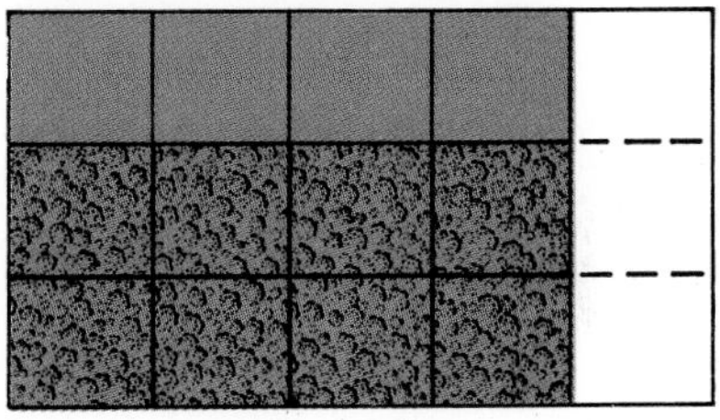

$\frac{2}{3} \times \frac{4}{5} = \frac{8}{15}$

Another way to find the answer is to multiply $\frac{2}{3}$ times $\frac{4}{5}$.

$$\frac{2}{3} \times \frac{4}{5} =$$

Multiply numerators. $$\frac{2}{3} \times \frac{4}{5} = \frac{2 \times 4}{} = \frac{8}{-}$$

Multiply denominators. $$\frac{2}{3} \times \frac{4}{5} = \frac{2 \times 4}{3 \times 5} = \frac{8}{15}$$

> The product of any two fractions is equal to the product of their numerators over the product of their denominators. So
>
> $\frac{a}{b} \times \frac{c}{d} = \frac{ac}{bd}$. *Example:* $\frac{2}{3} \times \frac{1}{5} = \frac{2 \times 1}{3 \times 5} = \frac{2}{15}$

Example 1: Multiply $\frac{4}{9}$ by $\frac{2}{5}$.

$$\frac{4}{9} \times \frac{2}{5} = \frac{8}{45}$$

Example 2: Multiply $\frac{1}{3}$ by 2.

$$\frac{1}{3} \times \frac{2}{1} = \frac{2}{3}$$ Express 2 as a fraction.

Exercises

A Multiply.

1. $\frac{1}{2} \times \frac{1}{5}$
2. $\frac{5}{12} \times \frac{1}{2}$
3. $\frac{1}{2} \times \frac{7}{8}$
4. $3 \times \frac{1}{4}$
5. $\frac{1}{10} \times \frac{1}{3}$
6. $\frac{1}{12} \times \frac{1}{3}$
7. $\frac{3}{5} \times \frac{2}{5}$
8. $\frac{1}{3} \times \frac{1}{4}$
9. $\frac{1}{3} \times \frac{1}{9}$

B Multiply.

10. $\frac{2}{7} \times \frac{2}{5}$
11. $\frac{1}{4} \times \frac{7}{9}$
12. $\frac{1}{6} \times \frac{7}{10}$
13. $\frac{1}{3} \times \frac{5}{8}$
14. $\frac{3}{8} \times \frac{3}{4}$
15. $\frac{3}{5} \times \frac{1}{8}$
16. $\frac{1}{7} \times \frac{3}{8}$
17. $\frac{1}{2} \times \frac{11}{12}$
18. $\frac{4}{5} \times \frac{1}{3}$
19. $\frac{1}{6} \times 5$
20. $3 \times \frac{2}{7}$
21. $\frac{9}{10} \times \frac{3}{4}$
22. $\frac{1}{5} \times \frac{2}{9}$
23. $\frac{1}{4} \times \frac{3}{5}$
24. $\frac{3}{10} \times 3$
25. $2 \times \frac{5}{5}$
26. $\frac{4}{7} \times \frac{4}{7}$
27. $8 \times \frac{3}{3}$
28. $\frac{2}{9} \times \frac{2}{5}$
29. $6 \times \frac{2}{11}$
30. $2 \times \frac{2}{3}$
31. How much is $\frac{1}{4}$ of 3 yd?
32. How much is $\frac{2}{3}$ of $\frac{4}{5}$ gallon?
33. A piece of rope is $\frac{5}{8}$ yd long. How long is $\frac{1}{2}$ of the rope?
34. It takes 2 gallons of paint to cover a fence. How much paint would it take to cover only $\frac{2}{5}$ of the fence?

C Compute.

35. $\frac{a}{2} \times \frac{3}{5}$
36. $\frac{a}{2} \times \frac{c}{5}$
37. $a \times \frac{1}{5}$
38. $\left(\frac{3}{4}\right)^2$
39. $\left(\frac{1}{2}\right)^3$
40. $\left(\frac{2}{3}\right)^4$

Simplifying Fractions 4.3

"$\frac{3}{6}$ of the doctors questioned preferred Hope Mouthwash." It would also be correct to say that $\frac{1}{2}$ of the doctors preferred Hope Mouthwash.

$$\frac{3}{6} = \frac{3 \div 3}{6 \div 3} = \frac{1}{2}$$

Since $\frac{3}{6}$ can be *simplified* to $\frac{1}{2}$, $\frac{3}{6}$ and $\frac{1}{2}$ are equivalent.

$\frac{1}{2}$ is a fraction *in lowest terms.*

> A fraction is **in lowest terms** if its numerator and denominator have no common whole-number factor other than 1. *Example:* $\frac{4}{7}$

Example 1: Express $\frac{8}{36}$ in lowest terms.

Step 1: Find the GCF of the numerator and denominator.

$$8 = 2^3$$
$$36 = 2^2 \times 3^2$$
$$2^2 = 4 \quad \text{GCF}$$

Step 2: Divide the numerator and denominator by the GCF.

$$\frac{8}{36} = \frac{8 \div 4}{36 \div 4} = \frac{2}{9}$$

Example 2: Express $\frac{10}{25}$ in lowest terms.

Step 1: The GCF of 10 and 25 is 5.

Step 2:

Long way

$$\frac{10}{25} = \frac{10 \div 5}{25 \div 5} = \frac{2}{5}$$

Short way

$$\frac{\not{10}^{\,2}}{\not{25}_{\,5}} = \frac{2}{5}$$

Example 3: Multiply $\frac{5}{3}$ by $\frac{3}{10}$.

You can simplify before you multiply.

$$\frac{5}{3} \times \frac{3}{10} = \frac{\cancel{15}^{1}}{\cancel{30}_{2}} = \frac{1}{2} \quad \text{or} \quad \frac{{}^{1}\cancel{5}}{\cancel{3}_{1}} \times \frac{\cancel{3}^{1}}{\cancel{10}_{2}} = \frac{1}{2}$$

Divide by 15, the GCF.

Let's agree to *always* express a fraction in lowest terms.

Exercises

A Find the GCF of the numerator and denominator. (The numerators and denominators are factored into primes.)

1. $\frac{3}{12} = \frac{3}{2^2 \times 3}$ **2.** $\frac{4}{8} = \frac{2^2}{2^3}$ **3.** $\frac{10}{15} = \frac{2 \times 5}{3 \times 5}$

4. $\frac{6}{10} = \frac{2 \times 3}{2 \times 5}$ **5.** $\frac{14}{18} = \frac{2 \times 7}{2 \times 3^2}$ **6.** $\frac{12}{30} = \frac{2^2 \times 3}{2 \times 3 \times 5}$

B Express each fraction in lowest terms.

7. $\frac{3}{12}$ **8.** $\frac{4}{8}$ **9.** $\frac{10}{15}$ **10.** $\frac{6}{10}$ **11.** $\frac{14}{18}$

12. $\frac{12}{30}$ **13.** $\frac{6}{9}$ **14.** $\frac{4}{6}$ **15.** $\frac{4}{16}$ **16.** $\frac{7}{21}$

17. $\frac{5}{20}$ **18.** $\frac{2}{8}$ **19.** $\frac{6}{12}$ **20.** $\frac{4}{12}$ **21.** $\frac{9}{15}$

22. $\frac{9}{12}$ **23.** $\frac{15}{20}$ **24.** $\frac{6}{8}$ **25.** $\frac{8}{10}$ **26.** $\frac{7}{35}$

27. $\frac{12}{20}$ **28.** $\frac{2}{16}$ **29.** $\frac{6}{16}$ **30.** $\frac{5}{15}$ **31.** $\frac{12}{18}$

Multiply. (Remember to express each answer in lowest terms.)

32. $\frac{4}{3} \times \frac{1}{2}$ **33.** $2 \times \frac{1}{8}$ **34.** $\frac{4}{3} \times \frac{3}{8}$ **35.** $\frac{1}{3} \times \frac{3}{5}$

36. $\frac{5}{4} \times \frac{2}{3}$ **37.** $\frac{5}{6} \times \frac{2}{5}$ **38.** $\frac{3}{2} \times \frac{4}{7}$ **39.** $\frac{3}{2} \times \frac{2}{9}$

40. $3 \times \frac{4}{15}$ **41.** $\frac{4}{5} \times \frac{5}{12}$ **42.** $\frac{1}{6} \times \frac{3}{4}$ **43.** $\frac{8}{9} \times \frac{1}{4}$

44. Gene travels a total of $\frac{4}{5}$ mile in a round trip from his home to school and back. How far is a one-way trip ($\frac{1}{2}$ of the trip)?

45. A recipe calls for $\frac{2}{3}$ cup milk. How much milk do you need for $\frac{1}{2}$ the recipe?

C Express each fraction in lowest terms.

Example: $\frac{3^2 \times 5}{2 \times 3} = \frac{3 \times \overset{1}{\cancel{3}} \times 5}{2 \times \underset{1}{\cancel{3}}} = \frac{15}{2}$

46. $\frac{2^3 \times 3 \times 5^2}{3^3 \times 5^3}$

47. $\frac{5^2 \times 7^3}{3^2 \times 5^3 \times 7}$

48. $\frac{3a^2}{15a}$

49. $\frac{10bc^3}{5b^3c^2}$

Another Way

Another way to simplify fractions by factoring the numerators and denominators follows:

Example 1:

$$\frac{8}{12} = \frac{2 \times 2 \times 2}{2 \times 2 \times 3} = \frac{2 \times 2}{2 \times 2} \times \frac{2}{3} = 1 \times \frac{2}{3} = \frac{2}{3}$$

Example 2:

$$\frac{15}{18} = \frac{3 \times 5}{2 \times 3 \times 3} = \frac{3}{3} \times \frac{5}{2 \times 3} = 1 \times \frac{5}{6} = \frac{5}{6}$$

Express each fraction in lowest terms.

1. $\frac{4}{6}$
2. $\frac{10}{15}$
3. $\frac{2}{12}$
4. $\frac{7}{28}$
5. $\frac{12}{20}$
6. $\frac{6}{16}$
7. $\frac{9}{21}$
8. $\frac{18}{36}$
9. $\frac{25}{75}$
10. $\frac{35}{45}$
11. $\frac{24}{40}$
12. $\frac{55}{99}$

4.4 Mixed Numbers

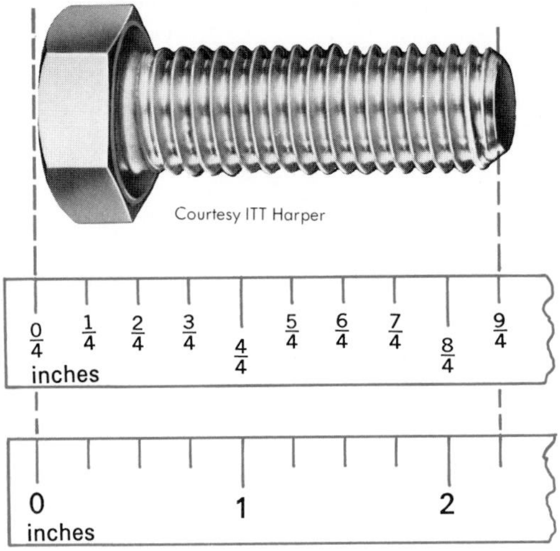

Courtesy ITT Harper

The length of the bolt can be given as either $\frac{9}{4}$ or $2\frac{1}{4}$ inches.

$2\frac{1}{4}$ stands for the sum of a whole number and a fraction.

Equivalent expressions

$$\frac{9}{4} = 2\frac{1}{4}$$

fraction ↑ — ↑ mixed number

$2\frac{1}{4}$ is read "two and one fourth."

$$2\frac{1}{4} = 2 + \frac{1}{4}$$

$$= (2 \times 1) + \frac{1}{4}$$

$$= \left(\frac{2}{1} \times \frac{4}{4}\right) + \frac{1}{4}$$

$$= \frac{8}{4} + \frac{1}{4}$$

$$= \frac{9}{4}$$

Example 1: Express $5\frac{3}{8}$ as a fraction.

Long way

$$5\frac{3}{8} = 5 + \frac{3}{8}$$

$$= \left(\frac{5}{1} \times \frac{8}{8}\right) + \frac{3}{8}$$

$$= \frac{40}{8} + \frac{3}{8}$$

$$= \frac{43}{8}$$

Short way

$$5\frac{3}{8} = \frac{40 + 3}{8} = \frac{43}{8}$$

$5 \times 8 = 40$

Since a fraction indicates division, you divide the numerator by the denominator to find the equivalent mixed number.

Example 2: Express $\frac{32}{5}$ as a mixed number.

$$\frac{32}{5} = 32 \div 5 \longrightarrow \begin{array}{r} 6 \text{ R}2 = 6\frac{2}{5} \\ 5\overline{)32} \\ \underline{30} \\ 2 \end{array} \qquad \text{So } \frac{32}{5} = 6\frac{2}{5}.$$

Example 3: Multiply $\frac{9}{4}$ by $\frac{2}{3}$. Express the answer as a mixed number in lowest terms (fraction in lowest terms and less than 1).

$$\frac{\overset{3}{\cancel{9}}}{\underset{2}{\cancel{4}}} \times \frac{\overset{1}{\cancel{2}}}{\underset{1}{\cancel{3}}} = \frac{3}{2} = 1\frac{1}{2}$$

Let's agree to *always* change a fraction to a mixed number in lowest terms whenever possible.

Exercises

A Express each of the following as the sum of a whole number and a fraction.

1. $2\frac{1}{3}$ **2.** $7\frac{3}{8}$ **3.** $21\frac{5}{6}$ **4.** $12\frac{9}{10}$

Show how you would divide to express each of the following as a mixed number.

Example: $\frac{3}{2} = 2\overline{)3}$

5. $\frac{5}{4}$ **6.** $\frac{8}{3}$ **7.** $\frac{14}{5}$ **8.** $\frac{27}{10}$

B Express each mixed number as a fraction.

9. $2\frac{1}{3}$ **10.** $4\frac{1}{6}$ **11.** $1\frac{1}{5}$ **12.** $1\frac{1}{4}$ **13.** $2\frac{1}{2}$

14. $3\frac{7}{10}$ **15.** $5\frac{4}{5}$ **16.** $7\frac{1}{2}$ **17.** $4\frac{2}{3}$ **18.** $8\frac{3}{4}$

Express each fraction as a mixed number.

19. $\frac{5}{2}$	**20.** $\frac{7}{6}$	**21.** $\frac{5}{3}$	**22.** $\frac{5}{4}$	**23.** $\frac{7}{5}$
24. $\frac{11}{3}$	**25.** $\frac{16}{5}$	**26.** $\frac{28}{3}$	**27.** $\frac{31}{4}$	**28.** $\frac{43}{8}$

Multiply.

29. $\frac{1}{2} \times \frac{12}{5}$	**30.** $\frac{4}{3} \times \frac{6}{5}$	**31.** $10 \times \frac{1}{3}$
32. $\frac{5}{7} \times \frac{7}{2}$	**33.** $\frac{3}{5} \times \frac{15}{8}$	**34.** $\frac{8}{9} \times 6$
35. $5 \times \frac{7}{10}$	**36.** $\frac{5}{3} \times \frac{11}{10}$	**37.** $\frac{25}{12} \times \frac{3}{5}$

38. The table shows the average amount of certain foods that an American eats in one day. Find the amounts per week. Express each answer in lowest terms.

	Daily average per person	*Weekly average per person*
Flour	$\frac{1}{3}$ pound	
Meat	$\frac{1}{2}$ pound	
Milk	$\frac{7}{10}$ pint	
Sugar	$\frac{2}{7}$ pound	

39. On the average, each American disposes of $\frac{7}{2}$ pounds of trash a day. How much is this per week? Per year (365 days)? Express each answer in lowest terms.

C Multiply.

Example: $\frac{1}{2} \times 4 \times \frac{2}{3} = \frac{1}{\cancel{2}_1} \times \frac{4}{1} \times \frac{\cancel{2}^1}{3} = \frac{4}{3} = 1\frac{1}{3}$

40. $\frac{3}{8} \times 3 \times \frac{2}{3}$	**41.** $12 \times \frac{3}{4} \times \frac{1}{6}$	**42.** $\frac{4}{3} \times \frac{5}{4} \times \frac{2}{3}$
43. $\frac{1}{2} \times \frac{3}{4} \times \frac{5}{6}$	**44.** $\frac{3}{4} \times \frac{3}{2} \times \frac{4}{5}$	**45.** $10 \times \frac{3}{5} \times \frac{1}{4}$

Solve.

46. $2u = 5$	**47.** $3v = 10$	**48.** $7w = 30$
49. $4x = 18$	**50.** $12y = 40$	**51.** $10z = 56$

4.5 Multiplying Mixed Numbers

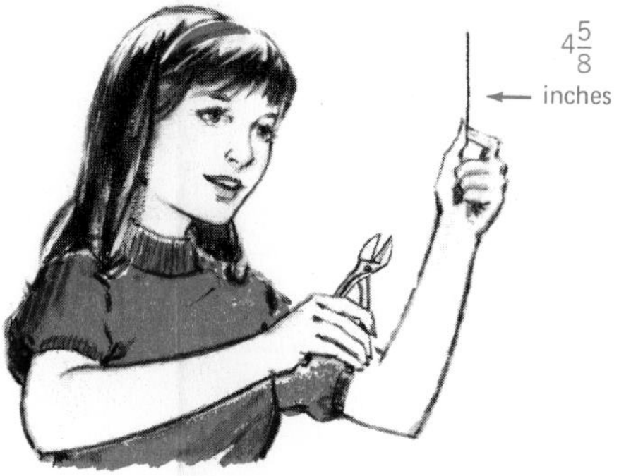

Terry wants to know how long $\frac{1}{2}$ of the wire is.

Example 1: Find $\frac{1}{2}$ of $4\frac{5}{8}$ inches.

Step 1: Express the mixed number as a fraction.

$$4\frac{5}{8} = \frac{32 + 5}{8} = \frac{37}{8}$$

Step 2: Multiply. $\frac{1}{2} \times \frac{37}{8} = \frac{37}{16}$

Step 3: Express the answer in lowest terms.

$$\begin{array}{r} 2\frac{5}{16} \\ 16\overline{)37} \\ \underline{32} \\ 5 \end{array} \qquad \frac{37}{16} = 2\frac{5}{16}$$

$\frac{1}{2}$ of $4\frac{5}{8}$ inches is $2\frac{5}{16}$ inches.

Example 2: Multiply $3\frac{1}{3} \times 1\frac{1}{2}$.

$$3\frac{1}{3} \times 1\frac{1}{2} = \frac{\overset{5}{\cancel{10}}}{\underset{1}{\cancel{3}}} \times \frac{\overset{1}{\cancel{3}}}{\underset{1}{\cancel{2}}}$$

$$= \frac{5}{1} \text{ or } 5$$

Example 3: How many feet are there in $2\frac{5}{6}$ yards?

Each yard contains 3 ft, so multiply $2\frac{5}{6}$ by 3.

$$2\frac{5}{6} \times 3 = \frac{17}{\cancel{6}_{2}} \times \frac{\cancel{3}^{1}}{1}$$

$$= \frac{17}{2} \text{ or } 8\frac{1}{2}$$

So $2\frac{5}{6}$ yd $= 8\frac{1}{2}$ ft.

Exercises

A What fraction would you use in place of each whole or mixed number?

1. $3 \times 4\frac{1}{2}$ **2.** $1\frac{1}{2} \times 1\frac{1}{3}$ **3.** $\frac{3}{5} \times 4\frac{1}{6}$

4. $2\frac{1}{3} \times 2\frac{1}{4}$ **5.** $3\frac{1}{3} \times \frac{1}{5}$ **6.** $2\frac{2}{9} \times 1\frac{1}{10}$

7. $8 \times 1\frac{1}{8}$ **8.** $5\frac{1}{4} \times 5\frac{1}{7}$ **9.** $1\frac{3}{7} \times 2\frac{4}{5}$

What two numbers would you multiply to complete each of the following?

10. $3\frac{1}{2}$ yd = ___ ft
1 yd = 3 ft

11. $6\frac{2}{3}$ ft = ___ in.
1 ft = 12 in.

12. $2\frac{3}{4}$ lb = ___ oz
1 lb = 16 oz

B Multiply.

13. $3 \times \frac{1}{3}$ **14.** $\frac{2}{5} \times 4$ **15.** $2\frac{1}{2} \times \frac{2}{3}$

16. $6 \times 2\frac{2}{9}$ **17.** $1\frac{1}{2} \times \frac{1}{2}$ **18.** $\frac{4}{5} \times 6\frac{1}{4}$

19. $3\frac{3}{4} \times 2$ **20.** $\frac{2}{3} \times 5\frac{5}{8}$ **21.** $2\frac{1}{2} \times 3\frac{1}{5}$

22. $\frac{3}{7} \times 4\frac{2}{3}$ **23.** $1\frac{1}{4} \times 1\frac{1}{4}$ **24.** $5 \times 2\frac{1}{10}$

25. $3\frac{1}{2} \times 2\frac{2}{3}$ **26.** $2\frac{5}{8} \times 10\frac{2}{3}$ **27.** $1\frac{2}{3} \times 2\frac{2}{5}$

28. $3\frac{3}{5} \times 3\frac{3}{4}$ **29.** $8\frac{1}{4} \times 7\frac{1}{3}$ **30.** $\frac{3}{4} \times 5\frac{1}{3}$

31. $5\frac{1}{3} \times 3\frac{3}{8}$ **32.** $7\frac{1}{5} \times 4\frac{4}{9}$ **33.** $4 \times 3\frac{1}{5}$

Complete. Refer to the table on page 50 for a list of equivalent measures.

34. $3\frac{1}{2}$ yd = ____ ft

35. $6\frac{2}{3}$ ft = ____ in.

36. $2\frac{3}{4}$ lb = ____ oz

37. $4\frac{5}{8}$ pt = ____ c

38. $5\frac{1}{3}$ gal. = ____ qt

39. $1\frac{3}{8}$ qt = ____ pt

C The formula for finding the area of a rectangle is $A = l \times w$. Find the area of each rectangle whose length and width is given below.

40. $l = 9\frac{3}{4}$ ft, $w = 5\frac{1}{3}$ ft

41. $l = 3\frac{1}{2}$ mi, $w = \frac{4}{5}$ mi

42. $l = 8\frac{2}{3}$ yd, $w = 6$ yd

43. $l = 6\frac{2}{3}$ in., $w = 5\frac{5}{8}$ in.

44. $l = 4\frac{1}{2}$ ft, $w = 1\frac{1}{6}$ yd

45. $l = 2\frac{2}{3}$ ft, $w = 1\frac{5}{16}$ in.

Quick Quiz

Sections 4.1 to 4.5

Express each of the following as a fraction.

1. $3 \div 5$

2. $7\overline{)4}$

3. $1\frac{2}{3}$

4. For $\frac{5}{8}$, 8 is the (*numerator, denominator*).

5. Express $\frac{7}{2}$ as a mixed number.

Add.

6. $\frac{1}{5} + \frac{2}{5}$

7. $\frac{5}{11} + \frac{3}{11}$

8. $\frac{7}{15} + \frac{7}{15}$

Multiply.

9. $\frac{3}{5} \times \frac{1}{7}$

10. $\frac{3}{4} \times \frac{2}{9}$

11. $\frac{18}{25} \times 5$

12. $3\frac{1}{8} \times 1\frac{3}{5}$

13. $12\frac{1}{2} \times 6$

14. $7\frac{1}{9} \times \frac{3}{8}$

CONSUMER CORNER

USING RECIPES

John wants to make 12 servings of spaghetti sauce. But his recipe is for only 8 servings. So John thinks:

servings needed → $\frac{12}{8} = 1\frac{1}{2}$ ← servings recipe makes

I'll make $1\frac{1}{2}$ times the recipe.

Spaghetti Sauce
$1\frac{1}{3}$ lb ground beef
24 oz tomato sauce
$\frac{2}{3}$ c water
1 tsp salt
$\frac{1}{2}$ tsp oregano
$\frac{1}{4}$ tsp pepper
$\frac{1}{8}$ tsp garlic powder
$\frac{3}{4}$ c chopped onion

Since he needs to make $1\frac{1}{2}$ times the recipe, he will use $1\frac{1}{2}$ times the amount of each ingredient. For example, find how much ground beef he should use.

amount recipe calls for ↓

$$1\frac{1}{2} \times 1\frac{1}{3} = \frac{\overset{1}{\cancel{3}}}{\underset{1}{\cancel{2}}} \times \frac{\overset{2}{\cancel{4}}}{\underset{1}{\cancel{3}}} = 2$$

He will use 2 lb ground beef.

1. Find how much of each remaining ingredient he should use.

2. Abby wants to make 30 servings from the same recipe. By what number should she multiply the amount of each ingredient?

3. Joe is going to make 4 servings from the recipe. By what number should he multiply the amounts? Find how much of each ingredient he should use.

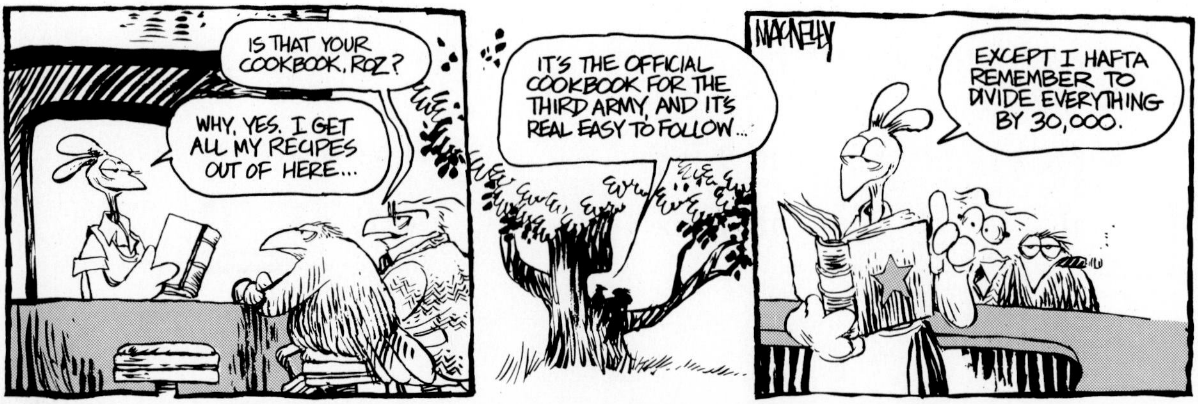

Chicago Tribune-New York News Syndicate

Dividing Fractions and Mixed Numbers

4.6

Divide $\frac{3}{4}$ yard of rope into $\frac{3}{8}$-yard pieces. How many pieces do you get? The diagram shows that $\frac{3}{4} \div \frac{3}{8} = 2$.

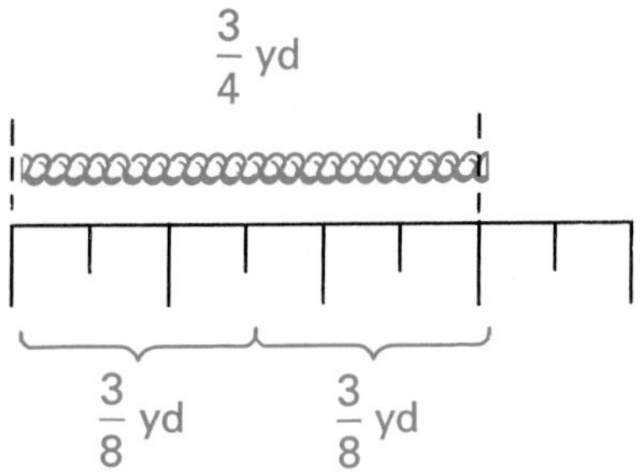

To find quotients, you can invert the divisor and multiply.

Example 1: Divide $\frac{3}{4}$ by $\frac{3}{8}$.

$$\frac{3}{4} \div \frac{3}{8} = \frac{3}{4} \times \frac{8}{3}$$ Invert divisor and multiply.

$$= \frac{\overset{1}{\cancel{3}}}{\underset{1}{\cancel{4}}} \times \frac{\overset{2}{\cancel{8}}}{\underset{1}{\cancel{3}}}$$

$$= \frac{2}{1} \text{ or } 2$$ Notice that this is the same answer you got from the diagram.

> To find the quotient of any two fractions, invert the divisor, then multiply the fractions. So, where c is not zero,
>
> $$\frac{a}{b} \div \frac{c}{d} = \frac{a}{b} \times \frac{d}{c}.$$ *Example:* $$\frac{1}{3} \div \frac{2}{5} = \frac{1}{3} \times \frac{5}{2} = \frac{5}{6}$$

Example 2: Divide $5\frac{1}{2}$ by $\frac{3}{4}$.

$$5\frac{1}{2} \div \frac{3}{4} = \frac{11}{2} \div \frac{3}{4}$$

$$= \frac{11}{\underset{1}{\cancel{2}}} \times \frac{\overset{2}{\cancel{4}}}{3}$$

$$= \frac{22}{3} \text{ or } 7\frac{1}{3}$$

Example 3: How many yards are there in $8\frac{1}{2}$ feet?

There are 3 ft in each yard, so divide $8\frac{1}{2}$ by 3.

$$8\frac{1}{2} \div 3 = \frac{17}{2} \div \frac{3}{1}$$
$$= \frac{17}{2} \times \frac{1}{3}$$
$$= \frac{17}{6} \text{ or } 2\frac{5}{6}$$

So $8\frac{1}{2}$ ft $= 2\frac{5}{6}$ yd.

Exercises

A Complete.

1. $\frac{1}{5} \div \frac{1}{2} = \frac{1}{5} \times$ ____
2. $\frac{1}{3} \div \frac{3}{4} = \frac{1}{3} \times$ ____
3. $2\frac{1}{2} \div 6 = \frac{5}{2} \times$ ____
4. $1\frac{3}{8} \div 1\frac{1}{2} = \frac{11}{8} \times$ ____
5. To find the number of yards in $7\frac{1}{2}$ ft, divide ____ by ____.
6. To find the number of feet in 56 in., divide ____ by ____.

B Divide.

7. $\frac{1}{5} \div \frac{1}{2}$
8. $\frac{1}{3} \div 3$
9. $3 \div \frac{1}{3}$
10. $\frac{3}{2} \div \frac{1}{2}$
11. $\frac{1}{6} \div 2$
12. $\frac{1}{3} \div \frac{1}{4}$
13. $\frac{2}{3} \div \frac{5}{6}$
14. $5 \div 1\frac{2}{3}$
15. $3\frac{1}{3} \div 2\frac{1}{2}$
16. $\frac{3}{4} \div 3$
17. $1\frac{1}{5} \div 3$
18. $3\frac{3}{4} \div \frac{5}{12}$
19. $3\frac{1}{2} \div 4\frac{1}{5}$
20. $\frac{4}{5} \div \frac{2}{3}$
21. $\frac{7}{10} \div 2\frac{4}{5}$
22. $4\frac{1}{2} \div 2\frac{2}{3}$
23. $4\frac{1}{3} \div \frac{1}{9}$
24. $2\frac{5}{8} \div 7$
25. $6 \div \frac{3}{5}$
26. $5\frac{1}{3} \div 1\frac{3}{5}$
27. $1\frac{1}{4} \div 1\frac{7}{8}$
28. $\frac{5}{8} \div 2\frac{1}{12}$
29. $10 \div 4\frac{1}{6}$
30. $2\frac{2}{9} \div \frac{5}{6}$

Complete. Refer to the table on page 50 for a list of equivalent measures.

31. $7\frac{1}{2}$ ft = ____ yd

32. 56 in. = ____ ft

33. $11\frac{1}{5}$ oz = ____ lb

34. $13\frac{3}{4}$ c = ____ pt

35. $20\frac{1}{2}$ qt = ____ gal.

36. 1750 ft = ____ mi

37. $8\frac{3}{4}$ in. of rain fell in 5 months. What is the average monthly rainfall?

38. Mr. Lauraitis has to find the number of panels he needs for a wall. Each panel is $1\frac{1}{3}$ feet wide. How many panels does he need for a 20-foot wall?

39. During a business trip, Mr. Levin traveled 125 miles in $2\frac{1}{2}$ hours. What was his average speed?

40. Each character typed by a pica typewriter takes $\frac{1}{10}$ inch. A character typed by an elite typewriter takes $\frac{1}{12}$ inch. How many characters are in a $7\frac{1}{2}$-inch line of pica type? Of elite type?

C Solve.

Example:

$$3x = 4\frac{1}{2}$$

$$\frac{3x}{3} = \frac{4\frac{1}{2}}{3}$$

$$x = 4\frac{1}{2} \div 3$$

$$x = \frac{\overset{3}{\cancel{9}}}{2} \times \frac{1}{\underset{1}{\cancel{3}}}$$

$$x = \frac{3}{2} \text{ or } 1\frac{1}{2}$$

Check:

$$3x = 4\frac{1}{2}$$

$$3 \times 1\frac{1}{2} = 4\frac{1}{2}$$

$$3 \times \frac{3}{2} = 4\frac{1}{2}$$

$$\frac{9}{2} = 4\frac{1}{2}$$

$$4\frac{1}{2} = 4\frac{1}{2}$$

41. $5a = 3\frac{1}{3}$

42. $9b = 6\frac{3}{4}$

43. $\frac{3}{7}c = 12$

44. $\frac{9}{16}d = 2\frac{7}{10}$

45. $2\frac{1}{8}e = 34$

46. $3\frac{5}{6}f = 5\frac{1}{9}$

4.7 Adding and Subtracting Like Fractions

A pizza was cut into 8 pieces. Jack and Pete ate 7 pieces, or $\frac{7}{8}$ of the pizza. If Jack ate $\frac{3}{8}$ of the pizza, what part of the pizza did Pete eat? To find the answer, subtract $\frac{3}{8}$ from $\frac{7}{8}$.

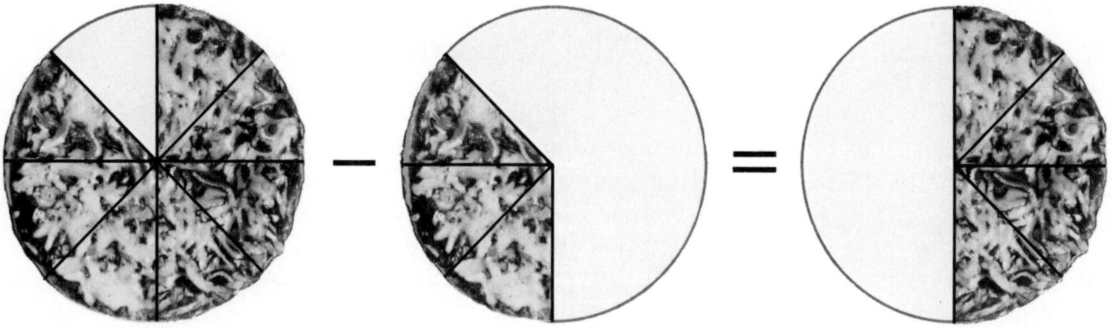

$$\frac{7}{8} \quad - \quad \frac{3}{8} \quad = \quad \frac{4}{8} \text{ or } \frac{1}{2}$$

Horizontal method:

$$\frac{7}{8} - \frac{3}{8} = \frac{7-3}{8}$$

$$= \frac{\cancel{4}^{1}}{\cancel{8}_{2}}$$

$$= \frac{1}{2}$$

Subtract numerators. Then simplify.

Vertical method:

$$\begin{array}{r} \frac{7}{8} \\ -\frac{3}{8} \\ \hline \frac{\cancel{4}^{1}}{\cancel{8}_{2}} = \frac{1}{2} \end{array}$$

Pete ate $\frac{1}{2}$ of the pizza.

> The difference of any two like fractions (fractions with a common denominator) is equal to the difference of their numerators over the common denominator. So
>
> $\frac{a}{c} - \frac{b}{c} = \frac{a-b}{c}$. *Example:* $\frac{3}{5} - \frac{2}{5} = \frac{3-2}{5} = \frac{1}{5}$

Example 1: Add $3\frac{3}{7}$ and $1\frac{6}{7}$.

Add numerators.
Add whole numbers.
Then simplify.

$$\begin{array}{r} 3\frac{3}{7} \\ +1\frac{6}{7} \\ \hline 4\frac{9}{7} \end{array} = 4 + 1\frac{2}{7} = 4 + 1 + \frac{2}{7} = 5\frac{2}{7}$$

Think: $\frac{9}{7} = 1\frac{2}{7}$

Example 2: Add $4\frac{3}{4}$ and $\frac{3}{4}$.

$$\begin{array}{r} 4\frac{3}{4} \\ +\ \frac{3}{4} \\ \hline 4\frac{6}{4} \end{array} = 4 + 1\frac{1}{2} = 5\frac{1}{2}$$

Think: $\frac{\cancel{6}^{3}}{\cancel{4}_{2}} = 1\frac{1}{2}$

Example 3: Subtract $1\frac{5}{8}$ from $8\frac{3}{8}$.

You cannot subtract $\frac{5}{8}$ from $\frac{3}{8}$, so rename $8\frac{3}{8}$.

Think: $8\frac{3}{8} = 7 + 1 + \frac{3}{8}$
$= 7 + \frac{8}{8} + \frac{3}{8}$
$= 7\frac{11}{8}$

Subtract numerators.
Subtract whole numbers.
Then simplify.

$$\begin{array}{r} 8\frac{3}{8} \\ -1\frac{5}{8} \\ \hline \end{array} \longrightarrow \begin{array}{r} 7\frac{11}{8} \\ -1\frac{5}{8} \\ \hline 6\frac{\cancel{6}^{3}}{\cancel{8}_{4}} \end{array} = 6\frac{3}{4}$$

Exercises

A Express each mixed number in lowest terms.

1. $1\frac{5}{4} = 2\frac{\square}{4}$ 2. $3\frac{11}{7} = 4\frac{\square}{7}$ 3. $2\frac{7}{6} = 3\frac{\square}{6}$

Complete each renaming.

4. $2\frac{1}{5} = 1\frac{\square}{5}$ 5. $4\frac{1}{6} = 3\frac{\square}{6}$ 6. $1\frac{1}{3} = \frac{\square}{3}$

B Find each sum or difference.

7. $\frac{3}{4} + \frac{1}{4}$ 8. $\frac{2}{3} - \frac{1}{3}$ 9. $\frac{7}{8} - \frac{3}{8}$ 10. $1\frac{5}{6} - \frac{1}{6}$ 11. $2\frac{1}{3} + \frac{1}{3}$

12. $1\frac{1}{8} + \frac{7}{8}$ 13. $1\frac{1}{3} - \frac{2}{3}$ 14. $2\frac{5}{12} + 5\frac{5}{12}$ 15. $2\frac{2}{3} + 1\frac{2}{3}$

16. $10\frac{5}{8} - 3\frac{3}{8}$ 17. $2\frac{1}{4} - \frac{3}{4}$ 18. $4\frac{4}{5} + 1\frac{3}{5}$ 19. $1\frac{9}{10} - 1\frac{3}{10}$

20. $3\frac{2}{5} - 2\frac{3}{5}$ 21. $2\frac{5}{6} + 1\frac{5}{6}$ 22. $4\frac{1}{6} - 1\frac{5}{6}$ 23. $5\frac{1}{8} - 2\frac{7}{8}$

24. $6\frac{4}{7} + \frac{2}{7}$ 25. $5\frac{2}{3} + 1\frac{2}{3}$ 26. $4\frac{5}{9} - \frac{2}{9}$ 27. $2\frac{3}{5} - 1\frac{4}{5}$

28. Sandy picked $5\frac{3}{4}$ quarts of strawberries in the morning and $2\frac{3}{4}$ quarts in the afternoon. How many quarts did she pick altogether?

29. Alex has $6\frac{2}{3}$ yards of string. If he uses $2\frac{1}{3}$ yards to tie a package, how much string will he have left?

Subtract.

Example 1: $1 - \frac{3}{5} = \frac{5}{5} - \frac{3}{5} = \frac{5-3}{5} = \frac{2}{5}$

Example 2: $5 - 1\frac{2}{3} = (4 + 1) - 1\frac{2}{3} = \left(4 + \frac{3}{3}\right) - 1\frac{2}{3} = 4\frac{3}{3} - 1\frac{2}{3} = 3\frac{1}{3}$

30. $1 - \frac{1}{4}$ **31.** $1 - \frac{5}{6}$ **32.** $1 - \frac{7}{12}$

33. $2 - \frac{1}{3}$ **34.** $8 - \frac{4}{5}$ **35.** $13 - \frac{5}{9}$

36. $2 - 1\frac{1}{5}$ **37.** $6 - 3\frac{2}{7}$ **38.** $10 - 4\frac{5}{8}$

39. English is spoken by about $\frac{1}{12}$ of the world's population. What part of the population does not speak English? (*Note:* 1, or $\frac{12}{12}$, represents the whole population.)

40. About $\frac{5}{7}$ of the earth's surface is covered with water. What part of the surface is land?

41. How much oil should you add to $\frac{3}{4}$ quart to have 5 quarts?

42. John has walked $2\frac{1}{3}$ miles of a 4-mile hike. How much farther does he have to walk?

Solve.

43. $m + \frac{2}{5} = \frac{4}{5}$ **44.** $n + 3\frac{1}{3} = 5\frac{2}{3}$ **45.** $p - \frac{7}{8} = \frac{5}{8}$

46. $q - 5\frac{1}{5} = 1\frac{2}{5}$ **47.** $r + 1\frac{3}{7} = 4\frac{1}{7}$ **48.** $s + \frac{10}{13} = 1$

C Use the distributive property to multiply.

Example:
$$2\frac{2}{5} \times 3 = \left(2 + \frac{2}{5}\right)3$$
$$= (2 \times 3) + \left(\frac{2}{5} \times 3\right)$$
$$= 6 + \frac{6}{5}$$
$$= 7\frac{1}{5}$$

49. $1\frac{5}{8} \times 2$ **50.** $4\frac{3}{4} \times 7$ **51.** $8\frac{5}{6} \times 3$

52. $10\frac{2}{9} \times 6$ **53.** $12\frac{5}{12} \times 10$ **54.** $15\frac{11}{18} \times 3$

4.8 Adding and Subtracting Unlike Fractions

In Section 4.7 you added and subtracted like fractions (fractions with a common denominator). Unlike fractions have different denominators. To add or subtract unlike fractions, you must first rename the fractions so they have a common denominator.

Example 1: Add $\frac{3}{8}$ and $\frac{5}{12}$.

Step 1: Find the *least common denominator* by finding the LCM of the denominators.

$$8 = 2^3$$

$$12 = 2^2 \times 3$$

$$2^3 \times 3 = 24 \quad \blacktriangleleft \text{ LCM}$$

Step 2: Express each fraction as an equivalent fraction with the least common denominator.

$$\frac{3}{8} = \frac{\square}{24} \qquad \frac{5}{12} = \frac{\square}{24}$$

$8 \times 3 = 24$, so $\qquad 12 \times 2 = 24$, so

$$\frac{3}{8} = \frac{3}{8} \times \frac{3}{3} = \frac{9}{24} \qquad \frac{5}{12} = \frac{5}{12} \times \frac{2}{2} = \frac{10}{24}$$

Step 3: Add.

$$\begin{array}{rcr} \frac{3}{8} & \rightarrow & \frac{9}{24} \\ +\frac{5}{12} & \rightarrow & +\frac{10}{24} \\ \hline & & \frac{19}{24} \end{array}$$

Example 2: Add $\frac{2}{5}$ and $\frac{3}{10}$.

Since 10 is a multiple of 5,
10 is the least common denominator.

$$\frac{2}{5} \longrightarrow \frac{2}{5} \times \frac{2}{2} \longrightarrow \frac{4}{10}$$

$$+\frac{3}{10} \longrightarrow +\frac{3}{10}$$

$$\frac{7}{10}$$

Example 3: How far is it between exits?
Subtract $\frac{1}{4}$ from $\frac{2}{3}$.

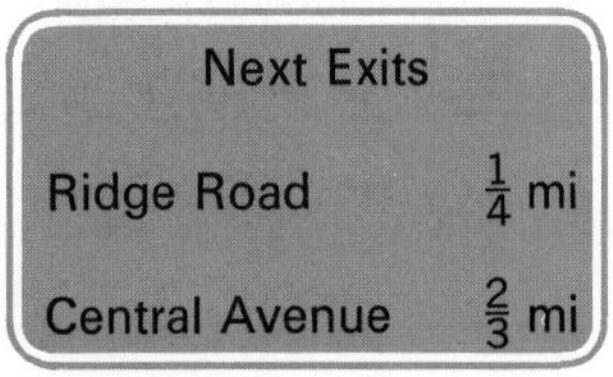

Since 3 and 4 have no common factors (except 1), 3×4, or 12, is the least common denominator.

$$\frac{2}{3} \longrightarrow \frac{2}{3} \times \frac{4}{4} \longrightarrow \frac{8}{12}$$

$$-\frac{1}{4} \longrightarrow \frac{1}{4} \times \frac{3}{3} \longrightarrow -\frac{3}{12}$$

$$\frac{5}{12}$$

The distance between the exits is $\frac{5}{12}$ mile.

Exercises

A Complete each pair of equivalent fractions.

1. $\frac{1}{4} = \frac{\square}{16}$ **2.** $\frac{1}{5} = \frac{\square}{15}$ **3.** $\frac{1}{2} = \frac{\square}{10}$

4. $\frac{1}{3} = \frac{\square}{12}$ **5.** $\frac{3}{4} = \frac{\square}{8}$ **6.** $\frac{2}{3} = \frac{\square}{6}$

B For each pair of fractions, find equivalent fractions with the least common denominator.

7. $\frac{3}{8}, \frac{1}{16}$ **8.** $\frac{1}{10}, \frac{2}{15}$ **9.** $\frac{1}{5}, \frac{5}{6}$ **10.** $\frac{1}{6}, \frac{2}{9}$

Find each sum or difference.

11. $\frac{1}{2} + \frac{1}{4}$ **12.** $\frac{2}{3} - \frac{1}{6}$ **13.** $\frac{3}{8} - \frac{1}{4}$ **14.** $\frac{1}{6} + \frac{1}{2}$

15. $\frac{1}{2} - \frac{1}{3}$ **16.** $\frac{5}{6} - \frac{3}{8}$ **17.** $\frac{1}{4} + \frac{2}{3}$ **18.** $\frac{7}{8} - \frac{1}{12}$

19. $\frac{1}{3} + \frac{5}{8}$ **20.** $\frac{1}{2} - \frac{2}{5}$ **21.** $\frac{3}{4} - \frac{5}{12}$ **22.** $\frac{1}{6} + \frac{4}{15}$

23. $\frac{2}{3} - \frac{1}{8}$ **24.** $\frac{5}{24} + \frac{5}{12}$ **25.** $\frac{9}{16} - \frac{1}{4}$ **26.** $\frac{3}{20} + \frac{2}{5}$

Solve.

27. $u + \frac{3}{4} = \frac{7}{8}$ **28.** $v + \frac{5}{6} = \frac{8}{9}$ **29.** $w - \frac{2}{7} = \frac{1}{4}$

30. $x - \frac{3}{10} = \frac{1}{2}$ **31.** $y - \frac{3}{8} = \frac{5}{12}$ **32.** $z + \frac{2}{9} = \frac{1}{2}$

C To arrange fractions in order, express the fractions as equivalent fractions with a common denominator. Then compare numerators.

Example: Which is the heaviest—$\frac{3}{4}$ oz, $\frac{2}{3}$ oz, or $\frac{5}{6}$ oz? The lightest?

12 is the LCM of 4, 3, and 6.

$$\frac{3}{4} = \frac{9}{12} \qquad \frac{2}{3} = \frac{8}{12} \qquad \frac{5}{6} = \frac{10}{12}$$

The order from least to greatest is $\frac{8}{12}, \frac{9}{12}, \frac{10}{12}$ or $\frac{2}{3}, \frac{3}{4}, \frac{5}{6}$.

The heaviest is $\frac{5}{6}$ oz and the lightest is $\frac{2}{3}$ oz.

Order each of the following sets from least to greatest.

33. $\frac{1}{2}, \frac{2}{5}, \frac{3}{10}$ **34.** $\frac{3}{8}, \frac{1}{4}, \frac{5}{16}$ **35.** $\frac{1}{6}, \frac{1}{2}, \frac{2}{3}$

36. $\frac{1}{4}, \frac{1}{5}, \frac{3}{10}$ **37.** $\frac{1}{4}, \frac{1}{2}, \frac{1}{3}$ **38.** $\frac{5}{9}, \frac{2}{3}, \frac{1}{2}$

Adding and Subtracting Mixed Numbers

A sewing pattern calls for $2\frac{7}{8}$ yards of fabric for a jacket and $1\frac{1}{4}$ yards of fabric for a skirt. How much fabric does Nancy need to make a matching jacket and skirt?

Example 1: Add $2\frac{7}{8}$ and $1\frac{1}{4}$.

The least common denominator of $\frac{7}{8}$ and $\frac{1}{4}$ is 8.

$$\begin{array}{rcr} 2\frac{7}{8} & \rightarrow & 2\frac{7}{8} \\ +\ 1\frac{1}{4} & \rightarrow & +\ 1\frac{2}{8} \\ \hline & & 3\frac{9}{8} \end{array}$$

$$3\frac{9}{8} = 3 + 1\frac{1}{8} = 4\frac{1}{8}$$

Nancy needs $4\frac{1}{8}$ yards.

Example 2: Subtract $2\frac{5}{6}$ from $5\frac{1}{4}$.

The least common denominator of $\frac{5}{6}$ and $\frac{1}{4}$ is 12.

You cannot subtract the numerators, so rename $5\frac{3}{12}$ as $4\frac{15}{12}$.

$$\begin{array}{rcrcr} 5\frac{1}{4} & \rightarrow & 5\frac{3}{12} & \rightarrow & 4\frac{15}{12} \\ -\ 2\frac{5}{6} & \rightarrow & -\ 2\frac{10}{12} & \rightarrow & -\ 2\frac{10}{12} \\ \hline & & & & 2\frac{5}{12} \end{array}$$

Exercises

A Express each mixed number in lowest terms.

1. $2\frac{5}{3} = 3\frac{\square}{3}$

2. $4\frac{3}{2} = 5\frac{\square}{2}$

3. $6\frac{7}{5} = 7\frac{\square}{5}$

Complete each renaming.

4. $1\frac{1}{4} = \frac{\square}{4}$

5. $2\frac{1}{5} = 1\frac{\square}{5}$

6. $5\frac{2}{3} = 4\frac{\square}{3}$

B Add or subtract.

7. $9\frac{1}{2} + 2\frac{1}{4}$

8. $8\frac{3}{5} - 3\frac{1}{2}$

9. $2\frac{1}{10} - 1\frac{2}{5}$

10. $\frac{7}{10} + 10\frac{1}{2}$

11. $7\frac{1}{8} - 4\frac{3}{4}$

12. $12\frac{3}{8} + 3\frac{5}{12}$

13. $1\frac{1}{3} - \frac{7}{12}$

14. $5\frac{1}{3} + 6\frac{5}{6}$

15. $5\frac{3}{4} - 2\frac{4}{5}$

16. $14\frac{11}{12} + 8\frac{1}{4}$

17. $9\frac{2}{3} + 7\frac{9}{10}$

18. $6\frac{1}{6} - 1\frac{4}{9}$

19. $6\frac{2}{5} + 1\frac{1}{4}$

20. $12\frac{1}{3} + 7\frac{5}{12}$

21. $7\frac{1}{12} - 3\frac{3}{8}$

22. $4\frac{1}{10} - 2\frac{3}{5}$

23. Kay cut $2\frac{5}{8}$ yards of material from a piece $4\frac{1}{2}$ yards long. How much material did she have left?

24. $10\frac{1}{2}$ in. of snow fell during the month of November and $14\frac{3}{4}$ in. fell during December. What was the total snowfall for both months?

25. It took a mechanic $5\frac{2}{3}$ hours of work one day and $2\frac{1}{2}$ hours on the next day to fix a car. What was the total number of hours the mechanic worked on the car?

C Add.

Example:

$$\begin{array}{rcr} 1\frac{2}{3} & \rightarrow & 1\frac{4}{6} \\ 2\frac{1}{2} & \rightarrow & 2\frac{3}{6} \\ +\,1\frac{5}{6} & \rightarrow & +\,1\frac{5}{6} \\ \hline & & 4\frac{12}{6} = 6 \end{array}$$

Think: $4\frac{\cancel{12}^{\,2}}{\cancel{6}_{\,1}} = 4 + 2 = 6$

26. $4\frac{1}{2} + 2\frac{1}{4} + 5\frac{1}{2}$

27. $3\frac{1}{2} + 2\frac{2}{3} + 1\frac{1}{6}$

28. $\frac{5}{8} + 2\frac{1}{4} + 3\frac{3}{8}$

29. $1\frac{3}{4} + 2\frac{1}{3} + 1\frac{5}{12}$

Use the method shown below to multiply.

Example: $2\frac{2}{5} \times 3\frac{1}{3} = (2 + \frac{2}{5})\ (3 + \frac{1}{3})$

Multiply both parts of one mixed number by each part of the other.

A B C D

$$= 6 + \frac{6}{5} + \frac{2}{3} + \frac{2}{15}$$

Then add the products.

$$= 6 + \frac{18}{15} + \frac{10}{15} + \frac{2}{15}$$

$$= 6 + \frac{\cancel{30}^{\,2}}{\cancel{15}_{\,1}}$$

$$= 8$$

30. $3\frac{1}{2} \times 2\frac{1}{4}$

31. $4\frac{3}{5} \times 5\frac{1}{3}$

32. $2\frac{3}{4} \times 2\frac{2}{5}$

33. $6\frac{7}{8} \times 1\frac{1}{3}$

34. $6\frac{2}{3} \times 2\frac{4}{5}$

35. $8\frac{1}{2} \times 3\frac{2}{3}$

4.10 Solving Problems With U.S. Units of Measure

A problem might require a whole-number answer, but the result of your computation is not a whole number. In such problems, the answer is usually the next larger or the next smaller whole number.

Example 1: Each chocolate bar weighs $2\frac{3}{4}$ ounces. How many bars would you buy to have the 10 ounces needed for the recipe?

$$10 \div 2\frac{3}{4} = \frac{10}{1} \div \frac{11}{4}$$
$$= \frac{10}{1} \times \frac{4}{11}$$
$$= \frac{40}{11} \text{ or } 3\frac{7}{11}$$

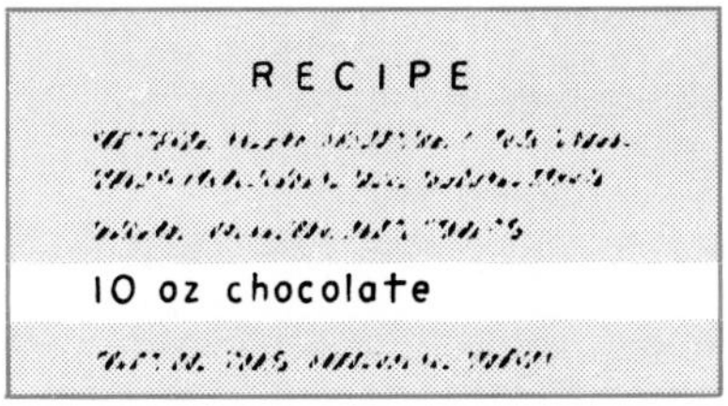

You can't buy $3\frac{7}{11}$ bars, and 3 bars would not be enough. So you would buy 4 bars.

Example 2: How many small boxes will fit on a 10-inch shelf?

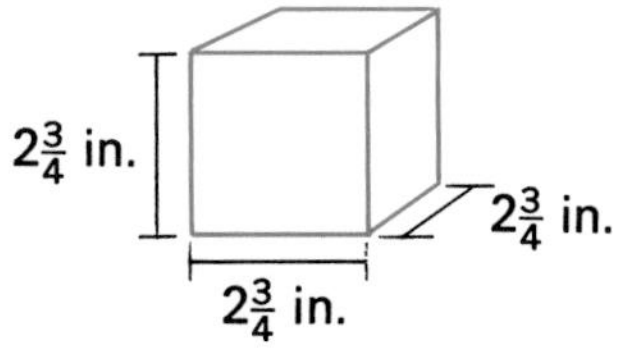

From Example 1, $10 \div 2\frac{3}{4} = 3\frac{7}{11}$.

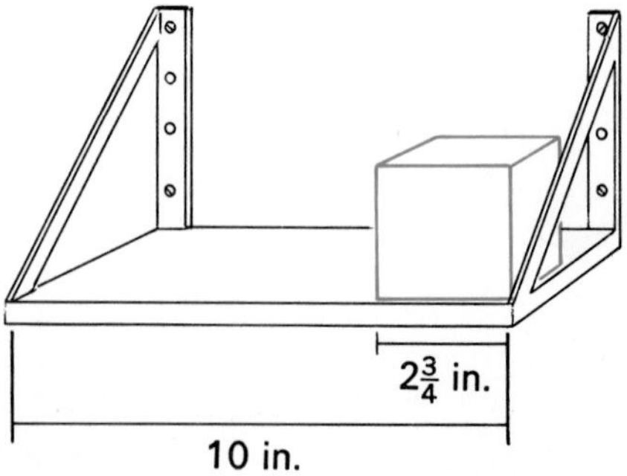

You can't have $3\frac{7}{11}$ boxes, and 4 boxes would not fit. So you can fit only 3 boxes on the 10-inch shelf.

In the examples, the best answer is not the mixed number that resulted from the computation.

Exercises

A The computation for each problem has a result that is not a whole number. Decide if the best answer would be

(a) the actual result,

(b) the next larger whole number, or

(c) the next smaller whole number.

1. Each wall panel is 4 feet wide. How many panels must you buy to panel a wall $18\frac{1}{2}$ feet wide?

2. A 19-inch wire is cut in half. How long is each piece?

3. Allen can make 8 posters in $2\frac{1}{2}$ hr. How many posters can he complete in 1 hr?

Mary Elenz Tranter Photographics

4. You're serving dinner to 11 people. How much meat should you buy to serve each person $\frac{1}{2}$ pound of meat?

5. How many $2\frac{1}{2}$-foot boards can be cut from a 12-foot board?

B Find the number that best answers each question.

6. On Jane's part-time job, she works $4\frac{1}{2}$ hours a day. How many days must she work to put in 15 hours per week?

7. There are $2\frac{1}{4}$ cups of rice in a pound box. Chris uses $\frac{1}{2}$ cup each time he makes rice pudding. How many times can he make rice pudding from a pound box?

8. Each theater seat is $2\frac{1}{4}$ feet wide. How many seats can fit in a 15-foot row?

9. Each can holds $1\frac{1}{2}$ quarts. How many cans are needed to hold 10 quarts of liquid?

Connie and PC Peri

10. It takes $1\frac{1}{6}$ yd of tissue paper to make 1 kite. How many kites can be made with $4\frac{1}{3}$ yd?

11. Fruit punch comes in 3-quart ($\frac{3}{4}$-gallon) bottles. How many bottles should you buy to have enough to fill a 2-gallon punch bowl?

12. The gas gauge on a car shows that $\frac{3}{8}$ of a tank of gas has been used since the tank was last filled. If the tank holds 20 gallons, how much gas was used?

13. A 28-inch piece of copper tubing is cut into 3 pieces of the same length. How long is each piece?

C The formula for finding the area of a circle is $A = \pi r^2$, where r stands for the radius and π is approximately equal to $\frac{22}{7}$.

Example: $A = \pi r^2$

$$= \frac{22}{7} \times \left(3\frac{1}{2}\right)^2$$

$$= \frac{22}{7} \times \left(\frac{7}{2}\right)^2$$

$$= \frac{22}{7} \times \frac{7}{2} \times \frac{7}{2}$$

$$= \frac{77}{2} \text{ or } 38\frac{1}{2}$$

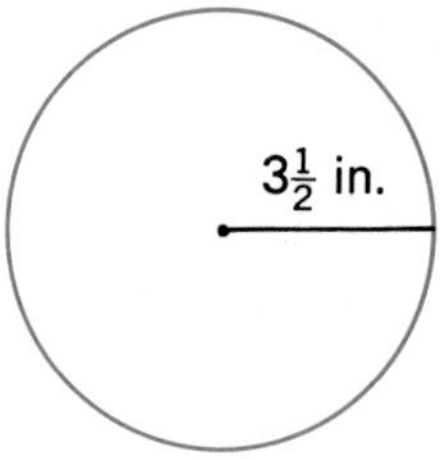

The area is $38\frac{1}{2}$ sq in.

Find the area of each circle. Use $\frac{22}{7}$ for π.

14. 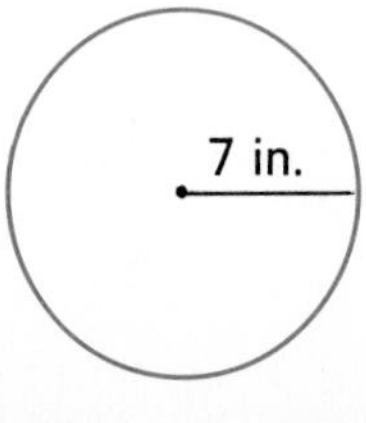

15. 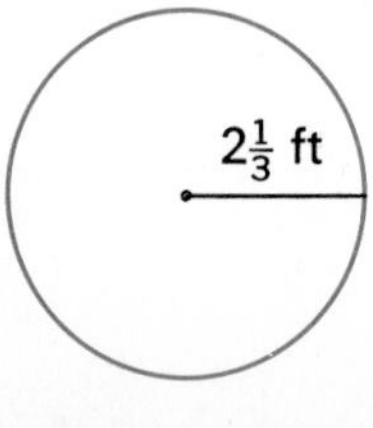

16. 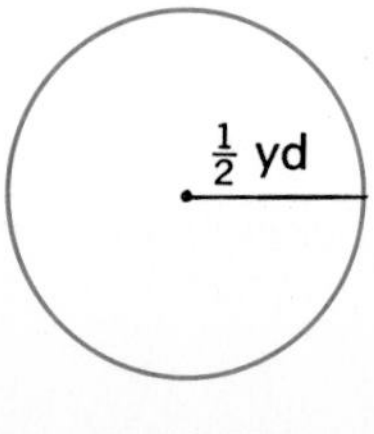

Terms and Symbols Review

Choose the best term.

1. 3 is the (*denominator, numerator*) of $\frac{3}{4}$.
2. $\frac{8}{12}$ is equivalent to ($\frac{2}{3}$, $\frac{5}{6}$, $\frac{3}{4}$).
3. ($\frac{2}{3}$, $\frac{2}{4}$, $\frac{2}{6}$) is a fraction in lowest terms.
4. ($\frac{3}{4}$, $2\frac{2}{3}$, $\frac{5}{10}$) is a mixed number.
5. (2, 12, $\frac{1}{5}$) is the least common denominator of $\frac{1}{4}$ and $\frac{1}{6}$.

Chapter 4 Review

Express as a fraction. 4.1

1. $2 \div 5$ 2. 4 3. $3\overline{)8}$ 4. $5 \div 2$

Add.

5. $\frac{1}{5} + \frac{1}{5}$ 6. $\frac{2}{7} + \frac{3}{7}$ 7. $\frac{2}{9} + \frac{5}{9}$ 8. $\frac{3}{8} + \frac{5}{8}$

Multiply. 4.2

9. $\frac{3}{4} \times \frac{3}{4}$ 10. $\frac{2}{3} \times \frac{4}{5}$ 11. $\frac{5}{16} \times \frac{1}{2}$ 12. $3 \times \frac{1}{4}$

Multiply. Express each answer in lowest terms. 4.3

13. $\frac{2}{3} \times \frac{3}{8}$ 14. $\frac{1}{16} \times \frac{4}{5}$ 15. $\frac{4}{3} \times \frac{3}{4}$ 16. $3 \times \frac{1}{6}$

Express each mixed number as a fraction. 4.4

17. $1\frac{2}{3}$ 18. $2\frac{1}{2}$ 19. $1\frac{3}{5}$ 20. $3\frac{3}{4}$

Express each fraction as a mixed number.

21. $\frac{10}{3}$ 22. $\frac{9}{2}$ 23. $\frac{7}{4}$ 24. $\frac{11}{5}$

Multiply.

25. $\frac{4}{5} \times \frac{11}{8}$ 26. $2 \times \frac{3}{4}$ 27. $\frac{8}{3} \times \frac{1}{6}$

28. $6 \times 1\frac{1}{2}$ 29. $1\frac{2}{3} \times \frac{3}{10}$ 30. $2\frac{1}{2} \times 1\frac{1}{3}$ 4.5

31. $2\frac{2}{5} \times 3\frac{1}{3}$ **32.** $\frac{1}{3} \times 1\frac{4}{5}$ **33.** $1\frac{1}{4} \times 4\frac{3}{5}$

4.6 Divide. Express each answer in lowest terms.

34. $\frac{5}{8} \div \frac{5}{12}$ **35.** $\frac{1}{3} \div 5$ **36.** $\frac{1}{2} \div 1\frac{1}{2}$

37. $6 \div 1\frac{1}{8}$ **38.** $1\frac{1}{2} \div 1\frac{1}{5}$ **39.** $2\frac{1}{4} \div 6$

4.7 Express each mixed number in lowest terms.

40. $3\frac{5}{4} = 4\frac{\square}{4}$ **41.** $2\frac{7}{5} = 3\frac{\square}{5}$ **42.** $5\frac{11}{6} = 6\frac{\square}{6}$

Complete each renaming.

43. $2\frac{2}{3} = 1\frac{\square}{3}$ **44.** $6\frac{2}{5} = 5\frac{\square}{5}$ **45.** $1 = \frac{\square}{8}$

Find each sum or difference. Express each answer in lowest terms.

46. $\begin{array}{r} 1\frac{1}{2} \\ +\ 2\frac{1}{2} \\ \hline \end{array}$ **47.** $\begin{array}{r} 2\frac{1}{3} \\ -\ 1\frac{2}{3} \\ \hline \end{array}$ **48.** $\begin{array}{r} 4\frac{2}{5} \\ +\ 1\frac{2}{5} \\ \hline \end{array}$ **49.** $\begin{array}{r} 5 \\ -\ 2\frac{5}{8} \\ \hline \end{array}$

4.8 Complete each pair of equivalent fractions.

50. $\frac{2}{3} = \frac{\square}{12}$ **51.** $\frac{3}{4} = \frac{\square}{8}$ **52.** $\frac{4}{5} = \frac{\square}{20}$

Find each sum or difference. Express your answers in lowest terms.

53. $\begin{array}{r} \frac{1}{3} \\ +\ \frac{1}{2} \\ \hline \end{array}$ **54.** $\begin{array}{r} \frac{3}{4} \\ -\ \frac{1}{6} \\ \hline \end{array}$ **55.** $\begin{array}{r} \frac{1}{4} \\ +\ \frac{5}{8} \\ \hline \end{array}$ **56.** $\begin{array}{r} \frac{3}{5} \\ -\ \frac{1}{2} \\ \hline \end{array}$

Find each sum or difference. Express your answers in lowest terms.

4.9 **57.** $\begin{array}{r} 2\frac{3}{5} \\ +\ 1\frac{3}{10} \\ \hline \end{array}$ **58.** $\begin{array}{r} 4\frac{1}{3} \\ -\ 3\frac{5}{6} \\ \hline \end{array}$ **59.** $\begin{array}{r} 5\frac{3}{4} \\ +\ 8\frac{2}{3} \\ \hline \end{array}$ **60.** $\begin{array}{r} 1\frac{1}{6} \\ -\ \frac{5}{8} \\ \hline \end{array}$

4.10 Find the number that best answers each question.

61. Mr. Sosnowski's students need wire for an experiment. How many $2\frac{1}{2}$-foot pieces can he cut from a 32-foot piece?

62. Tomato juice comes in $5\frac{1}{3}$-ounce cans. How many cans should you buy if the recipe calls for 12 ounces?

63. How many $\frac{3}{4}$-pound packages of bacon are needed to have at least 10 pounds of bacon?

Express as a fraction.

1. 6 **2.** $4\frac{1}{2}$ **3.** $3 \div 2$

Express in lowest terms.

4. $\frac{5}{15}$ **5.** $\frac{5}{2}$ **6.** $\frac{10}{6}$

Compute.

7. $\frac{1}{5} \times \frac{2}{3}$ **8.** $\frac{2}{5} \times \frac{5}{6}$ **9.** $10 \times \frac{1}{4}$

10. $1\frac{1}{2} \times 1\frac{1}{3}$ **11.** $3 \times \frac{1}{7}$ **12.** $\frac{2}{3} \div \frac{1}{2}$

13. $4\frac{1}{2} \div 3$ **14.** $6 \div \frac{3}{8}$ **15.** $8\frac{1}{3} \div 3\frac{1}{3}$

Complete each pair of equivalent fractions.

16. $\frac{1}{2} = \frac{\square}{12}$ **17.** $\frac{2}{3} = \frac{\square}{6}$ **18.** $\frac{3}{4} = \frac{\square}{8}$

Express each mixed number in lowest terms.

19. $2\frac{4}{3} = 3\frac{\square}{3}$ **20.** $1\frac{7}{4} = 2\frac{\square}{4}$ **21.** $3\frac{11}{8} = 4\frac{\square}{8}$

Complete each renaming.

22. $2\frac{1}{4} = 1\frac{\square}{4}$ **23.** $6\frac{2}{5} = 5\frac{\square}{5}$ **24.** $5\frac{3}{10} = 4\frac{\square}{10}$

Find each sum or difference.

25. $\begin{array}{r} \frac{1}{8} \\ +\ \frac{3}{8} \\ \hline \end{array}$ **26.** $\begin{array}{r} 10 \\ -\ 8\frac{2}{3} \\ \hline \end{array}$ **27.** $\begin{array}{r} 2\frac{5}{6} \\ -\ 2\frac{1}{6} \\ \hline \end{array}$ **28.** $\begin{array}{r} 6\frac{5}{8} \\ +\ 5\frac{5}{8} \\ \hline \end{array}$

29. $\begin{array}{r} \frac{2}{3} \\ -\ \frac{1}{2} \\ \hline \end{array}$ **30.** $\begin{array}{r} 8\frac{1}{2} \\ -\ 7\frac{3}{4} \\ \hline \end{array}$ **31.** $\begin{array}{r} 5\frac{1}{2} \\ +\ 3\frac{5}{6} \\ \hline \end{array}$ **32.** $\begin{array}{r} \frac{1}{3} \\ +\ \frac{1}{4} \\ \hline \end{array}$

Find the number that best answers each question.

33. How many $2\frac{1}{4}$-inch pieces of wire can be cut from a 10-inch piece?

34. How many $1\frac{1}{2}$-quart cans must you buy to have at least 8 quarts?

RATE YOURSELF

Number Correct	
32–34	Superior
29–31	Excellent
25–28	Good
18–24	Fair
0–17	Poor

CAREER CORNER

MATH AND TYPING

Photo by George Quinn
© Chicago Tribune, 1979, World Rights Reserved

Many people who work in offices must know how to type. Typing fast is important, but so is making as few errors as possible. That is why you must subtract for errors when finding your typing speed.

The formula below is used for a 20-minute typing test.

$$s = \frac{w - 10e}{20}$$

where s = speed in words per minute, w = number of words typed, e = number of errors

Find the speed for each of these scores on a 20-minute test.

1. 670 words with 5 errors

2. 720 words with 14 errors

3. 1000 words with 10 errors

4. 830 words with 7 errors

Getting Ready for Chapter 5

Find each answer.

1. $\begin{array}{r} 364 \\ +148 \\ \hline \end{array}$

2. $\begin{array}{r} 134 \\ -94 \\ \hline \end{array}$

3. $\begin{array}{r} 260 \\ 42 \\ +1486 \\ \hline \end{array}$

4. $\begin{array}{r} 36 \\ \times 8 \\ \hline \end{array}$

5. $\begin{array}{r} 425 \\ \times 5 \\ \hline \end{array}$

6. $\begin{array}{r} 34 \\ \times 25 \\ \hline \end{array}$

7. $6\overline{)504}$

8. $8\overline{)1928}$

9. $672 \div 32$

10. $34 + 186 + 7$

11. $406 - 38$

12. 16×42

Express each fraction in lowest terms. 4.3

13. $\frac{32}{100}$

14. $\frac{6}{10}$

15. $\frac{25}{1000}$

Find the value of each expression. 3.8

16. 10^3

17. 10^2

18. 10^1

19. $\frac{1}{10^3}$

20. $\frac{1}{10^2}$

21. $\frac{1}{10^1}$

Complete. 1.1

22. 1 kg = ____ g

23. 1 L = ____ mL

24. 1 m = ____ cm

25. 1 g = ____ mg

26. 1 km = ____ m

27. 1 cm = ____ mm

Write each mixed number as a fraction. 4.4

28. $3\frac{3}{8}$

29. $5\frac{7}{10}$

30. $6\frac{2}{3}$

5

5

DECIMALS AND ESTIMATING

In this chapter you will review the basic operations with decimals and learn how to solve equations involving decimals. You will also learn how to check answers by estimating them.

Decimals as Fractions or Mixed Numbers

5.1

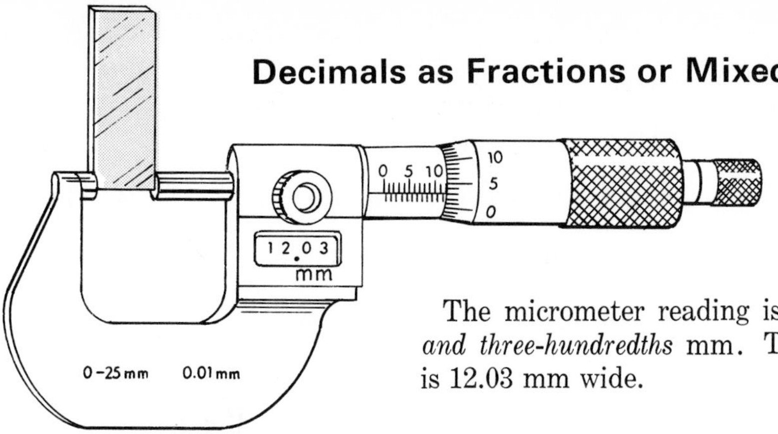

The micrometer reading is *twelve and three-hundredths* mm. The bar is 12.03 mm wide.

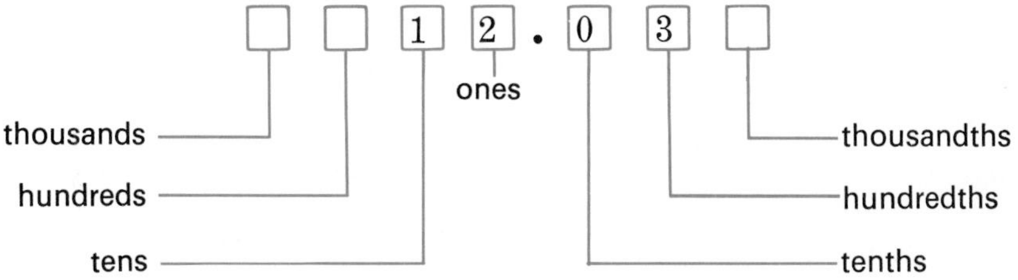

Example 1: Express 0.7, 12.03, and 123.456 as fractions or mixed numbers.

$$0.7 = \frac{7}{10} \qquad 12.03 = 12\frac{3}{100} \qquad 123.456 = 123\frac{456}{1000}$$

$$= 123\frac{57}{125}$$

Change to lowest terms whenever possible.

This 0 calls attention to the decimal point.

The number of digits here tells what the denominator should be.

The numbers 10, 100, 1000, and so on, are called *powers of ten,* since they can be written 10^1, 10^2, 10^3, and so on. A fraction whose denominator is a power of ten can easily be written as a decimal.

Example 2: Express $\frac{3}{10}$, $\frac{24}{100}$, and $2\frac{5}{1000}$ as decimals.

$$\frac{3}{10} = 0.3 \qquad \frac{24}{100} = 0.24 \qquad 2\frac{5}{1000} = 2.005$$

The denominator tells where the last digit of the numerator goes.

Use zeros here to put the 5 in the thousandths place.

Exercises

A Tell how to read each decimal.

1. 0.1 **2.** 1.5 **3.** 7.9 **4.** 14.6

5. 0.12 **6.** 0.02 **7.** 6.55 **8.** 35.09

9. 0.123 **10.** 0.402 **11.** 8.063 **12.** 14.839

B Write each decimal as a fraction or a mixed number.

13. 0.3 **14.** 0.8 **15.** 68.9 **16.** 6.5

17. 0.17 **18.** 0.36 **19.** 9.07 **20.** 5.25

21. 0.321 **22.** 0.055 **23.** 18.009 **24.** 6.025

25. 8.6 **26.** 9.24 **27.** 16.085 **28.** 3.125

Express each number as a decimal.

29. $\frac{5}{10}$ **30.** $\frac{7}{10}$ **31.** $3\frac{9}{10}$ **32.** $17\frac{8}{10}$

33. $\frac{16}{100}$ **34.** $\frac{6}{100}$ **35.** $4\frac{37}{100}$ **36.** $43\frac{75}{100}$

37. $\frac{225}{1000}$ **38.** $\frac{25}{1000}$ **39.** $6\frac{3}{1000}$ **40.** $24\frac{502}{1000}$

41. $6\frac{9}{10}$ **42.** $6\frac{9}{100}$ **43.** $6\frac{9}{1000}$ **44.** $4\frac{75}{1000}$

C Rewrite each fraction with a denominator that is a power of ten. Then rewrite as a decimal.

45. $\frac{2}{5}$ **46.** $\frac{1}{2}$ **47.** $\frac{9}{25}$ **48.** $3\frac{7}{50}$

49. $7\frac{3}{20}$ **50.** $4\frac{21}{500}$ **51.** $1\frac{121}{200}$ **52.** $\frac{13}{250}$

Courtesy U.S. Mint

The Three-Cent Dollar

The Susan B. Anthony dollar is 1.043 inches in diameter, weighs 8.1 grams, and costs $0.03 to make.

Rounding Numbers

5.2

Buffalo Bills Photo

When speaking of the same sporting event, different people report the attendance in different ways.

A sportscaster — — — — — — 42,400 excited fans are enjoying . . .

An accountant — — — — — 42,364 tickets sold . . .

A sports reporter — — — — 42,000 see X stomp Y . . .

For many purposes, an exact number is not needed. Two of the persons reporting have *rounded* the number in attendance.

Example 1: Round 42,364 to the nearest thousand.

To round here, you check here.

4 2, 3 6 4

This digit is less than 5, so replace it and all following digits with 0's.

$42{,}364 \approx 42{,}000$ (to the nearest thousand)

This symbol means "is approximately equal to."

Example 2: Round 42,364 to the nearest hundred.

To round here, you check here.

4 2, 3 6 4

This digit is 5 or greater, so
(1) replace it and all following digits with 0's.
(2) increase the hundreds digit by 1.

42,364 ≈ 42,400 (to the nearest hundred)

Example 3: Round as indicated.

	to the nearest		
number	one	tenth	hundredth
43.5762	44	43.6	43.58
1.6218	2	1.6	1.62
0.0421	0	0.0	0.04

Rounding can be used to **estimate** answers. An estimate serves as a check on whether a computed answer is reasonable.

Example 4: Estimate and then compute each answer. Compare the results.

34827 + 3207		82 × 97
35000 + 3000	← Round each number to any convenient place. →	80 × 100
38000	← estimates →	8000
34827 + 3207 = 38034	← computed answers →	82 × 97 = 7954

Exercises

A Tell which digit you would check when rounding **(a)** to the nearest ten, **(b)** to the nearest hundred, and **(c)** to the nearest thousand.

1. 5801 **2.** 546 **3.** 38,542 **4.** 645,123

5. 3592.1 **6.** 32,546.78 **7.** 50,613.82 **8.** 1624.578

Tell which digit you would check when rounding **(a)** to the nearest one, **(b)** to the nearest tenth, **(c)** to the nearest hundredth, and **(d)** to the nearest thousandth.

9. 6.0123 **10.** 0.2345 **11.** 0.9152 **12.** 8.0576

13. 0.5724 **14.** 9.13428 **15.** 19.60572 **16.** 742.0536

Tell how you would estimate each answer.

17. 32×32 **18.** $989 - 285$ **19.** 89×11 **20.** $896 \div 32$

B Round as indicated.

	to the nearest			
number	one	tenth	hundredth	thousandth
21. 0.4532				
22. 0.6051				
23. 9.0826				
24. 24.0580				
25. 132.5158				

	to the nearest		
number	ten	hundred	thousand
26. 1762			
27. 9835			
28. 14.508			
29. 672.54			
30. 80,521.3			

(a) Estimate the value; **(b)** then compute the value.

31. 888×71 **32.** $638 - 183$ **33.** $135 + 27 + 212$

C Round 3.14159265358973 as indicated.

34. nearest hundred thousandth **35.** nearest millionth

5.3

Adding and Subtracting Decimals

Brent Jones

By using the following rule, you can add or subtract with decimals just as you add or subtract whole numbers.

> **Keep the decimal points aligned when adding or subtracting with decimals.**

Example 1: A customer buys \$6.75 worth of groceries and gives the clerk a \$10 bill. How much change should the customer receive?

Align the decimal points.

These 0's do not change the value, but they are helpful in subtracting.

$$\begin{array}{r} \$10.00 \\ -6.75 \\ \hline \$\ 3.25 \end{array}$$

total cost (6.75)
change (\$ 3.25)

Example 2: Estimate and then compute the sum of 6, 0.41, 31.9, and 2.059.

Round each number to any convenient place.

$$\begin{array}{r} 6 \\ 0 \\ 32 \\ +2 \\ \hline 40 \end{array}$$ estimate

Align.

These 0's do not change the value.

$$\begin{array}{r} 6.000 \\ 0.410 \\ 31.900 \\ +2.059 \\ \hline 40.369 \end{array}$$ sum

Exercises

A Answer the questions.

1. What rule must you use when adding or subtracting with decimals?
2. How is adding with decimals like adding whole numbers?
3. How is subtracting with decimals like subtracting whole numbers?
4. Estimate 3.2 + 2.97 + 1.855 + 2.002.
5. Is 3.2 equal to 3.200? When might the 0's be helpful?

B Add or subtract.

6. 3.25 +4.3	**7.** 15.09 +2.3	**8.** 42.3 0.42 +1.093	**9.** 21.3 0.94 +36
10. 1.45 −1.05	**11.** 3.08 −1.4	**12.** 13.5 −0.25	**13.** 4.095 −1.5
14. 3.425 1.5 +0.93	**15.** 44.2 9.9 +9	**16.** 25.5 −5.35	**17.** 10.5 −0.22

(a) Estimate the value; **(b)** then compute the value.

18. 3.4 − 2.45

19. 36.2 + 14.85 + 1.256

20. 9.6 − 3.125

21. 4.2 + 4.02 + 3.5

22. 0.7 + 7.7 + 7.77 + 7.777

23. 5 − 0.25

24. 3.6 + 5.256 + 8 + 9.25

25. 16 − 1.75

C **26.** Mechanics use the gauge shown to measure gaps. The metal pieces are used one at a time or in combination of two or more. Which of them could you combine to measure a gap of the given width?

a. 0.09 mm **b.** 0.11 mm

c. 0.17 mm **d.** 0.40 mm

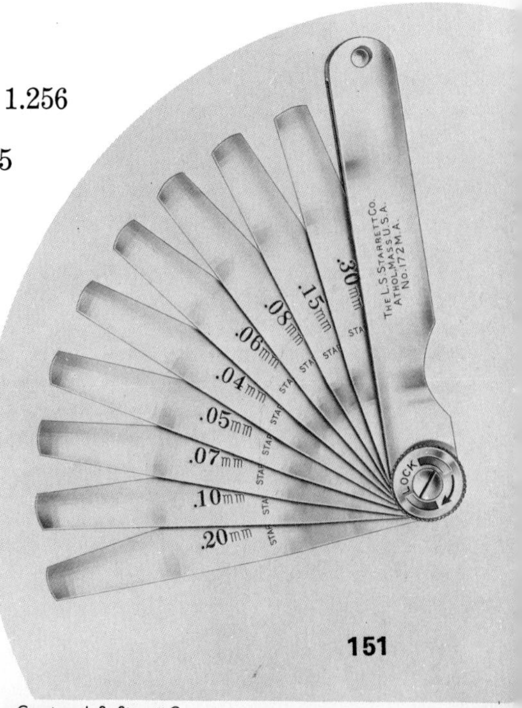

Courtesy L.S. Starrett Co.

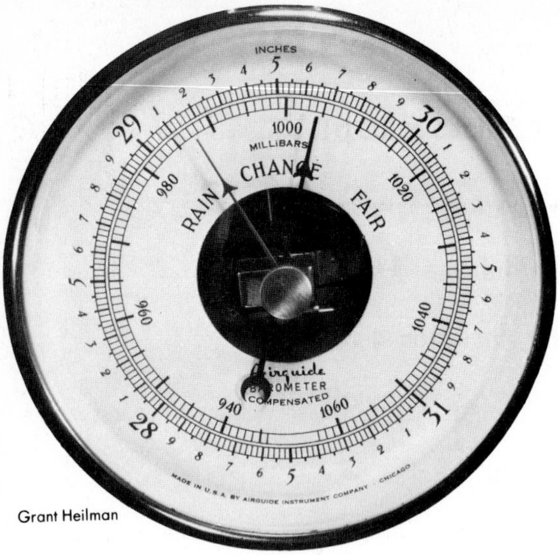

Grant Heilman

27. At 8 A.M. the barometer reading was 29.16. It rose steadily until 5 P.M., when the reading was 29.65. How much did the reading change?

28. For a three-minute phone call from Chicago to Atlanta, the charge is \$1.18 if you "dial direct." An operator-assisted call costs \$2.05. How much cheaper is the dial-direct call?

Solve.

29. $x + 2.7 = 5.9$

30. $8.36 = n + 4.61$

31. $5 = r + 0.2$

32. $d - 1 = 3.7042$

Rounding Pi

To describe a circle, you can state the circumference (C), the diameter (d), the radius (r), or the area (A). For every circle, of any size, $C \div d$ is the same number. This number cannot be named exactly as a fraction or as a decimal, so we say $C \div d = \pi$. (π is a Greek letter pronounced PĪ.) Computers have been used to find π to thousands of decimal places. Here are a few of them.

$$\pi = 3.14159265358973 \cdots$$

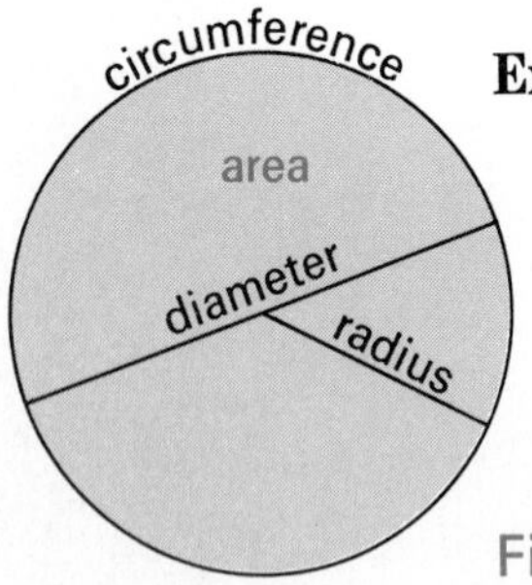

Example: Find the area of a circle with a radius of 6.

$$A = \pi r^2$$
$$= \pi \times 6^2$$
$$= \pi \times 36$$

So 36π is the exact area.

Find approximate values for this area by multiplying 36 by the decimal for π rounded to the place named.

1. the nearest one
2. the nearest tenth
3. the nearest hundredth
4. the nearest thousandth

The values you have found come closer and closer to the exact value of the area. But since π cannot be named exactly as a decimal, neither can the area.

Multiplying Decimals

Multiplying with decimals is like multiplying whole numbers. You must decide, however, where to place the decimal point.

Example 1: Find each product.

number of digits after the decimal point

12.3	1	12.3	1	1.23	2	0.123	3
×4	+0	×0.4	+1	×0.4	+1	×0.4	+1
49.2	1	4.92	2	0.492	3	0.0492	4

Write in as many 0's as needed to properly place the decimal point.

Example 2: How can an estimate be used to decide where to put the decimal point in an answer?

	estimate		estimate
12.3	12	24.326	24
×4	×4	×11	×10
49.2	48	267.586	240

Example 3: What shortcuts can be used to multiply by 10, 100, 1000, and so on?

$10 \times 3.49 = 34.9$

1 zero — 1 digit

$100 \times 3.49 = 349$

2 zeros — 2 digits

$1000 \times 3.490 = 3490$

3 zeros — 3 digits

Count 0's.

Move this decimal point right that many places.

"HE SURE MAKES A FUSS OVER ONE LITTLE DECIMAL POINT!"

Example 4: 2.4 kg = ___ g

Each kilogram contains 1000 grams.

So multiply 2.4 by 1000.

2.4 kg = <u>2400</u> g

Exercises

A Tell where the decimal point should be placed in each answer.

1. $\begin{array}{r} 56.7 \\ \times 12 \\ \hline 6804 \end{array}$ **2.** $\begin{array}{r} 5.67 \\ \times 12 \\ \hline 6804 \end{array}$ **3.** $\begin{array}{r} 0.567 \\ \times 12 \\ \hline 6804 \end{array}$ **4.** $\begin{array}{r} 0.0567 \\ \times 12 \\ \hline 6804 \end{array}$

5. $\begin{array}{r} 56.7 \\ \times 1.2 \\ \hline 6804 \end{array}$ **6.** $\begin{array}{r} 5.67 \\ \times 0.12 \\ \hline 6804 \end{array}$ **7.** $\begin{array}{r} 0.567 \\ \times 1.2 \\ \hline 6804 \end{array}$ **8.** $\begin{array}{r} 0.567 \\ \times 0.12 \\ \hline 6804 \end{array}$

Multiply.

9. $\begin{array}{r} 324 \\ \times 0.01 \\ \hline \end{array}$ **10.** $\begin{array}{r} 7.238 \\ \times 100 \\ \hline \end{array}$ **11.** $\begin{array}{r} 1000 \\ \times 97 \\ \hline \end{array}$ **12.** $\begin{array}{r} 0.1 \\ \times 5.2 \\ \hline \end{array}$

Complete.

13. To find how many meters in 75.6 kilometers, multiply by ___.

14. To find how many centimeters in 3.2 meters, multiply by ___.

B For each product, **(a)** estimate the result; **(b)** then compute the result.

15. $\begin{array}{r} 75 \\ \times 1.2 \\ \hline \end{array}$ **16.** $\begin{array}{r} 3.2 \\ \times 7 \\ \hline \end{array}$ **17.** $\begin{array}{r} 0.21 \\ \times 0.9 \\ \hline \end{array}$ **18.** $\begin{array}{r} 3.8 \\ \times 0.5 \\ \hline \end{array}$

19. $\begin{array}{r} 0.421 \\ \times 1.2 \\ \hline \end{array}$ **20.** $\begin{array}{r} 5.18 \\ \times 0.42 \\ \hline \end{array}$ **21.** $\begin{array}{r} 30.9 \\ \times 5.4 \\ \hline \end{array}$ **22.** $\begin{array}{r} 0.42 \\ \times 0.25 \\ \hline \end{array}$

23. $\begin{array}{r} 12.3 \\ \times 2.4 \\ \hline \end{array}$ **24.** $\begin{array}{r} 42.1 \\ \times 0.25 \\ \hline \end{array}$ **25.** $\begin{array}{r} 6.05 \\ \times 0.02 \\ \hline \end{array}$ **26.** $\begin{array}{r} 0.0031 \\ \times 6 \\ \hline \end{array}$

Multiply.

27. 4.012×3.1 **28.** 6.2×0.25 **29.** 3.1×3.1

30. 6×19.5 **31.** 7.5×0.75 **32.** 0.3×0.16

33. 0.001×63.2 **34.** 10×3.142 **35.** 0.079×0.01

36. 0.0037×1000 **37.** 100×0.001 **38.** 0.01×0.001

Complete.

39. 4.52 km = ____ m **40.** 0.023 km = ____ m

41. 1.9 m = ____ cm **42.** 2.34 cm = ____ mm

43. 0.476 kg = ____ g **44.** 37.2 g = ____ mg

45. The Morrows have found that it costs them \$0.30 a mile to operate the family automobile. If they drive 675.3 miles on vacation, how much are their auto expenses?

46. At Marsh's Supermarket, tomatoes cost 43 cents a can. How much does a case (24 cans) cost?

47. Steel is manufactured in sheets of various thicknesses and stacked in piles for storage. How high is a stack of 50 sheets that are each 0.375 inches thick?

A. Devaney, Inc.

C Solve.

48. $\frac{r}{5.2} = 4.1$ **49.** $7 = \frac{p}{0.01}$ **50.** $\frac{s}{6.25} = 1.9$

Compute.

51. $(0.5)^2$ **52.** $(2.01)^2$ **53.** $(0.2)^3$ **54.** $(0.01)^4$

55. $(3.4)(0.1)^2$ **56.** $(7.24)10^2$ **57.** $10(0.3)^2$ **58.** $2^5(0.1)^5$

Quick Quiz
Sections 5.1 to 5.4

Write each decimal as a fraction or mixed number.

1. 0.9 **2.** 3.71 **3.** 0.04 **4.** 7.25

Write each fraction or mixed number as a decimal.

5. $\frac{7}{10}$ **6.** $\frac{3}{100}$ **7.** $3\frac{23}{100}$ **8.** $4\frac{7}{1000}$

Round **(a)** to the nearest ten and **(b)** to the nearest hundredth.

9. 7.051 **10.** 3.975 **11.** 206.4237 **12.** 723.5773

(a) Estimate the value; **(b)** then compute the value.

13. $75.3 + 15.94 + 9.312$ **14.** 8.02×11.57

Math and Diving

H. Armstrong Roberts

In school diving competitions, the judges give points as follows:

Failed: 0
Unsatisfactory: $\frac{1}{2}$ to 2
Deficient: $2\frac{1}{2}$ to $4\frac{1}{2}$
Satisfactory: 5 to 6
Good: $6\frac{1}{2}$ to 8
Very good: $8\frac{1}{2}$ to 10

The score for a dive is found by adding the points given by the judges and multiplying that sum by the "degree of difficulty." Find the total points earned by the diver whose scores are shown.

No.	Dive Name	Pos.	Judges 1	Judges 2	Judges 3	Total	Degree of Difficulty	Total for Dive
101	Forward Dive	L	8	$8\frac{1}{2}$	8		1.4	
202	Back Somersault	P	$7\frac{1}{2}$	$7\frac{1}{2}$	$7\frac{1}{2}$		1.6	
302	Reverse Somersault	L	7	$6\frac{1}{2}$	$7\frac{1}{2}$		1.7	
401	Inward Dive	L	6	6	6		1.7	
5112	Forward Dive, 1 Twist	P	5	6	5		2.1	
3	Forward $1\frac{1}{2}$ Somersault	T	8	$8\frac{1}{2}$	9		1.6	
							Total Points	

Donald Dietz, Stock, Boston

Dividing Decimals by Whole Numbers

5.5

Example 1: Lee earned \$6.75 in 3 hours. How much did Lee earn per hour?

Place decimal point directly above the decimal point in 6.75.

$$\begin{array}{r} 2.25 \\ 3\overline{)6.75} \end{array}$$

Divide as you would whole numbers.

Lee earned \$2.25 per hour.

Example 2: Divide 2.3 by 8.

$$8\overline{)2.3} \qquad \begin{array}{r} 0.2875 \\ 8\overline{)2.3000} \end{array}$$

Continue including 0's until the remainder is 0 or the answer has as many digits as you'd like.

Example 3: What shortcut can be used to divide by 10, 100, 1000, and so on?

$23.49 \div 10 = 2.349$

1 digit 1 zero

$23.49 \div 100 = 0.2349$

2 digits 2 zeros

$023.49 \div 1000 = 0.02349$

3 digits 3 zeros

Count 0's.

Move this decimal point left that many places.

Example 4: 172.6 mL = ____ L

There are 1000 milliliters in each liter.

So divide 172.6 by 1000.

172.6 mL = $\underline{0.1726}$ L

Example 5: Write as decimals: **a.** $\frac{3}{8}$ **b.** $5\frac{3}{8}$ **c.** $\frac{2}{3}$

a. $8\overline{)3.000}$ = 0.375

b. $5\frac{3}{8} = 5 + \frac{3}{8}$
$= 5 + 0.375$
$= 5.375$

OR $5\frac{3}{8} = \frac{43}{8}$, $8\overline{)43.000}$ = 5.375

c. $3\overline{)2.000\cdots}$ = $0.666\cdots$ ➡ Write $0.\overline{6}$ to show that the 6 repeats.

Exercises

A Tell where the decimal point should be placed in each answer.

1. $8\overline{)9.6}$ = 1 2
2. $8\overline{)0.96}$ = 12
3. $8\overline{)0.096}$ = 12
4. 1234.5 ÷ 1000
5. 0.123 ÷ 100

Complete.

6. To find how many grams in 192 milligrams, divide by ____.
7. To find how many meters in 36 centimeters, divide by ____.
8. The bar in $3.\overline{6}$ shows that the ____ repeats.

B Divide.

9. $7\overline{)8.61}$
10. $8\overline{)99.2}$
11. $6\overline{)0.21}$
12. $5\overline{)6.3}$
13. $3\overline{)3.069}$
14. $2\overline{)9.006}$
15. $6\overline{)0.0312}$
16. $8\overline{)338.4}$
17. $16\overline{)6.72}$
18. $12\overline{)15.6}$
19. $43\overline{)53.75}$
20. $55\overline{)0.165}$

21. $28.26 \div 9$ 22. $0.258 \div 6$ 23. $45.6 \div 5$

24. $12.045 \div 3$ 25. $103.02 \div 1000$ 26. $3.045 \div 7$

27. $45.6 \div 12$ 28. $6.76 \div 100$ 29. $0.456 \div 10$

Complete.

30. 1471 mL = ____ L 31. 30 mL = ____ L

32. 975 cm = ____ m 33. 4356 m = ____ km

34. 96 mg = ____ g 35. 560 g = ____ kg

Write as decimals.

36. $\frac{1}{8}$ 37. $\frac{5}{8}$ 38. $\frac{1}{16}$ 39. $1\frac{3}{16}$

40. $2\frac{5}{16}$ 41. $\frac{3}{4}$ 42. $4\frac{7}{8}$ 43. $\frac{7}{16}$

44. $\frac{1}{3}$ 45. $2\frac{2}{3}$ 46. $\frac{1}{9}$ 47. $\frac{4}{9}$

H. Armstrong Roberts

48. If 15 fish weigh 10.5 kg, what is the average weight per fish?

49. The average annual rainfall in Mobile, Alabama, is 68.13 inches. What is the average monthly rainfall?

50. If a light plane uses 34.2 gallons of gasoline in 3 hours, how many gallons are used per hour?

C 51. The greatest recorded distance bicycled in 24 hours is 515.8 miles. What is the average number of miles the bicyclist rode each hour?

Write as decimals.

52. $\frac{5}{6}$ 53. $\frac{91}{18}$ 54. $\frac{78}{11}$ 55. $\frac{3}{11}$

Solve. Write each solution as a decimal.

56. $16n = 5$ 57. $100x = 2.9$ 58. $1 = 4x$

59. $7x = 2.1$ 60. $7 = 4n$ 61. $10y = 35$

5.6 Dividing by Decimals

Multiplying the numerator and the denominator of a fraction by the same number gives an equivalent fraction.

$$\frac{0.96}{1.2} = \frac{0.96}{1.2} \times \frac{10}{10} = \frac{9.6}{12}$$

But this is the same as $1.2\overline{)0.96}$

And this is the same as $12\overline{)9.6}$

So these two division problems have the same answer.

That is, if you move the decimal points in a division problem the same number of places, the answer is unchanged. You can use this idea to change division by a decimal to division by a whole number.

$1.2\overline{)0.96}$

$1.2\overline{)0.9\,6}$ — Change so divisor is a whole number.

$\begin{array}{r} 0.8 \\ 1.2\overline{)0.9\,6} \end{array}$ — Divide.

Example: Divide.

a. $2.4\overline{)76.8}$

$2.4\overline{)76.8}$

$\begin{array}{r} 32 \\ 2.4\overline{)76.8} \end{array}$

b. $0.09\overline{)6.3}$

$0.09\overline{)6.30}$

$\begin{array}{r} 70 \\ 0.09\overline{)6.30} \end{array}$

c. $0.34\overline{)2.7268}$

$0.34\overline{)2.72\,68}$

$\begin{array}{r} 8.02 \\ 0.34\overline{)2.72\,68} \end{array}$

Exercises

A How would you change each division problem so the divisor is a whole number?

1. $0.2\overline{)8.4}$ **2.** $8.1\overline{)9.72}$ **3.** $0.56\overline{)14}$

4. $2.4\overline{)0.6}$ **5.** $3.4\overline{)0.0068}$ **6.** $0.87\overline{)23.49}$

7. $0.002\overline{)0.016}$ **8.** $0.014\overline{)0.084}$ **9.** $0.09\overline{)0.225}$

Where should the decimal point be placed in each answer?

10. $0.6\overline{)7.2}$ with quotient 1 2

11. $0.18\overline{)1.116}$ with quotient 62

12. $1.3\overline{)0.0338}$ with quotient 26

B Divide.

13. $0.6\overline{)15.24}$

14. $0.4\overline{)9.04}$

15. $0.5\overline{)0.0125}$

16. $0.08\overline{)4.984}$

17. $0.003\overline{)0.01896}$

18. $0.07\overline{)0.168}$

19. $1.2\overline{)0.384}$

20. $0.13\overline{)0.0169}$

21. $2.5\overline{)0.9}$

22. $0.014\overline{)0.0448}$

23. $0.18\overline{)0.0756}$

24. $1.8\overline{)4.68}$

25. $2.2\overline{)7.92}$

26. $3.4\overline{)0.136}$

27. $0.14\overline{)9.1}$

28. $2.94 \div 0.7$

29. $1.62 \div 0.06$

30. $0.0144 \div 0.12$

31. $1.44 \div 1.2$

32. $8.704 \div 3.4$

33. $0.315 \div 0.015$

34. $9.8 \div 0.1$

35. $4.75 \div 0.01$

36. $7.2 \div 0.01$

37. $0.395 \div 0.001$

38. $5.6 \div 0.001$

39. $0.38 \div 0.1$

40. $632 \div 0.01$

41. $76.41 \div 0.001$

After a vacation trip, the Mortons wanted to know how much they had paid per gallon of gasoline at each stop. They had recorded only the number of gallons and the total cost. Complete the charts.

	gallons	total cost	paid per gallon
42.	9.8	$10.29	
44.	6.0	7.50	
46.	8.1	9.72	
48.	12.5	15.50	
50.	6.0	7.08	

	gallons	total cost	paid per gallon
43.	8.0	$10.08	
45.	8.5	10.37	
47.	3.5	3.85	
49.	8.6	9.89	
51.	10.0	11.10	

C Solve.

52. $7.5r = 317.25$

53. $4.19s = 1.0475$

54. $0.3125d = 1$

55. $0.75n = 3$

56. $50.92 = 6.365x$

57. $2.8384 = 0.887y$

58. $3.5t + 6.8 = 7.675$

59. $0.12v + 0.19 = 0.91$

60. $0.5a + 2.6 = 2.95$

61. $0.08b + 3.09 = 4.1028$

62. $1.19 = 1.2c - 0.25$

63. $0.6d - 0.55 = 1.49$

64. $3.2e - 0.9 = 0.7$

65. $0.006f - 0.152 = 1$

66. $7.2g - 16.5 = 163.5$

67. $5 = 0.25x + 4.85$

68. $1.3m - 22.5 = 11.3$

69. $0.12y + 2.5 = 3.256$

70. $0.25x + 0.75x = 5.9$

71. $1.34n + 0.06n = 4.2$

72. $8.2 = 1.09y + 0.91y$

73. $18 = 3.45a + 1.55a$

74. $6.24r - 0.74r = 2.75$

75. $1.68 = 9.1m - 4.9m$

Another way to decide where to put the decimal point in a quotient is by estimating.

Examples:

		estimate	quotient
a. $2.3\overline{)35.88}$	Round to the nearest one.	$\begin{array}{r}18\\2\overline{)36}\end{array}$	$\begin{array}{r}15.6\\2.3\overline{)35.88}\end{array}$
b. $0.41\overline{)0.8487}$	Multiply by 10 and round to the nearest one.	$\begin{array}{r}2\\4\overline{)8}\end{array}$	$\begin{array}{r}2.07\\0.41\overline{)0.8487}\end{array}$

(a) Estimate the value; **(b)** then compute the value.

76. $5.7\overline{)17.784}$

77. $0.21\overline{)4.998}$

78. $0.075\overline{)0.48}$

79. $3.9\overline{)5.538}$

80. $0.00126 \div 6.3$

81. $0.0003\overline{)0.168}$

UNIT PRICING

CONSUMER CORNER

Ed Hoppe Photography

The 312-gram box of cereal costs $1.19.

The 198-gram box of cereal costs $0.85.

Which is the better buy?

Probably the best way to find out is to find how much one gram of cereal costs in each case. To do this, divide price by amount.

$\frac{1.19}{312} \approx 0.0038$ ➡ **The cereal in the larger box costs $0.0038 or 0.38¢ a gram.**

$\frac{0.85}{198} \approx 0.0043$ ➡ **The cereal in the smaller box costs $0.0043 or 0.43¢ a gram.**

So the larger box is the better buy.

The price of one gram of cereal is called a **unit price.** For another product, a different unit could be used. It might be a pound, an ounce, a kilogram, a quart, a liter, a piece, or 100 pieces, depending on the product. But the same unit should be used for products that are to be compared.

Of course, it is not easy for shoppers to figure unit prices for each product they buy in a store. So many stores label their shelves to show the unit prices of the products they sell.

Use unit prices to tell which is the better buy.

1. notebook paper: 200 sheets for $1.24 or 300 sheets for $1.84

2. two-ply facial tissue: 70 for 30¢ or 200 for 84¢

3. shampoo: 230 mL for $1.61 or 360 mL for $2.59

4. potato chips: $8\frac{1}{2}$ ounces for $1.11, 9 ounces for $1.19, or $13\frac{1}{2}$ ounces for $1.74

5.7 Solving Problems With Metric Units

Example 1: Find the area of the circle. Use 3.14 for π. ($A = \pi r^2$)

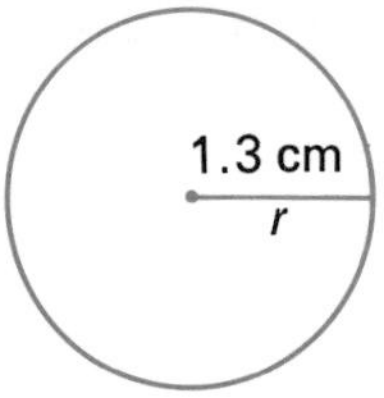

$$\begin{aligned} A &= \pi r^2 \\ &= 3.14(1.3)^2 \\ &= 3.14(1.69) \\ &= 5.3066 \end{aligned}$$

The area is 5.3066 square centimeters or 5.3066 cm^2.

To compute with metric measurements, you must express them in the same units.

Example 2: Add 8.9 cm, 37 mm, and 0.16 m.

Here are three ways to do this addition.

8.9 cm →	8.9 cm →	89 mm →	0.089 m
37 mm →	3.7 cm →	37 mm →	0.037 m
0.16 m →	+16.0 cm →	+160 mm →	+0.16 m
	28.6 cm	286 mm	0.286 m

Any one of these can be given as the answer.

Example 3: Find the area of a rectangle that is 13.2 centimeters wide and 2.4 meters long. ($A = lw$)

In meters	In centimeters
$13.2 \text{ cm} = (13.2 \div 100) \text{ m}$	$2.4 \text{ m} = (2.4 \times 100) \text{ cm}$
$= 0.132 \text{ m}$	$= 240 \text{ cm}$
$A = lw$ ➡ $A = 2.4(0.132)$	$A = 240(13.2)$
$= 0.3168$	$= 3168$

The area is 0.3168 m^2 or 3168 cm^2.

Exercises

A Tell what number should replace each ? .

1. 15.6 cm, 88 mm → ? mm + 88 mm

2. 15.6 cm, 88 mm → 15.6 cm + ? cm

3. 9.47 kg, 30 g → ? g + 30 g

4. 9.47 kg, 30 g → 9.47 kg + ? kg

B Compute.

5. 180 km − 31 007 m

6. 12.06 cm − 88 mm

7. 27.54 m + 3895 cm + 65.9 m

8. 3.4 km + 178 m + 5300 cm

9. There are 37.4 mL of orange juice in a bottle that held 236 mL of orange juice when bought. How much has been used?

10. René drove 79.8 km. When he started, the odometer read 1395.4 km. What did it read at the end of the drive?

11. The Kulik family has three suitcases packed for a trip to Europe. The suitcases weigh 17.8 kg, 13.7 kg, and 22.1 kg.

a. What is the total weight of the suitcases?

b. The airline will allow the Kuliks 60 kg for the three suitcases. Are they over or under the weight limit? By how much?

Solve. Use 3.14 for π.

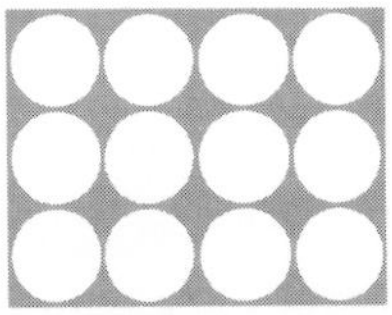

Ex. 12

12. Aluminum can lids are stamped from rectangular sheets 32 cm long and 24 cm wide. If each lid has a radius of 4 cm, how much of each sheet (in area) is used to make the lids? How much is wasted?

Courtesy Nebraska Dept. of Economic Development

13. In a center-pivot irrigation system, a length of pipeline mounted on wheels is attached at one end to a source of water. Driven by electricity or water power, the pipeline rotates around the source, spreading water in a circle whose radius is the pipeline. If the pipeline is 90 m long, what is the area of the circle it irrigates?

14. A section of highway 6.1 meters wide and 1.75 kilometers long needs repaving. What is the area of this section?

15. Gruener Park has a swimming pool that is 28.25 meters long. How many kilometers would a person swim in 20 lengths of the pool? 30 lengths? 45 lengths?

16. Jan's car gets an average of 6.8 kilometers per liter of gasoline. The tank holds 77.5 liters. About how far will the car go on one tank of gas?

17. If gasoline costs \$0.30 a liter, how much does it cost to fill a tank that holds 77.5 liters?

C 18. Some Olympic records for running and freestyle swimming are listed below. Using the formula $d = rt$, find each rate in meters per second to the nearest hundredth.

Eddie Adams/De Wys, Inc.

Sven Simon—Katherine Young

MEN'S RECORDS

	running		swimming	
distance	sec	rate	sec	rate
100 m	9.9		49.99	
200 m	19.8		110.29	
400 m	43.8		231.93	
1500 m	214.9		902.40	

Willi Ostgathe/De Wys, Inc.

WOMEN'S RECORDS

	running		swimming	
distance	sec	rate	sec	rate
100 m	11.0		55.65	
200 m	22.37		119.26	
400 m	49.29		249.89	
800 m	114.94		517.14	

Terms and Symbols Review

Choose the answer in ( ) that best completes each sentence.

1. The decimal for three and three tenths is (*0.33, 3.3,* $3\frac{3}{10}$).
2. The 1 in (*3.412, 3.142, 3.421*) is in the thousandths place.
3. The symbol for "is approximately equal to" is ($=$, $\neq$, $\approx$).
4. 4.185 rounded to the nearest hundredth is (*4.2, 4.18, 4.19*).
5. When (*adding, multiplying*) with decimals, always keep the decimal points aligned.
6. When you multiply 3.1 by 0.05, there should be (*one, two, three*) places after the decimal point in the answer.
7. To (*compute, estimate*) a product, round both factors and then multiply.

Chapter 5 Review

Express each decimal as a fraction or mixed number. 5.1

1. 0.7 **2.** 0.5 **3.** 2.9 **4.** 3.25

5. 1.035 **6.** 0.08 **7.** 5.42 **8.** 3.6

Express the following as decimals.

9. $\frac{5}{10}$ **10.** $6\frac{8}{10}$ **11.** $\frac{9}{100}$ **12.** $4\frac{125}{1000}$

13. $2\frac{16}{100}$ **14.** $\frac{75}{1000}$ **15.** $6\frac{6}{100}$ **16.** $\frac{3}{1000}$

Round as indicated. 5.2

	to the nearest			
number	ten	one	tenth	hundredth
17. 54.129				
18. 7.650				

(a) Estimate the value; **(b)** then compute the value.

19. 312×57 **20.** $416 + 273 + 550$ **21.** $526 - 288$

(a) Estimate the value; (b) then compute the value.

5.3 **22.** $68.2 + 25.4$ **23.** $73.4 - 26.6$

24. $3.1 + 2.42 + 0.196$ **25.** $13.12 - 4.221$

5.4 **26.** 6.8×26 **27.** 42.3×2.1

28. 0.04×3.02 **29.** 6.14×0.35

Multiply.

30. 6.247×100 **31.** 5.3×1000 **32.** 0.006×10

Complete.

33. 3.5 km = ____ m **34.** 0.054 L = ____ mL

5.5 Divide.

35. $21.24 \div 6$ **36.** $3.72 \div 3$ **37.** $0.336 \div 14$

38. $86.4 \div 10$ **39.** $4.32 \div 1000$ **40.** $1104.6 \div 100$

Complete.

41. 425 mm = ____ m **42.** 1954 g = ____ kg

Write as decimals.

43. $\frac{7}{8}$ **44.** $6\frac{2}{3}$ **45.** $\frac{5}{9}$ **46.** $2\frac{3}{5}$

5.6 Divide.

47. $5.06 \div 0.2$ **48.** $1.944 \div 0.6$ **49.** $0.02496 \div 0.008$

50. $28.8 \div 1.2$ **51.** $0.8 \div 0.25$ **52.** $9 \div 0.36$

5.7 Compute.

53. 416.04 m + 2509 cm **54.** 5042 g − 2.075 kg

55. 67.1 km × 2.3 m **56.** 350 m + 1.1 km + 5000 cm

57. A car averages 10.9 kilometers per liter of gasoline. At that rate, how many kilometers could the car travel on 30.2 liters?

Chapter 5 Test

Write each decimal as a fraction or mixed number. Write each fraction or mixed number as a decimal.

1. 0.9 **2.** 8.25 **3.** 0.035

4. $\frac{19}{1000}$ **5.** $\frac{3}{5}$ **6.** $5\frac{3}{4}$

Round as indicated.

	to the nearest		
number	hundred	one	tenth
7. 765.21			
8. 425.902			

(a) Estimate the value; **(b)** then compute the value.

9. $12 + 3.42 + 1.6$ **10.** $6.124 - 3.5$

11. 3.6×0.8 **12.** 4.25×1.8

13. 30.5×0.04 **14.** 7.5×6

Divide.

15. $40.8 \div 12$ **16.** $0.72 \div 0.02$

17. $3.5 \div 1.4$ **18.** $1.125 \div 0.5$

Complete.

19. 4.8 km = ____ m **20.** 1.6 cm = ____ m

21. 92 mm = ____ cm **22.** 5.8 g = ____ mg

Compute.

23. 675.42×100 **24.** 7.832×10 **25.** $8.55 \div 100$

26. 92.63 m − 45 mm **27.** 4.2 kg + 6200 g

28. 3.6 cm × 2 mm **29.** 9.76 m + 395 cm + 14.12 m

30. If the juice in a bottle that holds 3.78 liters is divided into four equal servings, how much is in each serving?

RATE YOURSELF

Number Correct	
29–30	Superior
26–28	Excellent
22–25	Good
16–21	Fair
0–15	Poor

CAREER CORNER

Courtesy ITT Harper

TOLERANCES IN INDUSTRY

In industry, **tolerance** is the amount a measurement can vary from the designed measurement. For example, the length of a bolt might be given as follows:

3.6 ± 0.1 cm (± read "plus or minus")

The tolerance is ±0.1. This means that the bolt should be as near as possible to 3.6 cm long, but it will work if its length is anywhere between two limits.

3.6 − 0.1 cm = 3.5 cm (lower limit) to 3.6 + 0.1 cm = 3.7 cm (upper limit)

(Another way to name a tolerance is by giving these upper and lower limits.)

Sometimes a measurement can be allowed to vary in one direction only. For example, if the bolt should be 3.6 cm long and it will not work if it is any shorter, the length might be given as

3.6 + 0.1 cm.

lower limit: 3.6; = 3.7 cm ← upper limit

Example: A gasoline intake valve is designed to have a stem length of 7.945 ± 0.005 mm. What are the limits on its size?

7.945 − 0.005 mm = 7.940 mm (lower limit) 7.945 + 0.005 mm = 7.950 mm (upper limit)

Copy and complete the chart.

Designed measurement	Tolerance	Lower limit	Upper limit
63.204 cm	±0.002 cm		
0.050 mm	±0.001 mm		
30.0 cm	−0.2 cm		
146.00 mm	+0.05 mm		

Getting Ready for Chapter 6

Which lettered choice best matches each numbered item?

1. $\{0, 1, 2, 3, \cdots\}$	**a.** identity number for addition	1.8
2. $\{1, 2, 3, 4, \cdots\}$	**b.** commutative property of addition	1.8
3. $n + 2 = 2 + n$	**c.** set of whole numbers	3.1
4. $n + 0 = n$	**d.** set of whole numbers greater than 0	3.3

Solve each equation. 2.2

5. $x + 7 = 16$

6. $x + 9 = 14$

7. $n - 7 = 6$

8. $10 = y - 8$

9. $28 = x + 16$

10. $x - 14 = 50$

Solve and graph each inequality. 2.4

11. $x + 4 < 9$

12. $y + 7 > 8$

13. $y - 8 > 11$

14. $12 > y - 5$

15. $38 < x - 7$

16. $y + 15 > 29$

6

ADDING AND SUBTRACTING INTEGERS

6

Harold M. Lambert

Opposites occur often in daily life. Coming down is the opposite of going up. A gain is the opposite of a loss. Moving backward is the opposite of moving forward. There are many other similar examples.

In algebra, these ideas are generalized and developed in terms of positive and negative numbers. In this chapter you will learn what positive and negative numbers are and begin to work with them.

Opposites of Whole Numbers

Notice how positive and negative numbers can be used to name some opposite activities.

Activity	*Number*	*Opposite Activity*	*Number*
earning $10	$^+10$	spending $10	$^-10$
gaining 8 yards	$^+8$	losing 8 yards	$^-8$
winning 6 points	$^+6$	losing 6 points	$^-6$
walking 2 blocks east	$^+2$	walking 2 blocks west	$^-2$

A "–" is always used when naming a negative number.

negative sixteen $^-16$

A "+" may (but need not) be used when naming a positive number.

positive sixteen $^+16$ or 16

On a number line, a number and its opposite are the same distance from 0 but in opposite directions. (0 is its own opposite.)

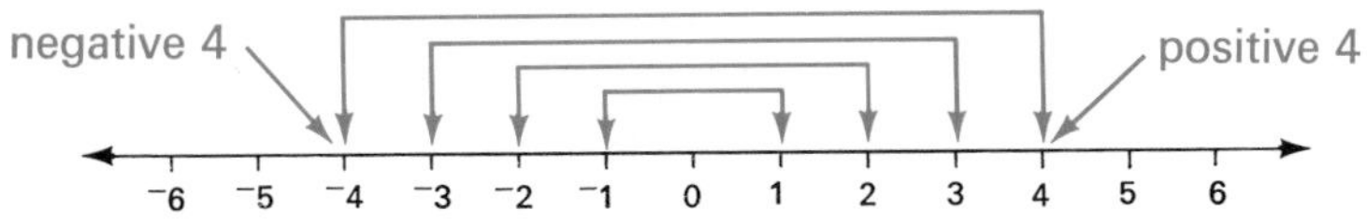

Example 1: How do you read $^-2$?

$^-2$ is read as "negative two."

Example 2: What is the opposite of $^-3$? Of 5?

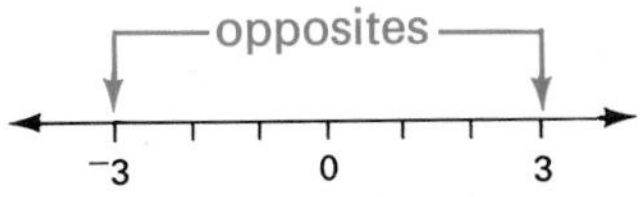

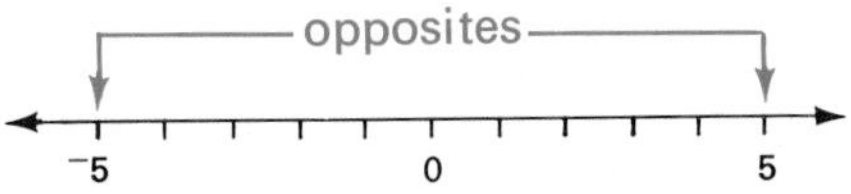

> The whole numbers and their opposites make up the set of numbers called the **integers**.

Integers = $\{\cdots, \underbrace{-5, -4, -3, -2, -1}_{\text{Negative Integers}}, 0, \underbrace{1, 2, 3, 4, 5, \cdots}_{\text{Positive Integers}}\}$

0: neither positive nor negative

Exercises

A Name the opposite of each number.

1. 2 **2.** +28 **3.** −17 **4.** 438

5. −2 **6.** −28 **7.** 86 **8.** 0

9. Which integer is neither positive nor negative?

10. Which integer is its own opposite?

B Complete the table below.

	Activity	*Integer*	*Activity*	*Integer*
11.	down 3 fathoms	−3	up 3 fathoms	______
12.	250 miles north	+250	______	−250
13.	five meters forward	+5	______	−5
14.	up 6 floors	+6	down 6 floors	______
15.	100 feet above sea level	+100	______	−100
16.	$1000 profit	______	$1000 loss	−1000
17.	8-yard loss	−8	8-yard gain	______
18.	increase of 10°	______	decrease of 10°	−10
19.	70 kilometers west	______	70 kilometers east	+70
20.	8 seconds before blast-off	−8	8 seconds after blast-off	______

The greater of two integers is farther to the right on the number line. Use the number line below to decide which integer in each pair is greater.

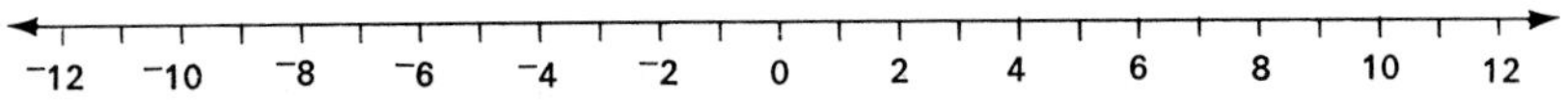

21. 0 or 10 **22.** 0 or $^{-}10$ **23.** $^{-}10$ or 10

24. $^{-}12$ or 4 **25.** $^{-}12$ or $^{-}7$ **26.** $^{-}8$ or $^{-}12$

For each exercise, arrange the numbers in order from least to greatest.

27. 5, $^{-}3$, 3, $^{-}1$

28. 2, $^{-}2$, 3, $^{-}3$

29. 0, $^{-}10$, $^{-}20$, 30, $^{-}25$

30. $^{-}5$, 10, $^{-}15$, $^{-}20$, 25

31. 3, $^{-}5$, 7, 0, 9, $^{-}8$

32. $^{-}2$, $^{-}6$, 1, 8, 0, $^{-}3$

33. 3, $^{-}3$, 4, $^{-}4$, 5, $^{-}5$, 0

34. 21, $^{-}12$, 48, $^{-}53$, 78, $^{-}91$

C **35.** Copy and complete the table.

Words	*Symbol*
the opposite of $^{-}7$	$-(^{-}7)$ or 7
________	$-(^{-}3)$ or ____
the opposite of $^{-}5$	____ or ____
the opposite of $^{+}5$	$-(^{+}5)$ or $^{-}5$
________	$-(^{+}7)$ or $^{-}7$

The expression ^{-}x is read *the opposite of x.* Find ^{-}x if

36. $x = {}^{-}8$ **37.** $x = 15$ **38.** $x = 19 - 9 + 5$

Find x if

39. $^{-}x = 9$ **40.** $^{-}x = {}^{-}9$ **41.** $^{-}x = {}^{-}3$

6.2 Addition on a Number Line

You can show addition of whole numbers on a number line.

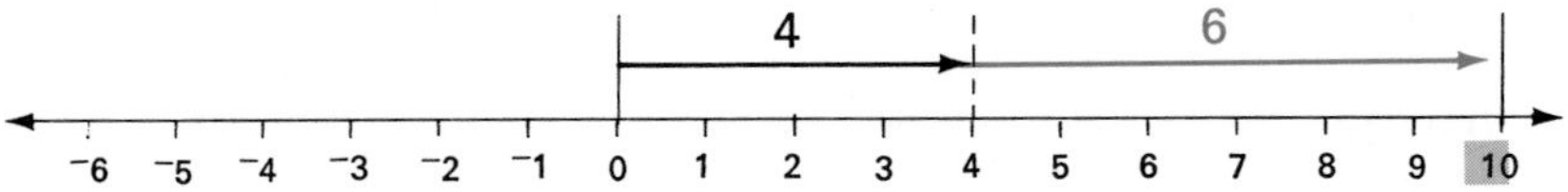

$4 + 6 = 10$

You can use the same methods to find sums of integers.

Example 1: Show $^{-}4 + 6$ on a number line.

Step 1: The first addend is $^{-}4$, so start at 0 and draw an arrow 4 units to the left (negative direction).

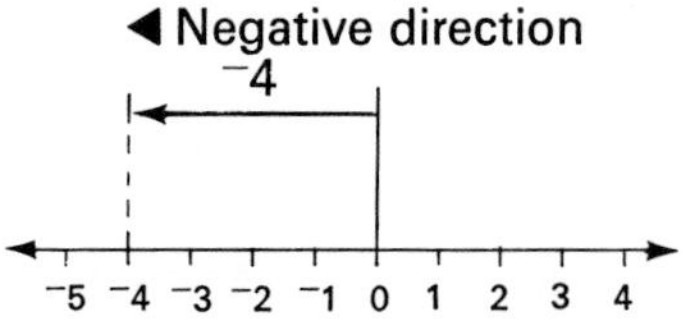

Step 2: The second addend is 6, so start at $^{-}4$ and draw an arrow 6 units to the right (positive direction).

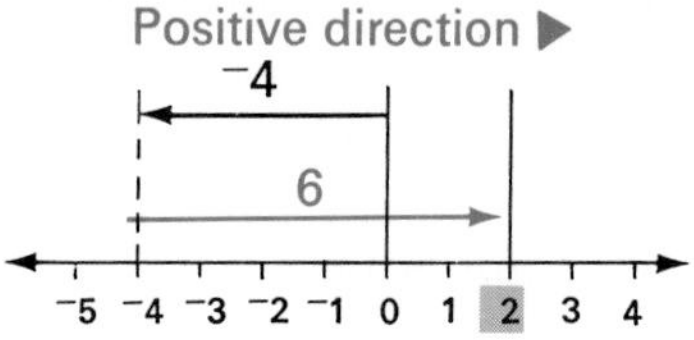

Step 3: The sum is given at the head of the second arrow.

$^{-}4 + 6 = 2$

Example 2: Show $4 + {}^{-}6$ on a number line.

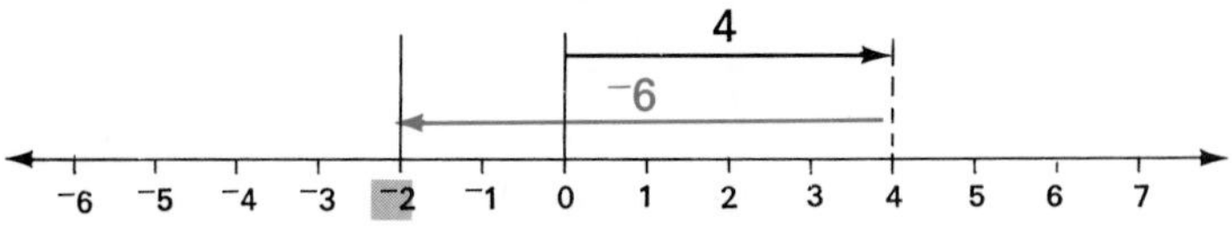

$4 + {}^{-}6 = {}^{-}2$

Example 3: Show $^{-}4 + {}^{-}6$ on a number line.

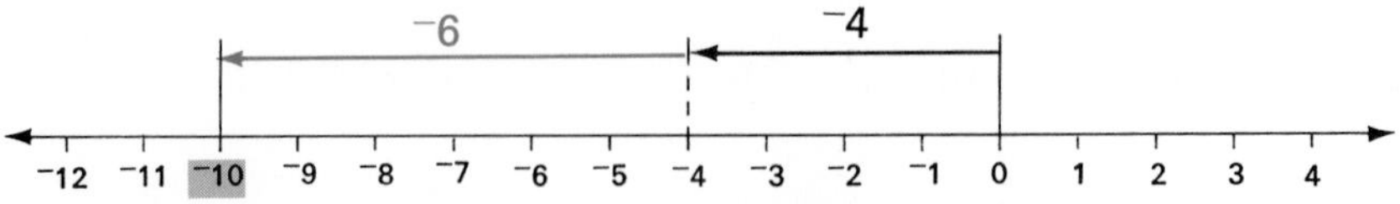

$^{-}4 + {}^{-}6 = {}^{-}10$

Exercises

A State an addition sentence for each drawing.

1.

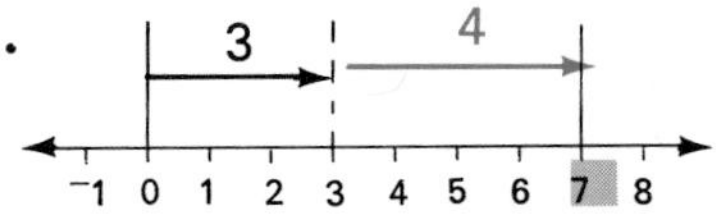

2.

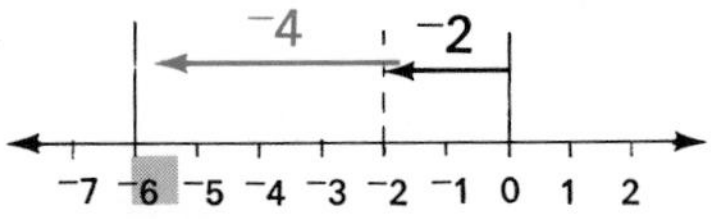

3.

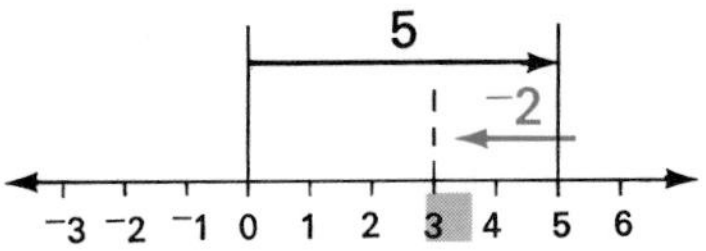

4.

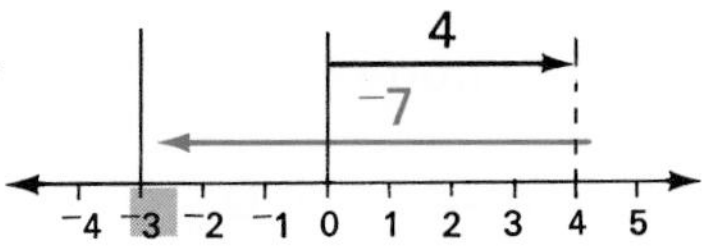

B Find each sum. Use a number line to help you.

5. $6 + 5$ **6.** $^-3 + ^-6$ **7.** $^-9 + 4$

8. $8 + ^-7$ **9.** $^-6 + ^-3$ **10.** $2 + ^-9$

11. $6 + ^-1$ **12.** $8 + ^-8$ **13.** $^-6 + 2$

14. $^-2 + 9$ **15.** $5 + 5$ **16.** $^-3 + 7$

17. $3 + ^-7$ **18.** $3 + 7$ **19.** $^-6 + 6$

20. $^-4 + ^-4$ **21.** $5 + ^-4$ **22.** $^-7 + 3$

23. $^-1 + 7$ **24.** $9 + ^-5$ **25.** $8 + ^-3$

C Use a number line to help you find each sum.

Example: $1 + 2 + 3$

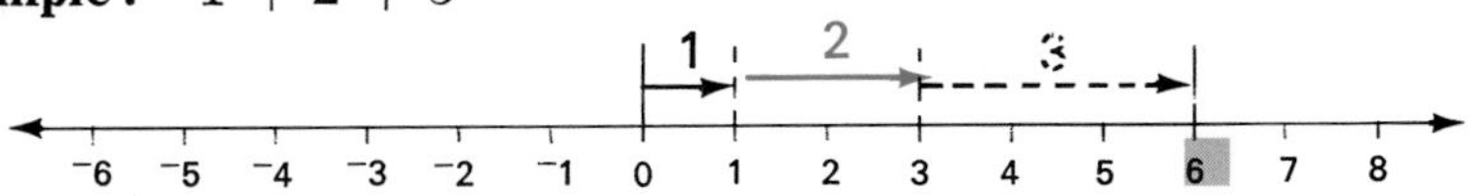

$$1 + 2 + 3 = 6$$

26. $2 + 3 + 4$ **27.** $6 + ^-1 + ^-3$ **28.** $10 + ^-8 + 5$

29. $^-3 + 4 + ^-6$ **30.** $7 + 7 + 3$ **31.** $^-1 + 1 + 8$

32. $^-2 + 3 + ^-4$ **33.** $6 + ^-7 + 1$ **34.** $2 + ^-3 + 2$

35. $^-7 + ^-5 + 4$ **36.** $^-2 + ^-4 + ^-3$ **37.** $^-6 + 5 + ^-3$

6.3 Adding Integers

Now that we have opposites of whole numbers, we have an important new property of addition.

Inverse Property of Addition

Any number a and its opposite ^{-}a have a sum of 0. So

$a + {}^{-}a = 0$ *Example:* $5 + {}^{-}5 = 0$

${}^{-}a + a = 0$ ${}^{-}5 + 5 = 0$

This new property and the idea of absolute value are helpful when adding integers.

Number	Its absolute value	
$^{+}4$ or 4	4	The absolute value of a positive number or 0 is that number itself.
0	0	
5	5	
$^{-}5$	5	The absolute value of a negative number is its opposite.
$^{-}3$	3	

Example 1: How do you add integers with the same sign?

	both negative	both positive
	${}^{-}4 + {}^{-}3$	${}^{+}4 + {}^{+}3$
Add the absolute values.	$4 + 3$	$4 + 3$
The result has the same sign as the addends.	$^{-}7$	$^{+}7$ or 7

Example 2: How do you add integers with different signs?

If the numbers are opposites, use the inverse property of addition.

${}^{+}4 + {}^{-}4 = 0$ $\qquad$ ${}^{-}7 + {}^{+}7 = 0$

If the numbers are not opposites,

${}^{-}4 + {}^{+}3$ $\qquad$ ${}^{+}4 + {}^{-}3$

Find the difference of the absolute values.

$4 - 3$ $\qquad$ $4 - 3$

The result has the same sign as the addend with the greater absolute value.

${}^{-}1$ $\qquad$ ${}^{+}1$ or 1

Example 3: How do you add ⁻4, 6, and ⁻5?

Take your choice of which integers to add first.

$({}^{-}4 + 6) + {}^{-}5$ $\qquad$ ${}^{-}4 + (6 + {}^{-}5)$

$2 + {}^{-}5$ $\qquad$ ${}^{-}4 + 1$

${}^{-}3$ $\qquad$ ${}^{-}3$

Exercises

A State the absolute value of each integer.

1. ${}^{+}16$ **2.** ${}^{-}24$ **3.** 325

4. ${}^{-}96$ **5.** 0 **6.** ${}^{-}1978$

Tell whether the sum is positive, negative, or zero.

7. $18 + 48$ **8.** ${}^{-}63 + {}^{-}49$ **9.** $18 + {}^{-}18$

10. ${}^{-}16 + 13$ **11.** $16 + {}^{-}34$ **12.** ${}^{-}83 + 149$

B Find each sum.

13. $16 + 12$
14. $^-17 + {}^-18$
15. $14 + {}^-14$
16. $32 + {}^-49$
17. $^-18 + {}^-39$
18. $^-47 + 21$
19. $37 + 48$
20. $^-23 + {}^-36$
21. $88 + {}^-72$
22. $^-17 + 12$
23. $103 + {}^-111$
24. $^-15 + 18$
25. $^-619 + {}^-832$
26. $173 + {}^-846$
27. $395 + {}^-395$
28. $792 + {}^-628$
29. $^-485 + {}^-96$
30. $278 + {}^-475$
31. $^-1692 + 1968$
32. $1795 + {}^-492$
33. $672 + 896$
34. $^-849 + {}^-782$
35. $6742 + {}^-4385$
36. $^-6275 + 4675$
37. $(2 + 4) + 3$
38. $(^-2 + 4) + 6$
39. $(8 + {}^-5) + 3$
40. $6 + (5 + {}^-7)$
41. $^-4 + (^-3 + 2)$
42. $^-5 + (7 + {}^-8)$
43. $2 + {}^-7 + {}^-4$
44. $^-2 + {}^-5 + {}^-7$
45. $^-6 + 5 + {}^-8$

C Copy and complete the table.

	Words	*Symbols*	*Sum*
	a temperature of 20° followed by a drop of 10°	$20 + {}^-10$	10
46.	a profit of \$3000 followed by a loss of \$5000	$3000 + {}^-5000$	___
47.	a loss of \$500 followed by a loss of \$200	___	___
48.	a deposit of \$75 followed by a withdrawal of \$20	___	___
49.	a deposit of \$80 followed by a withdrawal of \$100	___	___
50.	a 20-yard gain followed by a 12-yard loss	___	___

6.4 Subtracting Integers

Subtracting 2 from 6 gives the same answer as adding $^{-}2$ to 6.

subtraction	addition
$6 - 2 = 4$	$6 + {}^{-}2 = 4$

(2 and $^{-}2$: opposites)

It appears that subtracting a number is equivalent to adding its opposite. Let's try another example.

subtraction	addition
$5 - 3 = 2$	$5 + {}^{-}3 = 2$

(3 and $^{-}3$: opposites)

Again the pattern holds. Such examples suggest the following property.

To subtract an integer, add its opposite.

Example 1: How do you subtract 6 from $^{-}1$?

Add its opposite.

$$^{-}1 - 6 = {}^{-}1 + {}^{-}6$$
$$= {}^{-}7$$

Example 2: How do you subtract $^{-}7$ from $^{-}2$?

Add its opposite.

$$^{-}2 - {}^{-}7 = {}^{-}2 + 7$$
$$= 5$$

Exercises

A Tell how to change each subtraction to an addition.

1. $6 - 7$ **2.** $8 - {}^{-}5$ **3.** $9 - {}^{-}12$

4. ${}^{-}5 - 6$ **5.** ${}^{-}4 - {}^{-}2$ **6.** $19 - 15$

B Find each difference.

7. $15 - 19$ **8.** ${}^{-}6 - 8$ **9.** ${}^{-}12 - 17$

10. $11 - {}^{-}5$ **11.** ${}^{-}11 - 3$ **12.** $4 - 10$

13. ${}^{-}8 - {}^{-}12$ **14.** $26 - {}^{-}14$ **15.** ${}^{-}11 - {}^{-}33$

16. ${}^{-}6 - {}^{-}5$ **17.** ${}^{-}16 - {}^{-}4$ **18.** ${}^{-}8 - 32$

19. ${}^{-}18 - 16$ **20.** ${}^{-}12 - 12$ **21.** ${}^{-}38 - 54$

22. ${}^{-}518 - 303$ **23.** $219 - {}^{-}118$ **24.** $416 - {}^{-}303$

25. $1776 - {}^{-}1865$ **26.** ${}^{-}1069 - 433$ **27.** ${}^{-}600 - {}^{-}439$

C Find the value of each phrase.

28. $(7 - 3) - 5$ **29.** $7 - (3 - 5)$

30. ${}^{-}5 - (7 - 8)$ **31.** $({}^{-}5 - 7) - 8$

32. $({}^{-}4 - 3) - {}^{-}2$ **33.** ${}^{-}4 - (3 - {}^{-}2)$

34. $({}^{-}5 - {}^{-}6) - 7$ **35.** ${}^{-}5 - ({}^{-}6 - 7)$

Quick Quiz

Sections 6.1 to 6.4

Find each sum or difference.

1. $8 + {}^{-}9$ **2.** ${}^{-}4 + {}^{-}7$ **3.** $12 + {}^{-}27$

4. $12 + {}^{-}12$ **5.** ${}^{-}28 + 45$ **6.** ${}^{-}30 + 142$

7. $17 - {}^{-}8$ **8.** ${}^{-}23 - 75$ **9.** $16 - 19$

10. ${}^{-}14 - {}^{-}5$ **11.** ${}^{-}56 - {}^{-}56$ **12.** $87 - {}^{-}15$

Solving Addition Equations

Before, you solved addition equations by subtracting the same number from each side. You can still do that. But now you can also use a new way.

Example 1: Solve $x + 3 = 19$.

Old way

$$x + 3 = 19$$

$$x + 3 - 3 = 19 - 3$$ Inverse operation.

$$x + 0 = 16$$

$$x = 16$$

New way

$$x + 3 = 19$$

$$x + 3 + {}^{-}3 = 19 + {}^{-}3$$ Add opposite.

$$x + 0 = 16$$

$$x = 16$$

Check:

$$x + 3 = 19$$

$$16 + 3 = 19$$

$$19 = 19 \checkmark$$

Example 2: Solve $x + 3 = {}^{-}19$.

$$x + 3 = {}^{-}19$$

$$x + 3 + {}^{-}3 = {}^{-}19 + {}^{-}3$$ Add $^{-}3$ to each side.

$$x + 0 = {}^{-}22$$

$$x = {}^{-}22$$

Check: $x + 3 = {}^{-}19$

$${}^{-}22 + 3 = {}^{-}19$$ Replace x with $^{-}22$.

$${}^{-}19 = {}^{-}19 \checkmark$$

Example 3: Solve $6 = n + {}^{-}5$.

$$6 = n + {}^{-}5$$

$$6 + 5 = n + {}^{-}5 + 5$$ Add 5 to each side.

$$11 = n + 0$$

$$11 = n$$

Check: $6 = n + {}^{-}5$

$$6 = 11 + {}^{-}5$$ Replace n with 11.

$$6 = 6 \checkmark$$

Exercises

A To solve each equation, what number would you add to each side?

1. $n + 7 = ^{-}6$
2. $n + ^{-}4 = 6$
3. $14 = k + 9$
4. $^{-}6 = m + ^{-}11$
5. $x + 8 = 0$
6. $z + ^{-}9 = 0$

B Solve.

7. $n + 3 = 9$
8. $m + 8 = ^{-}16$
9. $8 = x + ^{-}9$
10. $p + ^{-}9 = ^{-}16$
11. $n + 16 = 9$
12. $^{-}6 = r + ^{-}6$
13. $k + ^{-}7 = 16$
14. $q + ^{-}17 = ^{-}9$
15. $^{-}7 = x + 14$
16. $x + ^{-}7 = 19$
17. $m + 9 = ^{-}32$
18. $^{-}72 = k + ^{-}6$
19. $10 = x + ^{-}1$
20. $y + 7 = ^{-}7$
21. $y + ^{-}7 = 7$
22. $^{-}16 = c + ^{-}2$
23. $13 = a + ^{-}5$
24. $r + ^{-}6 = ^{-}12$

C Solve as shown in the example. Notice that the commutative property of addition is used.

Example:

$$
\begin{aligned}
^{-}7 + n &= 10 \\
n + ^{-}7 &= 10 \\
n + ^{-}7 + 7 &= 10 + 7 \\
n + 0 &= 17 \\
n &= 17
\end{aligned}
$$

Check:

$$
\begin{aligned}
^{-}7 + n &= 10 \\
^{-}7 + 17 &= 10 \\
10 &= 10 \checkmark
\end{aligned}
$$

25. $7 + x = 5$
26. $^{-}5 + x = 9$
27. $9 + x = ^{-}4$
28. $^{-}9 + x = 6$
29. $6 = 7 + x$
30. $9 = ^{-}7 + z$

Solve as shown in the example. Notice that the associative property of addition is used.

Example: $(r + {}^-6) + {}^-3 = 7$

$$r + ({}^-6 + {}^-3) = 7$$
$$r + {}^-9 = 7$$
$$r + {}^-9 + 9 = 7 + 9$$
$$r + 0 = 16$$
$$r = 16$$

Check:
$$(r + {}^-6) + {}^-3 = 7$$
$$(16 + {}^-6) + {}^-3 = 7$$
$$10 + {}^-3 = 7$$
$$7 = 7 \checkmark$$

31. $(m + {}^-2) + 3 = 5$

32. $(x + 3) + {}^-1 = 5$

33. $(r + {}^-2) + 1 = 7$

34. $(y + {}^-5) + 2 = 6$

35. $7 = (a + {}^-8) + 2$

36. $10 = (t + {}^-3) + 2$

Solve each problem. First write an addition equation.

37. At dawn the temperature was $^-7°$. The temperature is $10°$ now. How much has the temperature changed?

Hint: Solve $^-7 + n = 10$.

38. Last year Eve Buckley's blood pressure was 6 millimeters above normal. This year it is 2 millimeters below normal. How much has her blood pressure changed?

Hint: Solve $6 + n = {}^-2$.

39. A submarine is at the $^-240$-foot level (240 feet below sea level). By how many feet will it have to change its depth to be at the $^-170$-foot level?

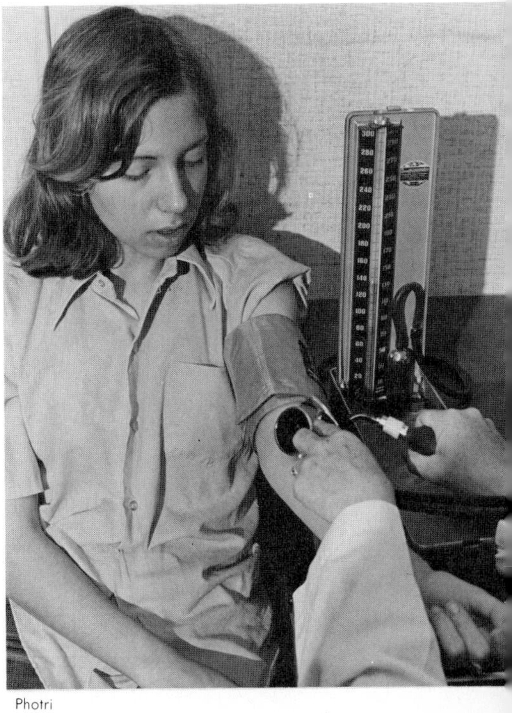

Photri

6.6 Solving Subtraction Equations

Before, you solved subtraction equations by adding the same number to each side. But in Section 6.4, you learned that

$$7 - {}^{-}2 \text{ is equivalent to } 7 + 2.$$

This idea can now be used in solving subtraction equations. Each subtraction equation below is first changed to an addition equation. Then the equation is solved by the method you used in the preceding section.

Example 1: Solve $x - {}^{-}5 = 14$.

$x - {}^{-}5 = 14$

$x + 5 = 14$ Change $x - {}^{-}5$ to $x + 5$.

$x + 5 + {}^{-}5 = 14 + {}^{-}5$ Add ${}^{-}5$ to each side.

$x + 0 = 9$

$x = 9$

Check: $x - {}^{-}5 = 14$

$9 - {}^{-}5 = 14$ Replace x with 9.

$9 + 5 = 14$

$14 = 14$ ✓

Example 2: Solve ${}^{-}6 = x - 4$.

${}^{-}6 = x - 4$

${}^{-}6 = x + {}^{-}4$ Change $x - 4$ to $x + {}^{-}4$.

${}^{-}6 + 4 = x + {}^{-}4 + 4$ Add 4 to each side.

${}^{-}2 = x + 0$

${}^{-}2 = x$

Check: ${}^{-}6 = x - 4$

${}^{-}6 = {}^{-}2 - 4$ Replace x with ${}^{-}2$.

${}^{-}6 = {}^{-}2 + {}^{-}4$

${}^{-}6 = {}^{-}6$ ✓

Exercises

A For each equation

a. Change the indicated subtraction to addition.

b. Tell what number you would add to each side of the resulting equation.

1. $n - 7 = {}^{-}6$ **2.** $n - {}^{-}4 = 6$ **3.** $14 = k - 7$

4. $m - {}^{-}11 = {}^{-}6$ **5.** $x - 8 = 0$ **6.** $0 = z - {}^{-}9$

B Solve.

7. $x - 9 = 7$ **8.** $t - 11 = {}^{-}6$ **9.** $13 = x - {}^{-}8$

10. $r - {}^{-}16 = {}^{-}9$ **11.** $k - 3 = 19$ **12.** ${}^{-}27 = t - 13$

13. $x - {}^{-}27 = 15$ **14.** $s - {}^{-}17 = {}^{-}48$ **15.** $16 = m - 16$

16. $b - 13 = {}^{-}49$ **17.** $c - {}^{-}9 = {}^{-}41$ **18.** $27 = d - {}^{-}93$

19. $t - 6 = 7$ **20.** $r - {}^{-}7 = 14$ **21.** ${}^{-}19 = s - 8$

C Solve as shown in the example.

Example:

$$
\begin{aligned}
{}^{-}7 - {}^{-}x &= 10 \\
{}^{-}7 + x &= 10 \\
x + {}^{-}7 &= 10 \\
x + {}^{-}7 + 7 &= 10 + 7 \\
x + 0 &= 17 \\
x &= 17
\end{aligned}
$$

Check:

$$
\begin{aligned}
{}^{-}7 - {}^{-}x &= 10 \\
{}^{-}7 - {}^{-}17 &= 10 \\
{}^{-}7 + 17 &= 10 \\
10 &= 10 \ \checkmark
\end{aligned}
$$

22. $5 - {}^{-}n = 14$ **23.** $11 - {}^{-}n = {}^{-}16$

24. ${}^{-}11 - {}^{-}x = 12$ **25.** ${}^{-}7 - {}^{-}a = {}^{-}5$

6.7 Inequalities With Integers

You already know how to solve such equations as $x + 4 = {}^-3$ and $x - {}^-3 = 2$. Notice how inequalities similar to these can be solved in the same way.

Example 1: Solve $x + 4 < {}^-3$.

$$x + 4 < {}^-3$$

$$x + 4 + {}^-4 < {}^-3 + {}^-4$$ Add $^-4$ to each side.

$$x + 0 < {}^-7$$

$$x < {}^-7$$

Check: Try any integer less than $^-7$.

$$x + 4 < {}^-3$$

$${}^-8 + 4 < {}^-3$$ Replace x with $^-8$.

$${}^-4 < {}^-3 \checkmark$$

But with inequalities, it is usually a good idea to draw a graph to help "see" the solutions.

Example 2: Graph $x + 4 < {}^-3$. (We solved this inequality in Example 1.)

Draw a number line and use dots and an arrowhead to show all integers less than $^-7$.

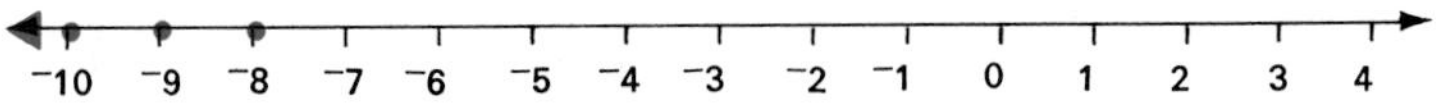

Example 3: Solve and graph $x - {}^-3 > 2$.

$$x - {}^-3 > 2$$

$$x + 3 > 2$$ Change $x - {}^-3$ to $x + 3$.

$$x + 3 + {}^-3 > 2 + {}^-3$$ Add $^-3$ to each side.

$$x + 0 > {}^-1$$

$$x > {}^-1$$

Check: Try any integer greater than $^-1$.

$$x - {}^-3 > 2$$

$$0 - {}^-3 > 2$$ Replace x with 0.

$$0 + 3 > 2$$

$$3 > 2 \checkmark$$

Graph:

Exercises

A To solve each inequality, what number would you add to each side?

1. $x + {}^-5 > 2$ **2.** $y + 6 < {}^-4$ **3.** $m + {}^-7 > {}^-2$

For each inequality.

a. Change the indicated subtraction to addition.

b. Tell what number you would add to each side of the resulting inequality.

4. $n - {}^-8 < 2$ **5.** $t - 6 > {}^-9$ **6.** $k - {}^-19 < {}^-64$

B Solve and graph each inequality.

7. $x + 5 > 4$ **8.** $n + 15 < {}^-6$ **9.** $a + {}^-7 > 6$

10. $t + {}^-8 < {}^-6$ **11.** $z + 7 > 9$ **12.** $m + 13 < {}^-19$

13. $b + {}^-8 > 14$ **14.** $u + {}^-15 < {}^-17$ **15.** $n + 8 < 6$

16. $k + 26 > {}^-7$ **17.** $c + {}^-9 < 3$ **18.** $w + {}^-11 > {}^-19$

19. $k - 5 < 3$ **20.** $a - 4 > {}^-6$ **21.** $t - {}^-5 < 2$

22. $v - {}^-8 > {}^-3$ **23.** $j - 8 < 12$ **24.** $b - 4 > {}^-3$

25. $r - {}^-11 < 13$ **26.** $w - {}^-14 > {}^-19$ **27.** $m - 6 > 2$

28. $c - 5 < {}^-9$ **29.** $s - {}^-7 > 19$ **30.** $y - {}^-23 < {}^-19$

C **31.** $6 < a + {}^-7$ **32.** ${}^-7 + a > 6$ **33.** ${}^-8 < y + 2$

34. $3 + x < {}^-5$ **35.** ${}^-1 > m + 4$ **36.** ${}^-3 > a + {}^-5$

37. $(a - 1) + {}^-2 < 10$ **38.** $(y - 5) + {}^-3 > {}^-8$

39. $(x - {}^-5) + {}^-5 < 8$ **40.** $(z - {}^-6) + 7 > {}^-5$

6.8 Using Equations to Solve Problems

Here is a good problem-solving method:

- Read the problem carefully to get a general understanding.
- Read the problem as many more times as necessary to determine all the given facts.
- Represent any unknown facts with variables.
- Translate the word statement of the problem into an equation.
- Solve the equation.
- Check the solution against the conditions of the problem.
- Answer the problem.

Note: This can replace checking the solution in the equation. If you made a mistake in setting up the equation, the solution might check in it, but still be wrong for the problem.

Example 1: Since noon, the temperature has changed ${}^{-}11$ °C. The temperature now is ${}^{-}9$ °C. What was the temperature at noon?

Let x = the temperature at noon.

Then $x + {}^{-}11 = {}^{-}9$

temperature at noon (x); change since noon (${}^{-}11$); temperature now (${}^{-}9$)

$$x + {}^{-}11 = {}^{-}9$$

$$x + {}^{-}11 + 11 = {}^{-}9 + 11$$

$$x + 0 = 2$$

$$x = 2$$

You can check this in the equation if you want to.

Check: To check against the conditions of the problem, ask yourself this question: Does a temperature of 2 °C followed by a ${}^{-}11$ °C change give a temperature of ${}^{-}9$ °C? ✓

So the temperature at noon was 2 °C.

Example 2: A mountain climber starts from an elevation of $^{-}282$ feet (282 feet below sea level) and climbs to an elevation of 2000 feet (above sea level). What is the change in elevation?

Let n = the change in elevation.

Then $^{-}282 + n = 2000$

starting elevation ($^{-}282$) — change (n) — ending elevation (2000)

$$^{-}282 + n = 2000$$

$$n + {}^{-}282 = 2000$$

$$n + {}^{-}282 + 282 = 2000 + 282$$

$$n + 0 = 2282$$

$$n = 2282$$

Check: Does a climb from 282 feet below sea level to 2000 feet above sea level give a change of 2282 feet? ✓

So the change in elevation is 2282 feet.

A. Devaney, Inc.

Exercises

A Match each problem in **1–6** with an equation in **a–f**.

a. $150 + n = 100$ **b.** $^{-}100 + n = 150$ **c.** $n + {}^{-}30 = 15$

d. $150 + n = {}^{-}100$ **e.** $^{-}150 + n = {}^{-}100$ **f.** $x - 2 = {}^{-}25$

1. The sum of a number and $^{-}30$ is 15. What is the number?

2. When 2 is subtracted from a number, the difference is $^{-}25$. What is the number?

3. A checking account had a balance of $^{-}100$ dollars. (It was overdrawn.) After a deposit was made, the account had a balance of 150 dollars. How much money was deposited?

4. A submarine is at the $^{-}150$-foot level. How many feet will it have to rise to be at the $^{-}100$-foot level?

5. In a card game, Ceil made 150 points on the first hand. After the second hand, her total score was 100 points. What was her score on the second hand?

6. A cable car goes from an elevation of 150 feet to an elevation of $^{-}100$ feet. What is the change in elevation?

B Solve each problem by using an equation.

7. The sum of a number and $^{-}10$ is $^{-}30$. What is the number?

8. When 12 is subtracted from a number, the difference is $^{-}18$. What is the number?

9. In May the balance on a charge account was $^{-}78$ dollars. In June the balance was $^{-}95$ dollars. What was the change in the balance?

10. The temperature at 8 A.M. was $^{-}8$ °C. By noon it had changed to 7 °C. What was the change in temperature?

11. A sky diver jumped out of a plane at an elevation of 4500 feet. The sky diver landed in a valley where the elevation was $^{-}121$ feet. What was the change in elevation?

12. A checking account had a balance of $250. A month later the balance was $135. What was the change in the balance?

13. The elevation of the Dead Sea is $^{-}1296$ feet. The highest point in the world is Mount Everest. The elevation of Mount Everest is 29,028 feet. What is the change in elevation from the Dead Sea to Mount Everest?

14. Mr. Ortíz's savings account had a balance of $1500. Four months later the balance was $650. What was the change in the balance?

15. The regular price of a stereo was $499. The sale price is $439. What was the change in price?

16. The temperature has changed $^{+}6$ °C since 7 A.M. The temperature is now $^{-}2$ °C. What was the temperature at 7 A.M.?

C 17. If you add 6 to a number and then subtract $^{-}8$ from the result, you get 13. What is the number?

18. The temperature changed $^{-}2$ °C. Then it changed $^{+}5$ °C. The resulting temperature was 20 °C. What was the starting temperature?

CONSUMER CORNER

WEATHER REPORTS

Two terms that you frequently hear in a weather report are *windchill* and *temperature-humidity index*.

The chart below shows the chilling effect of wind (windchill). For example, when there is a reported temperature of 50 °F and a wind of 20 mph, the windchill is 32 °F. (Your body loses heat as fast as on a calm day at 32 °F.)

WINDCHILL CHART (in °F)

Wind (mph)	Reported Temperature					
	50	**40**	**30**	**20**	**10**	**0**
5	48	37	27	16	6	-5
10	40	28	16	4	-9	-24
15	36	22	9	-5	-18	-32
20	32	18	4	-10	-25	-39
25	30	16	0	-15	-29	-44
30	28	13	-2	-18	-33	-48
35	27	11	-4	-20	-35	-51
40	26	10	-6	-21	-37	-53

Chicago Tribune

What is the windchill when

1. the reported temperature is 20 °F and the wind is 10 mph?

2. the reported temperature is 0 °F and the wind is 15 mph?

The temperature-humidity index (THI) is based on the air temperature (t) and the temperature (w) of a wet-bulb thermometer. A wet-bulb thermometer has a moistened cloth on its bulb, and its reading depends on both air temperature and humidity. The temperature (w) represents the lowest temperature to which the skin can be cooled by evaporation of perspiration. The following formula can be used to find the THI.

$$\text{THI} = 0.4(t + w) + 15$$ (Temperatures are Fahrenheit.)

People begin to feel discomfort when the THI is 70 or above. When the THI reaches 80, there is danger of heat exhaustion.

3. Find the THI when $t = 80°$ and $w = 60°$.

4. Find the THI when $t = 65°$ and $w = 50°$.

Chicago Tribune

activities

SUM 0

Equipment An ordinary deck of 52 playing cards

Black cards (clubs and spades) stand for positive numbers; red cards (hearts and diamonds) stand for negative numbers as follows:

A♣	2♠	...	10♣	J♠	Q♠	K♣	A♥	2♦	...	10♦	J♦	Q♥	K♥
$^{+}1$	$^{+}2$		$^{+}10$	$^{+}11$	$^{+}12$	$^{+}13$	$^{-}1$	$^{-}2$		$^{-}10$	$^{-}11$	$^{-}12$	$^{-}13$

Setup Two to four players take seats around a table. One of them deals four cards to each player. The remaining cards become a draw pile, placed facedown on the table. The dealer puts the top two cards from the draw pile into the field of play by turning them faceup on the table.

Play (VARIATION 1) START AND ORDER OF PLAY: The first player to the left of the dealer starts, and play proceeds around the table to the left.

OBJECT: The object is to use *one* card in your hand to pick up *one* or *two* cards from the field of play. A pickup can be made only when a card in your hand and the card(s) in the field of play have a sum of 0. *Examples:*

Ed Hoppe Photography

7♥ picks up 7♣ because $^{-}7 + {}^{+}7 = 0$

K♠ picks up K♦ because $^{+}13 + {}^{-}13 = 0$

10♦ picks up 7♣ and 3♠ because $^{-}10 + ({}^{+}7 + {}^{+}3) = 0$

Q♣ picks up J♥ and A♦ because $^{+}12 + ({}^{-}11 + {}^{-}1) = 0$

NOTE: The two cards picked up must be the *same* color. (See also Variation 2.)

POINT PILE: The card played and those it picks up are placed in the player's point pile (to be scored at the end of the game).

WHEN IT IS YOUR TURN:

If you can make at least one pickup:

a. Make *all* possible pickups in succession.

b. Then draw a card from the draw pile.

c. Your turn ends.

If you cannot make a pickup:

a. Discard a card into the field of play.

b. Then draw a card from the draw pile.

c. Your turn ends.

EXHAUSTING THE FIELD: If there are no cards left in the field of play (because of pickups), play your turn as at the right above.

EXHAUSTING THE DRAW PILE: If there are no cards left in the draw pile, play continues as before, except that no more cards are drawn as in **b**.

END OF GAME: The game ends when the draw pile has been exhausted and any one player has no cards left to play.

Challenging

A misplay occurs when a player discards a card that could have been used to make a pickup. Any other player can challenge a misplay by saying "Sum 0." If the challenge is correct, the misplayed card and those it could pick up are added to the challenger's point pile. If the challenge is in error (no misplay has occurred), the challenger loses his or her next turn, and the cards involved stay in play. A challenge *must* be made *before* the next player has started play.

Scoring

Any picture card (jack, queen, or king) counts 2 points. Any other card counts 1 point. Your score is the total points in your point pile minus any points left in your hand at the end of the game. High score wins.

VARIATION 2

Play is the same as in Variation 1, except that two cards to be picked up may be the same color (as in Variation 1) or different colors. *Examples:*

8♠ picks up 10♦ and 2♣ because $^{+}8 + (^{-}10 + ^{+}2) = 0$

J♥ picks up K♠ and 2♥ because $^{-}11 + (^{+}13 + ^{-}2) = 0$

Terms and Symbols Review

Match each item with the best description.

1. 9 and $^-9$	**a.** $x + 9$
2. $\{1, 2, 3, 4, \cdots\}$	**b.** set of negative integers
3. 10	**c.** set of positive integers
4. 9	**d.** opposites
5. $\{^-1, ^-2, ^-3, ^-4, \cdots\}$	**e.** absolute value of $^-10$
6. $x - {}^-9$	**f.** absolute value of 9

Chapter 6 Review

6.1 Name the opposite of each integer.

1. 6
2. $^-7$
3. 0
4. $^+9$

6.2 Find each sum.

5. $6 + {}^-3$
6. $4 + 7$
7. $^-8 + 6$
8. $^-7 + {}^-5$

6.3
9. $37 + 19$
10. $16 + {}^-23$
11. $^-18 + 37$
12. $^-15 + {}^-39$
13. $100 + {}^-100$
14. $^-75 + 95$

6.4 Find each difference.

15. $^-3 - 8$
16. $^-6 - {}^-8$
17. $37 - 84$
18. $^-18 - 37$
19. $^-76 - 38$
20. $39 - {}^-16$

Solve. 6.5

21. $n + 7 = 2$

22. $s + {}^{-}6 = 4$

23. ${}^{-}7 = x + {}^{-}2$

24. $w + {}^{-}5 = 12$

25. $m + {}^{-}41 = {}^{-}12$

26. $17 = a + {}^{-}20$

27. $x - 5 = 14$

28. $y - {}^{-}2 = 6$ 6.6

29. $16 = y - {}^{-}7$

30. $t - {}^{-}6 = 14$

31. $r - 12 = 28$

32. $29 = s - 50$

Solve and graph. 6.7

33. $y + 17 < 10$

34. $x + {}^{-}6 > 5$

35. $t + {}^{-}5 > 5$

36. $m - 7 < 20$

37. $x - 14 < 21$

38. $v - {}^{-}6 > {}^{-}10$

Solve each problem. 6.8

39. Since 4 P.M., the temperature has changed ${}^{-}7$ °C. The temperature now is 4 °C. What was the temperature at 4 P.M.?

40. Last month the balance in a charge account was ${}^{-}38$ dollars. This month the balance is ${}^{-}57$ dollars. What was the change in balance?

Chapter 6 Test

Find each sum.

1. $8 + {}^{-}6$

2. ${}^{-}7 + 8$

3. ${}^{-}16 + {}^{-}23$

4. $18 + {}^{-}26$

5. ${}^{-}48 + {}^{-}23$

6. ${}^{-}27 + {}^{-}49$

Find each difference.

7. $16 - 42$

8. ${}^{-}18 - 16$

9. $92 - {}^{-}16$

10. ${}^{-}84 - {}^{-}48$

11. ${}^{-}48 - {}^{-}84$

12. ${}^{-}36 - 52$

Solve.

13. $x + {}^{-}4 = 17$

14. $y + {}^{-}7 = {}^{-}13$

15. $x - 9 = {}^{-}14$

16. $z - {}^{-}4 = 15$

Solve and graph.

17. $x - 4 < {}^{-}7$

18. $x + {}^{-}3 > 2$

19. $n + {}^{-}7 < 6$

20. $x - {}^{-}4 > 5$

Solve this problem.

21. In going from 1750 feet elevation to ${}^{-}175$ feet elevation, what is the change in elevation?

RATE YOURSELF

Number Correct	
20–21	Superior
18–19	Excellent
16–17	Good
11–15	Fair
0–10	Poor

Getting Ready for Chapter 7

Which lettered choice best matches each numbered item?

1. $3 \times 5 = 5 \times 3$

2. $(2 \times 3) \times 4 = 2 \times (3 \times 4)$

3. $\frac{n}{6}$

a. inverse of dividing by 6 — 3.1

b. $n \div 6$ — 3.2

c. commutative property of multiplication — 4.1

d. associative property of multiplication — 2.1

m = 1/5 (5, -3) Quiz 15 pts.

Write in:
pt-slope form
slope-intercept form
standard form

$(y+3) = \frac{1}{5}(x-5)$

$-3 = \frac{1}{5}(5)+b$

$y = \frac{1}{5}x - 4$

$-3 = 1+b$

$-1 \quad -1$

$-4 = b$

$5y = x - 20$

$-x \quad -x$

$-x + 5y = -20$

6. $\frac{15}{3}$ — 4.1

8. $0 \div 41$ — 3.3

10. $2m = 14$ — 2.3

12. $\frac{a}{5} = 20$

14. $3y - 28 = 20$ — 2.7

16. $\frac{n}{4} - 7 = 6$

18. $\frac{z}{6} > 5$ — 2.4

20. $8w > 32$

7

7

7 MULTIPLYING AND DIVIDING INTEGERS

In Chapter 6 you added and subtracted integers. Now you will extend your skills to include multiplying and dividing integers. You will also continue to use integers to solve problems.

Multiplying a Positive and a Negative Integer

7.1

You already know how to multiply positive integers. That's just like multiplying whole numbers.

But how can you find a product like $3 \times {}^{-}4$?

Think of multiplication as repeated addition. Thus, $3 \times {}^{-}4$ can be shown on a number line as follows.

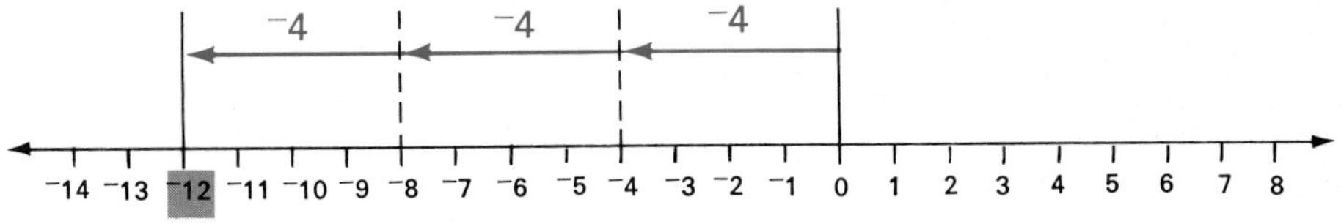

$$3 \times {}^{-}4 = {}^{-}12$$

How can you find a product like ${}^{-}4 \times 3$?

Since you can change the order of the factors without changing the product,

$$3 \times {}^{-}4 = {}^{-}4 \times 3.$$

You already know $3 \times {}^{-}4 = {}^{-}12$, so ${}^{-}4 \times 3 = {}^{-}12$ also.

The examples above suggest the following rule.

> If two integers have *different* signs, then their product is *negative*.

Example 1: Multiply 8 by ⁻9.

$$8 \times {}^{-}9 = {}^{-}(8 \times 9)$$
$$= {}^{-}72$$

Example 2: Multiply ⁻14 by 6.

$${}^{-}14 \times 6 = {}^{-}(14 \times 6)$$
$$= {}^{-}84$$

In Chapter 3 you learned that the product of 0 and any number n is 0. This property is true when n is an integer.

Example 3: $0 \times {}^{-}5 = 0$ $\qquad$ ${}^{-}8 \times 0 = 0$

Exercises

A Tell whether the product is positive, negative, or zero.

1. 3×4 **2.** ${}^{-}3 \times 4$ **3.** $3 \times {}^{-}4$

4. $6 \times {}^{-}5$ **5.** $5 \times {}^{-}7$ **6.** ${}^{-}8 \times 0$

7. ${}^{-}42 \times 79$ **8.** 8×79 **9.** ${}^{-}85 \times 69$

B Find each product.

10. 7×3 **11.** $3 \times {}^{-}6$ **12.** ${}^{-}6 \times 4$

13. ${}^{-}3 \times 7$ **14.** 9×14 **15.** $5 \times {}^{-}8$

16. $7 \times {}^{-}3$ **17.** ${}^{-}5 \times 8$ **18.** 8×17

19. $8 \times {}^{-}10$ **20.** ${}^{-}9 \times 7$ **21.** $0 \times {}^{-}10$

22. $9 \times {}^{-}7$ **23.** ${}^{-}13 \times 12$ **24.** ${}^{-}16 \times 22$

25. $84 \times {}^{-}3$ **26.** $11 \times {}^{-}11$ **27.** ${}^{-}76 \times 6$

28. $38 \times {}^{-}19$ **29.** ${}^{-}42 \times 17$ **30.** ${}^{-}11 \times 0$

31. $8 \times {}^{-}119$ **32.** ${}^{-}476 \times 12$ **33.** $692 \times {}^{-}48$

C Compute as indicated.

34. $8({}^{-}7) + 8(6)$ **35.** $8({}^{-}7 + 6)$

36. $9({}^{-}7) + 9({}^{-}8)$ **37.** $9({}^{-}7 + {}^{-}8)$

38. $12(8 + {}^{-}13)$ **39.** $6(18 + {}^{-}24)$

40. ${}^{-}18(24 + 37)$ **41.** $19(12 + {}^{-}19)$

Multiplying Two Negative Integers

7.2

To learn how to find the product of two negative integers, consider the following pattern.

These factors are decreasing by 1.

$$3 \times -6 = -18$$

$$2 \times -6 = -12$$

$$1 \times -6 = -6$$

$$0 \times -6 = 0$$

$$-1 \times -6 = ?$$

$$-2 \times -6 = ?$$

+6 +6 +6

These products are increasing by 6.

For the pattern to continue, you have the following.

$$-1 \times -6 = 6$$

$$-2 \times -6 = 12$$

Many other examples suggest this conclusion.

> The product of two negative integers is positive.

Example 1: Multiply -5 by -75.

$$-5 \times -75 = 5 \times 75$$
$$= 375$$

Example 2: How do you multiply -3, 4, and -6?

Take your choice of which integers to multiply first.

$$(-3 \times 4) \times -6 \qquad \text{or} \qquad -3 \times (4 \times -6)$$

Then proceed as follows to find the product.

$$(-3 \times 4) \times -6 = -12 \times -6 = 72$$

$$-3 \times (4 \times -6) = -3 \times -24 = 72$$

Exercises

A Tell whether each product is positive or negative.

1. 7×6
2. $18 \times {}^-6$
3. ${}^-16 \times 18$
4. ${}^-48 \times {}^-27$
5. ${}^-76 \times 7$
6. ${}^-83 \times {}^-72$

B Find each product.

7. ${}^-7 \times {}^-6$
8. ${}^-9 \times {}^-10$
9. ${}^-8 \times {}^-4$
10. ${}^-12 \times {}^-13$
11. ${}^-15 \times {}^-17$
12. ${}^-11 \times {}^-16$
13. ${}^-19 \times {}^-20$
14. ${}^-23 \times {}^-23$
15. ${}^-18 \times {}^-18$
16. ${}^-4 \times {}^-5 \times {}^-6$
17. $11 \times {}^-4 \times {}^-5$
18. ${}^-8 \times 6 \times {}^-2$
19. $8 \times 7 \times {}^-6$
20. ${}^-14 \times {}^-4 \times {}^-8$
21. $1 \times {}^-8 \times {}^-19$
22. ${}^-25 \times {}^-25 \times 25$
23. ${}^-72 \times {}^-73 \times 43$
24. $48 \times {}^-99 \times {}^-101$
25. $18 \times {}^-19 \times {}^-21$

C

26. $7 \times 6 \times 3$
27. $8 \times {}^-7 \times 5$
28. ${}^-7 \times {}^-4 \times 2$
29. ${}^-6 \times {}^-7 \times {}^-8$
30. ${}^-7 \times 4 \times {}^-9$
31. ${}^-8 \times 7 \times {}^-17 \times {}^-5$
32. ${}^-17 \times {}^-4 \times {}^-8 \times {}^-3$
33. ${}^-8 \times {}^-17 \times {}^-13 \times 3$

Use your answers to Exercises 26–33 to decide if the following statements are true or false.

34. If there is an *even number of negative factors* and no other factor is 0, then the product is positive.
35. If there is an *odd number of negative factors* and no other factor is 0, then the product is negative.

Dividing Integers 7.3

Multiplication and division are inverse operations. You can use this idea to discover how to divide integers.

both positive

If $3 \times 4 = 12$, then $12 \div 4 = 3$.

If $3 \times {}^-4 = {}^-12$, then ${}^-12 \div {}^-4 = 3$.

both negative — *positive quotients*

If two integers have the *same* sign, then their quotient is *positive.*

Example 1: Divide ${}^-18$ by ${}^-2$.

same sign

$$ {}^-18 \div {}^-2 = 18 \div 2 $$

$$ = 9 $$ *positive quotient*

What if the signs are different?

different signs

If ${}^-3 \times 4 = {}^-12$, then ${}^-12 \div 4 = {}^-3$.

If ${}^-3 \times {}^-4 = 12$, then $12 \div {}^-4 = {}^-3$.

different signs — *negative quotients*

If two integers have *different* signs, then their quotient is *negative.*

Example 2: Divide 28 by ${}^-4$.

different signs

$$ 28 \div {}^-4 = {}^-(28 \div 4) $$

$$ = {}^-7 $$ *negative quotient*

Example 3: Find the quotient $\frac{^-84}{7}$.

different signs

$$\frac{^-84}{7} = \overbrace{^-84 \div 7} = ^-(84 \div 7)$$

$$= ^-12$$ *negative quotient*

Exercises

A Tell whether the quotient is positive or negative.

1. $8 \div 2$ **2.** $\frac{18}{^-6}$ **3.** $^-24 \div 8$

4. $\frac{^-36}{4}$ **5.** $84 \div {^-12}$ **6.** $\frac{^-42}{^-7}$

7. $^-48 \div {^-16}$ **8.** $\frac{96}{8}$ **9.** $78 \div {^-3}$

B Find each quotient.

10. $48 \div 16$ **11.** $16 \div {^-4}$ **12.** $^-21 \div 3$

13. $^-27 \div {^-3}$ **14.** $81 \div {^-9}$ **15.** $30 \div {^-5}$

16. $^-18 \div 6$ **17.** $72 \div {^-8}$ **18.** $^-30 \div {^-6}$

19. $^-121 \div 11$ **20.** $96 \div 16$ **21.** $91 \div 13$

22. $^-100 \div 5$ **23.** $91 \div {^-7}$ **24.** $^-70 \div 5$

25. $\frac{^-9}{3}$ **26.** $\frac{20}{^-5}$ **27.** $\frac{^-15}{^-3}$

28. $\frac{78}{13}$ **29.** $\frac{^-75}{5}$ **30.** $\frac{225}{^-25}$

31. $\frac{^-144}{^-16}$ **32.** $\frac{^-288}{9}$ **33.** $\frac{324}{^-18}$

Find each value. (Remember the order of operations, pages 6–7.)

34. $9 + {^-42} \div 3$ **35.** $^-6 \times 14 \div {^-2}$

36. $^-81 \div 9 + {^-16}$ **37.** $^-84 \div {^-7} \times 6$

38. $16 + {^-9} \times 4 \div 2$ **39.** $^-6 \times 12 \div 3 + {^-5}$

40. $^-20 + 12 \div {^-3} \times 6$ **41.** $16 \times {^-3} \div 4 + {^-8}$

42. $10 \times {^-5} \div 2 - {^-2}$ **43.** $^-50 + 36 \times {^-2} \div {^-2}$

C Study the following statements and examples before you do Exercises 44–52.

0 cannot be divided by itself, but 0 can be divided by any other number.

Dividing by 0 is meaningless.

Examples: $0 \div {}^{-}5 = 0$ $\qquad$ ${}^{-}5 \div 0 = ?$

Check: $\begin{array}{r} 0 \\ \times\ {}^{-}5 \\ \hline 0 \end{array}$ $\qquad$ *Check:* $\begin{array}{r} ? \\ \times\ 0 \\ \hline 5 \end{array}$ ← No number works. So there is no answer for $^{-}5 \div 0$.

Find each quotient or product, if possible. Write *meaningless* if division by 0 is involved.

44. $0 \div {}^{-}8$ $\qquad$ **45.** $\frac{^{-}8}{0}$ $\qquad$ **46.** $0 \div 0$

47. $0 \times {}^{-}8$ $\qquad$ **48.** ${}^{-}6 \div 0$ $\qquad$ **49.** 0×0

50. ${}^{-}8 \times 0$ $\qquad$ **51.** $\frac{0}{^{-}5}$ $\qquad$ **52.** $\frac{0}{0}$

Do You Speak Mathematics?

Sometimes words in other languages are very similar to English words with the same meaning. Can you guess the English words which have the same meaning as these?

Spanish:	**French:**	**German:**
número positivo	*nombre positif*	*positive zahl*
cero	*zéro*	*null*
número negativo	*nombre négatif*	*negative zahl*

If you speak another language, can you name foreign words from mathematics which are similar to English words?

7.4 Solving Multiplication Equations

You already know how to solve equations like $3x = 12$.

$$3x = 12$$

$$\frac{3x}{3} = \frac{12}{3} \quad \text{Divide each side by 3.}$$

$$x = 4$$

Check:

$$3x = 12$$

$$3(4) = 12$$

$$12 = 12 \checkmark$$

The same method is used to solve equations involving integers.

Example 1: Solve $3n = {}^-12$.

$$3n = {}^-12$$

$$\frac{3n}{3} = \frac{{}^-12}{3} \quad \text{Divide each side by 3.}$$

$$n = {}^-4$$

Check: $3n = {}^-12$

$$3({}^-4) = {}^-12 \quad \text{Replace } n \text{ with } {}^-4.$$

$$-12 = {}^-12 \checkmark$$

Example 2: Solve $15 = {}^-5z$.

$$15 = {}^-5z$$

$$\frac{15}{{}^-5} = \frac{{}^-5z}{{}^-5} \quad \text{Divide each side by } {}^-5.$$

$${}^-3 = z$$

Check: $15 = {}^-5z$

$$15 = {}^-5({}^-3) \quad \text{Replace } z \text{ with } {}^-3.$$

$$15 = 15 \checkmark$$

Exercises

A To solve each equation, what would you do to each side?

1. $7x = 42$ **2.** $8y = {}^-48$ **3.** $27 = {}^-9x$

4. ${}^-18z = {}^-90$ **5.** $12x = 0$ **6.** ${}^-70 = 14b$

Find each quotient.

7. $\frac{16}{8}$ **8.** $\frac{-16}{8}$ **9.** $\frac{16}{-8}$

10. $\frac{-24}{-6}$ **11.** $\frac{35}{-7}$ **12.** $\frac{-42}{-6}$

B Solve each equation.

13. $9x = 54$ **14.** $8y = {}^-40$ **15.** $36 = {}^-9t$

16. ${}^-7n = {}^-21$ **17.** $6x = {}^-96$ **18.** $72 = 12x$

19. ${}^-8t = 96$ **20.** ${}^-9k = {}^-117$ **21.** ${}^-168 = 12n$

22. $24z = 192$ **23.** ${}^-14s = 252$ **24.** ${}^-512 = {}^-32p$

25. $27n = {}^-243$ **26.** ${}^-18t = 126$ **27.** ${}^-138 = {}^-23n$

28. ${}^-17t = 153$ **29.** ${}^-16t = {}^-192$ **30.** ${}^-1056 = 48n$

Solve each problem.

31. A submarine left the surface of the water at a rate of ⁻2 feet per second. At that rate, how long would it take the submarine to reach the ⁻100-foot level?

32. The stock market changed ⁻18 points in 3 days. What was the average change each day?

33. The Mills Company profit-and-loss statement showed a change of ⁻$1200 in 3 weeks. What was the average change each week?

Harold M. Lambert

34. On four running plays, a back for the Bears' football team made $^-16$ yards net yardage. What was the average per run?

C Solve each equation.

Example:

$$\begin{aligned} {}^-7x - 3x &= 50 \\ ({}^-7 - 3)x &= 50 \\ {}^-10x &= 50 \\ \frac{{}^-10x}{{}^-10} &= \frac{50}{{}^-10} \\ x &= {}^-5 \end{aligned}$$

Check:

$$\begin{aligned} {}^-7x - 3x &= 50 \\ {}^-7({}^-5) - 3({}^-5) &= 50 \\ 35 - {}^-15 &= 50 \\ 35 + 15 &= 50 \\ 50 &= 50 \ \checkmark \end{aligned}$$

35. $7z - 2z = {}^-35$

36. $3n - 5n = 42$

37. ${}^-5k - 2k = {}^-49$

38. $7x + 2x = {}^-54$

39. ${}^-7x + 4x = 36$

40. ${}^-2x + {}^-3x = {}^-25$

Quick Quiz

Sections 7.1 to 7.4

Find each product.

1. $8 \times {}^-7$

2. ${}^-6 \times 9$

3. ${}^-7 \times {}^-6$

4. ${}^-10 \times 5$

5. $15 \times {}^-18$

6. ${}^-26 \times 14$

7. $4 \times {}^-6 \times {}^-2$

8. ${}^-3 \times {}^-4 \times {}^-5$

Find each quotient.

9. ${}^-18 \div 2$

10. ${}^-25 \div {}^-5$

11. $56 \div {}^-8$

Solve each equation.

12. $8m = {}^-64$

13. $56 = {}^-7x$

14. ${}^-12x = {}^-48$

Solving Division Equations

You already know how to solve equations like $\frac{n}{7} = 2$.

$$\frac{n}{7} = 2$$

$$\frac{n}{7} \times 7 = 2 \times 7 \quad \text{Multiply each side by 7.}$$

$$n = 14$$

Check:

$$\frac{n}{7} = 2$$

$$\frac{14}{7} = 2$$

$$2 = 2 \quad \checkmark$$

The same method is used to solve equations involving integers.

Example 1: Solve $\frac{k}{3} = {}^{-}8$.

$$\frac{k}{3} = {}^{-}8$$

$$\frac{k}{3} \times 3 = {}^{-}8 \times 3 \quad \text{Multiply each side by 3.}$$

$$k = {}^{-}24$$

Check:

$$\frac{k}{3} = {}^{-}8$$

$$\frac{{}^{-}24}{3} = {}^{-}8 \quad \text{Replace } k \text{ with } {}^{-}24.$$

$$ {}^{-}8 = {}^{-}8 \quad \checkmark$$

Example 2: Solve $15 = \frac{m}{{}^{-}2}$.

$$15 = \frac{m}{{}^{-}2}$$

$$15 \times {}^{-}2 = \frac{m}{{}^{-}2} \times {}^{-}2 \quad \text{Multiply each side by } {}^{-}2.$$

$$ {}^{-}30 = m$$

Check: $15 = \frac{m}{^-2}$

$15 = \frac{^-30}{^-2}$ Replace *m* with $^-30$.

$15 = 15$ ✓

Exercises

A To solve each equation, what would you do to each side?

1. $\frac{m}{3} = {}^-5$ **2.** $\frac{x}{^-2} = 3$ **3.** $4 = \frac{s}{^-5}$

4. $6 = \frac{x}{^-4}$ **5.** $\frac{d}{^-6} = {}^-8$ **6.** $\frac{d}{5} = {}^-7$

Find each product.

7. $8 \times {}^-7$ **8.** $^-8 \times {}^-7$ **9.** $^-8 \times 7$

10. $^-4 \times 9$ **11.** $^-5 \times 20$ **12.** $^-8 \times {}^-11$

B Solve each equation.

13. $\frac{n}{3} = 9$ **14.** $\frac{m}{2} = {}^-8$ **15.** $5 = \frac{k}{^-3}$

16. $\frac{t}{^-2} = {}^-9$ **17.** $\frac{a}{6} = 12$ **18.** $^-15 = \frac{a}{5}$

19. $\frac{d}{^-6} = 13$ **20.** $\frac{c}{^-7} = {}^-21$ **21.** $^-2 = \frac{x}{11}$

22. $\frac{n}{4} = 4$ **23.** $\frac{x}{18} = {}^-1$ **24.** $^-12 = \frac{x}{^-3}$

25. $\frac{y}{82} = 6$ **26.** $\frac{n}{101} = {}^-4$ **27.** $^-16 = \frac{x}{12}$

28. $\frac{n}{^-17} = {}^-5$ **29.** $\frac{p}{^-13} = 6$ **30.** $^-13 = \frac{a}{14}$

Solve each problem.

31. A number is divided by 3. The result is $^-14$. What is the number?

32. In a certain experiment, the temperature of a solution is lowered in 5 stages from 0 °C to $^-90$ °C. If the temperature is lowered the same amount in each stage, what is the temperature after the first stage?

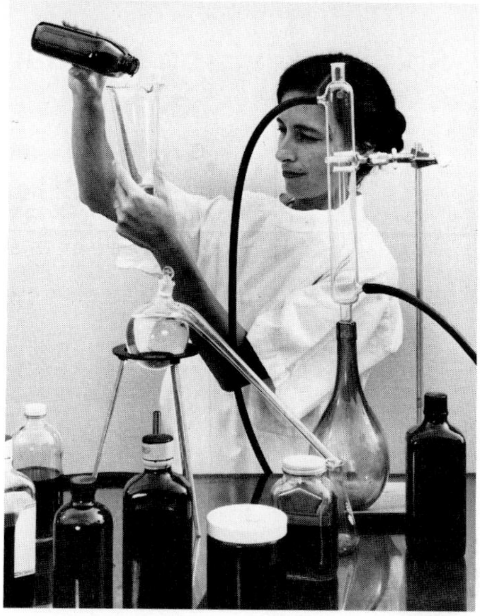

Camerique

C Solve each equation.

Example: $\frac{^-10}{n} = 5$

$\frac{^-10}{n} \times n = 5 \times n$ Multiply each side by n.

$^-10 = 5n$

$\frac{^-10}{5} = \frac{5n}{5}$ Divide each side by 5.

$^-2 = n$

Check: $\frac{^-10}{n} = 5$

$\frac{^-10}{^-2} = 5$ Replace n with $^-2$.

$5 = 5$ ✓

33. $\frac{12}{n} = 6$ **34.** $\frac{^-18}{n} = 6$ **35.** $\frac{24}{n} = {^-8}$

36. $\frac{^-27}{n} = {^-3}$ **37.** $\frac{36}{n} = 9$ **38.** $\frac{42}{n} = {^-6}$

39. $\frac{^-18}{n} = 9$ **40.** $\frac{^-56}{n} = {^-4}$ **41.** $\frac{63}{n} = {^-9}$

7.6 Solving Division Inequalities

If each side of a true inequality is multiplied by a *positive* integer, the resulting inequality has the same inequality symbol.

$^-3 > {}^-4$	$6 < 10$	$^-5 < 2$
$^-3 \times 5 > {}^-4 \times 5$	$6 \times 5 < 10 \times 5$	$^-5 \times 5 < 2 \times 5$
$^-15 > {}^-20$	$30 < 50$	$^-25 < 10$

same symbol

Notice what happens when each side of an inequality is multiplied by a negative integer.

$^-3 > {}^-4$	Multiplying by $^-5$ changes the inequality symbol.	$^-5 < 2$
$^-3 \times {}^-5 < {}^-4 \times {}^-5$		$^-5 \times {}^-5 > 2 \times {}^-5$
$15 < 20$		$25 > {}^-10$

Multiplying each side of an inequality by a negative integer changes $<$ to $>$, and vice versa.

You can use multiplication as follows to solve inequalities. We will also draw graphs to help "see" the solutions.

Example 1: Solve and graph $\frac{n}{4} < {}^-6$.

$$\frac{n}{4} < {}^-6$$

$$\frac{n}{4} \times 4 < {}^-6 \times 4$$

Multiply each side by 4.
Keep the same inequality symbol.

$$n < {}^-24$$

Check: Try any integer less than $^-24$ in the original inequality.

$$\frac{n}{4} < {}^-6$$

$$\frac{^-28}{4} < {}^-6$$

Replace *n* with $^-28$.

$$^-7 < {}^-6 \quad \checkmark$$

Graph: 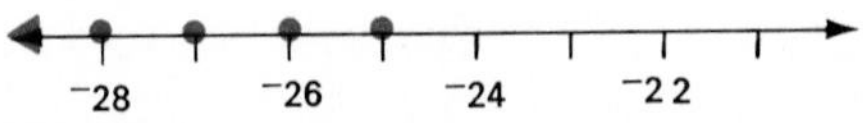

The red dots and arrow show the integers less than $^-24$.

Example 2: Solve and graph $4 > \frac{n}{-3}$.

$$4 > \frac{n}{-3}$$

$$4 \times {}^{-}3 < \frac{n}{-3} \times {}^{-}3$$ Multiply each side by $^{-}3$. Change the inequality symbol.

$$^{-}12 < n$$

Check: Try any integer greater than $^{-}12$ in the original inequality.

$$4 > \frac{n}{-3}$$

$$4 > \frac{-9}{-3}$$ Replace n with $^{-}9$.

$$4 > 3 \checkmark$$

Graph:

Exercises

A Tell whether the inequality symbol will change when each side is multiplied by the number given.

1. $^{-}5 < 8$ 7

2. $10 > 7$ $^{-}3$

3. $^{-}10 > {}^{-}15$ 4

4. $^{-}8 < 2$ $^{-}4$

5. $\frac{x}{-4} < 7$ $^{-}4$

6. $\frac{x}{7} < {}^{-}5$ 7

B Multiply each side of the given inequality by the number indicated, and write the resulting inequality.

7. $6 < 4$ 3

8. $10 > 7$ $^{-}4$

9. $8 > {}^{-}2$ $^{-}7$

10. $^{-}11 < 10$ $^{-}2$

11. $^{-}6 < 0$ 5

12. $5 > 3$ $^{-}3$

13. $\frac{x}{4} < {}^-8$ 4

14. $\frac{x}{{}^-6} > {}^-7$ ${}^-6$

15. $\frac{x}{{}^-7} < 10$ ${}^-7$

16. $\frac{x}{9} > 9$ 9

Solve and graph each inequality.

17. $\frac{x}{4} < {}^-9$

18. $\frac{m}{{}^-4} > 8$

19. $8 < \frac{k}{6}$

20. $\frac{x}{{}^-9} > {}^-2$

21. $\frac{x}{3} < {}^-2$

22. $8 > \frac{n}{{}^-9}$

23. $\frac{t}{11} < 12$

24. $\frac{x}{5} > {}^-9$

25. $7 < \frac{n}{{}^-8}$

26. $\frac{m}{5} > 7$

27. $\frac{x}{{}^-6} < {}^-4$

28. $7 > \frac{t}{{}^-16}$

29. $\frac{a}{{}^-15} > {}^-4$

30. $\frac{n}{18} > {}^-9$

31. $16 < \frac{d}{{}^-18}$

32. $\frac{b}{{}^-13} < {}^-13$

33. $\frac{c}{35} > {}^-7$

34. ${}^-32 < \frac{f}{{}^-15}$

C Should $>$, $<$, or $=$ replace each ● to make each sentence true?

35. ${}^-6 < 2$

${}^-6 \times 0$ ● 2×0

36. $4 > {}^-3$

4×0 ● ${}^-3 \times 0$

37. $8 > 7$

8×0 ● 7×0

38. ${}^-5 < {}^-3$

${}^-5 \times 0$ ● ${}^-3 \times 0$

39. What is the effect of multiplying each side of a true inequality by 0?

Solving Multiplication Inequalities

If each side of a true inequality is divided by a *positive* integer, the resulting inequality has the same inequality symbol.

$6 < 10$	$4 > {}^-4$	${}^-8 > {}^-12$
$\frac{6}{2} < \frac{10}{2}$	$\frac{4}{2} > \frac{^-4}{2}$	$\frac{^-8}{2} > \frac{^-12}{2}$
$3 < 5$	$2 > {}^-2$	${}^-4 > {}^-6$

Notice what happens when each side of an inequality is divided by a *negative* integer.

$6 < 10$		${}^-8 > {}^-12$
$\frac{6}{^-2} > \frac{10}{^-2}$	Dividing by $^-2$ changes the inequality symbol.	$\frac{^-8}{^-2} < \frac{^-12}{^-2}$
${}^-3 > {}^-5$		$4 < 6$

Dividing each side of an inequality by a negative integer changes $>$ to $<$, and vice versa.

Example 1: Solve and graph $3n < {}^-12$.

$$3n < {}^-12$$

$$\frac{3n}{3} < \frac{^-12}{3}$$ Divide each side by 3. Keep the same inequality symbol.

$$n < {}^-4$$

Check: Try any integer less than $^-4$ in the original inequality.

$$3n < {}^-12$$

$$3\,({}^-5) < {}^-12$$ Replace n with $^-5$.

$$^-15 < {}^-12 \ \checkmark$$

Graph:

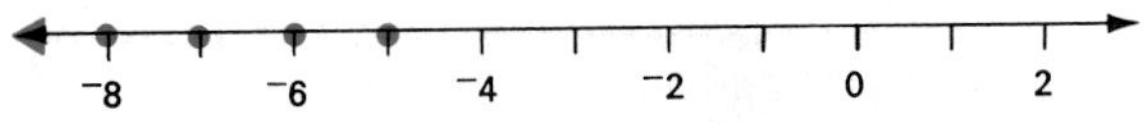

Example 2: Solve and graph $20 > {}^-4n$.

$$20 > {}^-4n$$

$$\frac{20}{{}^-4} < \frac{{}^-4n}{{}^-4}$$ Divide each side by $^-4$. Change the inequality symbol.

$${}^-5 < n$$

Check: Try any integer greater than $^-5$ in the original inequality.

$$20 > {}^-4n$$

$$20 > {}^-4\,({}^-4)$$ Replace n with $^-4$.

$$20 > 16 \checkmark$$

Graph:

Exercises

A Tell whether the inequality symbol will change when each side is divided by the given number.

1.	$6 < 8$	2	**2.**	$14 > 10$	$^-2$
3.	$^-8 > {}^-12$	$^-4$	**4.**	$^-12 < {}^-6$	6
5.	$^-4x > 8$	4	**6.**	$3x < {}^-9$	3

B Divide each side of the given inequality by the number indicated, and write the resulting inequality.

7.	$8 > 4$	2	**8.**	$15 < 25$	$^-5$
9.	$36 < 64$	$^-4$	**10.**	$12 > {}^-4$	$^-4$
11.	$^-14 > {}^-16$	2	**12.**	$^-18 < {}^-12$	$^-6$
13.	$3x > 15$	3	**14.**	$^-5x < 25$	$^-5$
15.	$^-6x < 24$	$^-6$	**16.**	$10x > {}^-10$	10

Solve and graph each inequality.

17. $6x < 48$
18. $7x > -42$
19. $81 > -9x$
20. $-3x < 6$
21. $8x > 16$
22. $-15 < 5x$
23. $-10x > -100$
24. $-2x < 12$
25. $-64 > 4x$
26. $9x > -108$
27. $-6x < 36$
28. $-121 > -11x$
29. $16x > 256$
30. $-2x > -24$
31. $196 > -4x$
32. $-8x < 24$
33. $-24x < 72$
34. $-52 > 13x$

C

35. $2x + 3x > 15$
36. $7x - 2x < 25$
37. $3(4x) < 72$
38. $\frac{8x}{2} < 60$
39. $-5x + 2x < 9$
40. $5x - 8x > 36$
41. $-3(2x) < 54$
42. $\frac{9x}{3} > -54$
43. $4x - 7x < -54$
44. $-3(2x) > -36$
45. $8x - 5x < -39$
46. $15x - 36x > -84$

Quick Quiz

Sections 7.5 to 7.7

Solve each equation.

1. $\frac{n}{5} = -6$
2. $\frac{n}{-5} = -10$
3. $-6 = \frac{w}{4}$
4. $\frac{n}{4} = 7$
5. $-12 = \frac{a}{-5}$
6. $15 = \frac{c}{-4}$

Solve and graph each inequality.

7. $\frac{n}{3} < -2$
8. $1 > \frac{a}{-4}$
9. $\frac{x}{-8} < -2$
10. $-10 < 5x$
11. $-9 > -3x$
12. $12t > 36$

7.8 Equations With Two Operations

Earlier you have solved equations with two operations involving whole numbers. Now you will solve such equations involving integers.

Example 1: Solve $3n + {}^-7 = {}^-19$.

$$3n + {}^-7 = {}^-19$$

$$3n + {}^-7 + 7 = {}^-19 + 7 \qquad \text{Add 7 to each side.}$$

$$3n + 0 = {}^-12$$

$$3n = {}^-12$$

$$\frac{3n}{3} = \frac{{}^-12}{3} \qquad \text{Divide each side by 3.}$$

$$n = {}^-4$$

Check: $3n + {}^-7 = {}^-19$

$$3({}^-4) + {}^-7 = {}^-19 \qquad \text{Replace } n \text{ with } {}^-4.$$

$$^-12 + {}^-7 = {}^-19$$

$$^-19 = {}^-19 \quad \checkmark$$

Example 2: Solve ${}^-3 = \frac{n}{{}^-6} + 9$.

$$^-3 = \frac{n}{{}^-6} + 9$$

$$^-3 + {}^-9 = \frac{n}{{}^-6} + 9 + {}^-9$$

$$^-12 = \frac{n}{{}^-6} + 0$$

$$^-12 = \frac{n}{{}^-6}$$

$$^-12 \times {}^-6 = \frac{n}{{}^-6} \times {}^-6$$

$$72 = n$$

Check: ${}^-3 = \frac{n}{{}^-6} + 9$

$$^-3 = \frac{72}{{}^-6} + 9$$

$$^-3 = {}^-12 + 9$$

$$^-3 = {}^-3 \quad \checkmark$$

Example 3: Solve $\frac{k-6}{3} = {}^{-}12$.

$$\frac{k-6}{3} = {}^{-}12$$
$$\frac{k-6}{3} \times 3 = {}^{-}12 \times 3$$
$$k - 6 = {}^{-}36$$
$$k + {}^{-}6 = {}^{-}36$$
$$k + {}^{-}6 + 6 = {}^{-}36 + 6$$
$$k + 0 = {}^{-}30$$
$$k = {}^{-}30$$

Check:
$$\frac{k-6}{3} = {}^{-}12$$
$$\frac{{}^{-}30 - 6}{3} = {}^{-}12$$
$$\frac{{}^{-}36}{3} = {}^{-}12$$
$${}^{-}12 = {}^{-}12 \checkmark$$

Exercises

A What would you do to each side to solve each equation?

1. $2n + {}^{-}7 = 7$
2. $\frac{m}{6} + {}^{-}7 = 2$
3. $\frac{k-9}{{}^{-}4} = 6$
4. ${}^{-}2k + 7 = 9$
5. $\frac{x}{{}^{-}7} + 5 = {}^{-}2$
6. $3t + {}^{-}9 = {}^{-}18$

B Solve each equation.

7. $2k + {}^{-}5 = {}^{-}9$
8. $\frac{m}{8} + {}^{-}5 = 6$
9. $6 = \frac{k-5}{4}$
10. $\frac{k}{{}^{-}6} + 8 = 4$
11. $5n - 7 = 18$
12. $9 = \frac{n + {}^{-}7}{6}$
13. $\frac{m+5}{{}^{-}4} = 16$
14. $\frac{m}{8} - 6 = {}^{-}14$
15. ${}^{-}27 = {}^{-}6x + {}^{-}9$
16. ${}^{-}4t + 8 = 40$
17. $\frac{x + {}^{-}5}{3} = 7$
18. $10 = \frac{r}{{}^{-}9} - 5$
19. $\frac{t}{5} + {}^{-}7 = {}^{-}14$
20. $8m + {}^{-}7 = 41$
21. $5 = \frac{x-8}{{}^{-}16}$
22. $\frac{x+9}{4} = {}^{-}5$
23. $\frac{m}{{}^{-}11} - 7 = {}^{-}9$
24. $33 = {}^{-}7t + {}^{-}9$

C

25. $7 + 2x = {}^{-}5$
26. ${}^{-}7 + 3x = {}^{-}10$
27. $5 + {}^{-}4x = 13$
28. $3 + {}^{-}5x = {}^{-}17$
29. $2n + (3 + {}^{-}2) = 7$
30. $(3m + 3) + {}^{-}7 = 14$

7.9 Solving Problems

Problems about *rates of change* and *averages* can often be solved by using multiplication and division of negative integers. Such problems also involve the following two formulas.

distance rate time

$$d = rt$$

total amount

$$\frac{T}{n} = a$$

average amount per item

number of items

De Wys, Inc.

Example 1: A hot-air balloon changes its altitude ⁻2000 feet in 40 minutes. What is the rate of change in altitude?

Let r = rate of change in altitude.

Then $^{-}2000 = r(40)$ ⟸ $d = rt$

$$^{-}2000 = 40r$$

$$\frac{^{-}2000}{40} = \frac{40r}{40}$$

$$^{-}50 = r$$

Note: Since the distance is in feet and the time is in minutes, the rate has been found in *feet per minute*.

Check: At ⁻50 ft/min for 40 min, will the balloon change its altitude ⁻2000 feet? ✓

So the rate of change in altitude is ⁻50 feet per minute.

Example 2: A chain of restaurants had an average profit-and-loss balance of $^-4100$ dollars per restaurant for a total of 8 restaurants. What was the total balance for all the restaurants?

Let T = total balance.

Then $\frac{T}{8} = {}^-4100$. ◀ $\frac{T}{n} = a$

$\frac{T}{8} \times 8 = {}^-4100 \times 8$

$T = {}^-32{,}800$

Check: Does a total balance of $^-32{,}800$ dollars for 8 restaurants give an average balance of $^-4100$ dollars per restaurant? ✓

The total balance was $^-32{,}800$ dollars. (Another way to say this is that the chain of restaurants lost $32,800.)

Exercises

A

1. What does each letter in the formula $d = rt$ stand for?

2. What does each letter in the formula $\frac{T}{n} = a$ stand for?

B Solve each problem.

3. A submarine descends from the surface (0 feet) to $^-55$ feet in 5 minutes. What is the rate of change?

4. An airplane changes its altitude $^-18{,}000$ feet in 15 minutes. What is the rate of change in altitude?

5. In a certain city, the average change in population has been $^-143$ people per year. What has been the population change during the last 5 years?

6. A company showed an average profit-and-loss balance of $^-345$ dollars per month for 12 months. What was the total balance for 12 months?

7. Until recently, the city of Venice, Italy, was changing its elevation an average of $^-5$ millimeters per year. At that rate, what was the change during 25 years?

8. The temperature changed $^-21$ degrees in 7 hours. What was the average change per hour?

Harold M. Lambert

9. A helicopter changed altitude $^{-}840$ meters in 7 minutes. What was the average change per minute?

10. An insurance company had 152 customers in a region which suffered a flood. The company recorded the average amount it paid out to each customer as $^{-}8200$ dollars. How would they record the total amount paid out?

11. A miner descended from the surface (0 feet) to $^{-}128$ feet in 16 minutes. What was the rate of change?

12. In a 7-day period, an airline reported an average change in income of $^{-}150{,}000$ dollars per day because of a strike. What was the total change in income?

C 13. A family reported the following monthly budget balances: January, 17 dollars; February, $^{-}3$ dollars; March, 8 dollars; April, $^{-}2$ dollars. What was the average monthly budget balance for the four months?

14. A business showed the following profit-and-loss balances: 7350 dollars for the first quarter, $^{-}850$ dollars for the second quarter, $^{-}1450$ dollars for the third quarter, and 6150 dollars for the fourth quarter. What was the average balance per quarter?

CONSUMER CORNER

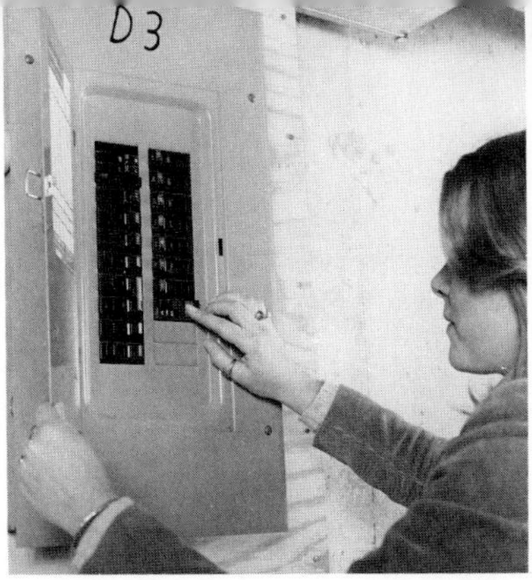

Courtesy General Electric Co., Circuit Protective Devices Dept.

WATTS THE LIMIT?

Your house or apartment has a circuit-breaker box like the one at the left. Each circuit breaker, which is a switch, is there to protect part of the electrical wiring in the building from catching on fire.

Here's how it works. Suppose your living room has a 120-volt line (you can tell this by looking in the circuit-breaker box) and a 15-ampere circuit breaker. How many 100-watt light bulbs could you operate on that line? Watts, volts, and amperes are related by this formula:

watts → P, volts → E, amperes → I

$$P = EI$$

$$P = 120 \times 15$$

$$P = 1800$$

So a 120-volt, 15-ampere circuit could handle 1800 watts and you could operate 18 light bulbs, each rated at 100 watts.

Appliances have watt ratings printed on them too. Could you operate the following on a 120-volt, 20-ampere line?

Blender	450 watts
Refrigerator	300 watts
Dishwasher	740 watts
Toaster	750 watts
Light bulbs	400 watts
total	2640 watts

$$P = EI$$

$$2640 = 120I$$

$$\frac{2640}{120} = \frac{120I}{120}$$

$$22 = I$$

This is greater than the 20-ampere circuit rating. So you could not use all the appliances and bulbs. The circuit breaker would stop the flow of electricity.

1. Find if you can operate the following on a 120-volt, 20-ampere line: iron, 1000 watts; hair dryer, 740 watts; refrigerator, 300 watts; microwave oven, 470 watts; light bulbs, 610 watts.

2. Find if you can operate the following on a 240-volt, 30-ampere line: air conditioner, 2400 watts; water heater, 4080 watts.

Terms and Symbols Review

Give the letter of the best ending for each sentence.

1. Multiplying each side of $\frac{x}{3} > {}^{-}7$ by 3
2. Dividing each side of ${}^{-}3x < {}^{-}9$ by ${}^{-}3$
3. The product of two negative integers is
4. The product of one positive and one negative integer is
5. The quotient of two negative integers is
6. The quotient of one positive and one negative integer is

a. does not change the inequality symbol.

b. changes the inequality symbol.

c. positive.

d. negative.

Chapter 7 Review

7.1 Find each product.

1. 7×9	**2.** $4 \times {}^{-}7$
3. ${}^{-}8 \times 6$	**4.** ${}^{-}11 \times 7$
5. $11 \times {}^{-}13$	**6.** ${}^{-}26 \times 17$
7.2 **7.** ${}^{-}8 \times {}^{-}3$	**8.** ${}^{-}10 \times {}^{-}10$
9. ${}^{-}13 \times {}^{-}14$	**10.** ${}^{-}18 \times {}^{-}16$

7.3 Find each quotient.

11. $8 \div {}^{-}2$	**12.** ${}^{-}16 \div 8$
13. ${}^{-}24 \div {}^{-}6$	**14.** $48 \div 4$
15. $\frac{69}{{}^{-}13}$	**16.** $\frac{{}^{-}72}{4}$
17. $\frac{{}^{-}96}{{}^{-}6}$	**18.** $\frac{144}{{}^{-}9}$

Solve each equation. 7.4

19. $8x = 72$

20. $^{-}48 = 6y$

21. $^{-}7x = 84$

22. $^{-}5m = {}^{-}35$

23. $\frac{n}{3} = 6$

24. $\frac{n}{2} = {}^{-}7$ 7.5

25. $\frac{m}{^{-}4} = 7$

26. $^{-}12 = \frac{k}{^{-}8}$

Solve and graph each inequality.

27. $\frac{x}{4} < {}^{-}6$

28. $\frac{t}{6} > 8$ 7.6

29. $8 < \frac{m}{^{-}3}$

30. $\frac{y}{^{-}2} < {}^{-}9$

31. $6x > 54$

32. $^{-}35 > 7t$ 7.7

33. $84 > {}^{-}7x$

34. $^{-}108 < {}^{-}9w$

Solve each equation. 7.8

35. $3x + {}^{-}5 = 10$

36. $^{-}8 = {}^{-}5x - 3$

37. $5 = \frac{x + {}^{-}8}{^{-}2}$

38. $\frac{x}{5} + 3 = 7$

Solve each problem. 7.9

39. An airplane changes its altitude $^{-}20{,}000$ feet in 10 minutes. What is the rate of change in altitude?

40. According to the United States Chamber of Commerce, the buying power of the average American family changed $^{-}612$ dollars in a recent year. If this continued, what would the total change be over 3 years?

Chapter 7 Test

Find each product or quotient.

1. $3 \times {}^{-}3$

2. ${}^{-}8 \times {}^{-}5$

3. ${}^{-}19 \times {}^{-}21$

4. ${}^{-}24 \times 32$

5. ${}^{-}120 \div 8$

6. ${}^{-}196 \div {}^{-}14$

7. $\frac{{}^{-}64}{16}$

8. $\frac{360}{{}^{-}45}$

Solve each equation.

9. ${}^{-}5c = 45$

10. ${}^{-}16 = 4x$

11. ${}^{-}72 = {}^{-}8w$

12. $\frac{a}{{}^{-}9} = {}^{-}18$

13. $\frac{k}{3} = {}^{-}7$

14. ${}^{-}12 = \frac{m}{{}^{-}5}$

Solve and graph each inequality.

15. $\frac{r}{4} < {}^{-}8$

16. $15 < \frac{w}{{}^{-}6}$

17. ${}^{-}10 < \frac{c}{{}^{-}2}$

18. $7m > {}^{-}28$

19. ${}^{-}50 > {}^{-}10x$

20. ${}^{-}9r > 45$

Solve each equation.

21. $2x + 5 = {}^{-}15$

22. $\frac{x}{4} + {}^{-}1 = 7$

23. ${}^{-}14 = {}^{-}3x - 2$

24. $\frac{y + {}^{-}3}{2} = 10$

25. A union figured that because of inflation, the purchasing power of each member changed an average of ${}^{-}20$ dollars a month for the last 12 months. What was the total change in the 12 months?

RATE YOURSELF

Number Correct	
24–25	Superior
21–23	Excellent
18–20	Good
13–17	Fair
0–12	Poor

CAREER CORNER

POWER LINES AND PIPELINES

Metal expands and contracts with changes in temperature. When power lines are strung during warm weather, a certain amount of slack must be left. Otherwise, the wires might contract and break in colder weather.

A person who strings copper wire can use the following formula to compute the change in length of a copper wire due to temperature changes.

$$c = 0.017\,\ell\,(T - t)$$

- c: change in length in millimeters
- ℓ: length in meters
- T: ending Celsius temperature
- t: starting Celsius temperature

© Yoram Kahana Photo

A pipefitter who lays brass pipe can use the following formula to compute the change in length of brass pipe because of temperature changes.

$$c = 0.0001248\,\ell\,(T - t)$$

- c: change in length in inches
- ℓ: length in feet
- T: ending Fahrenheit temperature
- t: starting Fahrenheit temperature

Use the formulas above to solve these problems.

1. When the temperature changes from $^{-}10\,°C$ to $14\,°C$, what is the change in length of a copper wire that is 15 meters long?

2. When the temperature changes from $150\,°F$ to $40\,°F$, what is the change in the length of a 300-foot brass pipe?

Terms and Symbols Review: Chapters 1–7

Which term or symbol in parentheses is the best choice?

Ch. 1

1. The (*liter, meter, gram*) is a metric unit of weight.

2. The prefix (*kilo-, centi-, milli-*) means "hundredth."

3. The symbol ($<$, $>$, $=$) is read "is less than."

Ch. 2

4. The pound is a unit for measuring (*weight, capacity, length*).

5. The inverse operation of addition is (*multiplication, subtraction*).

6. If the replacement set is the whole numbers, the graph of $x < 2$ contains (*0, 1, 2*) points.

Ch. 3

7. The (*commutative, associative*) property of multiplication is illustrated by the equation $3a = a \times 3$.

8. The number 7 is (*prime, composite*).

9. The exponent in the expression 3^2 is (*3, 2*).

Ch. 4

10. 5 is the (*numerator, denominator*) of $\frac{5}{8}$.

11. $\frac{9}{12}$ is equivalent to ($\frac{2}{3}$, $\frac{3}{4}$, $\frac{5}{6}$).

12. The least common denominator of $\frac{1}{6}$ and $\frac{1}{8}$ is (*2, 24,* $\frac{1}{7}$).

Ch. 5

13. The decimal for two and two tenths is (*0.22, 2.2,* $2\frac{2}{10}$).

14. The 3 in (*1.234, 4.123, 4.321*) is in the hundredths place.

15. When you multiply 1.8 by 0.3, there should be (*one, two, three*) places after the decimal point in the product.

Ch. 6

16. The absolute value of $^-8$ is (8, $^-8$, 0).

17. $x - {}^-3$ is equivalent to ($x - 3$, $x + 3$, $3 - x$).

Ch. 7

18. The product of two negative integers is (*positive, negative*).

19. The quotient of one positive and one negative integer is (*positive, negative*).

Cumulative Review: Chapters 1–7

Ch. 1

Find each value.

1. $10 + 4 \div 2$
2. $(7 + 3) \times (4 - 2)$
3. $(n + 4) \times 5$ if n is replaced with 2
4. $3 + 6x$ if x is replaced with 3

Translate into symbols.

5. four plus twice y
6. a number n divided by three
7. The product of six and a number z is thirty.
8. The quotient of a number s divided by two is less than ten.

Classify as *True, False,* or *Open*.

9. $3x + 2 = 13$
10. $12 - 3 < 9$
11. $8 > 4$

Solve. Use {1, 2, 3, 4, 5} as the replacement set.

12. $x + 4 = 7$
13. $12 = a + 8$
14. $m + 13 = 22$

Ch. 2

Simplify.

15. $13 \times 6 \div 6$
16. $11 - 8 + 8$
17. $34 + 7 - 7$

Solve.

18. $m + 8 = 14$
19. $16 = y - 5$
20. $42 = 6n$
21. $\frac{x}{4} < 13$
22. $t - 4 > 5$
23. $5a + 4 = 24$
24. $12 = \frac{y}{2} + 8$
25. $\frac{t - 6}{5} = 4$
26. $16 = 3t + 1$

Solve and graph.

27. $7 = x + 4$
28. $4n < 28$
29. $21 > t + 19$

Complete.

30. 4 ft = ____ in. **31.** 64 oz = ____ lb **32.** 8 qt = ____ gal.

33. Find the area of a rectangle with length 29 meters and width 18 meters.

34. Find the volume of a rectangular solid with length 12 inches, width 9 inches, and height 8 inches.

Translate into symbols.

35. One number is four times another number. The sum of the two numbers is thirty.

Ch. 3 Using a property of numbers, solve.

36. $25 \times 1 = a$ **37.** $0 \times 17 = b$ **38.** $12 + 0 = c$

39. $0 \div 8 = d$ **40.** $5 \div 5 = e$ **41.** $5(4f) = 40$

42. $5 + g = 13$ **43.** $10h + h = 66$ **44.** $25j - 12j = 39$

45. Find all the factors of 42.

46. Is 310 divisible by 2? By 3? By 5? By 10?

47. Write the prime factorization of 40.

48. Find the GCF of 30 and 12.

49. Find the LCM of 8 and 12.

Ch. 4 Compute. Express each answer in lowest terms.

50. $\frac{1}{3} \times \frac{2}{5}$ **51.** $8 \times \frac{1}{4}$ **52.** $1\frac{2}{3} \times 2\frac{1}{2}$

53. $\frac{3}{7} \div \frac{1}{3}$ **54.** $3\frac{1}{3} \div 5$ **55.** $6\frac{1}{4} \div 1\frac{7}{8}$

56. $\frac{2}{7} + \frac{3}{7}$ **57.** $5\frac{3}{8} + 7\frac{5}{8}$ **58.** $3\frac{1}{3} + 5\frac{1}{4}$

59. $5\frac{3}{4} - 1\frac{1}{4}$

60. $\frac{2}{5} - \frac{1}{3}$

61. $9\frac{1}{2} - 7\frac{2}{3}$

Answer each question.

62. How many $1\frac{1}{2}$-foot boards can be cut from a 6-foot board?

63. If 1 can of juice holds $8\frac{1}{2}$ ounces, how many ounces are in 4 cans of the juice?

Round as indicated.

Ch. 5

number	to the nearest: hundred	one	tenth
64. 128.38			
65. 763.248			

(a) Estimate each answer; **(b)** then compute each answer.

66. $19 + 2.8 + 5.62$

67. $3.188 - 2.5$

68. 5.4×0.6

69. 7.4×3.58

70. 0.09×78.3

71. $19.5 \div 6$

Divide.

72. $57.6 \div 18$

73. $0.78 \div 0.04$

74. $6.8 \div 1.7$

75. $2.484 \div 0.04$

Complete.

76. 2.9 km = ____ m

77. 8.4 cm = ____ m

78. 47 mm = ____ cm

79. 8.9 g = ____ mg

Compute.

80. 138.46×100

81. 4.63 m + 186 cm + 1.38 m

82. 5.2 cm × 3 mm

Ch. 6 Find each sum or difference.

83. $^-27 + {^-18}$ **84.** $^-46 + 38$ **85.** $50 + {^-12}$

86. $^-14 - 17$ **87.** $25 - {^-26}$ **88.** $^-19 - {^-13}$

Solve.

89. $x + 12 = {^-6}$ **90.** $^-22 = y + {^-10}$

91. $y - {^-29} = 17$ **92.** $a - 5 = {^-32}$

Solve and graph.

93. $a - 9 < {^-6}$ **94.** $x + {^-6} > 3$

95. $m + {^-19} < {^-16}$ **96.** $d - {^-3} > 2$

97. Before a deposit was made, a checking account had a balance of $^-16$ dollars. After the deposit was made, the balance was 34 dollars. How much money was deposited?

Ch. 7 Find each product or quotient.

98. $18 \times {^-5}$ **99.** $^-7 \times {^-14}$ **100.** $^-28 \times 12$

101. $^-48 \div 8$ **102.** $95 \div {^-5}$ **103.** $^-84 \div {^-12}$

Solve.

104. $3k = {^-21}$ **105.** $^-18x = {^-90}$

106. $\frac{x}{^-6} = {^-7}$ **107.** $\frac{t}{4} = {^-6}$

108. $6x + {^-2} = {^-14}$ **109.** $1 = \frac{x}{5} - {^-3}$

Solve and graph.

110. $^-8y > {^-40}$ **111.** $^-55 < 11t$

112. $\frac{m}{4} < {^-8}$ **113.** $^-14 > \frac{s}{^-2}$

114. An airplane changes its altitude $^-12{,}000$ feet in 10 minutes. What is the rate of change in altitude?

Getting Ready for Chapter 8

Compute. 1.2

1. $5 + 2(\frac{12}{3})$
2. $15 \div (21 - 18)$
3. $(38 - 15) \times 2$
4. $(5 + 4) \times (17 - 8)$

Find the value of each phrase. 1.3

5. $8y - 11$ if $y = 4$
6. $7(\frac{x}{8}) + 16$ if $x = 56$
7. $(5a \div 2) + 7$ if $a = 6$
8. $\frac{n+5}{3} - 1$ if $n = 7$

Compute.

9. $^-3 + 7$ 10. $^-8 + {}^-9$ 11. $(2 + {}^-5) + 7$ 6.3

12. $^-10 - 4$ 13. $8 - {}^-7$ 14. $^-8 - {}^-12$ 6.4

15. $^-10 \times {}^-5$ 16. $^-4 \times 5$ 17. $8 \times {}^-3 \times {}^-2$ 7.2

18. $18 \div {}^-3$ 19. $^-20 \div {}^-5$ 20. $\frac{15}{^-5}$ 7.3

Solve these problems.

Wide World

21. The Wildcats made 23 field goals and 14 free throws. What was their score? 1.9

$p = 2g + f$

score ↗ field goals ↑ free throws ↖

22. The Cardinals scored 71 points in a game. They made 29 field goals. How many free throws did they make?

23. The base of a triangle is 18 cm long. The altitude is 5 cm long. Find the area of the triangle. 2.8

area ↓ base ↓ altitude ↓

$A = \frac{b \times a}{2}$

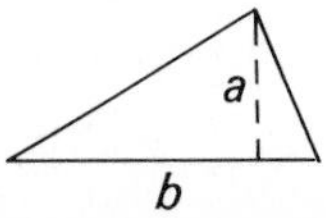

8

GRAPHING

Reprinted courtesy of the Chicago Tribune

Graphs are used for many things in math and in everyday life. In this chapter you will draw graphs like those above. You will also see how graphs are used in other ways.

Ordered Pairs

Mary Elenz Tranter Photographics

In a math game, Ann drew a rule card. She will apply that rule to any number you give her.

If your number is 2, Ann's number is 2 + 3 or 5. If your number is 4, what is Ann's number? If your number is x, what is Ann's number?

The rule could also be given as an equation.

$$a = x + 3$$

a: Ann's number; x: Your number

Example 1: Use Ann's rule to complete the table.

Your number (x)	0	1	2	3	4	5
Ann's number (a)	3	4	5	6	7	8

$$a = x + 3 = 0 + 3 = 3 \qquad a = x + 3 = 1 + 3 = 4$$

Replace x with each number. Solve for a.

You can list these pairs of numbers in another way. In each pair, list your number first and Ann's number second.

$$(0, 3), (1, 4), (2, 5), (3, 6), (4, 7), (5, 8)$$

Since we have specified an order, these are called **ordered pairs** of numbers.

Example 2: Write the rule as an equation.
Use the rule to complete the table.

Rule: To find the second number,
multiply the first number by 2. Then add 3.

Let x be the first number and y be the second number.

$$y = 2x + 3$$

x	0	1	2	3	4	5	6	7	8
y	3	5	7	9	11	13	15	17	19

$$\begin{aligned} y &= 2x + 3 \\ &= 2(0) + 3 \\ &= 0 + 3 \\ &= 3 \end{aligned}$$

$$\begin{aligned} y &= 2x + 3 \\ &= 2(1) + 3 \\ &= 2 + 3 \\ &= 5 \end{aligned}$$

Replace x with each number. Solve for y.

Exercises

A State each rule as an equation. Let x be the first number. To find the second number y:

1. Add 7 to the first number.
2. Divide the first number by 2.
3. Multiply the first number by 8.
4. Subtract 2 from the first number.
5. Multiply the first number by 3. Then subtract 2.
6. Multiply the first number by 4. Then add 1.
7. Divide the first number by 3. Then add 2.

Interchange the numbers in each ordered pair. Then tell what the new ordered pair means.

Example: The date 2–12 means February 12th.
The date 12–2 means December 2nd.

8. The date 5–10 means May 10th.
9. Section 8.1 means chapter 8, section 1.
10. A count of 1–2 in baseball means 1 ball, 2 strikes.
11. A volleyball score of 11–6 means the serving team has 11, the other team has 6.

B Use the rule to complete the table.

12. $y = x - 2$

x	5	6	7	8	9	10	11
y	3	4					

13. $y = 4x - 3$

x	1	2	3	4	5	6	7
y							

14. $y = \frac{x}{2} + 5$

x	2	4	6	8	10	12	14
y							

15. $y = 7x$

x	0	1	2	3	4	5	6
y							

Use the rule to complete the ordered pairs.
The values of *x* are given first.

16. $y = 3x + 2$

(2, 8), (3, 11), (4,), (5,), (6,), (7,)

17. $y = 10x$

(3,), (5,), (7,), (9,), (11,), (13,)

18. $y = x + 6$

(3,), (4,), (5,), (6,), (7,), (8,)

C Discover the rule for each table.

19.

length of side (s)	1	2	3	4	5	6
perimeter (p)	4	8	12	16	20	24

20.

millimeters (m)	10	20	30	40	50	60	70
centimeters (c)	1	2	3	4	5	6	7

8.2 Graphing Ordered Pairs

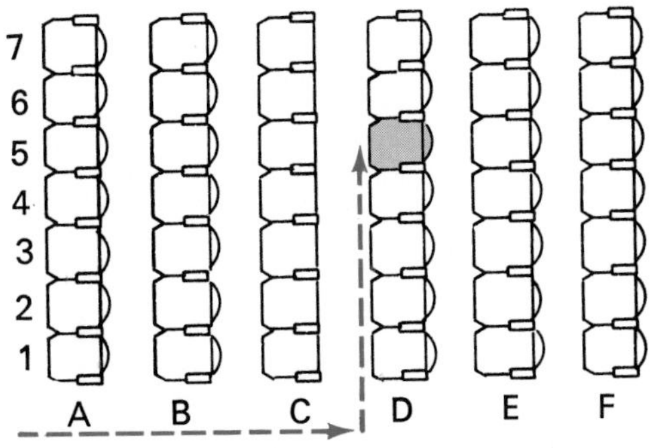

Suppose this is your ticket stub.
To find your seating location, you would go to row D, then to seat 5. The letter D tells you how far to go in one direction. The number 5 tells you how far to go in another direction.

An *ordered pair* of numbers like (2, 4) can be graphed in the same way. You can use graph paper as shown below.

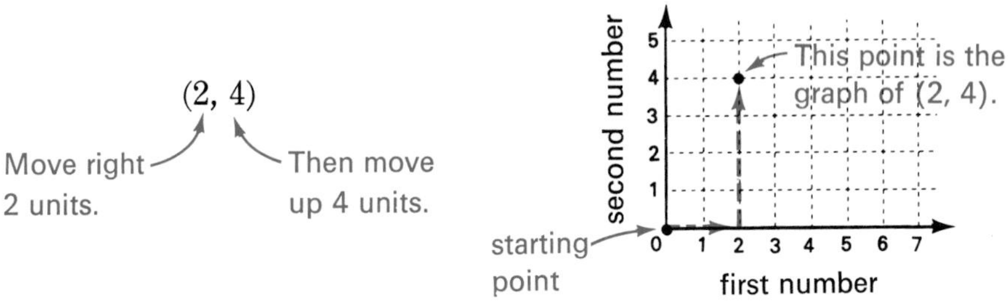

The dashed arrows show the moves. Do not draw them as part of the graph. Just draw a dot at the ending point.

Example 1: Graph the ordered pairs (3, 0) and (0, 3).

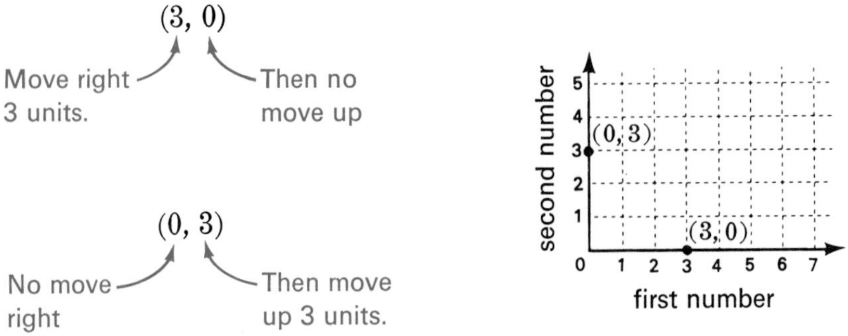

Example 2: Graph the ordered pairs.

x (first number)	0	1	2	3	4	5	6
y (second number)	3	2	6	5	4	0	1

If it helps, list the ordered pairs as follows.

(0, 3), (1, 2), (2, 6), (3, 5), (4, 4), (5, 0), (6, 1)

On a piece of graph paper, draw and label two number scales as shown at the right. Then graph each ordered pair as shown in Example 1.

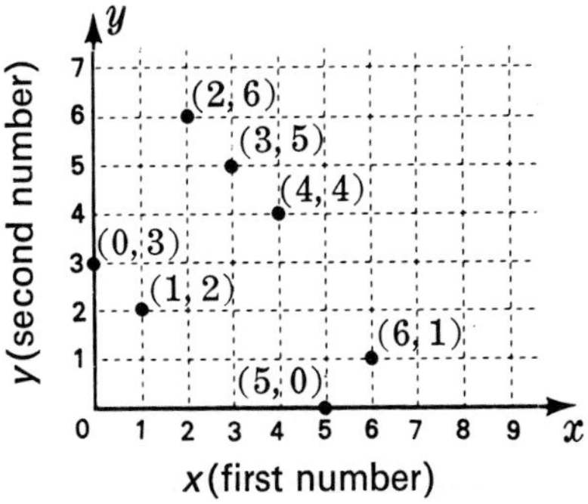

Exercises

A Tell the moves you would make to graph each ordered pair.

1. (3, 4) **2.** (5, 8) **3.** (0, 5) **4.** (3, 3)

5. (6, 2) **6.** (1, 0) **7.** (10, 7) **8.** (2, 9)

Name the ordered pair for each point.

9. A **10.** B

11. C **12.** D

13. E **14.** F

15. G **16.** H

17. I **18.** O

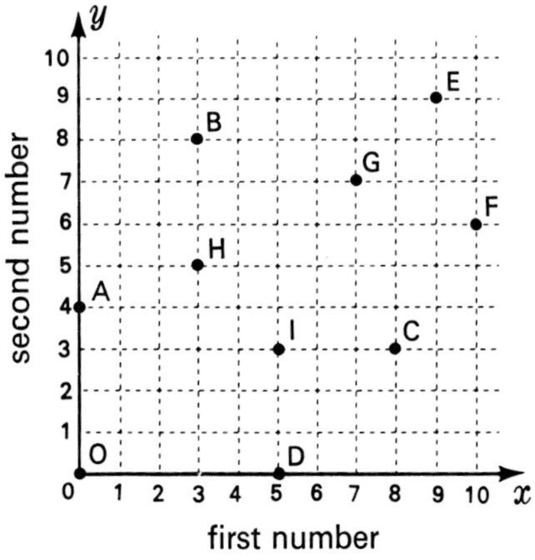

B Graph each set of ordered pairs, using a different pair of number scales for each set.

19.

x	1	2	3	4	5	6
y	4	5	6	7	8	9

20.

x	0	2	4	6	8	10
y	4	3	2	3	4	5

21.

x	0	1	2	3	4	55
y	4	4	4	4	4	4

22.

x	0	1	2	3	4	5
y	0	1	2	3	4	5

23. (0, 5), (1, 4), (2, 3), (3, 2), (4, 1), (5, 0)

24. (3, 0), (3, 1), (3, 2), (3, 3), (3, 4), (3, 5)

25. (1, 2), (2, 3), (3, 4), (3, 5), (4, 6), (5, 7)

26. (1, 1), (2, 4), (3, 1), (4, 4), (5, 1), (6, 4)

C Graph the set of ordered pairs, using a different pair of number scales for each set. Then join the points by line segments in the order listed.

27. (2, 0), (1, 2), (2, 1), (3, 2), (5, 3), (8, 3),
(10, 2), (9, 4), (9, 5), (10, 6), (11, 6), (12, 5),
(15, 4), (12, 4), (11, 3), (12, 2), (12, 1), (11, 0)

28. (3, 0), (2, 2), (5, 2), (5, 8), (8, 3), (6, 2), (11, 2),
(11, 11), (16, 3), (12, 2), (18, 2), (22, 4), (21, 0)

29. Make up your own list of ordered pairs for a picture. Let a friend draw the picture.

Integers and the Coordinate System

In Chapter 6, we graphed integers on a number line. If we use two number lines, called **axes,** we can graph ordered pairs of integers.

coordinate system

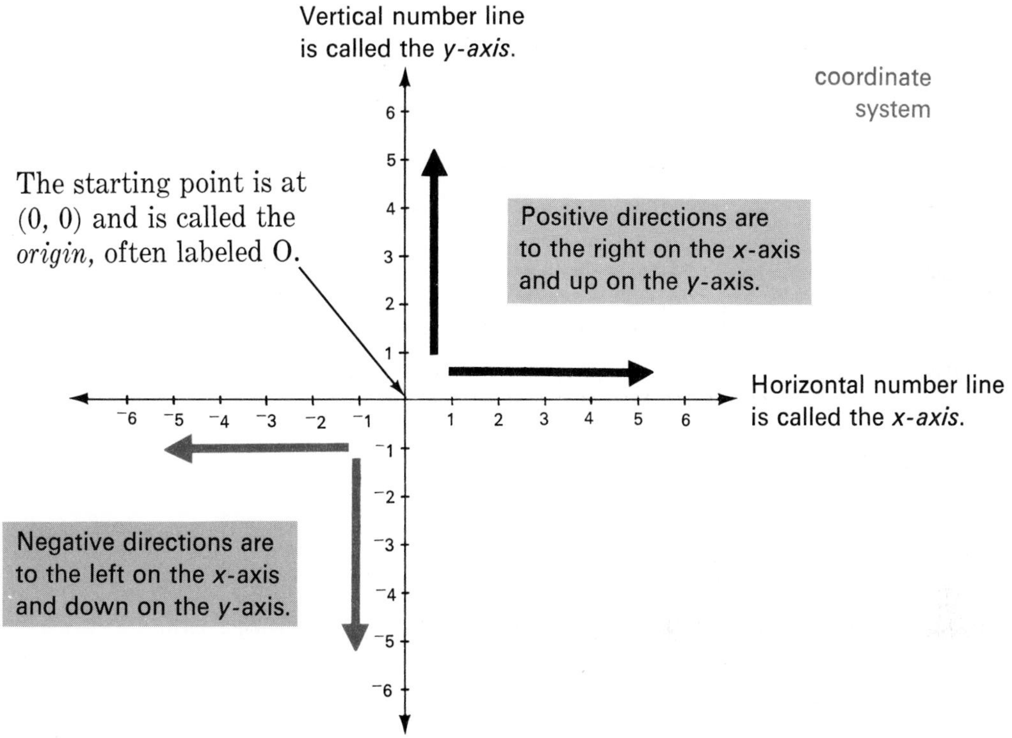

Example 1: Graph (-2, 5) and (5, -2).

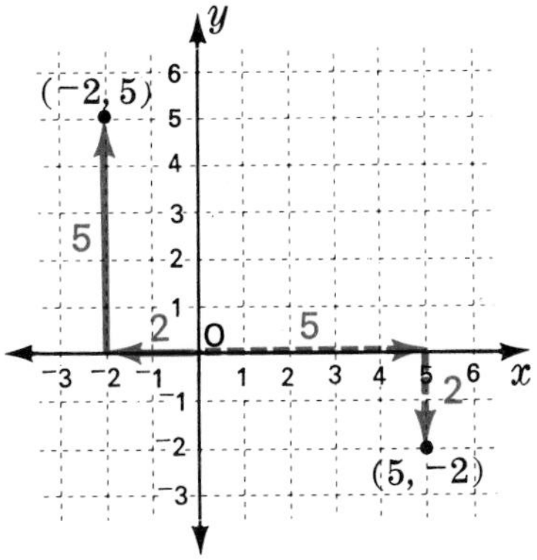

(-2, 5)

Move left 2 units. Then move up 5 units.

(5, -2)

Move right 5 units. Then move down 2 units.

Notice that (-2, 5) and (5, -2) name different points.

The numbers of an ordered pair are called **coordinates.**

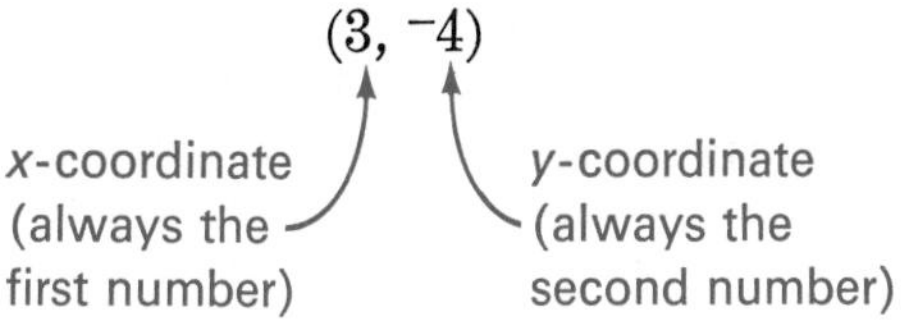

Example 2: Name the coordinates of each point shown on the graph.

Point	*Coordinates*
A	(3, 4)
B	$(^-3, 4)$
C	$(^-3, ^-4)$
D	$(3, ^-4)$
E	(0, 3)
F	(4, 0)
G	$(0, ^-3)$
H	$(^-4, 0)$
O	(0, 0)

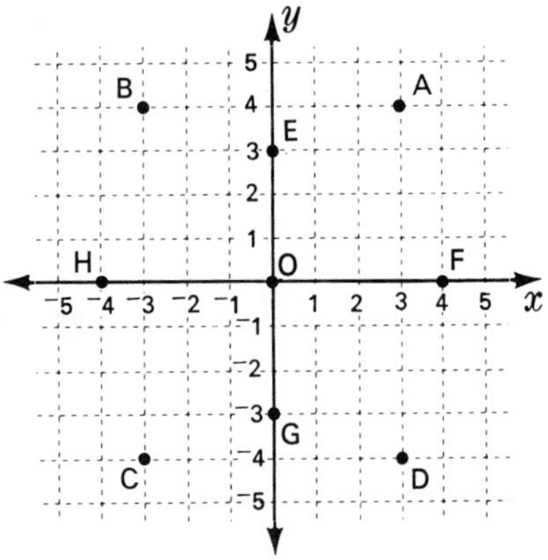

Exercises

A **1.** The positive direction on the x-axis is to the ____.

2. The negative direction on the y-axis is ____.

3. The coordinates of the origin are ____.

4. For (3, 6), the x-coordinate is ____.

Tell the moves you would make to graph each ordered pair.

5. $(1, ^-2)$ **6.** $(^-3, ^-6)$ **7.** (1, 4) **8.** (0, 8)

9. $(^-3, 8)$ **10.** $(10, ^-7)$ **11.** $(^-18, ^-25)$ **12.** (0, 0)

Name the coordinates of each point.

13. A **14.** E **15.** M

16. F **17.** B **18.** J

19. N **20.** G **21.** C

22. H **23.** D **24.** I

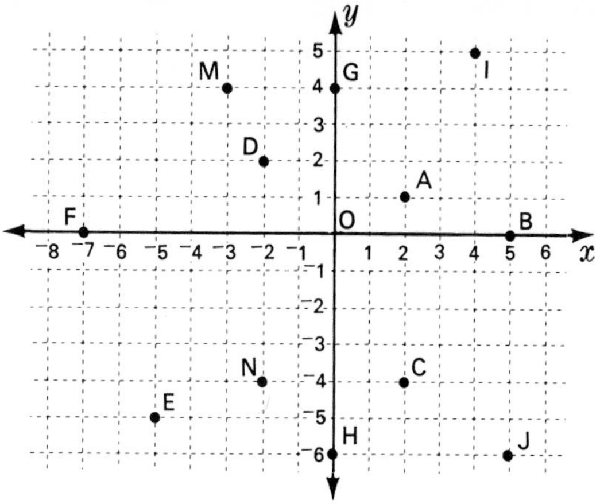

B On graph paper, draw a pair of axes. Then graph the points given below. Label each point with its letter.

25. K(5, 6) **26.** O(0, 0) **27.** R(⁻5, ⁻4)

28. U(⁻8, 2) **29.** L(⁻7, ⁻3) **30.** P(⁻5, 4)

31. S(5, ⁻4) **32.** V(⁻6, 0) **33.** M(6, 0)

34. Q(5, 4) **35.** T(2, 1) **36.** W(5, ⁻2)

C Use the rule to complete the table. Then graph each set of ordered pairs on its own pair of axes.

37. $y = 6x$

x-coordinate	⁻3	⁻2	⁻1	0	1	2	3	4
y-coordinate	⁻18							

38. $y = 2x - 3$

x-coordinate	⁻3	⁻2	⁻1	0	1	2	3	4
y-coordinate								

39. $y = {}^{-}4x$

x-coordinate	⁻3	⁻2	⁻1	0	1	2	3	4
y-coordinate								

40. $y = {}^{-}3x + 8$

x-coordinate	⁻4	⁻2	0	2	4	6	8	10
y-coordinate								

8.4 Drawing Line Graphs

A pair of axes can be used to graph many things. For example, Elizabeth kept the following record of a bicycle trip.

hour of the trip	0	1	2	3	4	5	6
number of miles traveled in the hour	0	2	5	1	3	4	2

Shawn Walker/Taurus Photos

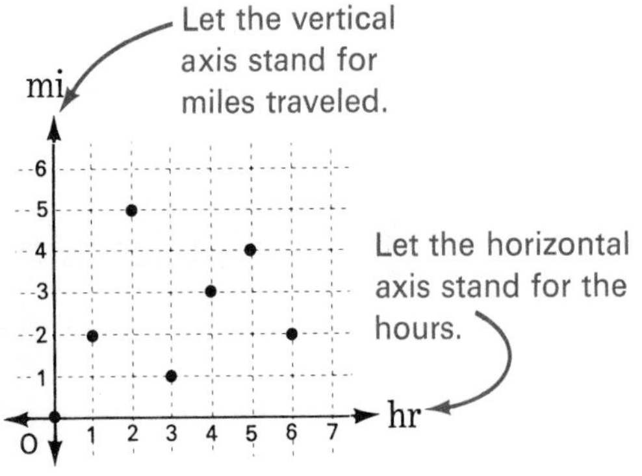

figure 1

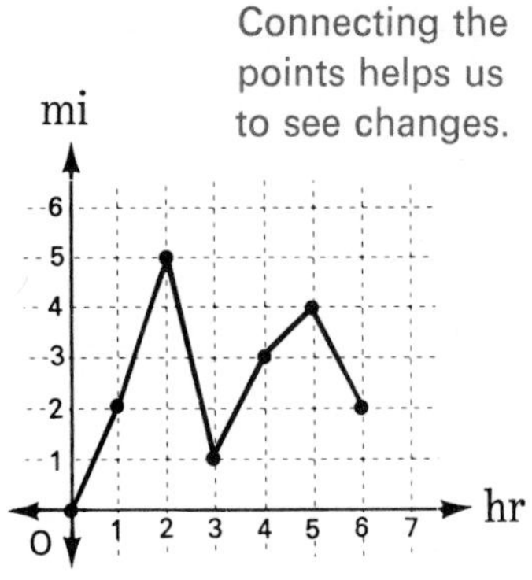

figure 2

The graph in figure 2 is called a *line graph.*

Example 1: Draw a line graph for the table below.

meters	0	1	2	3	4	5	6	7
centimeters	0	100	200	300	400	500	600	700

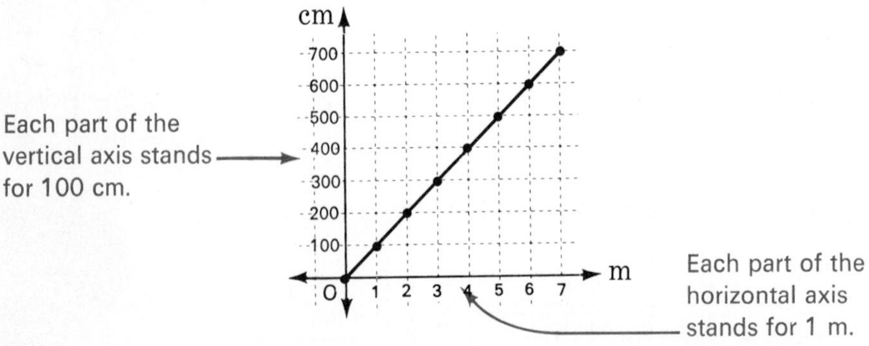

Example 2: Draw a line graph for each table.

a.

time (hr)	0	2	4	6	8	10	12
temp. (°C)	−6	−2	1	5	6	3	2

b.

x	0	0.1	0.2	0.3	0.5	0.7	0.9
y	0	10	20	30	50	70	90

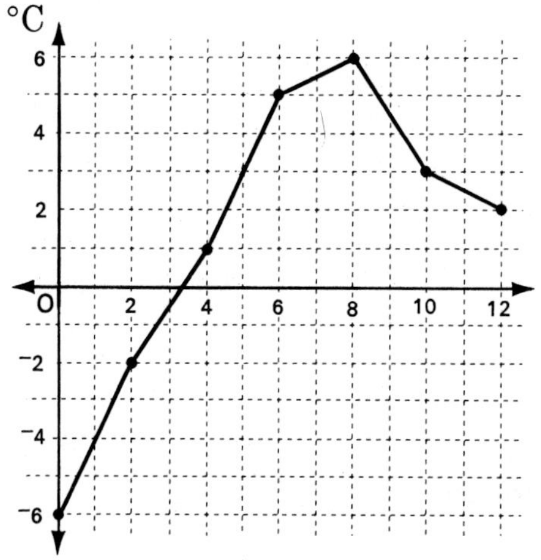

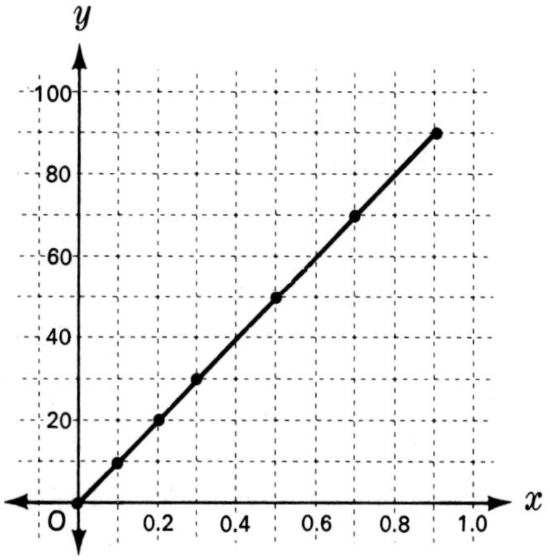

Exercises

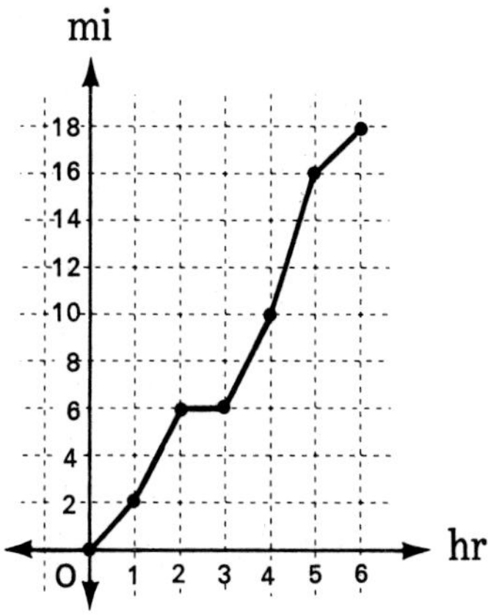

[A] **1.** The graph at left is called a ____ graph.

2. What does each part of the horizontal axis stand for?

3. What does each part of the vertical axis stand for?

4. Complete the table from the graph at left.

hours	0	1	2	3	4	5	6
miles	0	2	6	?	?	?	?

[B] Draw a line graph for each table.

5.

x	0	1	2	3	4	5	6	7
y	0	5	7	6	9	3	1	1

6.

x	−3	−2	−1	0	1	2	3
y	9	4	1	0	1	4	9

7.

ft	0	1	2	3	4	5	6	7
in.	0	12	24	36	48	60	72	84

8.

min	0	60	120	180	240	300	360	420
hr	0	1	2	3	4	5	6	7

9.

cm	0	1	2	3	4	5	6	7
approx. in.	0	0.4	0.8	1.2	1.6	2.0	2.4	2.8

10.

km	0	1	2	3	4	5	6	7
approx. mi	0	0.6	1.2	1.8	2.4	3.0	3.6	4.2

11.

pounds bought	1	2	3	4	5	6	7
price per lb ($)	5	5	4	4	3	3	3

12.

weight of object on moon (lb)	0	5	10	15	20	25	30
weight of object on earth (lb)	0	30	60	90	120	150	180

13.

age of a car (yr)	0	1	2	3	4	5
change in value ($)	0	−900	−1200	−1600	−1800	−2000

14.

snowfall (in.)	0	2	4	6	8	10	12	14
equivalent rainfall (in.)	0	0.2	0.4	0.6	0.8	1.0	1.2	1.4

15.

time (hr)	0	1	2	3	4	5	6	7
temp. (°C)	−10	−7	−2	4	5	2	−1	−5

16.

price ($)	0	5	10	15	20	25	30	35
discount ($)	0	−1	−2	−3	−4	−5	−6	−7

C The reported temperature on two different days may have been the same, but you felt colder on one day than you did on the other. This is partly because of the wind. For example, if the reported temperature is 30 °F and the wind speed is 10 mph, then it feels like a reported temperature of 16 °F on a calm day (no wind). 16 °F is called the *windchill*. Draw a line graph for each table below.

17. Windchill for a reported temperature of 30 °F.

wind speed (mph)	0	5	10	15	20	25	30	35	40	45
windchill (°F)	30	27	16	9	4	1	−2	−4	−5	−6

18. Windchill for a reported temperature of 0 °F.

wind speed (mph)	0	5	10	15	20	25	30	35	40	45
windchill (°F)	0	−5	−22	−31	−39	−44	−49	−52	−53	−54

19. Use the rule for changing Celsius temperatures to Fahrenheit temperatures to complete the table below. Then draw a line graph.

degrees Fahrenheit → F ; degrees Celsius → C

$$F = \frac{9C}{5} + 32$$

Example: Change −25 °C to degrees Fahrenheit.

$$F = \frac{9C}{5} + 32$$

$$F = \frac{9(\overset{-5}{\cancel{-25}})}{\underset{1}{\cancel{5}}} + 32$$

$$F = -45 + 32$$

$$F = -13$$

°C	−25	−20	−15	−10	−5	0	5	10	15	20	25
°F	−13										

8.5 Functions

$$a = b - 2$$

- a: actual speed
- b: speed of boat (in still water)
- 2: speed of current

speed of boat (b)	4	5	6	7	8	9
actual speed (a)	2	3	4	5	6	7

The ordered pairs in the table can be written as

$$(4, 2), (5, 3), (6, 4), (7, 5), (8, 6), (9, 7).$$

Are any values of b (*first numbers*) ever repeated?

For every value of b, there is only one value of a. So, no two ordered pairs have the same first number. Such a set of ordered pairs is called a *function.*

> A **function** is a set of ordered pairs whose first numbers are all different.

For this number of dollars	2	4	5	6	7	7	8
You can use it for this number of hours	1	2	3	4	5	6	7

The ordered pairs in the table can be written as

$$(2, 1), (4, 2), (5, 3), (6, 4), (7, 5), (7, 6), (8, 7).$$

This set of ordered pairs is *not* a function. Why? Because the first numbers of the ordered pairs are not all different. The ordered pairs (7, 5) and (7, 6) have the *same* first number.

Example 1: Is (2, 3), (3, 4), (3, 5), (4, 6) a function?

(2, 3), (3, 4), (3, 5), (4, 6)

NO. There are two ordered pairs with the same first number.

Example 2: Is (4, 6), (5, 6), (6, 6), (7, 6) a function?

YES. Every first number is different.

Let's look at the graph of the function.

Every first number is different. So the graph of a function *never* has one point directly above another.

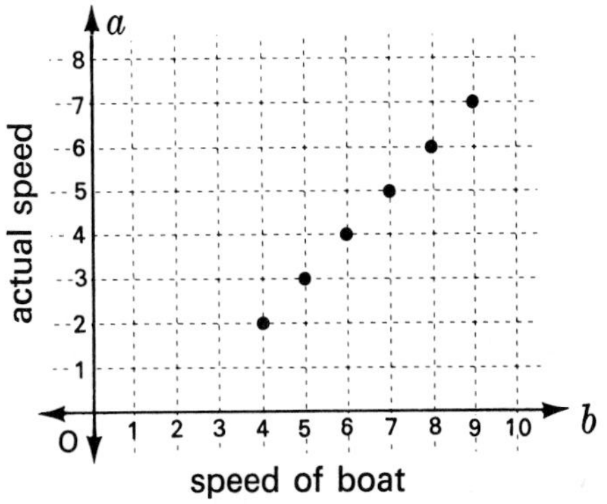

Example 3: Is the following the graph of a function?

NO. One point is directly above another.

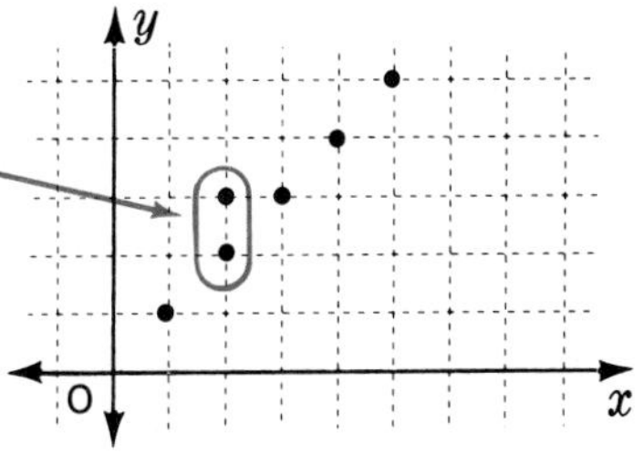

Example 4: Is the following the graph of a function?

YES. No point is directly above another.

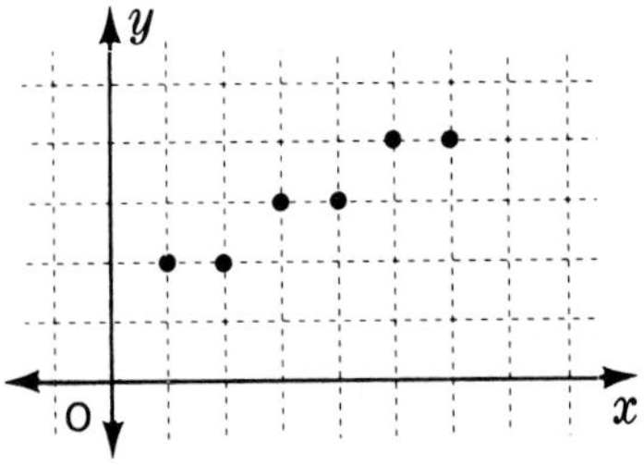

Exercises

A Is each set of ordered pairs a function? If not, tell why not.

1. (7, 7), (8, 6), (9, 5), (10, 4), (11, 3)

2. (5, 0), (6, 1), (7, 2), (7, 3), (8, 4)

3.

first number	2	4	6	8	10
second number	3	5	5	7	9

4.

first number	1	3	5	7	9
second number	$^-1$	$^-9$	$^-25$	$^-49$	$^-81$

Is each graph the graph of a function? If not, tell why not.

5.

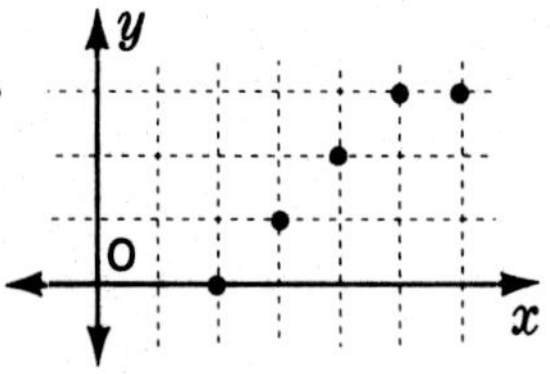

6.

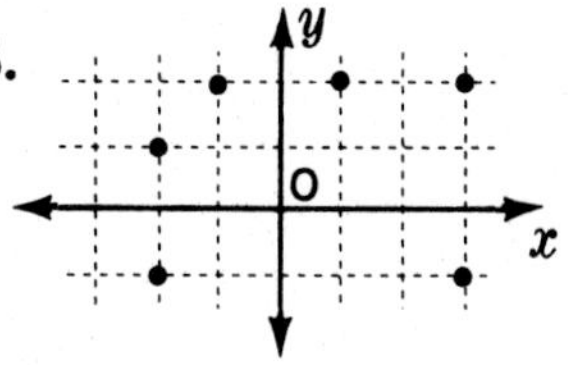

B Tell whether each set of ordered pairs is a function.

7. (1, 6), (2, 7), (3, 8), (4, 9), (5, 10)

8. (5, 7), (5, 8), (6, 9), (7, 10), (8, 11)

9. ($^-3$, $^-2$), ($^-2$, $^-1$), ($^-3$, 0), ($^-3$, 1), ($^-4$, 2)

10.

first number	4	5	6	7	8
second number	2	2	2	2	2

11.

first number	1	2	3	4	5
second number	2	4	6	8	10

12.

first number	0	1	2	3	4
second number	0	$^-1$	$^-2$	$^-3$	$^-4$

Tell whether each graph is the graph of a function.

13.

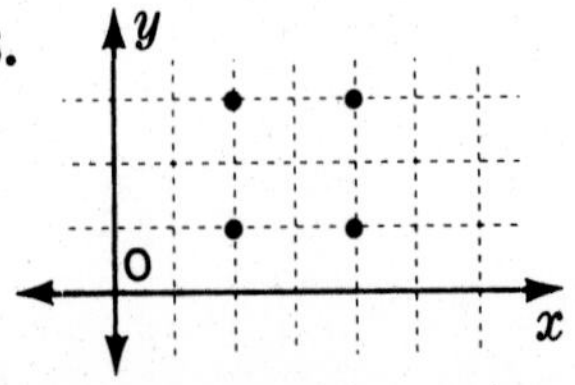

14.

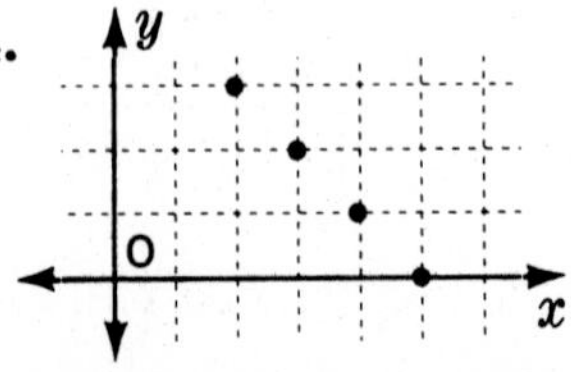

15.

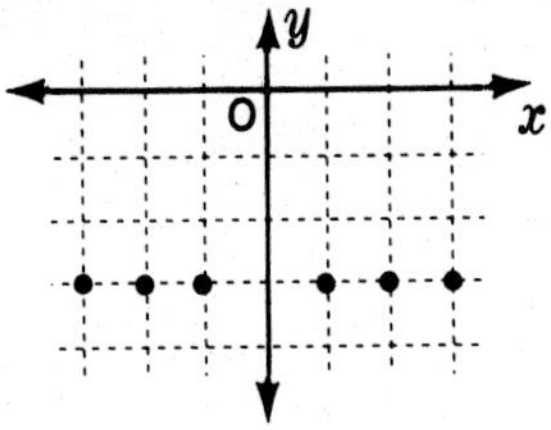

16.

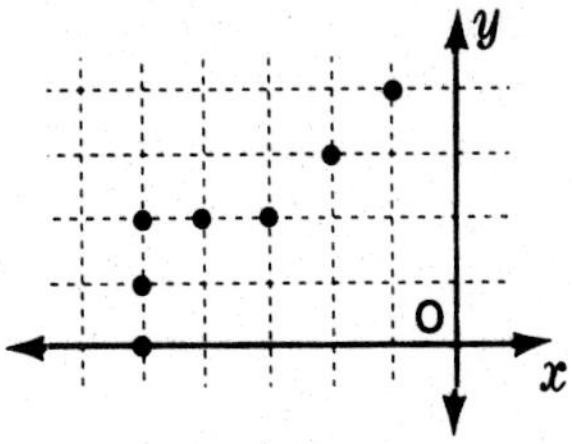

17.

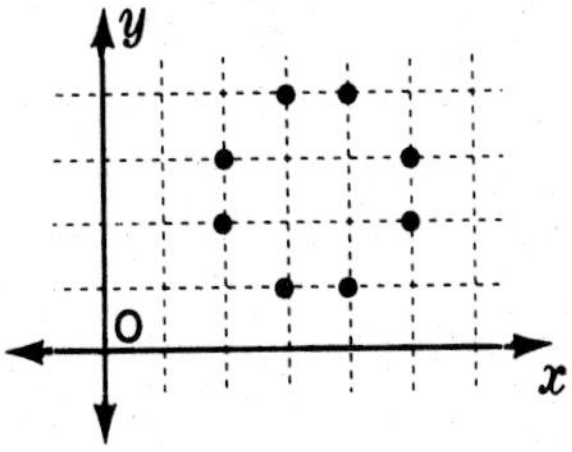

18.

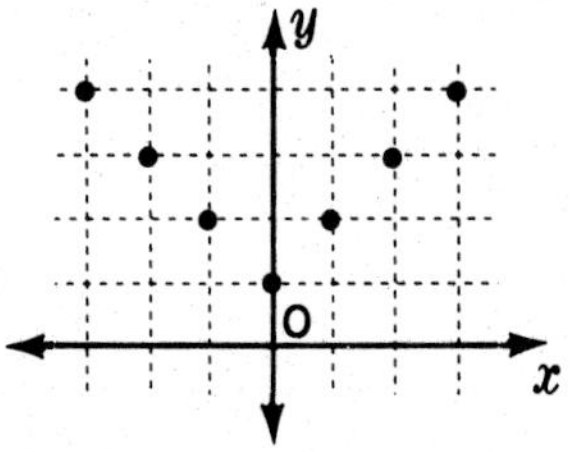

C Make a table of 6 ordered pairs for each rule. Then tell whether each rule describes a function.

19. Multiply the first number by itself to get the second number.

20. The first number is always 1. The second number can be any whole number.

21. The first number can be any whole number. The second number is always 3.

22. The second number is the same as the first number.

Quick Quiz
Sections 8.1 to 8.5

1. Use the rule to complete the table.

$y = 3x + 1$

x	0	1	2	3	4	5	6
y							

2. Name the coordinates of each point on the graph at the right.

a. A **b.** B **c.** C **d.** D

Ex. 2

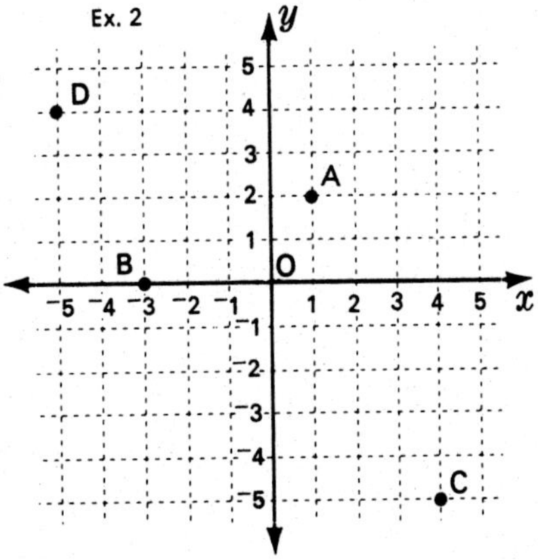

3. Draw a line graph for the table.

x	0	1	2	3	4	5	6	7	8
y	−5	−2	0	3	5	4	1	−3	−6

4. Is the set of ordered pairs in Exercise 3 a function?

8.6 Using Functions

Erich Bach/Photri

Jim heard the thunder 4 seconds after he saw the lightning. He wondered how far away the lightning was.

Sound travels about 1100 feet per second through air. So the following equation shows how *distance* and *time* are related.

distance (ft) time (sec)

$$d = 1100\,t$$

Let's solve Jim's problem.

$$d = 1100t$$
$$= 1100\,(4) \quad \text{Replace } t \text{ with 4.}$$
$$= 4400$$

The lightning was 4400 feet away.

Let's make a table and a graph for $d = 1100t$.

t	d
0	0
1	1100
2	2200
3	3300
4	4400
5	5500
6	6600

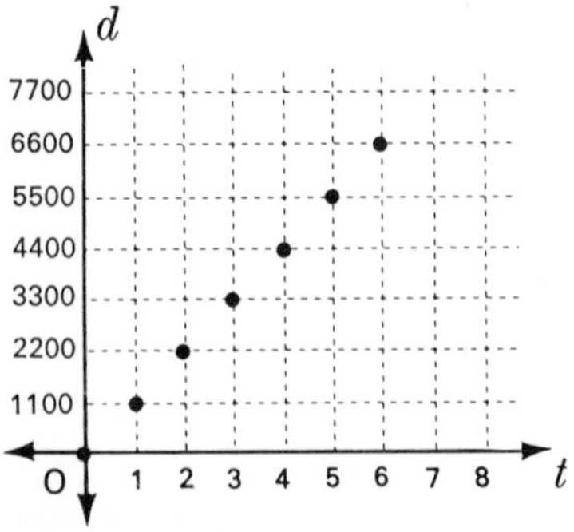

Are any values of t repeated in the table?

Suppose you try 3 again. Would d still be 3300?

Does the value of d depend on the value of t?

Is the graph the graph of a function?

Such a time-distance relationship is a function. Other functions from nature and everyday life are used in the exercises.

Exercises

A Answer these questions.

1. Jim saw lightning strike a tree that was 5500 feet away. How long after that did he hear the noise? (See the table and graph on page 254.)

2. Light travels about 186,000 miles per second. Give an equation that tells the distance d that light will travel in t seconds.

3. How can you find the number of seconds it takes for light to travel from the sun to the earth?

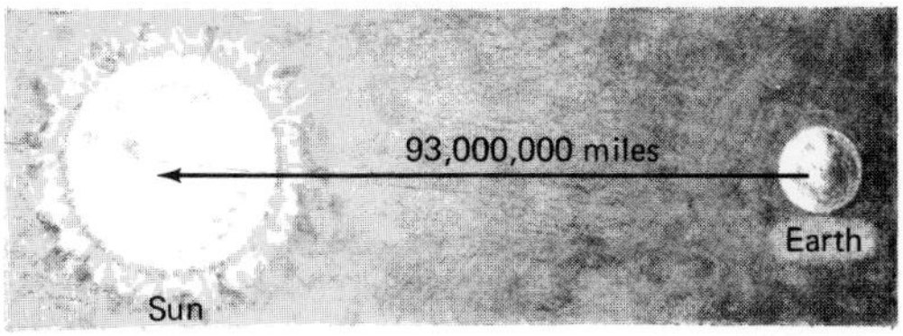

B Solve these problems.

speed of wind directly against plane

$$g = a - 34$$

ground speed (speed over ground) — g

airspeed (speed through the air) — a

4. If the plane's airspeed is 140 mph, what is its ground speed?

5. To be on time, the plane must make a ground speed of 126 mph. At what airspeed should it fly?

Courtesy Boeing

speed of wind directly behind plane

$$g = a + 45$$

ground speed (speed over ground)

airspeed (speed through the air)

6. To be on time, a passenger jet must make a ground speed of 520 mph. At what airspeed should it fly?

7. If the passenger jet's airspeed is 465 mph, what is its ground speed?

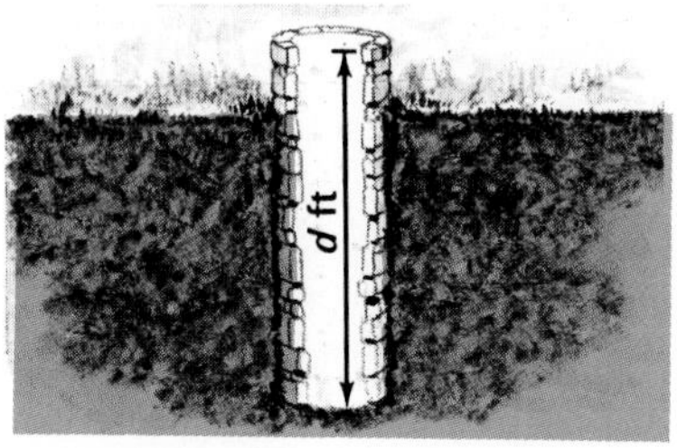

Free-falling object

$$d = 16t^2$$

distance (ft)

time (sec)

8. Tom dropped a stone in the well. It hit bottom in 2 seconds. How deep was the well?

9. A helicopter dropped a life raft. It hit the water in 10 seconds. How high was the helicopter?

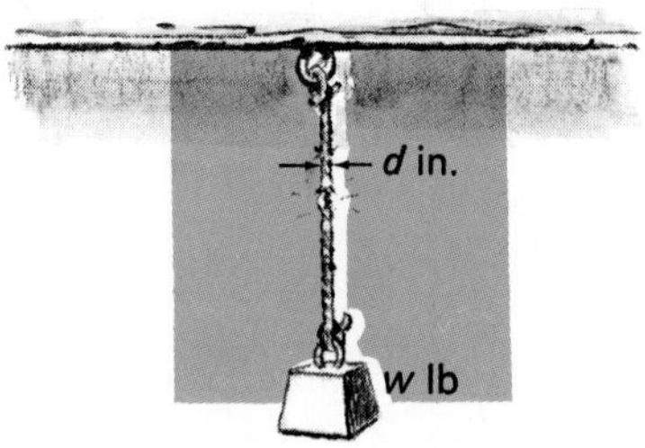

Breaking strength of a certain kind of rope

$$w = 5000d(d + 1)$$

weight (lb)

diameter of rope (in.)

10. At what weight would a 1-inch rope break?

11. At what weight would a 2-inch rope break?

degrees Celsius → $C = \frac{5(F - 32)}{9}$ ← degrees Fahrenheit

$$C = \frac{5(F - 32)}{9}$$

12. What is the temperature in degrees Celsius if the Fahrenheit temperature is $^{-}22°$?

13. What is the temperature in degrees Fahrenheit if the Celsius temperature is $^{-}40°$?

C 14. To see n miles out to sea, you must be h feet above sea level, where $h = \frac{2n^2}{3}$. How tall should the lighthouse be if you are to see 9 miles out to sea?

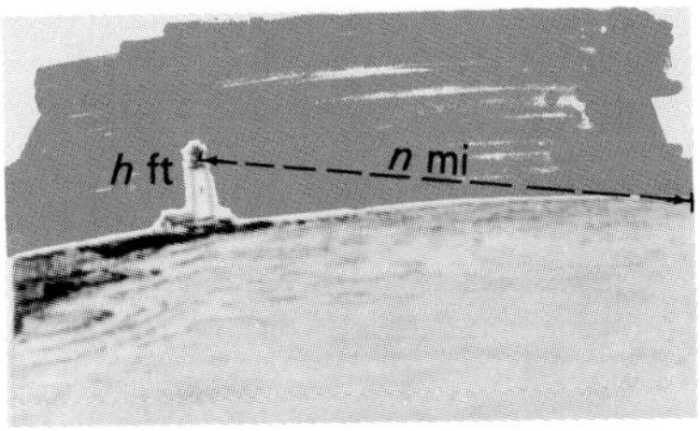

15. During a search at sea, a helicopter crew wanted to see at least 18 miles. They must be at least how high?

16. A sonar set measures the time it takes for sound waves to reach an object and return. Sound travels through water about 4800 feet per second.

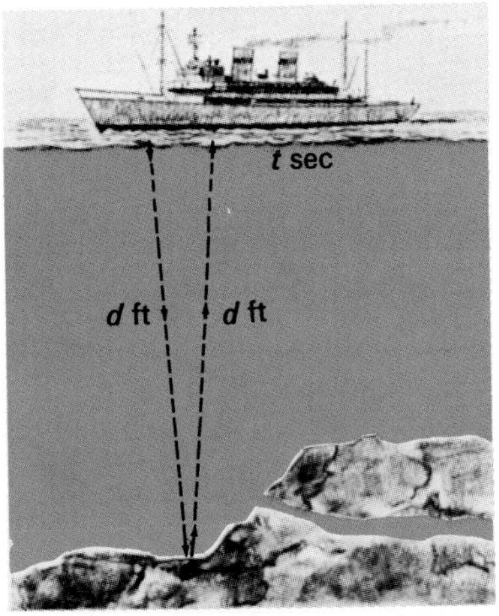

distance (ship to object in feet) → d; time in seconds for "round trip" of sound waves → t

$$d = \frac{4800t}{2}$$

or

$$d = 2400t$$

It took 3 seconds for the sound waves to reach the ocean floor and return. How deep is the ocean at that point?

17. A submarine was 4800 feet from the ship. How long did it take the sound waves to reach the submarine and return?

8.7 Using Graphs to Enlarge and Reduce

Herb Taylor, Jr.

A lab worker sometimes studies enlarged pictures of germs.

Feminist Resources for Equal Education

A construction worker or drafter often uses reduced drawings of buildings.

Example 1: Make a 1-to-2 enlargement of the square.

"1-to-2 enlargement" means that all measurements of the new square will be 2 times those of the original square.

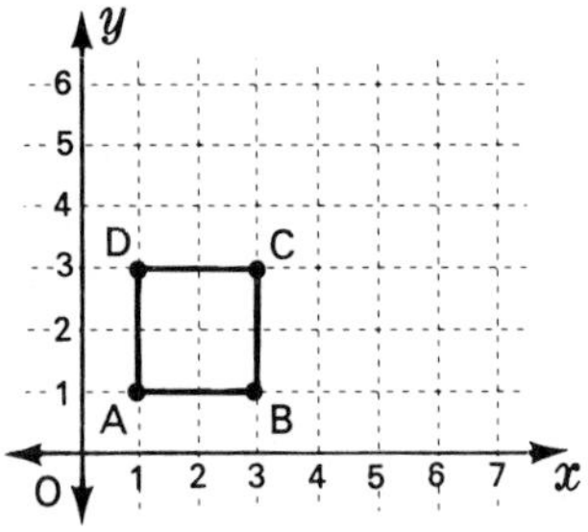

Step 1: For a 1-to-2 enlargement, multiply both numbers in each original ordered pair by 2.

Point / *Original ordered pair*	*Point* / *New ordered pair*
A(1, 1)	A′(2, 2)
B(3, 1)	B′(6, 2)
C(3, 3)	C′(6, 6)
D(1, 3)	D′(2, 6)

A′ is read *A prime*. Using A′ rather than some other letter makes it easy to see that point A′ corresponds to point A.

Step 2: Graph the new ordered pairs. Draw the new square.

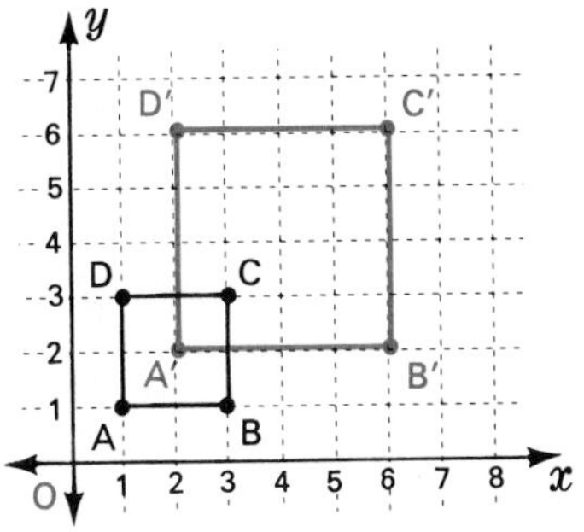

Example 2: Make a 1-to-3 reduction of the triangle.

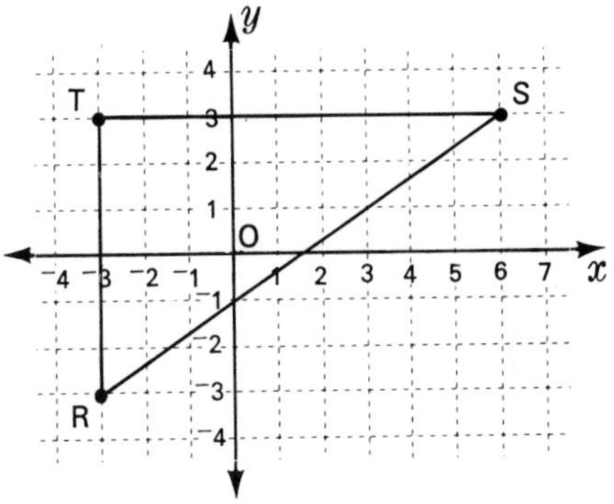

For a 1-to-3 reduction, divide both numbers in each original ordered pair by 3.

Original triangle	*New triangle*
R(⁻3, ⁻3)	R′(⁻1, ⁻1)
S(6, 3)	S′(2, 1)
T(⁻3, 3)	T′(⁻1, 1)

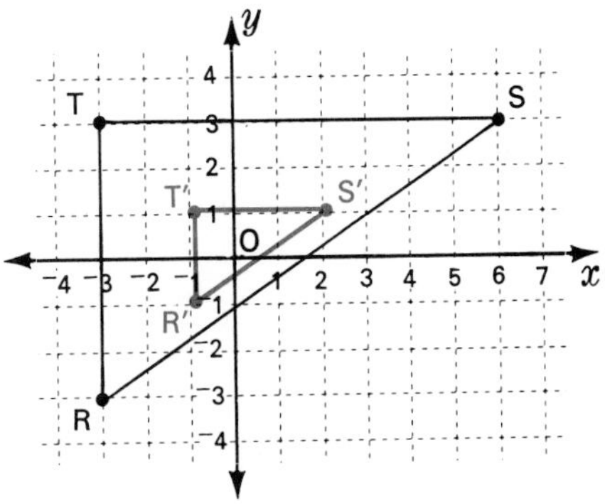

Exercises

A What would you do with the numbers in each ordered pair to make each of the following?

1. a 1-to-4 enlargement

2. a 1-to-10 enlargement

3. a 1-to-2 reduction

4. a 1-to-5 reduction

B Copy and graph the following.

5. a 1-to-3 enlargement of

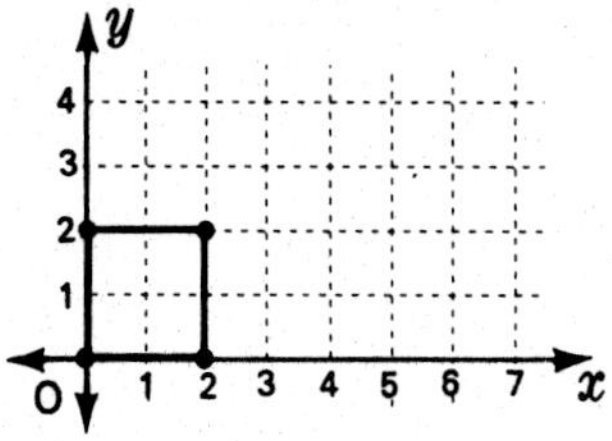

6. a 1-to-5 enlargement of

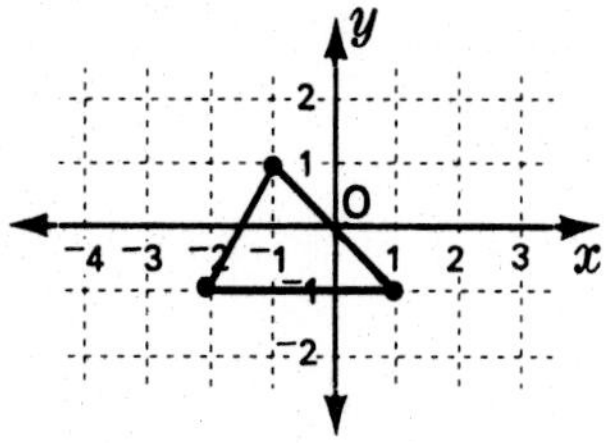

7. a 1-to-2 reduction of

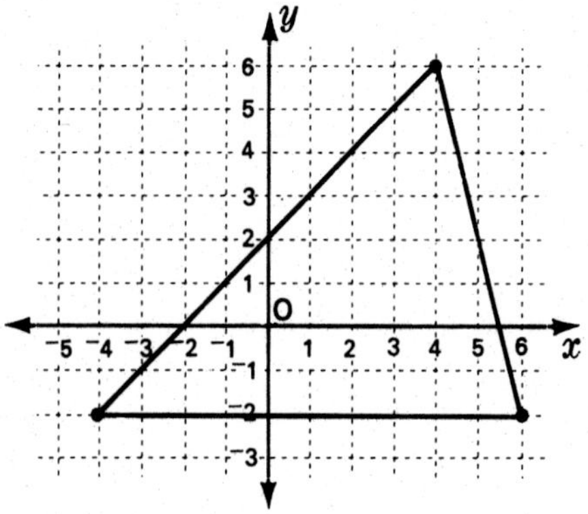

8. a 1-to-4 reduction of

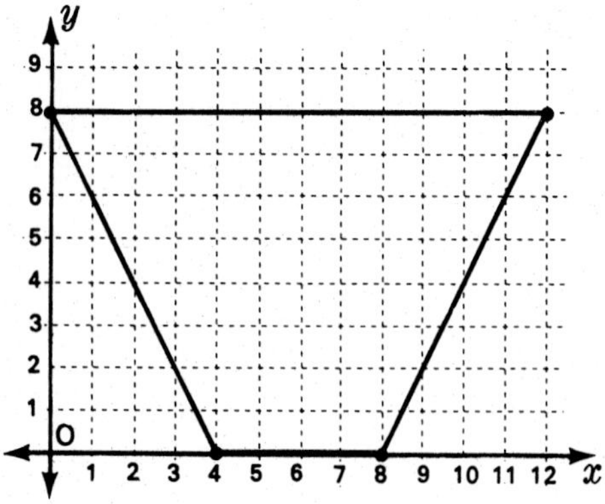

C Complete each set of ordered pairs. Graph all four triangles on the same pair of axes.

9.

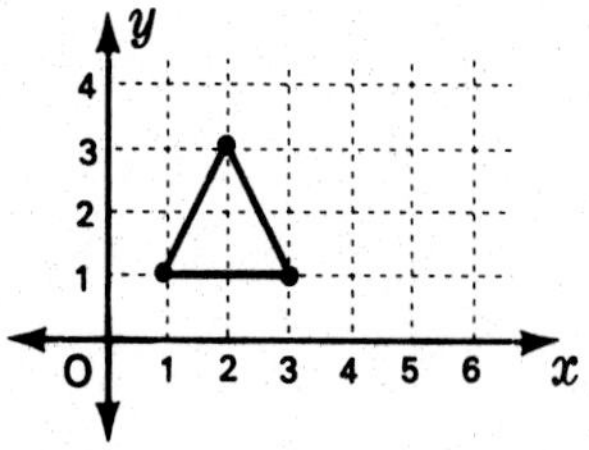

Original ordered pair	Multiply first number by 4.	Multiply second number by 4.	Multiply both numbers by 4.
(1, 1)	(4, 1)	(1, 4)	(4, 4)
(3, 1)	(____, 1)	(3, ____)	(____, ____)
(2, 3)	(____, 3)	(2, ____)	(____, ____)

a. How does multiplying only the first numbers change the shape of a figure?

b. How does multiplying only the second numbers change the shape of a figure?

c. How does multiplying both numbers change the shape of a figure?

Complete each set of ordered pairs. Graph all four triangles on the same pair of axes.

10.

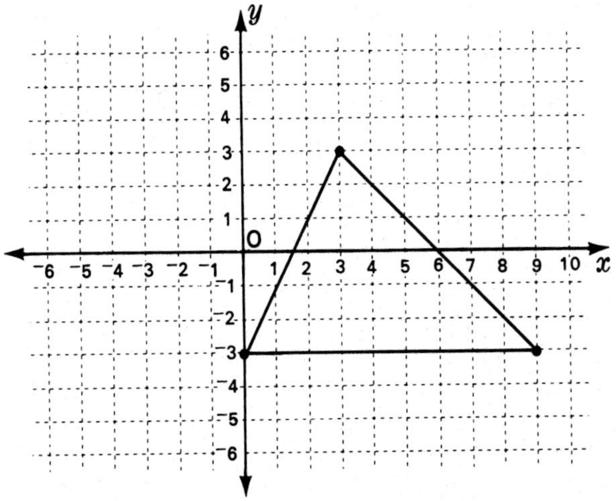

Original ordered pair	Divide first number by 3.	Divide second number by 3.	Divide both numbers by 3.
(0, ⁻3)	(0, ⁻3)	(0, ⁻1)	(0, ⁻1)
(9, ⁻3)	(___, ⁻3)	(9, ___)	(___, ___)
(3, 3)	(___, 3)	(3, ___)	(___, ___)

a. How does dividing only the first numbers change the shape of a figure?

b. How does dividing only the second numbers change the shape of a figure?

c. How does dividing both numbers change the shape of a figure?

8.8 Sliding by Graphing

After Image/Herbeck

You can slide or move a drawing by graphing.

Example 1: Slide the triangle 5 units to the right.

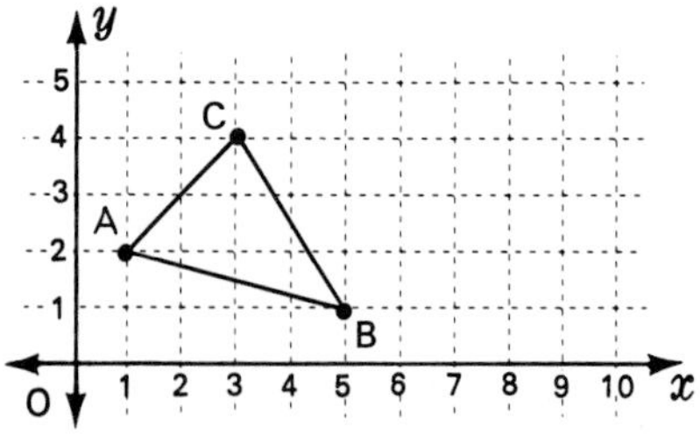

Step 1: To slide a drawing 5 units to the right, add 5 to the first number in each ordered pair.

Point / *Original ordered pair*	*Point* / *New ordered pair*
A(1, 2)	A′(6, 2)
B(5, 1)	B′(10, 1)
C(3, 4)	C′(8, 4)

Step 2: Graph the new ordered pairs. Draw the new triangle.

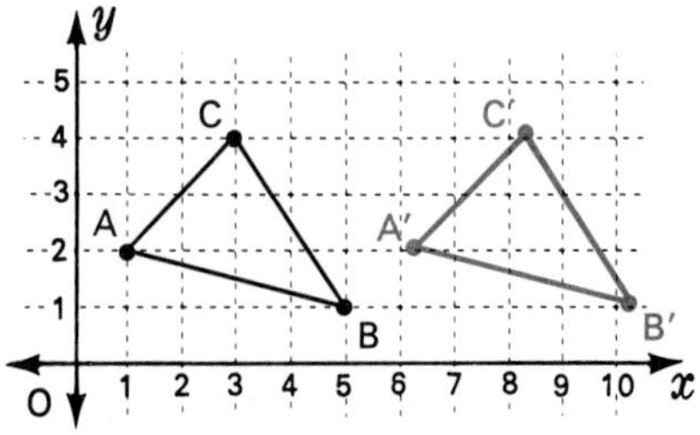

How would you slide a drawing *to the left* by graphing?

Example 2: Slide the figure 4 units down.

To slide a figure 4 units down, subtract 4 from the second number in each ordered pair.

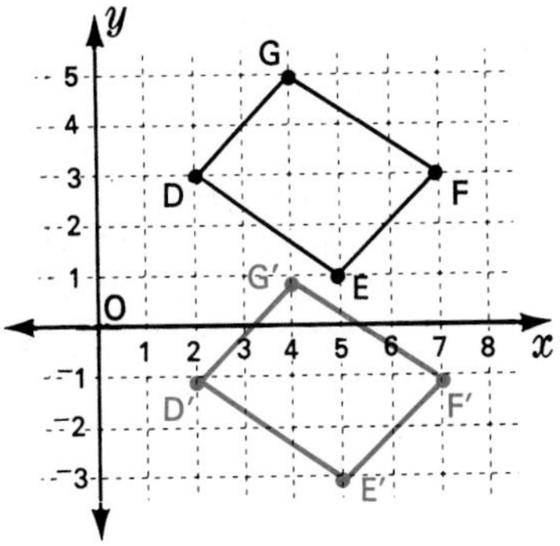

Original figure	*New figure*
D(2, 3)	D′(2, $^-1$)
E(5, 1)	E′(5, $^-3$)
F(7, 3)	F′(7, $^-1$)
G(4, 5)	G′(4, 1)

How would you slide a figure *up* by graphing?

Exercises

A What would you do with the numbers in each ordered pair to make the following slides?

1. 6 units to the right

2. 5 units down

3. 3 units to the left

4. 7 units up

5. 2 units to the right and 5 units up

6. 4 units down and 6 units to the left

B Copy and make the following slides by graphing.

7. 3 units to the right

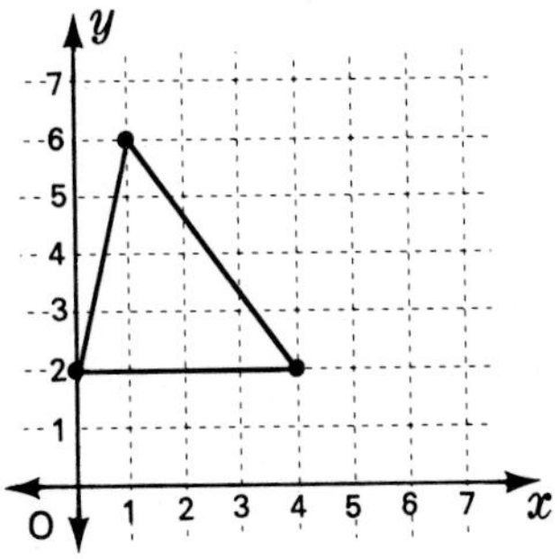

8. 5 units to the left

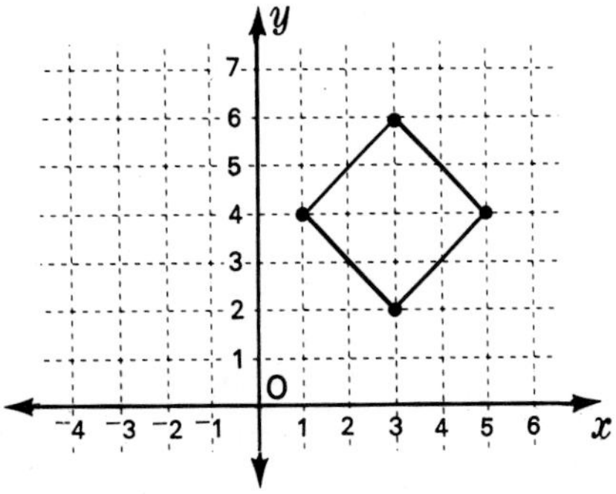

9. 4 units down

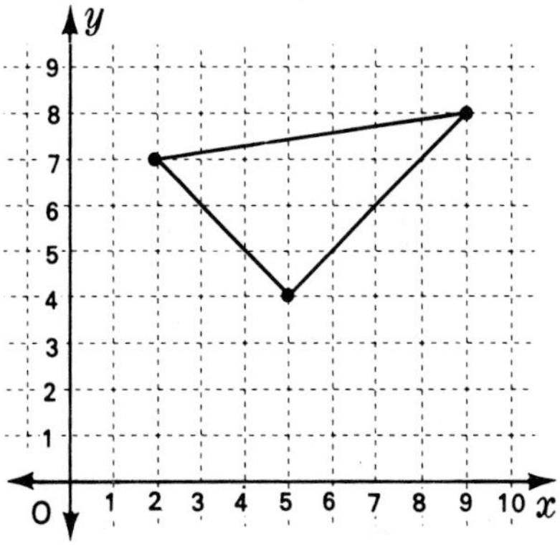

10. 6 units up

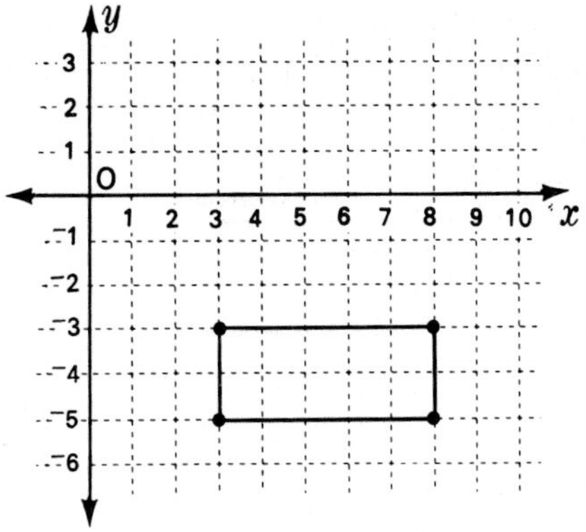

11. 4 units to the right
and 2 units down

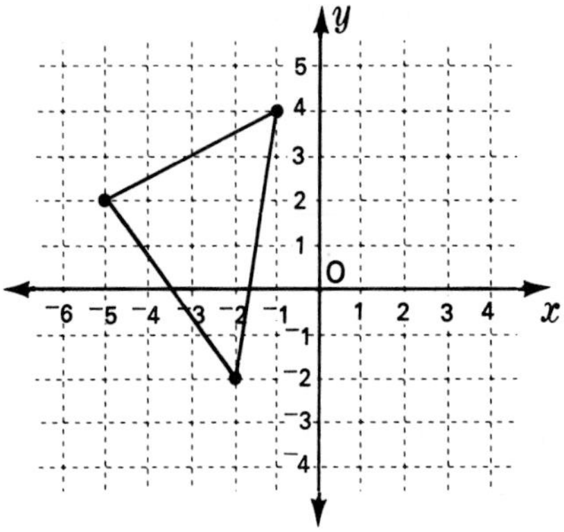

12. 5 units up and
3 units to the left

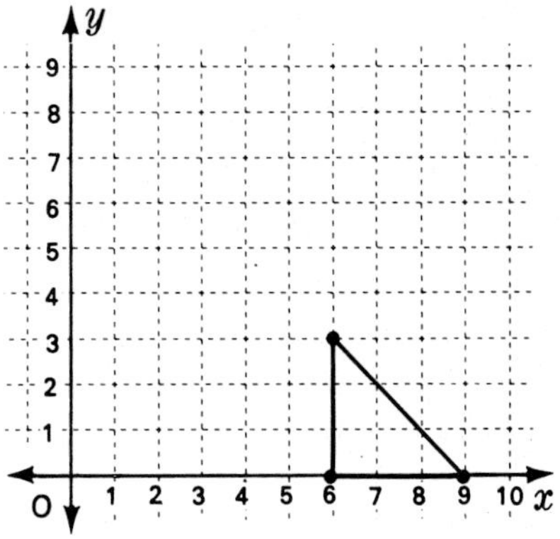

C Copy and graph the following.

13. a 1-to-3 enlargement,
then a slide 4 units
to the right

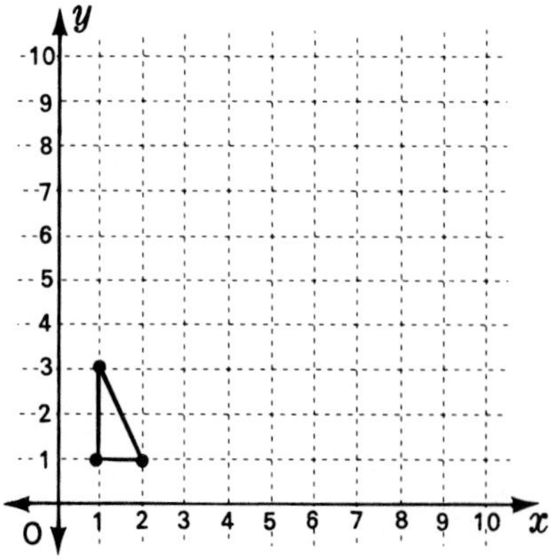

14. a slide 5 units down,
then a 1-to-2 reduction

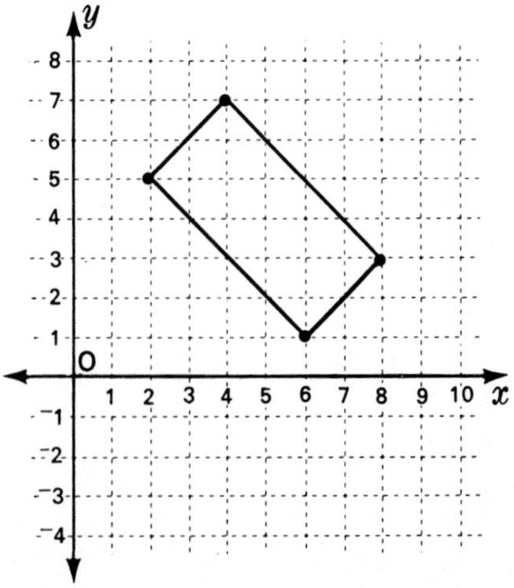

Terms and Symbols Review

Which term best completes each sentence?

a. x-axis
b. y-axis
c. origin
d. ordered pair
e. point
f. to the right
g. up
h. coordinates
i. (5, 6), (7, 8), (9, 8)
j. (4, $^-3$), ($^-4$, 3), (4, 2)

1. Two numbers listed in a certain order are a(n) ____.
2. When you draw a pair of axes, the horizontal number line is the ____.
3. The point at (0, 0) is the ____.
4. The numbers 3 and 5 are the ____ of the point at (3, 5).
5. The graph of (3, 5) is a(n) ____.
6. The positive direction on the y-axis is ____.
7. An example of a set of ordered pairs that is a function is ____.

Chapter 8 Review

Use the rule to complete each table. 8.1

1. $y = 2x + 5$

x	0	1	2	3	4	5
y						

2. $y = \frac{x}{3} - 1$

x	3	6	9	12	15	18
y						

Graph each set of ordered pairs on a different pair of axes.

8.2 **3.** (1, 3), (2, 4), (3, 5), (4, 6), (4, 7)

4.

x	0	1	2	3	4	5
y	3	4	5	2	3	1

8.3

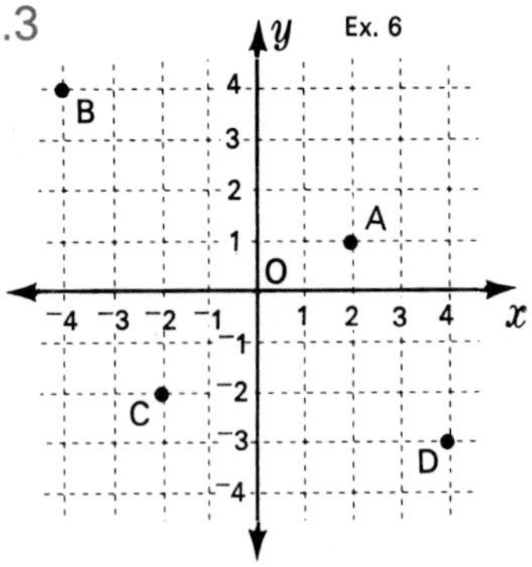

5. What moves would you make to graph $(5, {}^-6)$?

6. Name the coordinates of each point on the graph at the right.

a. A **b.** B **c.** C **d.** D

7. Draw a coordinate system on graph paper. Then graph the following points:

W(0, 0) X$({}^-2, {}^-1)$ Y(5, 5) Z$(1, {}^-2)$

8.4 Draw a line graph for each table.

8.

x	0	2	4	6	8	10
y	$^-5$	$^-4$	$^-3$	$^-2$	$^-1$	0

9.

yd	0	1	2	3	4	5	6
ft	0	3	6	9	12	15	18

8.5 Is each set of ordered pairs a function?

10. (0, 2), (1, 2), (2, 4), (3, 4), (4, 5)

11. (3, 4), (3, 5), (4, 6), (5, 7), (6, 8)

Tell whether each graph is the graph of a function.

12.

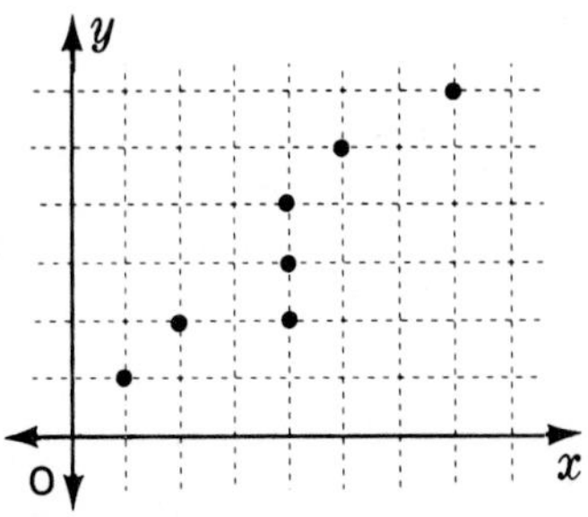

13.

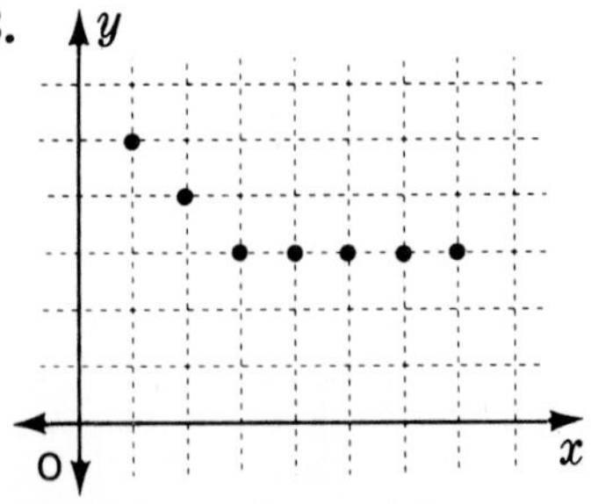

Solve each problem. 8.6

14. A plane's airspeed (a) is 135 mph, and the speed of the wind directly against the plane is 34 mph. What is the plane's ground speed (g)? $g = a - 34$

15. To be on time, a passenger jet must make a ground speed (g) of 515 mph. If the speed of the wind directly behind the plane is 45 mph, at what airspeed should the plane fly? $g = a + 45$

Copy and graph the following. 8.7

16. a 1-to-4 enlargement of

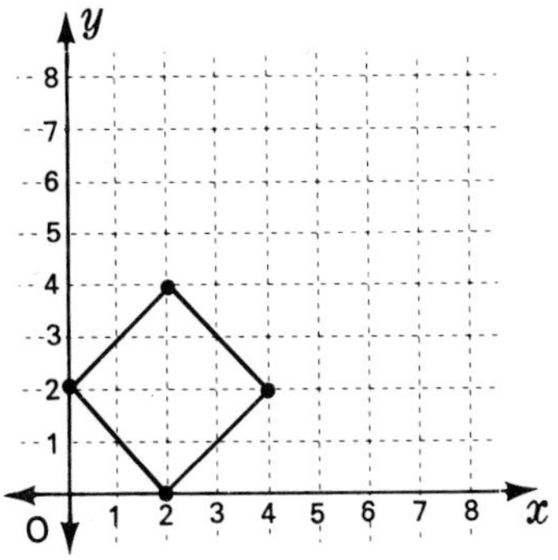

17. a 1-to-3 reduction of

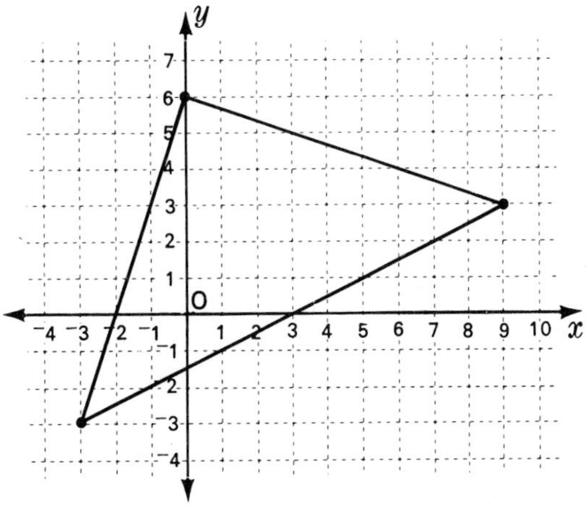

Copy and make the following slides by graphing. 8.8

18. 4 units up

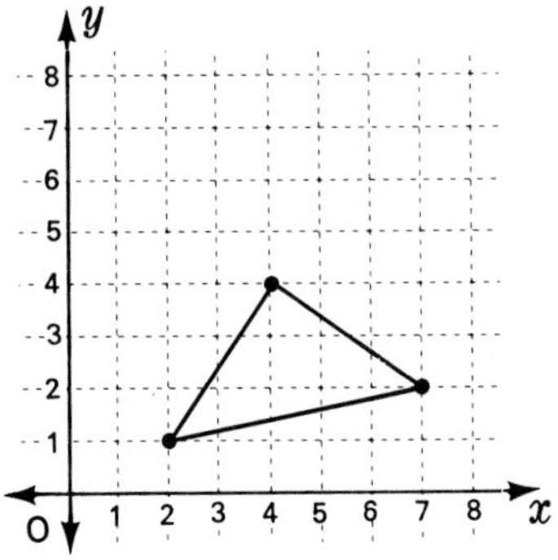

19. 5 units to the right

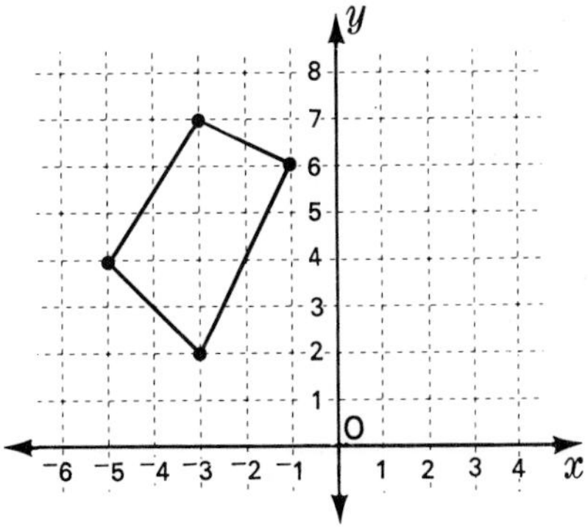

Chapter 8 Test

Use the rule to complete the ordered pairs. *x* is given first.

1. $y = 4x - 3$

x	2	3	4	5	6	7
y						

2. $y = x + 6$

(0, __), (1, __), (3, __), (4, __)

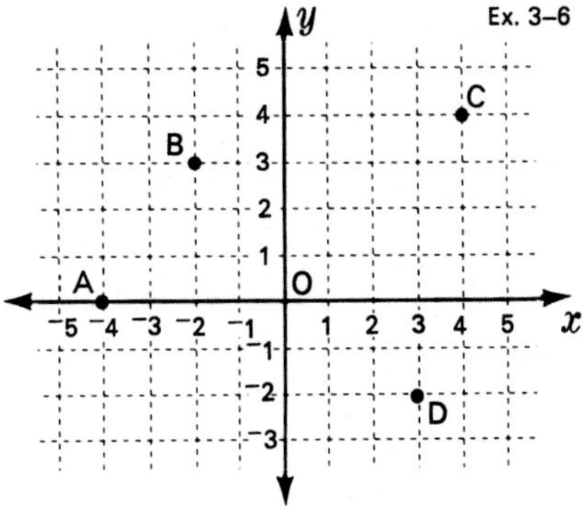

Write the ordered pair for each point on the graph at the right.

3. A **4.** B

5. C **6.** D

Draw a line graph for each table.

7.

fluid ounces	0	1	2	3	4	5
tablespoons	0	2	4	6	8	10

8.

x	0	1	2	3	4	5
y	3	3	3	0	−1	−2

Answer these questions.

9. Is the graph for Exercises 3–6 the graph of a function?

10. Is the set of ordered pairs (2, 5), (2, 6), (2, 7), and (2, 8) a function?

11. Is the set of ordered pairs in Exercise 8 a function?

12. You notice the flash of an explosion. You hear the "boom" 9 seconds (t) later. How far (d) are you from the explosion? $d = 1100t$

RATE YOURSELF

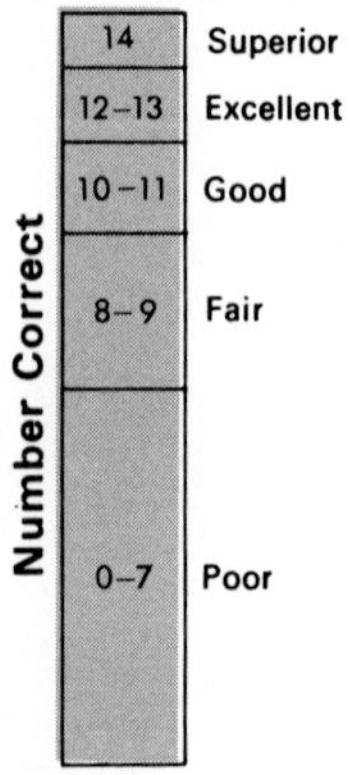

Copy and graph the following.

13. a slide 4 units right

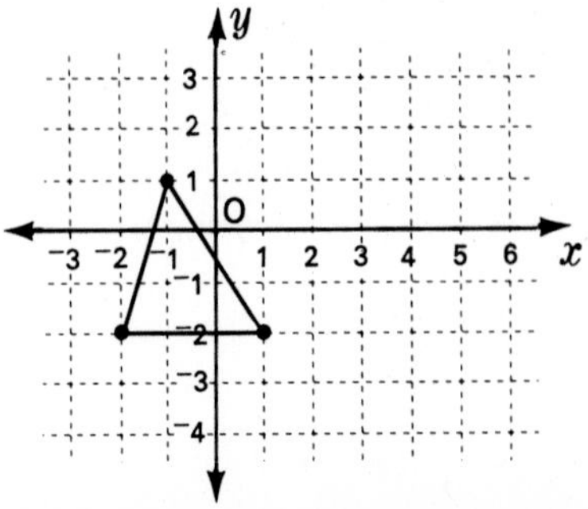

14. a 1-to-2 reduction

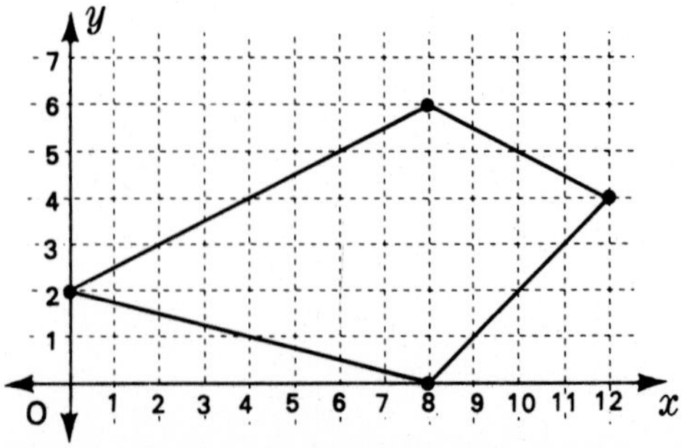

MISLEADING GRAPHS

Line graphs are sometimes used to show trends. But beware! The way information is put on a graph can change the appearance of a trend. At first glance, which graph below makes it look like the number of subscriptions has increased more and faster? Why?

SUBSCRIPTIONS, 1970–1980
SKATEBOARD MONTHLY

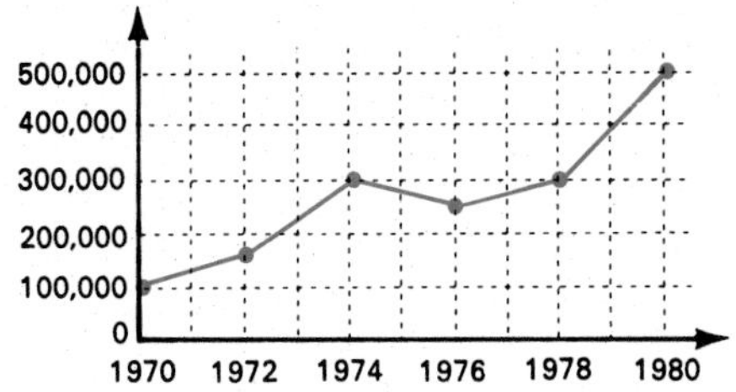

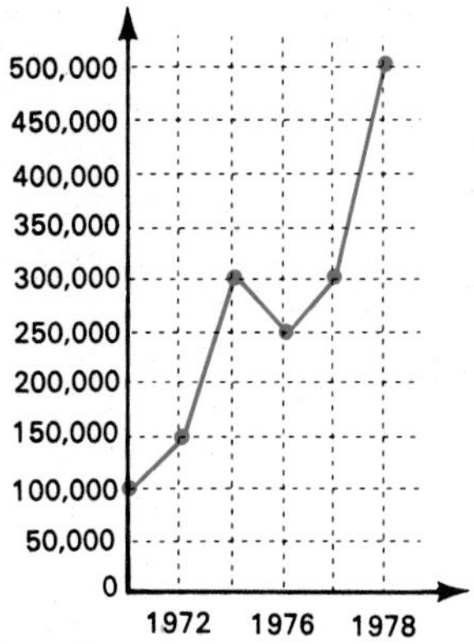

At first glance, which graph below makes it look as if profits had been going up each year? What really happened?

PROFIT RECORD FOR ZAPPO, INC.

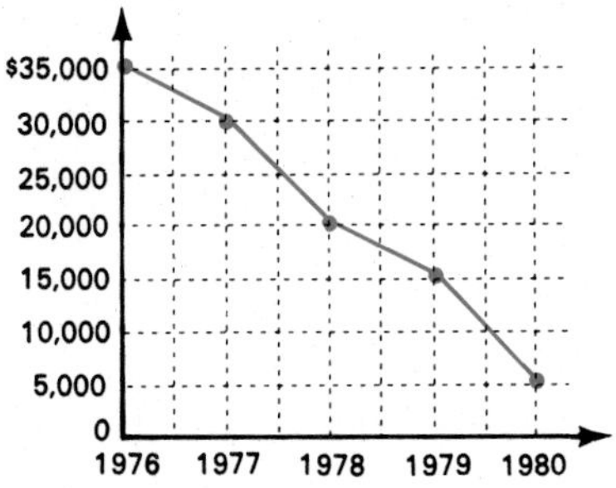

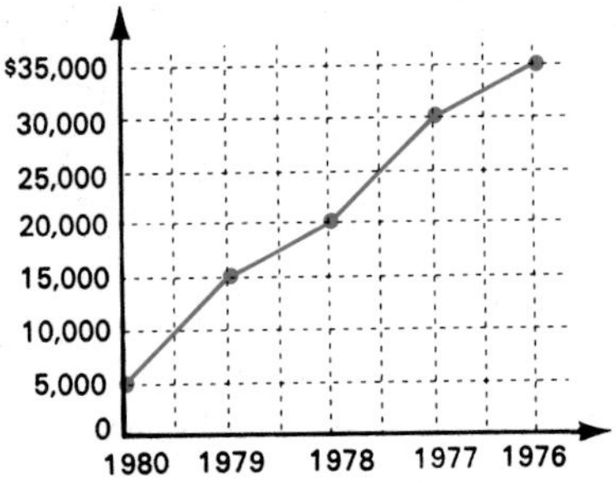

Which graph below makes it look like the price of stock has always been going up? How do the prices for 1970–1972 change the trend?

PRICE OF ROUND WHEEL CO. STOCK

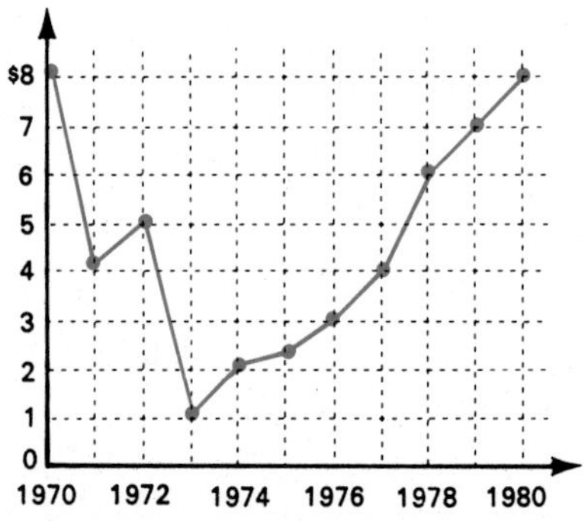

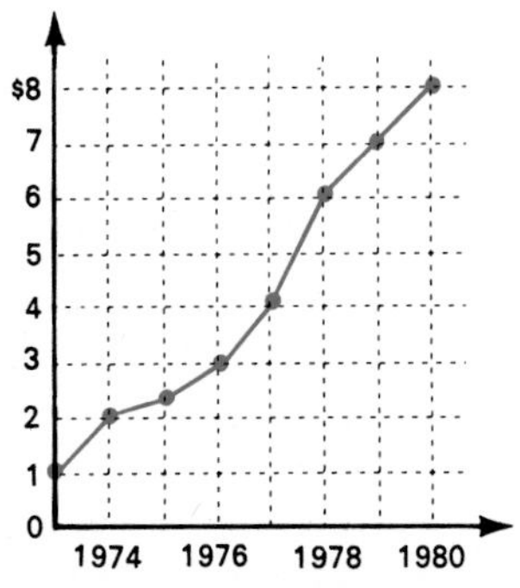

CAREER CORNER

"MAGIC NUMBER 30" FORMULA

One of the first things a wallpaper hanger must do is estimate the amount of wallpaper needed for a room. One way to do this is to use the "Magic Number 30" formula. Most wallpapers come in rolls that contain 36 square feet of paper. That is, a roll of 18-inch-wide paper is 24 feet long (18 in. $= 1\frac{1}{2}$ ft and $1\frac{1}{2}$ ft $\times$ 24 ft $=$ 36 ft^2) and a roll of 27-inch-wide paper is 16 feet long (27 in. $= 2\frac{1}{4}$ ft and $2\frac{1}{4}$ ft $\times$ 16 ft $=$ 36 ft^2). Waste and allowances for matching patterns are taken care of by assuming that a roll will cover only 30 square feet of wall (instead of 36 ft^2). Also, $\frac{1}{2}$ roll of paper is subtracted for each normal-size door or window.

$$r = \frac{p \times h}{30} - \frac{1}{2}n$$

- r: number of rolls of wallpaper needed
- p: perimeter of room (in feet)
- h: height of walls (in feet)
- n: number of normal-size doors and windows

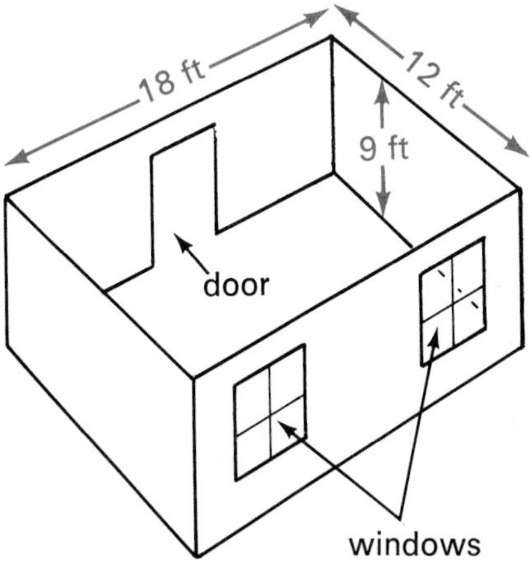

For the room shown at left:

$p = 2(18 \text{ ft} + 12 \text{ ft}) = 60$ ft

$h = 9$ ft

$n = 3$

$$r = \frac{60 \times 9}{30} - \frac{1}{2}(3)$$

$$= 18 - 1\frac{1}{2}$$

$$= 16\frac{1}{2}$$

So, it will take about 17 rolls to paper the room.

Sometimes a wall of a room has several large areas that are not to be covered. Then the amount of paper needed can be found by making a reduced drawing of the wall on graph paper. Vertical lines are drawn to show each strip of wallpaper. For the wall below, the paper being used is 18 inches (or $1\frac{1}{2}$ ft) wide. The number (r) of rolls needed is found by adding the number of feet in each strip, then dividing by 24 (24 ft in each roll).

$$
\begin{aligned}
r &= \frac{5(9) + 3(2\frac{1}{2}) + 2(2)}{24} \\
&= \frac{45 + 7\frac{1}{2} + 4}{24} \\
&= \frac{56\frac{1}{2}}{24} \\
&= 56\frac{1}{2} \div 24 \\
&= \frac{113}{2} \times \frac{1}{24} \\
&= 2\frac{17}{48}
\end{aligned}
$$

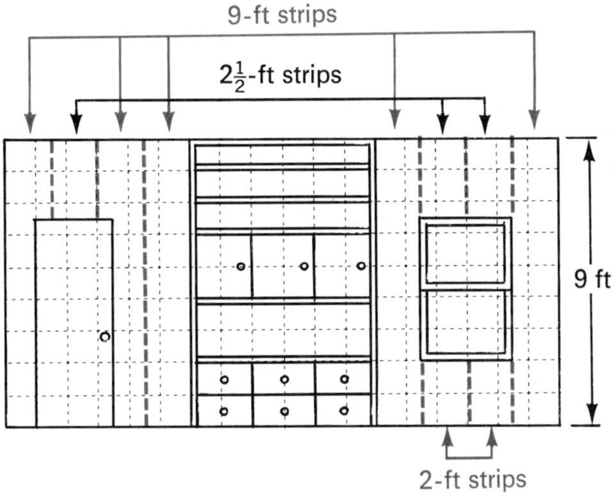

So, it will take about 3 rolls plus 1 roll for waste and allowance for matching patterns, or 4 rolls, to paper the wall.

activities

TREASURE HUNT

Players: Two (The instructions are the same for each player.)

Materials for each player: Graph paper, pencil

Prepare to play: Draw two graphs with units from $^{-}10$ to 10 on each axis. (See example below.) One is your *island* and the other is your *map*. Do not let the other player see your *island* after this (place your hand or a book in front of it).

Example of an island:

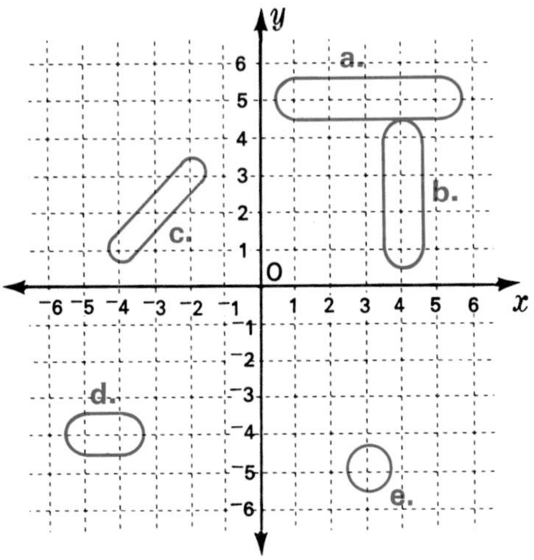

You will bury treasure chests on your *island*, and each contains a certain number of points.

Kind of treasure chest	Number of points
a. diamonds	5
b. emeralds	4
c. rubies	3
d. gold coins	2
e. silver coins	1

Bury one of each kind of treasure chest by circling horizontal, vertical, or diagonal rows of points on your *island*.

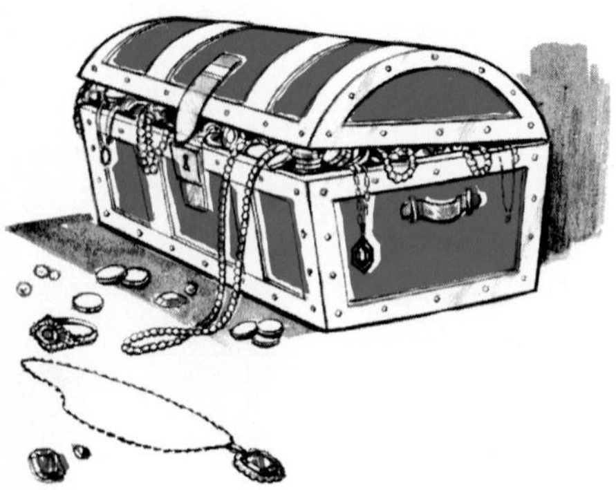

To play: Take turns "digging" for buried treasure by saying the coordinates of a point. The object is to find all the treasure chests on the other player's *island*. (A treasure chest is found when all its points have been named.)

When you dig, the other player must say "in" or "out" to tell you whether or not the point is inside or outside a treasure chest. Mark your "ins" (X) and "outs" (O) on your *map* so you can plan your next move.

Mark the other player's "ins" on your *island*. Do *not* tell the other player what *kind* of treasure chest is being dug. But if a point is the last one inside a chest, you must say "in and found."

The first player to find all the other player's buried treasure wins.

Getting Ready for Chapter 9

Express as a fraction or mixed number in lowest terms.

1. $\frac{3}{6}$	**2.** $\frac{16}{48}$	**3.** $\frac{20}{80}$	**4.** $\frac{25}{100}$	4.3
5. $\frac{178}{100}$	**6.** $\frac{185}{100}$	**7.** $\frac{142}{100}$	**8.** $\frac{120}{100}$	4.4

Solve.

9. $4x = 60$	**10.** $25n = 250$	2.3
11. $4.20 = 12a$	**12.** $8y = 76$	5.5
13. $0.1x = 0.25$	**14.** $1.5n = 6$	5.6

Multiply 120 by each fraction or decimal.

15. $\frac{1}{4}$	**16.** $\frac{1}{3}$	**17.** $\frac{2}{3}$	**18.** $\frac{3}{4}$	4.2
19. 0.3	**20.** 0.34	**21.** 0.6	**22.** 0.68	5.4

Express as a fraction in lowest terms. 4.4

23. $1\frac{3}{5}$	**24.** $3\frac{7}{8}$	**25.** $5\frac{1}{4}$	**26.** $11\frac{1}{2}$

Express as a fraction with a denominator of 100. 5.1

27. 0.5	**28.** 0.25	**29.** 0.68	**30.** 2.33
31. 0.75	**32.** 0.875	**33.** 0.05	**34.** 7

Express as a decimal. 5.5

35. $\frac{3}{5}$	**36.** $\frac{1}{4}$	**37.** $\frac{1}{2}$	**38.** $\frac{1}{3}$
39. $\frac{3}{10}$	**40.** $\frac{11}{20}$	**41.** $\frac{17}{50}$	**42.** $\frac{2}{3}$
43. $\frac{31}{100}$	**44.** $\frac{38}{5}$	**45.** $\frac{235}{100}$	**46.** $\frac{19.5}{100}$

Round to the nearest tenth. 5.2

47. 0.32	**48.** 0.45	**49.** 0.76	**50.** 0.64

Round **(a)** to the nearest ten and **(b)** to the nearest hundred. 5.2

51. 327	**52.** 787	**53.** 1243	**54.** 974

RATIOS, PROPORTIONS, AND PER CENTS

9

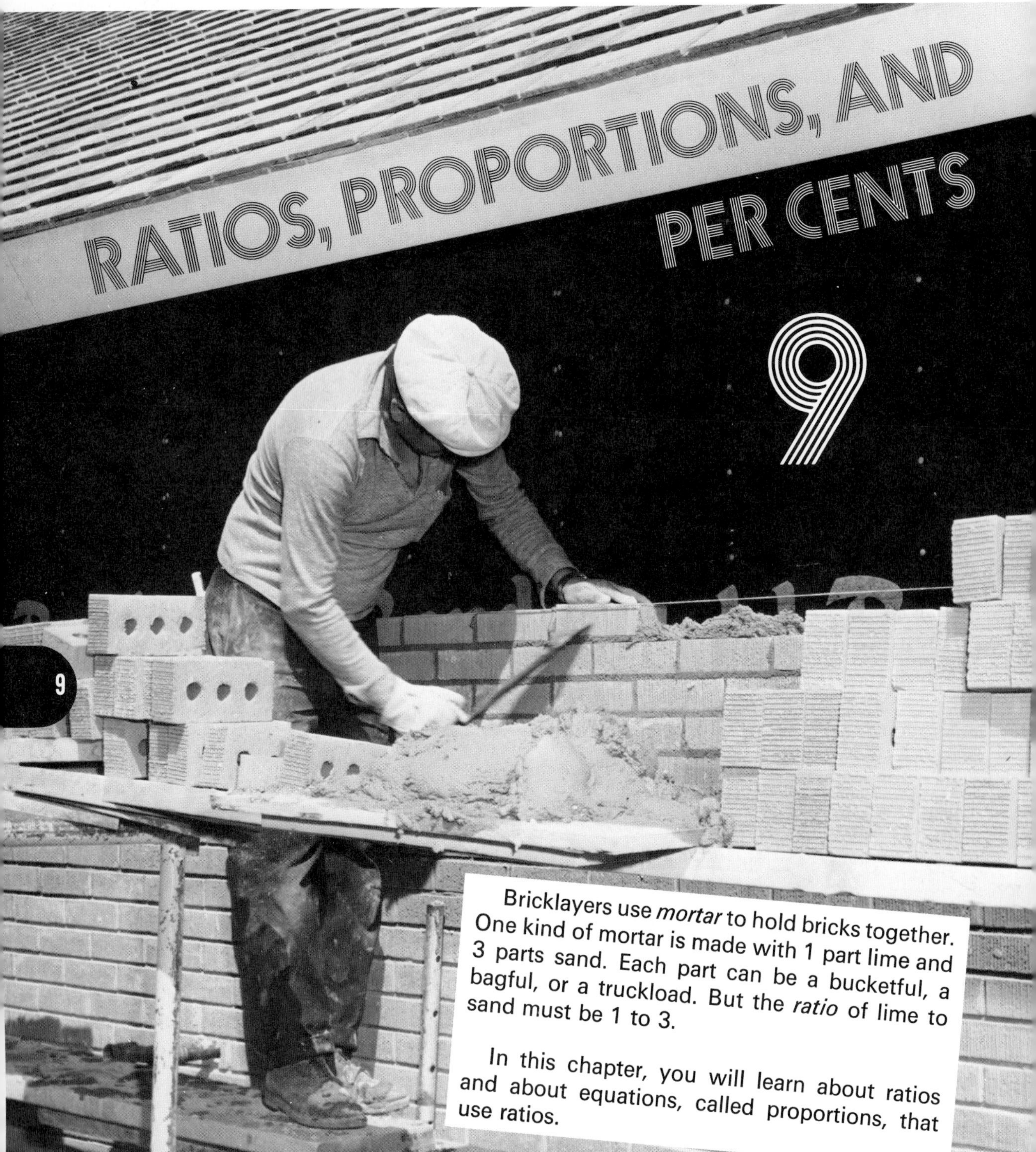

Bricklayers use *mortar* to hold bricks together. One kind of mortar is made with 1 part lime and 3 parts sand. Each part can be a bucketful, a bagful, or a truckload. But the *ratio* of lime to sand must be 1 to 3.

In this chapter, you will learn about ratios and about equations, called proportions, that use ratios.

H. Armstrong Roberts

Ratios 9.1

Courtesy Schwinn

Scale: $\frac{1}{4}$

> The jury foreman told news reporters that the jury voted for conviction by an 11-to-1 ratio on most of the charges.

A **ratio** compares two numbers by division. The ratio of *a* to *b* can be written

$$a \text{ to } b \quad \text{or} \quad a:b \quad \text{or} \quad \frac{a}{b}.$$

Example: Give each ratio in three ways.

a. colored tiles to total tiles: 2 to 5 or 2:5 or $\frac{2}{5}$

b. total tiles to colored tiles: 5 to 2 or 5:2 or $\frac{5}{2}$

c. colored tiles to white tiles: 2 to 3 or 2:3 or $\frac{2}{3}$

d. white tiles to total tiles: 3 to 5 or 3:5 or $\frac{3}{5}$

In mathematics, we usually write a ratio as a fraction.

Exercises

A Give each ratio as a fraction.

1. **a.** circles to stars

   b. stars to circles

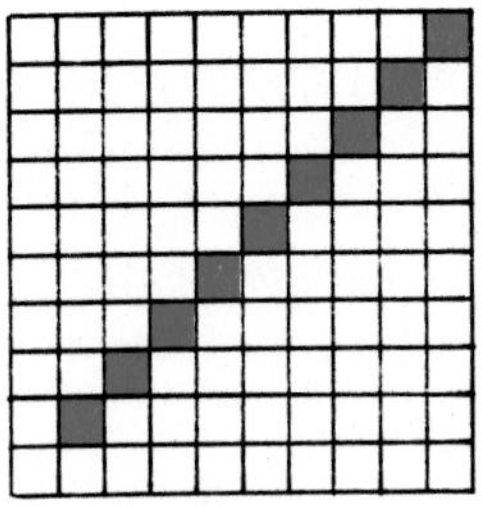

2. **a.** total squares to shaded squares

   b. shaded squares to total squares

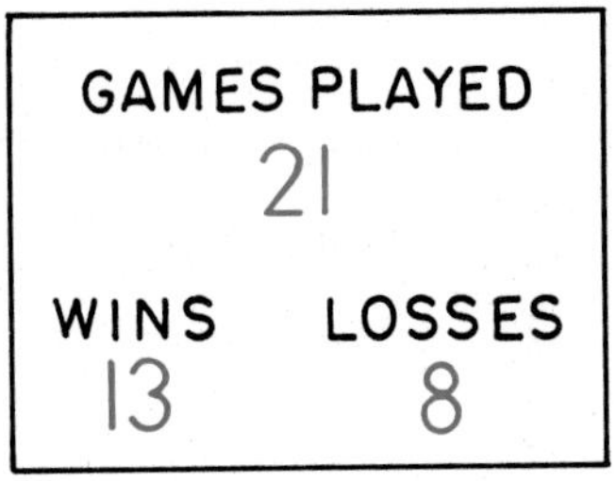

3. **a.** wins to losses

   b. losses to games played

   c. wins to games played

Choose the correct ratio for each of the following.

4. 15 squares to 11 circles

   $\frac{15}{26}$ $\frac{11}{15}$ $\frac{15}{11}$ $\frac{26}{15}$

5. 2400 boys to 100 girls

   $\frac{100}{2400}$ $\frac{2400}{2500}$ $\frac{100}{2500}$ $\frac{2400}{100}$

6. 27 pounds to 1 cubic foot

   $\frac{1}{27}$ $\frac{27}{1}$ $\frac{1}{28}$ $\frac{28}{1}$

7. 65 miles to 2 hours

   $\frac{2}{65}$ $\frac{67}{2}$ $\frac{2}{67}$ $\frac{65}{2}$

B Give each ratio in three ways.

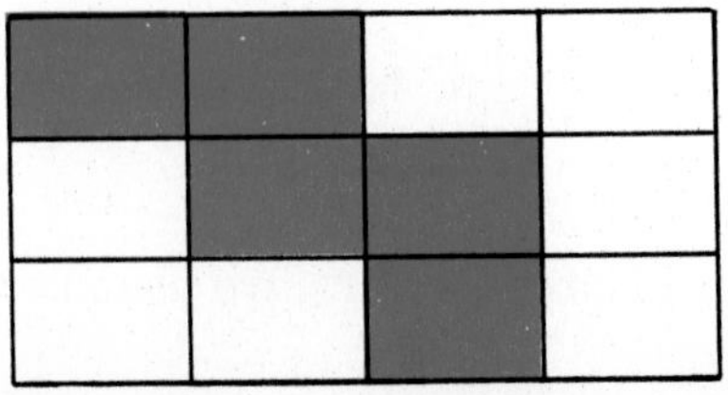

8. shaded parts to unshaded parts

9. unshaded parts to total parts

Express each ratio as a fraction.

10. Write the ratio of 27 pounds to 50 pounds.

11. A rock that weighs 6 kg on earth would weigh only 1 kg on the moon. Write the ratio of the weight on moon to weight on earth.

12. Most cars have 4 tires in use and carry 1 spare tire. Write the usual ratio of cars to tires.

13. A pinch hitter was at bat 4 times and got 1 hit. What is the ratio of hits to times at bat?

14. The girls' basketball team won 7 games and lost 3. What is the ratio of games won to games played?

15. Donna received a 3 to 2 vote over Jackie for class president. Write the ratio of Jackie's votes to total votes.

16. A recipe calls for 3 cups of milk and 1 cup of water. What is the ratio of water to milk?

Decide what property of the figures each ratio compares.

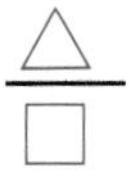 $\frac{3}{4}$ 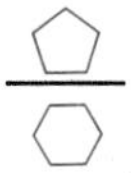 $\frac{5}{6}$ 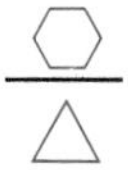 $\frac{6}{3}$

Use the same method to compare the figures below.

17. 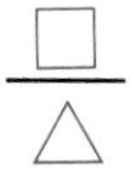 **18.** 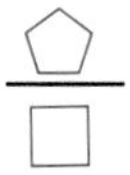 **19.** 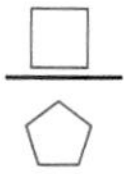

20. 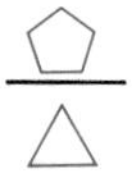 **21.** 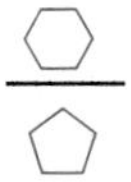 **22.** 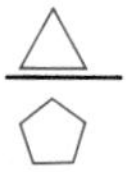

C Decide what property of the sets of points each ratio compares.

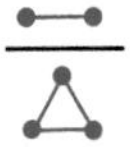 $\frac{1}{3}$ 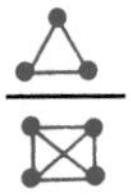 $\frac{3}{6}$

Use the same method to compare the sets of points below.

23. 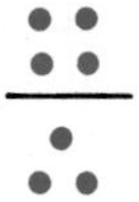 **24.** 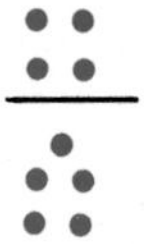 **25.** 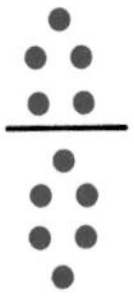

CAREER CORNER

GEAR RATIOS

Millions of people in the United States work in industrial production. Most of these workers are employed in factories. Semiskilled workers, such as assemblers and certain machine operators, may need only brief on-the-job training. Skilled workers, such as patternmakers and machinists, may have to complete a 3- or 4-year apprenticeship program. Many of these skilled factory workers must know about gear ratios.

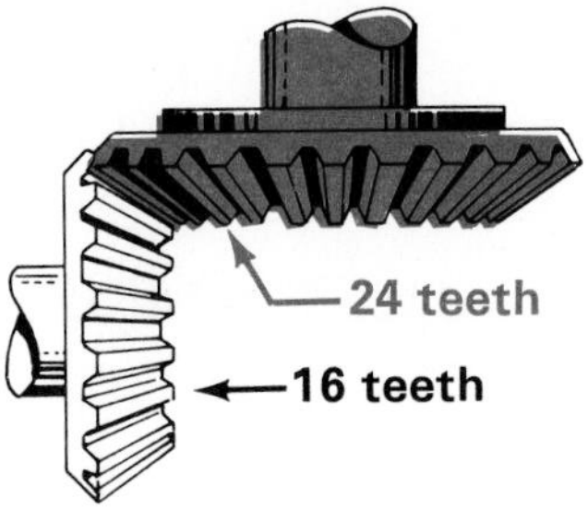

When power is applied to gear **A,** it causes gear **B** to revolve 3 times for every 2 times gear **A** revolves. So the gear ratio is 3 to 2. If power is applied to gear **B,** it causes gear **A** to revolve 2 times for every 3 times gear **B** revolves. So the gear ratio is 2 to 3. These ratios can be found by comparing the number of teeth on the two gears.

teeth on powered gear

$$\frac{24}{16} = \frac{3}{2} \qquad \frac{16}{24} = \frac{2}{3}$$

teeth on other gear

Find the gear ratio for each pair of gears below. (Power is applied to each gear shown in color.)

a.

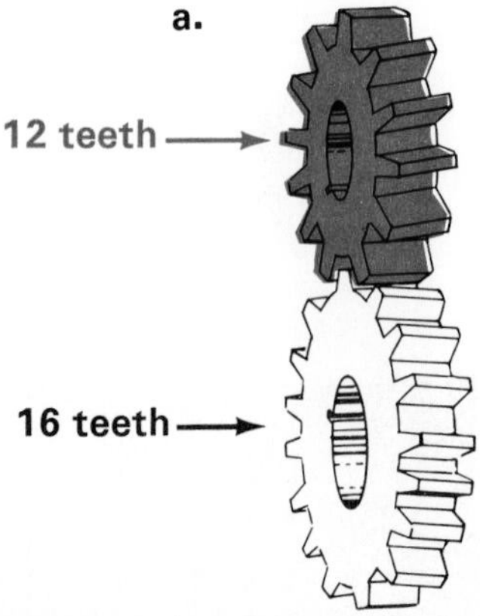

b.

c.

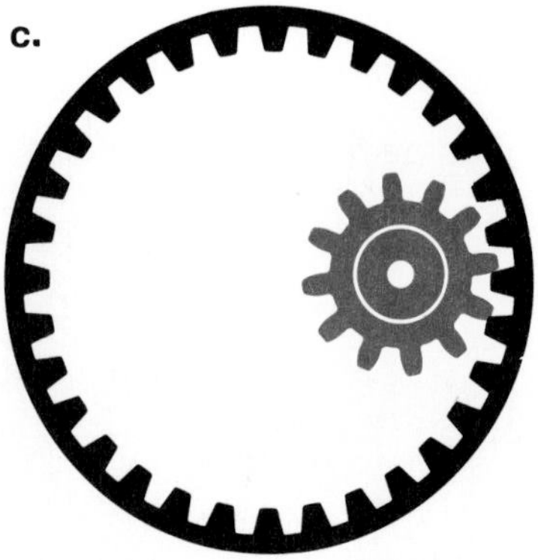

9.2 Equivalent Ratios

Three ways of comparing four ■'s to eight △'s are shown below.

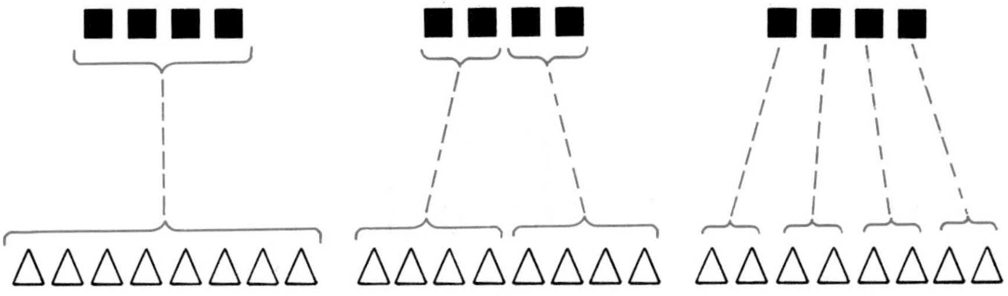

$\frac{4}{8}$ $\qquad$ $\frac{2}{4}$ $\qquad$ $\frac{1}{2}$

The ratios $\frac{4}{8}$, $\frac{2}{4}$, and $\frac{1}{2}$ are different ways of comparing the same sets. They are called **equivalent ratios.**

For the equivalent ratios $\frac{4}{8}$, $\frac{2}{4}$, and $\frac{1}{2}$, the ratio $\frac{1}{2}$ is in *lowest terms* because the fraction $\frac{1}{2}$ is in lowest terms. (The numerator and the denominator have no common whole-number factor other than 1.)

> A ratio can be changed to an equivalent ratio by multiplying the numerator and the denominator by the same number (but not zero).

Example 1: Find two ratios equivalent to $\frac{3}{5}$.

$$\frac{3}{5} = \frac{3 \times 2}{5 \times 2} = \frac{6}{10} \qquad \frac{3}{5} = \frac{3 \times 3}{5 \times 3} = \frac{9}{15}$$

> A ratio can be changed to an equivalent ratio by dividing the numerator and the denominator by the same number (but not zero).

Example 2: Change each ratio to lowest terms.

$$\frac{6}{10} = \frac{6 \div 2}{10 \div 2} = \frac{3}{5} \qquad \frac{24}{32} = \frac{24 \div 8}{32 \div 8} = \frac{3}{4}$$

GCF of 6 and 10 $\qquad$ GCF of 24 and 32

Exercises

A Answer the following.

1. What is the ratio of shaded sections to unshaded sections in each circle? Are they equivalent ratios?

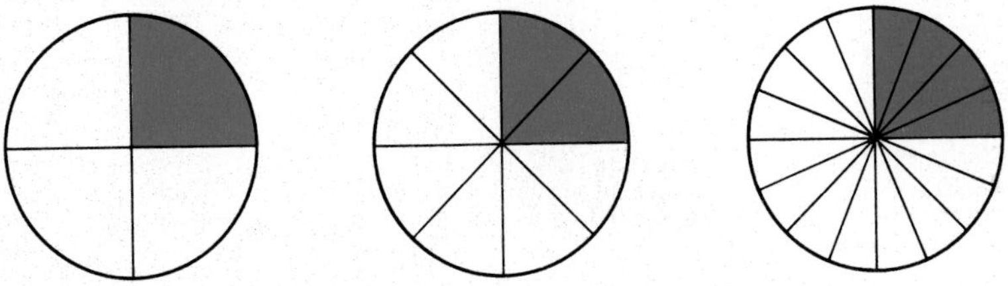

2. What is the ratio of ●'s to △'s in each comparison? Are they equivalent ratios?

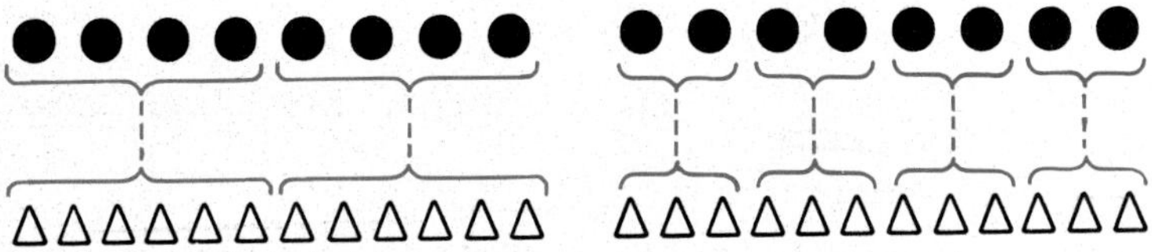

Tell what number should replace each ?.

3. $\frac{3}{5} = \frac{3 \times ?}{5 \times 20}$

4. $\frac{4}{9} = \frac{4 \times 6}{? \times 6}$

5. $\frac{5}{7} = \frac{? \times 2}{7 \times ?}$

6. $\frac{6}{18} = \frac{6 \div 6}{18 \div ?}$

7. $\frac{48}{72} = \frac{48 \div ?}{72 \div 24}$

8. $\frac{150}{250} = \frac{? \div 75}{? \div 75}$

B Find two equivalent ratios for each ratio below.

9. $\frac{1}{4}$ 10. $\frac{2}{5}$ 11. $\frac{6}{7}$ 12. $\frac{4}{7}$ 13. $\frac{10}{13}$ 14. $\frac{9}{11}$

15. $\frac{1}{5}$ 16. $\frac{7}{9}$ 17. $\frac{14}{17}$ 18. $\frac{15}{23}$ 19. $\frac{20}{31}$ 20. $\frac{30}{31}$

21. $\frac{5}{8}$ 22. $\frac{3}{4}$ 23. $\frac{5}{9}$ 24. $\frac{19}{21}$ 25. $\frac{7}{12}$ 26. $\frac{5}{7}$

Change each ratio to lowest terms.

27. $\frac{2}{6}$ 28. $\frac{8}{6}$ 29. $\frac{6}{12}$ 30. $\frac{18}{24}$ 31. $\frac{15}{35}$

32. $\frac{14}{28}$ 33. $\frac{18}{81}$ 34. $\frac{20}{50}$ 35. $\frac{20}{45}$ 36. $\frac{30}{100}$

37. $\frac{60}{24}$ 38. $\frac{8}{10}$ 39. $\frac{21}{9}$ 40. $\frac{150}{200}$ 41. $\frac{18}{54}$

C When a ratio compares two similar measurements (such as two distances or two capacities), both measurements should be in the same unit.

Example: Use a ratio to compare 2 feet to 6 inches.
First express both measurements in the same unit.

$$\frac{2 \text{ feet}}{6 \text{ inches}} \longrightarrow \frac{24 \text{ inches}}{6 \text{ inches}} \longrightarrow \frac{24}{6} = \frac{24 \div 6}{6 \div 6} = \frac{4}{1}$$

Write a ratio in lowest terms to compare the measurements.

42. 4 yards to 3 feet

43. 3 hours to 5 seconds

44. 6 pints to 1 gallon

45. 75 centimeters to 2 meters

46. 2 pounds to 1 ton

47. 8 ounces to 3 pounds

48. 40 minutes to 2 hours

49. 450 grams to 2 kilograms

50. 9 grams to 18 milligrams

51. 5000 milligrams to 10 kilograms

52. 70 milliliters to 14 liters

Artstreet

When a ratio compares the *number of units* in two measurements, the measurements need not be in the same unit. In fact, they need not even be similar measurements.

Example: Use a ratio to express "135 miles in 3 hours."

$$\frac{135 \text{ miles}}{3 \text{ hours}} \longrightarrow \frac{(135 \div 3) \text{ miles}}{(3 \div 3) \text{ hours}} \longrightarrow \frac{45 \text{ miles}}{1 \text{ hour}}$$ or 45 miles per hour

Write a ratio in lowest terms to compare the number of units in the measurements.

53. 100 miles for every 5 gallons

54. \$500 for 100 hours of work

55. 200 feet in 4 minutes

56. 8 pounds lost in 4 weeks

57. 96¢ for 12 pencils

58. 60 meters every 5 minutes

59. 80 kilometers for 8 liters

60. 10 °C drop every 5 hours

CONSUMER CORNER

RATIOS IN ADVERTISING

In a nationwide survey, veterinarians preferred Ken-L Ration over any other canned dog food—and by 6 to 1 over the other leading canned food.

Reprinted courtesy Quaker Oats

This ad compares two canned dog foods.

1. If 7 veterinarians (animal doctors) took part in the survey, how many preferred Ken-L Ration? How many preferred the other food?
2. If 42 veterinarians took part in the survey, how many preferred Ken-L Ration? How many preferred the other food?
3. Use the ad to find a comparison that would be described by the ratio $\frac{1}{7}$; by the ratio $\frac{6}{7}$.

> You'd probably never dream of writing a love letter to the company that built your car. Yet at Volvo, we get them all the time.
>
> Maybe because 9 out of 10 people who buy new Volvos are happy.

Reprinted courtesy Volvo of America Corp.

This ad compares certain automobile buyers.

1. If 10 people bought new Volvos, how many of them does this ad claim are happy?
2. If 10,000 people bought new Volvos, how many of them should be happy?
3. Use the ad to find a comparison that would be described by the ratio $\frac{1}{10}$; by the ratio $\frac{9}{1}$.

> In blindfold tests, 3 out of every 4 women chose piecrusts made with digestible all-vegetable Crisco as tasting flakier than those made with the leading part-vegetable shortening.

Reprinted courtesy Proctor and Gamble

This ad compares piecrust made with Crisco to piecrust made with another shortening.

1. If 4 women took part in the tests, how many thought the Crisco piecrust tasted flakier? How many did not?
2. If 20 women took part in the tests, how many thought the Crisco piecrust tasted flakier? How many did not?
3. Use the ad to find a comparison that would be described by the ratio $\frac{3}{1}$; by the ratio $\frac{1}{4}$.

9.3 Proportions

In Section 9.2, you learned to find equivalent ratios. You probably wrote them in equations like these:

$$\frac{1}{4} = \frac{2}{8} \qquad \frac{2}{6} = \frac{1}{3} \qquad \frac{8}{10} = \frac{4}{5}$$

> A **proportion** is an equation that names two equivalent ratios.

$$\frac{1}{4} = \frac{2}{8}$$

1 and 8 are called the **extremes.**

4 and 2 are called the **means.**

1×8 and 4×2 are called the **cross products.**

Example 1: Find the cross products in each proportion.

a. $\frac{2}{6} = \frac{1}{3}$: $2 \times 3 = 6$ and $6 \times 1 = 6$

b. $\frac{8}{10} = \frac{4}{5}$: $8 \times 5 = 40$ and $10 \times 4 = 40$

c. $\frac{2}{3} = \frac{6}{9}$: $2 \times 9 = 18$ and $3 \times 6 = 18$

Notice that the cross products for each proportion are equal.

> In a proportion, the product of the extremes equals the product of the means.

Example 2: Use cross products to solve $\frac{2}{3} = \frac{34}{n}$.

$$\frac{2}{3} = \frac{34}{n}$$

multiply the extremes; multiply the means

$$2n = 3 \times 34$$

$$2n = 102$$

$$\frac{2n}{2} = \frac{102}{2}$$

$$n = 51$$

Check:

$$\frac{2}{3} = \frac{34}{n}$$

$$\frac{2}{3} = \frac{34}{51}$$

$$2 \times 51 = 3 \times 34 \quad \text{cross products}$$

$$102 = 102 \ \checkmark$$

Exercises

A Use cross products to tell whether each sentence is true.

Examples:

$\frac{2}{3} = \frac{6}{9}$

$2 \times 9 = 18 \qquad 3 \times 6 = 18$

True

$\frac{4}{6} = \frac{9}{10}$

$4 \times 10 = 40 \qquad 6 \times 9 = 54$

False

1. $\frac{21}{7} = \frac{3}{1}$ **2.** $\frac{5}{2} = \frac{10}{4}$ **3.** $\frac{6}{8} = \frac{2}{3}$

4. $\frac{7}{5} = \frac{9}{3}$ **5.** $\frac{6}{9} = \frac{4}{6}$ **6.** $\frac{4}{7} = \frac{8}{10}$

7. $\frac{10}{3} = \frac{50}{9}$ **8.** $\frac{10}{18} = \frac{5}{9}$ **9.** $\frac{5}{6} = \frac{10}{12}$

B Solve each proportion.

10. $\frac{3}{4} = \frac{n}{20}$ **11.** $\frac{2}{3} = \frac{6}{n}$ **12.** $\frac{6}{n} = \frac{3}{8}$

13. $\frac{1}{2} = \frac{n}{24}$ **14.** $\frac{45}{90} = \frac{n}{100}$ **15.** $\frac{3}{4} = \frac{n}{40}$

16. $\frac{8}{6} = \frac{32}{n}$ **17.** $\frac{n}{8} = \frac{25}{40}$ **18.** $\frac{24}{36} = \frac{n}{12}$

19. $\frac{4}{5} = \frac{n}{15}$ **20.** $\frac{3}{8} = \frac{n}{16}$ **21.** $\frac{n}{5} = \frac{10}{25}$

22. $\frac{4}{n} = \frac{3}{3}$ **23.** $\frac{2}{3} = \frac{4}{n}$ **24.** $\frac{n}{7} = \frac{9}{63}$

25. $\frac{n}{4} = \frac{18}{8}$ **26.** $\frac{6}{n} = \frac{60}{70}$ **27.** $\frac{5}{12} = \frac{75}{n}$

28. $\frac{0.2}{n} = \frac{1}{3}$ **29.** $\frac{n}{1.4} = \frac{3}{1}$ **30.** $\frac{2}{5} = \frac{n}{1.5}$

31. $\frac{2.4}{32} = \frac{n}{10}$ **32.** $\frac{n}{7} = \frac{9}{6.3}$ **33.** $\frac{5}{n} = \frac{0.5}{1}$

The four proportions below all have equal cross products. They are *equivalent proportions.*

given proportion	switch means	switch extremes	invert both ratios
$\frac{2}{5} = \frac{4}{10}$	$\frac{2}{4} = \frac{5}{10}$	$\frac{10}{5} = \frac{4}{2}$	$\frac{5}{2} = \frac{10}{4}$

Write three proportions equivalent to the given proportion. Then find the cross products.

34. $\frac{3}{7} = \frac{9}{21}$ **35.** $\frac{12}{18} = \frac{2}{3}$ **36.** $\frac{4}{5} = \frac{16}{20}$

37. $\frac{1.2}{1.6} = \frac{3}{4}$ **38.** $\frac{5}{1} = \frac{3.5}{0.7}$ **39.** $\frac{2.6}{5.2} = \frac{7.8}{15.6}$

C **40.** $\frac{n}{3} = \frac{15}{9}$ **41.** $\frac{12}{n} = \frac{15}{2}$ **42.** $\frac{3}{11} = \frac{13}{n}$

Solve.

43. $\frac{0.25}{0.75} = \frac{1}{n}$ **44.** $\frac{4.45}{0.25} = \frac{n}{2.6}$ **45.** $\frac{70}{0.35} = \frac{6.25}{n}$

46. $\frac{n}{6.22} = \frac{9.93}{18.66}$ **47.** $\frac{0.95}{1.5} = \frac{n}{0.3}$ **48.** $\frac{0.26}{7.8} = \frac{1.2}{n}$

Postal Ratios

The United States Postal Service can refuse or charge extra for mail that is not a standard size. A standard-size envelope must fit the description below.

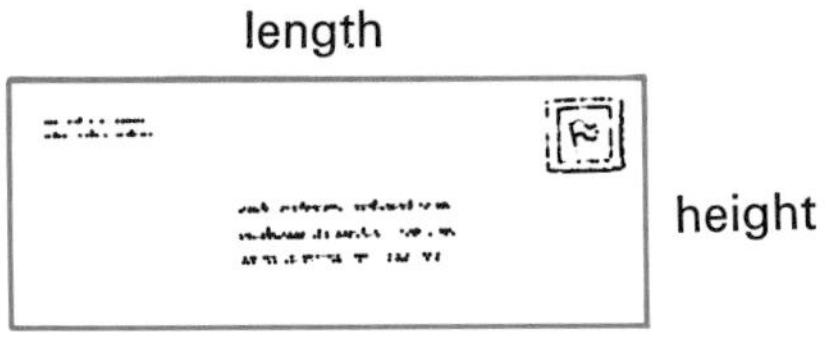

a. height: from $3\frac{1}{2}$ to $6\frac{1}{8}$ inches

b. length: from 5 to $11\frac{1}{2}$ inches

c. the ratio $\frac{\text{height}}{\text{length}}$: from $\frac{2}{5}$ to $\frac{10}{13}$

To be standard, how long may an envelope be if it is 4 inches high?

Hint: To find the longest and shortest possible lengths, solve $\frac{4}{x} = \frac{2}{5}$ and $\frac{4}{x} = \frac{10}{13}$.

Courtesy U.S. Postal Service

9.4

Using Proportions to Solve Problems

Example: There are 150 calories in 12 ounces of limeade. How many calories are there in 8 ounces?

METHOD 1

1st amount → 150; 2nd amount → x

calories → 150, ounces → 12

$$\frac{150}{12} = \frac{x}{8}$$

$$150 \times 8 = 12x$$

$$\frac{1200}{12} = \frac{12x}{12}$$

$$100 = x$$

cross products

METHOD 2

calories → 150; ounces → 12

1st amount → 150, 2nd amount → x

$$\frac{150}{x} = \frac{12}{8}$$

$$150 \times 8 = x \times 12$$

$$\frac{1200}{12} = \frac{x \times 12}{12}$$

$$100 = x$$

Check: Is 100 calories in 8 ounces equivalent to 150 calories in 12 ounces? (Use cross products or reduce ratios to lowest terms.) ✓

So there are 100 calories in 8 ounces of limeade.

Exercises

A Find the cross products.

1. $\frac{1}{5} = \frac{3}{x}$ **2.** $\frac{x}{7} = \frac{2}{3.5}$ **3.** $\frac{6}{x} = \frac{0.3}{2}$

4. $\frac{x}{0.5} = \frac{1}{10}$ **5.** $\frac{1.8}{36} = \frac{1}{x}$ **6.** $\frac{2}{9} = \frac{x}{0.3}$

B Use a proportion to solve each problem.

7. Out of 3514 voters in Hay County, 502 are chosen for jury duty. At this rate, how many more voters are needed to get 86 more jurors?

8. If a 3-pound roast requires 60 minutes to cook, how long should a 4-pound roast be cooked?

For some 1-inch diameter fluorescent lights, the ratio of watts to length in inches is $\frac{5}{6}$. Use this ratio and a proportion to solve.

9. How long is a 15-watt fluorescent light?

10. Find the number of watts for a 36-inch fluorescent light.

11. Find the number of watts for a 24-inch fluorescent light.

12. How long is a 40-watt fluorescent light?

Use a proportion to solve each problem.

13. At 60 mph a car travels 88 feet per second. How many feet per second does a car travel at 15 mph?

14. A car used 6 gallons of gasoline in 120 miles. At this rate, how much gasoline will the car use in 360 miles?

15. Mrs. Rackow won an election by a 5 to 2 margin. Her opponent got 2800 votes. How many votes did Mrs. Rackow get?

16. There are 180 calories in 3 ounces of veal. How many calories are there in 4 ounces?

17. If a lawn mower uses a fuel mixture of 4 ounces of oil for each 0.5 gallon of gasoline, how much oil should be mixed with 5 gallons of gasoline?

18. If 32 bags of cement are needed to make 5 cubic yards of concrete, how many cubic yards of concrete will 12 bags of cement make?

Courtesy Commonwealth Edison Co.

19. It costs the Mahans 36 cents a month to operate their electric frying pan, which uses 8 units of electricity a month. If their slow cooker uses 12 units a month, how much does it cost to operate?

20. The Georges have two solid-state TV sets. Their black-and-white set uses 6 units of electricity a month and costs 27 cents to operate. If their color set uses 28 units a month, how much does it cost to operate?

John Running/After Image

[C] **21.** A water tank in the shape of a cylinder is 18 feet deep and holds 1200 gallons of water. How many gallons are in the tank when it is filled to the 15-foot level?

22. According to the United States Department of Agriculture, the best light for growing plants indoors uses 3 watts of fluorescent light for each watt of regular (incandescent) light. If a regular 75-watt bulb is used, how many 75-watt fluorescent lights should be used? If a regular 100-watt bulb is used, how many 75-watt fluorescent lights should be used?

23. The ratio of weight to volume of a substance is called *density*. If the density of silver is 10.5 g/cm^3, what is the weight of 15 cm^3 of silver? What is the volume of 21 g of silver?

Use a proportion to solve as in the example.

Example: In making plate glass, 18 kilograms of sand are used for every 7 kilograms of other ingredients. How many kilograms of sand are needed to make 125 kilograms of glass? (A diagram can help you set up the proportion.)

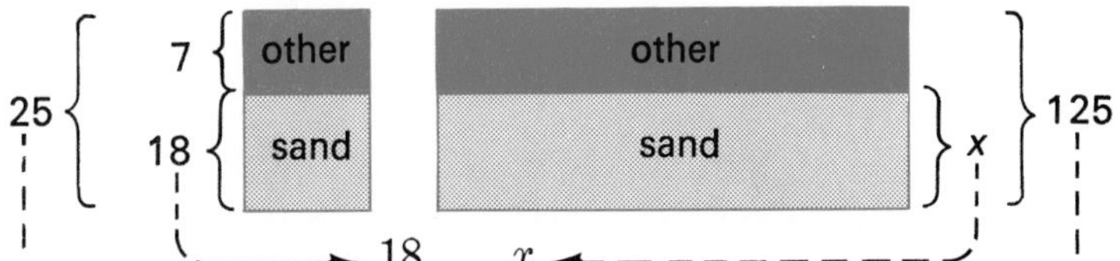

$$\frac{18}{25} = \frac{x}{125}$$

$$18 \times 125 = 25x$$

$$\frac{2250}{25} = \frac{25x}{25}$$

$$90 = x$$

Check: Is 90 kg out of 125 equivalent to 18 kg out of 25? ✓

So 90 kilograms of sand are needed.

24. To make violet food coloring, you mix 3 drops of red for every 5 drops of blue. How much of each color should you mix to make 16 drops of violet food coloring?

25. Brass is an alloy made by adding 1 kilogram of zinc for every 4 kilograms of copper. How much copper is needed to make 500 kilograms of brass?

26. The alloy for 18-karat gold is made by adding 6 grams of gold for every 2 grams of other ingredients (silver and copper). How much gold is in an 18-karat bracelet that weighs 24 grams?

27. Bronze is an alloy made by adding 1 kilogram of tin for every 19 kilograms of copper. How much tin is needed to make 300 kilograms of bronze?

28. To make the alloy for solid-silver tableware, you add 1 pound of copper for every 9 pounds of silver. How much silver is in a 50-piece service that weighs 8 pounds?

Quick Quiz

Sections 9.1 to 9.4

1. Write the ratio 6 to 5 in two other forms.

Write three equivalent ratios for each given ratio.

2. $\frac{4}{7}$

3. $\frac{6}{12}$

4. $\frac{30}{100}$

Solve.

5. $\frac{3}{4} = \frac{n}{16}$

6. $\frac{2}{3} = \frac{8}{n}$

7. $\frac{n}{8} = \frac{25}{40}$

8. A syrup for use in freezing fruits can be made by mixing 6 cups of sugar with water to make 11 cups of syrup. If 72 cups of sugar are available, how many cups of syrup can be made?

9.5 Meaning of Per Cent

> A ratio that compares a number to 100 is a **per cent.** The symbol for per cent is %.

Example 1: Express each ratio as a per cent.

3 to 100   3:100 $\frac{3}{100}$

3 per 100   3 out of 100

These are all equal to 3%.

Any per cent can be changed to a fraction with a denominator of 100. But the fraction should then be reduced or simplified if possible. Or the fraction may be changed to a decimal.

Example 2: Change each per cent to a fraction or mixed number.

a. $35\% = \frac{35}{100} = \frac{7}{20}$

b. $166\% = \frac{166}{100} = \frac{83}{50} = 1\frac{33}{50}$

c. $37\frac{1}{2}\% = \frac{37\frac{1}{2}}{100} = \frac{37\frac{1}{2} \times 2}{100 \times 2} = \frac{75}{200} = \frac{3}{8}$

Example 3: Change each per cent to a decimal.

a. $35\% = \frac{35}{100} = 0.35$

b. $166\% = \frac{166}{100} = 1.66$

c. $37\frac{1}{2}\% = 37.5\% = \frac{37.5}{100} = 0.375$

Shortcut: $35\% = 0.35$ $166\% = 1.66$ $37.5\% = 0.375$

To write a per cent as a decimal: Move the decimal point two places to the left and drop the symbol %.

Exercises

A Give each of the following as a per cent.

1. 50 out of 100

2. 70 per 100

3. $\frac{9}{100}$

4. 45 to 100

5. 59 out of 100

6. 85 per 100

7. $\frac{64}{100}$

8. n out of 100

9. $\frac{135}{100}$

Change each per cent to a decimal.

10. 4%

11. 3.75%

12. 5.5%

13. A per cent (*greater than, less than*) 100% can be changed to a number less than 1.

14. A per cent (*greater than, less than*) 100% can be changed to a number greater than 1.

What number should replace each *n*?

15. $68\% = \frac{n}{100}$

16. $28\% = \frac{n}{100}$

17. $135\% = \frac{n}{100}$

18. $232\% = \frac{n}{100}$

B Copy and complete each table.

	per cent	fraction	decimal
19.	21%	___	___
21.	61%	___	___
23.	70%	___	___
25.	50%	___	___
27.	35%	___	___
29.	$12\frac{1}{2}\%$	___	___
31.	6.3%	___	___

	per cent	fraction	decimal
20.	7%	___	___
22.	49%	___	___
24.	30%	___	___
26.	20%	___	___
28.	75%	___	___
30.	$62\frac{1}{2}\%$	___	___
32.	7.9%	___	___

Copy and complete each table.

	per cent	fraction or mixed number	decimal
33.	33.3%	___	___
35.	$8\frac{3}{4}\%$	___	___
37.	101%	___	___
39.	127%	___	___
41.	250%	___	___

	per cent	fraction or mixed number	decimal
34.	71.7%	___	___
36.	$9\frac{1}{4}\%$	___	___
38.	143%	___	___
40.	125%	___	___
42.	342%	___	___

Change each per cent to a fraction or a whole number.

43. 10% **44.** 40% **45.** 60% **46.** 100%

47. 400% **48.** 600% **49.** 1000% **50.** 5000%

51. 6000% **52.** $x\%$ **53.** $(a+3)\%$ **54.** $4n\%$

C Change each per cent to a decimal.

55. 0.3% **56.** 0.01% **57.** $\frac{1}{4}\%$ **58.** $\frac{3}{5}\%$

Change each per cent to a fraction.

59. 0.02% **60.** $\frac{1}{3}\%$ **61.** $\frac{1}{12}\%$ **62.** 0.5%

% % % % % % % % % % % % % % % % % % % % % %

The use of the per cent symbol developed slowly over many centuries. By the fifteenth century (the century in which Columbus came to America), the words *per cento,* from the Latin *per centum,* were used to mean "for a hundred." Then the words were abbreviated, and gradually the abbreviation changed in form.

15th century → modern

per cento → per c̊ or p c̊ → per $\frac{o}{o}$ → $\frac{o}{o}$ → %

RATIOS AT WORK

CAREER CORNER

If water is to flow through a pipe, one end must be lower than the other. If a ramp is to raise a car from one level to another, one end must be higher than the other. In many construction trades, rate of rise or fall (called *grade*) is written as a ratio. Sometimes this ratio is expressed as a per cent.

Courtesy Chicago Rehabilitation Center

Courtesy General Motors

Archivo Mas, Barcelona

9.6

Changing Numbers to Per Cents

A baseball player's batting average is written as a decimal. Lou Gehrig had a lifetime batting average of 0.340, while Babe Ruth's was 0.342.

Example 1: What per cent of his times at bat did each player hit safely?

a. Lou Gehrig

$$0.340 = 0.34 = \frac{34}{100} = 34\%$$

$$0.340 = 34\%$$

b. Babe Ruth

$$0.342 = \frac{34.2}{100} = 34.2\%$$

$$0.342 = 34.2\%$$

To write a decimal as a per cent: Move the decimal point two places to the right and write the symbol %.

Example 2: Change each fraction to a per cent.

	a. $\frac{3}{4}$	**b.** $\frac{3}{8}$	**c.** $\frac{2}{3}$
Change the fraction to a decimal.	$4\overline{)3.00}$ = 0.75	$8\overline{)3.000}$ = 0.375	$3\overline{)2.00}$ = $0.66\frac{2}{3}$
Change the decimal to a per cent.	75%	37.5%	$66\frac{2}{3}\%$

This form is usually used rather than $66.\overline{6}\%$.

Example 3: Change $2\frac{3}{5}$ to a per cent.

Write $2\frac{3}{5}$ as a fraction. $2\frac{3}{5} = \frac{13}{5}$

Change the fraction to a per cent as in Example 2. $5\overline{)13.00}$ = 2.60 → 260%

Wide World

Exercises

A Change each of the following to a per cent.

1. 0.28	**2.** 7.21	**3.** 4.6	**4.** 0.5
5. 1	**6.** 4	**7.** $\frac{31}{100}$	**8.** $\frac{300}{100}$

B

9. 0.53	**10.** 0.06	**11.** 0.7	**12.** 0.002
13. 1.12	**14.** 2.5	**15.** 4	**16.** 23
17. 0.125	**18.** 0.075	**19.** 1.375	**20.** $2.33\frac{1}{3}$
21. $\frac{3}{10}$	**22.** $\frac{1}{20}$	**23.** $\frac{1}{2}$	**24.** $\frac{3}{4}$
25. $\frac{1}{5}$	**26.** $\frac{1}{6}$	**27.** $\frac{3}{8}$	**28.** $\frac{2}{5}$
29. $\frac{1}{4}$	**30.** $\frac{1}{3}$	**31.** $\frac{3}{5}$	**32.** $\frac{5}{6}$
33. $\frac{1}{8}$	**34.** $\frac{4}{5}$	**35.** $\frac{5}{8}$	**36.** $\frac{7}{10}$
37. $\frac{7}{8}$	**38.** $\frac{9}{20}$	**39.** $\frac{4}{25}$	**40.** $\frac{7}{50}$
41. $\frac{9}{10}$	**42.** $\frac{2}{25}$	**43.** $\frac{7}{20}$	**44.** $\frac{9}{25}$
45. $1\frac{1}{3}$	**46.** $1\frac{3}{4}$	**47.** $1\frac{1}{2}$	**48.** $1\frac{1}{4}$
49. $2\frac{5}{8}$	**50.** $1\frac{7}{8}$	**51.** $3\frac{5}{6}$	**52.** $3\frac{1}{2}$

53. A 20% alcohol solution means there are 20 parts alcohol for 100 parts solution. How would you describe a solution which is 15 parts alcohol for 100 parts solution?

54. The interest for a new-car loan is stated as $8 per $100. What is the per cent of interest?

C Change each ratio to a per cent.

55. 3 to 2	**56.** 6:5	**57.** 4 to 3
58. $\frac{3}{4}$ to $\frac{1}{2}$	**59.** $\frac{7}{8}:\frac{5}{8}$	**60.** $1\frac{1}{2}$ to $1\frac{1}{4}$
61. 7.5 to 5.0	**62.** 3.2:2.4	**63.** 3.25 to 2.5

9.7 The Three Kinds of Per Cent Problems

When a proportion involves per cent, one denominator is 100. In a problem, you might have to find any one of the other three numbers.

$$\frac{3}{4} = \frac{75}{100}$$

part (3), whole (4), per cent amount (75), 100 (100)

What per cent?

Example 1: 12 is what per cent of 30?

part (12), per cent amount (what), 100 (per cent), whole (30)

$$\frac{12}{30} = \frac{p}{100}$$

$$p = 40$$

So 12 is 40% of 30.

Check:

$$\frac{12}{30} = \frac{p}{100}$$

$$\frac{12}{30} = \frac{40}{100}$$

$$12 \times 100 = 30 \times 40$$

$$1200 = 1200 \checkmark$$

What part?

Example 2: What is 71% of 142?

part (What), per cent amount (71), 100 (%), whole (142)

$$\frac{x}{142} = \frac{71}{100}$$

$$x = 100.82$$

So 71% of 142 is 100.82.

Check:

$$\frac{x}{142} = \frac{71}{100}$$

$$\frac{100.82}{142} = \frac{71}{100}$$

$$100.82 \times 100 = 142 \times 71$$

$$10082 = 10082 \checkmark$$

What whole?

Example 3: 7 is 25% of what?

part (7), per cent amount (25), 100 (%), whole (what)

$$\frac{7}{n} = \frac{25}{100}$$

$$n = 28$$

So 7 is 25% of 28.

Check:

$$\frac{7}{n} = \frac{25}{100}$$

$$\frac{7}{28} = \frac{25}{100}$$

$$7 \times 100 = 28 \times 25$$

$$700 = 700 \checkmark$$

Exercises

A Match each question with the correct proportion.

a. $\frac{75}{x} = \frac{60}{100}$ **b.** $\frac{x}{90} = \frac{45}{100}$ **c.** $\frac{x}{75} = \frac{60}{100}$

d. $\frac{45}{90} = \frac{x}{100}$ **e.** $\frac{60}{75} = \frac{x}{100}$ **f.** $\frac{90}{x} = \frac{45}{100}$

1. What is 60% of 75?
2. 60 is what per cent of 75?
3. 75 is 60% of what?
4. What is 45% of 90?
5. 45 is what per cent of 90?
6. 90 is 45% of what?

B Use proportions to solve.

7. 45 is what per cent of 75?
8. 80 is what per cent of 120?
9. 90 is what per cent of 150?
10. 66 is what per cent of 90?
11. What per cent of 80 is 24?
12. 8.5 out of 68 is what per cent?

See Example 1.

13. What is 16% of 85?
14. What is 40% of 25?
15. What is 60% of 80?
16. What is $33\frac{1}{3}$% of 6?
17. 25% of 28 is what?
18. How much is 40% of 60?

See Example 2.

19. 60 is 75% of what?
20. 90 is 40% of what?
21. 18 is 45% of what?
22. 88 is 80% of what?
23. 30% of what is 48?
24. 50% is 19 out of what?

See Example 3.

C

25. What is 100% of 28?
26. What is 125% of 28?
27. 92.4 is 28% of what?
28. 22 is what per cent of 50?
29. 43% of 628 is what?
30. 48% of what is 300?
31. How much is 46% of 120?
32. 6 out of 25 is what per cent?
33. 75% of what is 0.69?
34. 92% of 4000 is what?
35. 62% of what is 38.44?
36. What per cent of 100 is 23?

9.8 Solving Per Cent Problems

Per cent problems can be solved using almost the same method you use for other problems.

- Read the problem as many times as necessary to determine the given facts.
- Decide which of these questions is asked:
  What per cent? What part? What whole?
- Represent the unknown fact with a variable.
- Translate the problem into a proportion and solve.
- Check the solution against the conditions of the problem.
- Answer the problem.

Example 1: Wes made 9 out of 15 field-goal attempts. What per cent of his field-goal attempts did he make?

Question: 9 out of 15 is what per cent?

Let n = the per cent amount.

Proportion: $\frac{9}{15} = \frac{n}{100}$ *Solution:* $n = 60$

Check: Is 60% of 15 equal to 9? ✓

So Wes made 60% of his field-goal attempts.

Russ Reed—Photo Trends

Example 2: Jan must score at least 70% to pass an exam. If 150 points are possible, how many are needed to pass?

Question: What part out of 150 is 70%?

Let n = the part.

Proportion: $\frac{n}{150} = \frac{70}{100}$ *Solution:* $n = 105$

Check: Is 105 points out of 150 equivalent to 70 out of 100? ✓

So Jan must score at least 105 points to pass.

Example 3: At a sale, each item was reduced 20%. What was the regular price of a radio that was reduced $8?

Question: 8 out of <u>what whole</u> is 20%?

Let n = the whole.

Proportion: $\frac{8}{n} = \frac{20}{100}$ *Solution:* $n = 40$

Check: Is 20% of $40 equal to $8? ✓

So the regular price of the radio was $40.

Exercises

Webb Photos

A Decide what is asked in each problem. Express it as a question as in the examples.

1. At Lyle's restaurant, Iris received $28 in tips on customer bills of $200. What per cent did her customers tip?

2. A certain cereal is 12% protein. How many ounces of protein are in a 14-ounce package?

3. Salespeople at Thorn's make 3% commission. How much must a person sell to make $150 in commissions?

B Use a proportion to solve. (See Example 1 on page 298.)

4. Exercise 1 above.

5. Rona answered 32 out of 40 test questions correctly. What per cent did she answer correctly?

6. Ruth paid $640 in income tax on a gross income of $8000. What per cent of her gross income was the tax?

7. The Crusade of Mercy has collected $21,000. Their goal is $28,000. What per cent of their goal have they reached?

8. The body of a 140-pound person has 56 to 91 pounds of water in the tissues. At least what per cent of the person's weight is due to the water? At most what per cent?

9. In a contest, Wally scored 37 points out of a possible 40. Express his score as a per cent.

10. There were 80 flights into the air terminal yesterday. Of these, 68 were jets. What per cent of the flights were jets?

11. Elaine needs 720 points to win a prize. She has 630 points now. What per cent of the number of points needed does she have now?

Collier Photographics

Use a proportion to solve. (See Example 2 on page 298.)

12. Exercise 2 on page 299.

13. Joan can save $33\frac{1}{3}\%$ by buying some clothing at a sale. How much can she save on clothes that regularly sell for $120?

14. James borrowed $680 at 8.5% interest for one year. How much interest will he pay if he pays off the loan on time?

15. About 7.5% of men are color-blind. Out of every 2000 men, about how many are color-blind?

16. About 0.1% of women are color-blind. Out of every 2000 women, about how many are color-blind?

17. At Davis Realty Company, a broker gets a 3% commission on each sale. What is the commission for selling a $70,000 house?

18. The monthly carrying charge on many charge accounts is 1.5% of the unpaid balance. What is the carrying charge on a balance of $160?

19. For adults, the recommended daily allowance (RDA) of calcium is 1 gram. One cup of whole milk contains 28.8% of the RDA. How much calcium is in a cup of milk?

20. For teenagers, the RDA (see Exercise 19) of iron is 18 milligrams. One whole egg contains about 6.5% of the RDA. How much iron is in an egg?

Use a proportion to solve. (See Example 3 on page 299.)

21. Exercise 3 on page 299.

22. The profit on each item Helen sells is 5%. How much must she sell to make a profit of $50?

23. The Badgers won $66\frac{2}{3}\%$ of their games. If they won 12 games, how many did they play?

24. At the age of 7, a girl is about 74% of her adult height. If a 7-year-old girl is 48 inches tall, how tall can she expect to be? Give your answer to the nearest inch.

25. At the age of 10, a boy is about 78% of his adult height. If a 10-year-old boy is 56 inches tall, how tall can he expect to be? Give your answer to the nearest inch.

26. One cup of pineapple juice supplies about 22.2 milligrams, or 37% of the RDA, of vitamin C. (See Exercise 19.) What is the RDA of vitamin C?

C Solve each problem.

27. What is 220% of 30?

28. What is 0.1% of 20?

29. 150% of what is 72?

30. 40 is what per cent of 20?

31. What is 0.01% of 153?

32. 75 is what per cent of 25?

33. 230 is what per cent of 100?

34. 132 is what per cent of 100?

35. 152% of what is 152?

36. 300% of what is 3?

De Wys, Inc.

37. The speedometer on a car may be as much as 5% off. If a speedometer reads 55 miles per hour, by how many miles per hour may it be wrong? What is the fastest the car might be going? The slowest?

38. The largest mountain lion on record weighed 276 pounds. This is 184% of the weight of the average mountain lion. How much does the average mountain lion weigh?

9.9 Estimating Per Cents

You have seen that per cent problems can be translated into proportions. But a problem that asks "What part?" can also be translated directly into an equation that is not a proportion.

Example 1: What is 71% of 142?

$$x = 0.71 \times 142$$

Write the per cent as a decimal.

Now the answer to the question can easily be estimated.

Example 2: Estimate 71% of 142.

$x = 0.71 \times 142$

0.7×140 — Round the per cent to the nearest tenth. Round the other number to any convenient place.

$7 \times 0.1 \times 140$ — Rewrite 0.7 as 7×0.1.

7×14.0 — Use the shortcut to multiply by 0.1.

98 — Estimate

Notice how close the estimate is to the exact amount. ⇨ exact amount $0.71 \times 142 = 100.82$

Exercises

A Express each per cent as a decimal.

1. 23%	**2.** 50%	**3.** 64.5%
4. $33\frac{1}{3}\%$	**5.** 122%	**6.** 0.1%
7. 43%	**8.** 140%	**9.** 1.5%

How would you round to estimate each answer?

10. 0.92×239 **11.** 0.83×19 **12.** 0.48×78

13. 1.23×64 **14.** 5.66×22 **15.** $0.66\frac{2}{3} \times 46$

16. 0.625×73 **17.** 0.68×93.6 **18.** 0.07×138

Express as a product in which one factor is 0.1.

19. 0.3 **20.** 0.9 **21.** 0.5

22. 1.2 **23.** 5.7 **24.** 11.6

B Copy and complete each table.

	%	of	estimate	exact
25.	37%	113		
27.	19%	369		
29.	27%	238		
31.	73%	188		

	%	of	estimate	exact
26.	62%	212		
28.	8%	783		
30.	41%	28		
32.	94%	64		

For each exercise listed below, estimate the answer.

33. Exercise 2 on page 299 **34.** Exercise 13 on page 300

35. Exercise 14 on page 300 **36.** Exercise 19 on page 300

C The results of some recent elections are given below. The total vote and the per cent of those voting for each candidate is listed. Estimate how many people voted for each candidate. Express your answers in hundred thousands.

Jim Anderson/Woodfin Camp & Associates, Inc.

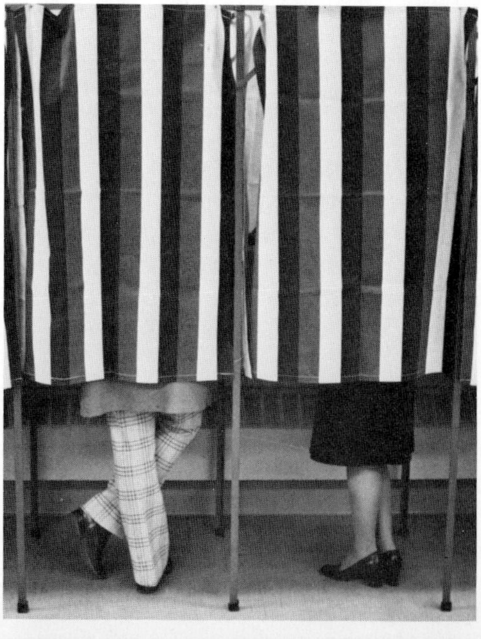

37. 523,527; Babbit 56%, Mecham 44%

38. 530,695; Clinton 63%, Lowe 37%

39. 6,621,313; Brown 61%, Younger 39%

40. 800,535; Lanam 60%, Strickland 40%

9.10 More Per Cent Problems

Often you must do some computing before writing a proportion.

Examples: Write a proportion for each problem below.

1. A shirt sells for \$12.60 after it is reduced 30%. What is the regular price?

The regular price is the full amount.		This much is taken off.		The selling price is the amount left.
100%	−	30%	=	70%

\$12.60 out of what is 70%?

$$\frac{12.60}{p} = \frac{70}{100}$$

2. Food that cost \$10 last month cost \$10.90 this month. What was the per cent of increase (or per cent of *inflation*)?

cost this month		cost last month		increase in cost
\$10.90	−	\$10.00	=	\$0.90

\$0.90 out of \$10 is what per cent?

$$\frac{0.90}{10} = \frac{p}{100}$$

3. If 1 pound (16 ounces) of ground meat makes 12 ounces of cooked meat patties, what is the per cent of decrease?

raw weight		cooked weight		decrease in weight
16 oz	−	12 oz	=	4 oz

4 out of 16 is what per cent?

$$\frac{4}{16} = \frac{p}{100}$$

Exercises

A What operation must be done in each case before a proportion can be written?

1. If the price was \$4 after it was reduced 20%, what was the regular price?

2. If \$5546 was left after a 6% commission was taken out, what was the original amount?

3. If the price of gasoline rises from \$1.25 to \$1.50 a gallon, what is the per cent of increase?

4. If the price of a shirt is reduced from \$7 to \$5.60, by what per cent is it reduced?

B Write and solve a proportion for each problem.

5. Exercise 1 6. Exercise 2 7. Exercise 3 8. Exercise 4

	per cent reduced	sale price	regular price
9.	20%	\$ 8.56	
11.	30%	\$ 42.63	
13.	45%	\$137.50	
15.	15%	\$ 6.80	

	per cent reduced	sale price	regular price
10.	25%	\$ 15.99	
12.	$33\frac{1}{3}$%	\$ 63.60	
14.	42%	\$348	
16.	50%	\$ 6.50	

17. An actor's agent receives 10% commission. How much must the actor make to have \$450 left after the commission is deducted?

18. The Bartons are selling their house. The real-estate agent's commission is 7%. The Bartons want to have \$46,500 left after the commission is deducted. What should be the selling price?

19. Mark works for Stein's Department Store. He gets a 20% discount on everything he buys at Stein's. He has \$16 to spend on a ski sweater. How expensive a sweater can he buy, if he buys the sweater at Stein's?

20. An increase from 10 to 15 is what per cent of increase?

21. An increase from 8 to 10 is what per cent of increase?

22. An increase from 3.2 to 3.6 is what per cent of increase?

23. An increase from $2\frac{1}{2}$ to $3\frac{3}{4}$ is what per cent of increase?

24. Mr. Larson's salary increased from \$160 to \$180. What was the per cent of increase?

25. At N Enterprises, sales increased from \$250,000 to \$350,000. What was the per cent of increase?

26. A decrease from 10 to 7 is what per cent of decrease?

27. A decrease from 20 to 16 is what per cent of decrease?

28. A decrease from $\frac{3}{4}$ to $\frac{1}{2}$ is what per cent of decrease?

29. A decrease from 3.2 to 2.4 is what per cent of decrease?

30. An item which regularly sells for \$25 was purchased on sale for \$17.50. What was the per cent of decrease?

31. Mrs. Catalano sold 16 houses last year. This year she sold 14. What was the per cent of decrease in her number of sales?

C. E. Pefley

C When a hole is dug, the dirt removed is looser and occupies more space than before its removal. Builders often use the rule that there is a 25% increase in the volume of excavated material. Use this rule to do the following problems.

32. For a basement, a contractor digs a hole 6 by 9 by 2 meters. What volume of dirt must he get rid of?

33. A landscaper needs 20 cubic yards of loose dirt for a garden. About how large a hole must be dug to supply it?

Terms and Symbols Review

Which example would you give for each item?

1. ratio of 2 to 5

2. 3 ratios equivalent to $\frac{3}{4}$

3. proportion

4. per cent

5. 3 ways to write a ratio

6. cross products for $\frac{3}{4} = \frac{12}{16}$

7. means for $\frac{3}{4} = \frac{12}{16}$

a. $\frac{3}{4} = \frac{12}{16}$

b. $3 \times 16 = 4 \times 12$

c. 4 and 12

d. $\frac{6}{8}, \frac{9}{12}, \frac{12}{16}$

e. $\frac{1}{2}$, 1 to 2, 1:2

f. $16\frac{2}{3}\%$

g. 2:5

h. 3 and 16

Chapter 9 Review

Write a ratio for each of the following. 9.1

1. 3 hits to 4 times at bat

2. 3 votes to 2 votes

3. 4 baskets to 9 attempts

4. 7 baseballs to 10 bats

Write two equivalent ratios for each ratio. 9.2

5. $\frac{1}{2}$

6. $\frac{3}{4}$

7. $\frac{10}{16}$

8. $\frac{5}{3}$

9. $\frac{8}{6}$

10. $\frac{3}{3}$

Solve each proportion. 9.3

11. $\frac{1}{4} = \frac{n}{20}$

12. $\frac{2}{3} = \frac{6}{n}$

13. $\frac{n}{8} = \frac{10}{16}$

14. $\frac{8}{n} = \frac{16}{18}$

15. $\frac{4}{5} = \frac{n}{10}$

16. $\frac{n}{8} = \frac{14}{16}$

Use a proportion to solve each problem. 9.4

17. There are 90 calories in 2 slices of bacon. How many calories are in 5 slices?

18. If a 200-meter roll of wire weighs 480 kg, how much do 93 meters of the wire weigh?

9.5 Copy and complete the tables below.

	per cent	fraction	decimal
19.	72%	___	___
21.	$6\frac{1}{2}$%	___	___

	per cent	fraction or mixed number	decimal
20.	2.8%	___	___
22.	121%	___	___

9.6 Express as a per cent.

23. 0.47 **24.** 1.03 **25.** 0.426

26. $\frac{3}{4}$ **27.** $\frac{3}{12}$ **28.** $\frac{7}{20}$

29. $\frac{3}{2}$ **30.** 1 **31.** 2

32. $\frac{5}{2}$ **33.** $3\frac{1}{4}$ **34.** $3\frac{1}{2}$

9.7 Solve each of the following.

35. 50% of 75 is what number? **36.** 56% of 56 is what number?

37. 20% of what number is 9? **38.** 6% of what number is 18?

39. 12 is what per cent of 16? **40.** 8 is what per cent of 10?

9.8 Solve.

41. Jean bought a coat marked down 35% from the regular price of \$60. How much did she save?

42. Mr. Bathke sold 16 cases of merchandise last week. This was 40% of his monthly quota. What was his monthly quota?

9.9 **43.** Estimate 48% of 281.

9.10 **44.** The price of the book was reduced 20%. What is the regular price?

Change each ratio to lowest terms.

1. $\frac{30}{50}$ 2. $\frac{36}{48}$ 3. $\frac{16}{24}$

4. $\frac{27}{81}$ 5. $\frac{21}{12}$ 6. $\frac{18}{54}$

Solve each proportion.

7. $\frac{2}{3} = \frac{n}{24}$ 8. $\frac{5}{8} = \frac{15}{n}$ 9. $\frac{7}{8} = \frac{n}{16}$

10. $\frac{5}{n} = \frac{20}{48}$ 11. $\frac{n}{6} = \frac{20}{24}$ 12. $\frac{3}{4} = \frac{18}{n}$

Solve.

13. 6% of 200 is what number? 14. 2.5% of 40 is what number?

15. 12 is what per cent of 25? 16. 9 is what per cent of 20?

17. 25% of what number is 8? 18. 75% of what number is 90?

Complete the following tables.

	fraction	decimal	per cent
19.	$\frac{1}{5}$	_____	_____
21.	_____	0.9	_____
23.	_____	_____	63%

	fraction or mixed number	decimal	per cent
20.	_____	0.875	_____
22.	$\frac{3}{8}$	_____	_____
24.	_____	_____	150%

RATE YOURSELF

Number Correct	
27–28	Superior
24–26	Excellent
21–23	Good
15–20	Fair
0–14	Poor

25. Estimate 52% of 679.

Use a proportion to solve each problem.

26. At a fast walk, you use about 80 calories in 15 minutes. How long must you walk fast to use up the calories in a 360-calorie slice of pie?

27. An author received a check for $150. This was 5% of the sales of her book. What were the sales for the book?

28. If a wrench sells for $4 after it is reduced 20%, what is the regular price?

H. Armstrong Roberts

activities

SCRAMBLED CROSSWORD

Copy the pattern below on graph paper. Then unscramble each term and write it in the proper boxes.

ACROSS

2. EVAQUELINT
6. TROFY
7. HELOW
8. BRAVELIAS
9. THIGE
12. CUNEO
14. ABES
17. LAQUE
19. TREME
21. FOURLAM
23. ELUVA
24. IP
25. TSE
28. TRAMENOUR
30. ITGID
31. IXS
32. LIME
34. VEGATINE
35. RAGAVEE
38. NET
39. LYMBOS
41. THIXS
44. WEVELT
46. ANDTHUSHOT
48. MOULVE
49. ATRIO
50. DUNHERD

DOWN

1. RINGIO
2. PLAXEME
3. TUNI
4. WOT
5. SEDGERE
9. MEERSTEX
10. TRUMPERATEE
11. CARTOF
13. TUMTAMVOICE
15. LAHF
16. EMDRAINER
18. RORED
20. NEVE
22. TIXSY
26. USADIR
27. TIFFY
29. NOE
32. MHAT
33. THENGL
36. DADED
37. VEENEL
39. VOLES
40. TRILE
42. THENT
43. FOTO
45. PUC
47. ONT

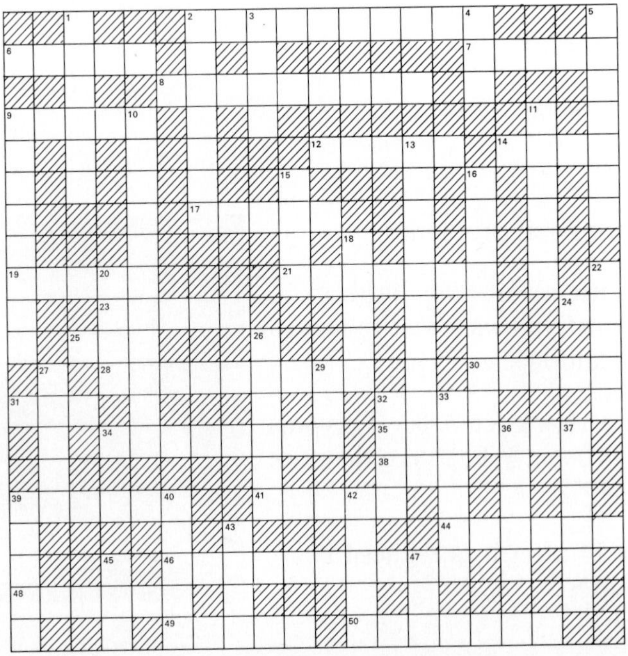

Getting Ready for Chapter 10

Tell which figures are named by each of these words.

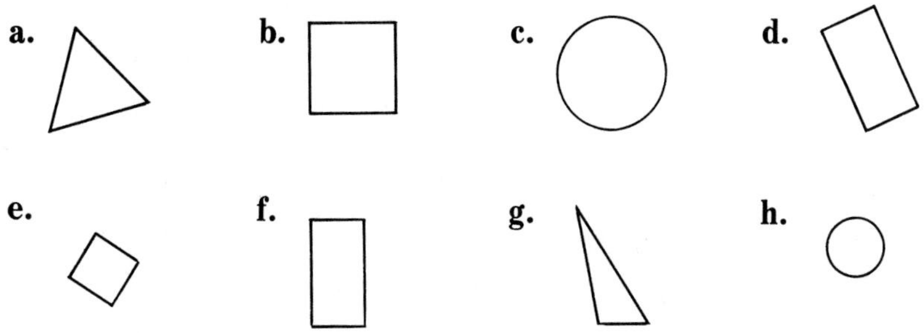

1. circles **2.** rectangles

3. squares **4.** triangles

Write two equivalent ratios for each ratio. 9.2

5. $\frac{1}{3}$ **6.** $\frac{3}{4}$ **7.** $\frac{2}{5}$

8. $\frac{5}{2}$ **9.** $\frac{9}{4}$ **10.** $\frac{3}{2}$

11. $\frac{12}{15}$ **12.** $\frac{24}{20}$ **13.** $\frac{18}{72}$

Solve each proportion. 9.3

14. $\frac{3}{4} = \frac{n}{20}$ **15.** $\frac{n}{8} = \frac{1}{4}$

16. $\frac{6}{9} = \frac{24}{n}$ **17.** $\frac{3}{n} = \frac{9}{15}$

10

Compute.

18. $8 \times 2\frac{3}{4}$ **19.** $3\frac{1}{2} \times 16$ 4.5

20. 0.6×14 **21.** 12×3.5 5.4

10

INDIRECT MEASUREMENT

Courtesy Robertshaw Controls Co.

Courtesy Sears, Roebuck & Co.

There's an old mathematical joke that goes something like this:

Problem: Give three ways a clock can be used to find the height of a tall building:

Answer:

1. Lower the clock by a tape measure from the roof to the ground.
2. Drop the clock off the roof, time the fall, and find the distance by using the formula $d = 16t^2$ for falling bodies.
3. On a sunny day, find the ratio of the clock's height to the length of its shadow. Measure the building's shadow and use a proportion to find the height.

The first method is a *direct measurement* because you are actually measuring the building itself. The other two methods are *indirect measurements* because you are really measuring something else. You'll learn how to make indirect measurements in this chapter.

Similar Figures 10.1

H. Armstrong Roberts

When a photograph is enlarged, you expect it to look like the original. You wouldn't want the picture made 5 times as tall but only 2 times as wide. Everything would look tall and skinny in the enlargement. You want everything to keep the same shape.

In mathematics, when figures have the same shape, we say the figures are *similar*.

similar figures

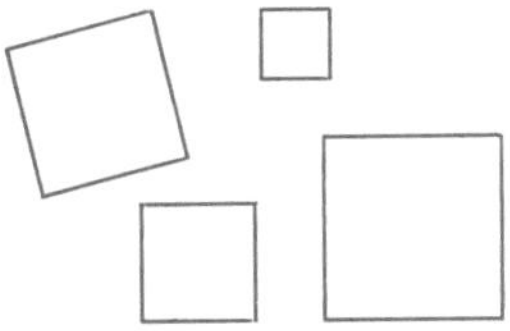

figures that are not similar

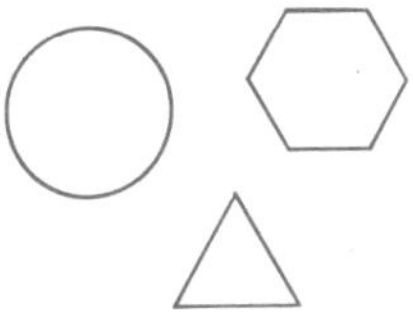

> **Similar figures** have exactly the same shape but may have different sizes.

Similar figures could be the same size. In that case, one figure is an exact copy of the other. If similar figures have different sizes, then one figure can be enlarged or reduced to make it an exact copy of the other.

These two triangles are similar. You could enlarge the first figure to make it an exact copy of the other.

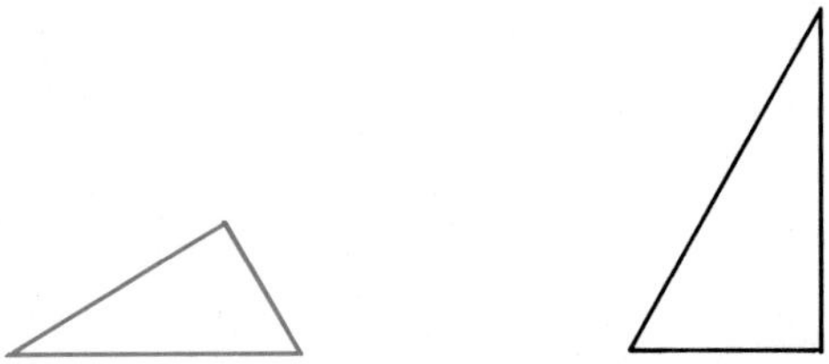

These figures may not look similar at first. If you "turn" one of the triangles, it makes it easier to see that they have the same shape.

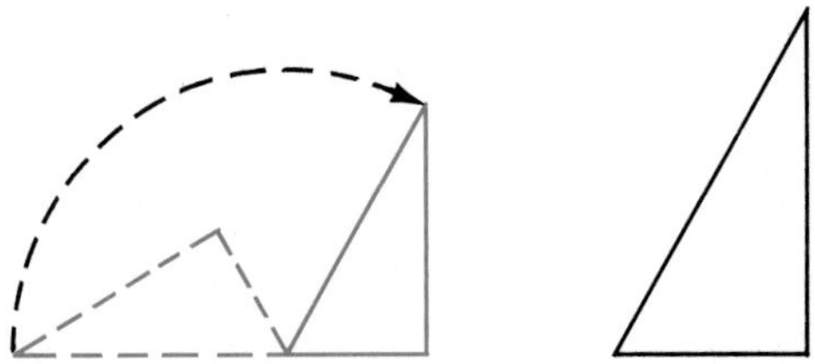

The two figures below are also similar. You could reduce the first figure to make it an exact copy of the other.

Again, the figures may not look similar at first. Turning either figure does not help. But you can "flip" one of them to make it easier to see that they are similar.

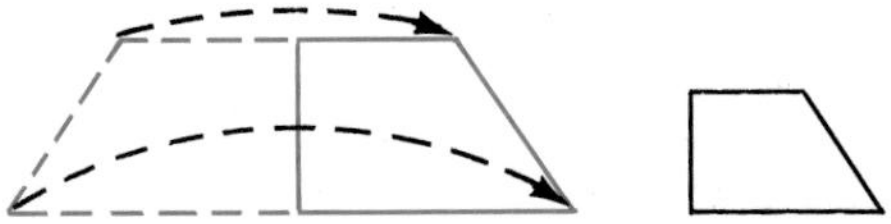

When we use triangles, the angles are usually labeled with letters. We name a triangle by using these letters. The letters can be named in any order. (△ is the symbol for "triangle.")

Example 1: Give six names for the triangle shown.

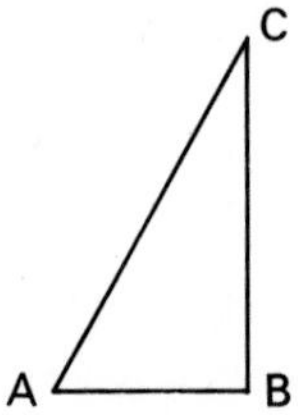

can be named

△ABC	△BAC	△CAB
△ACB	△BCA	△CBA

Example 2: Tell which triangles are similar.

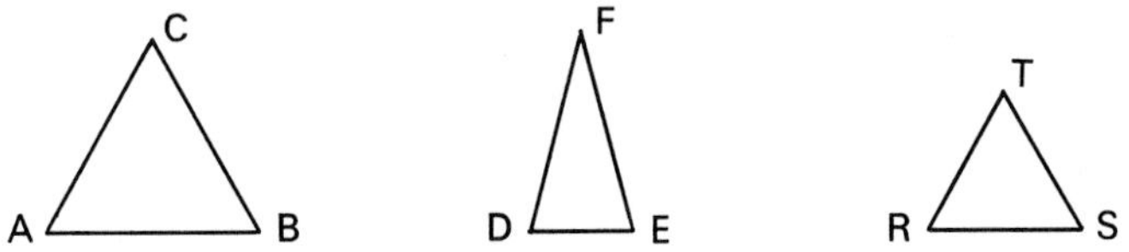

$\triangle ABC$ is similar to $\triangle RST$ because it could be reduced to be an exact copy. $\triangle DEF$ is not similar to either of the other triangles. It could never be enlarged or reduced so that it would be an exact copy of either of the other two triangles.

Exercises

A Choose the figure in each row that is similar to the colored figure.

1. a. b. c. d.

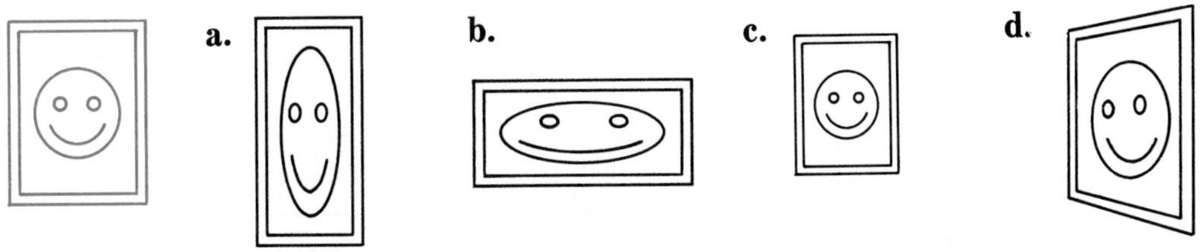

2. a. b. c. d.

3. a. b. c. d.

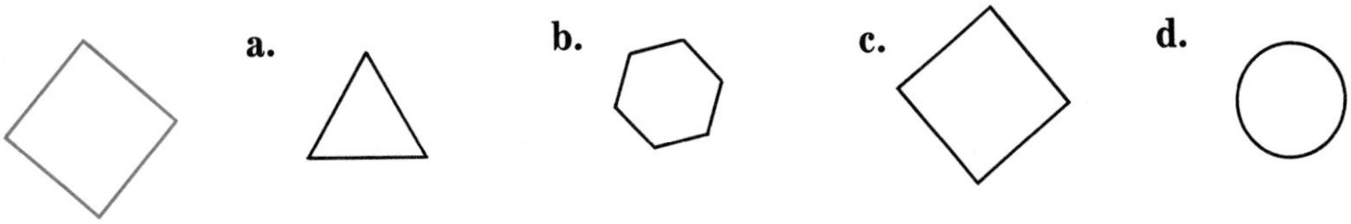

4. a. b. c. d.

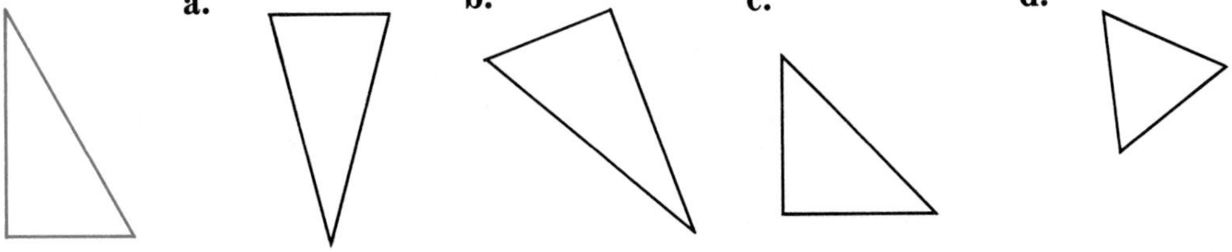

B Are the two figures similar? (*Hint:* Could you enlarge or reduce the first figure to make it an exact copy of the other?)

5.

6.

7.

8.

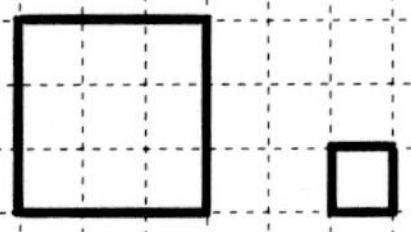

9.

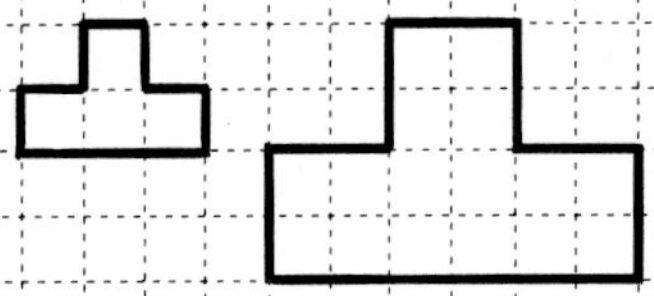

10.

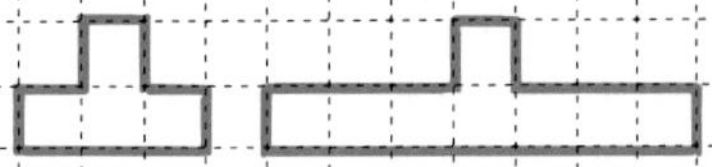

11.

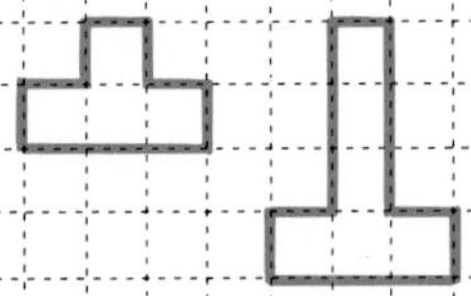

12.

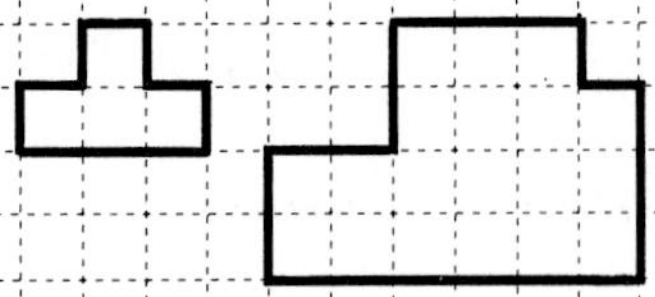

13.

14.

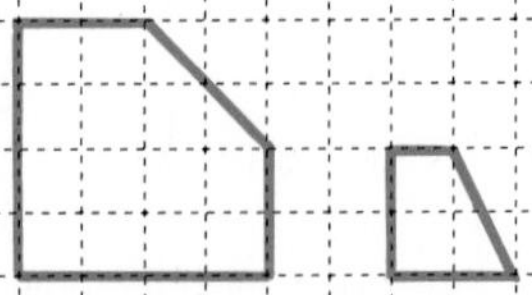

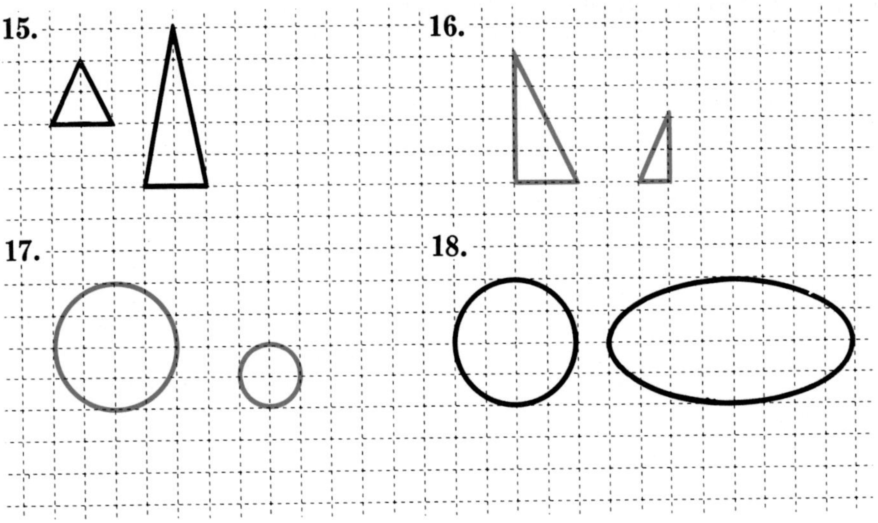

19. Using the figures below, name the triangles that are similar.

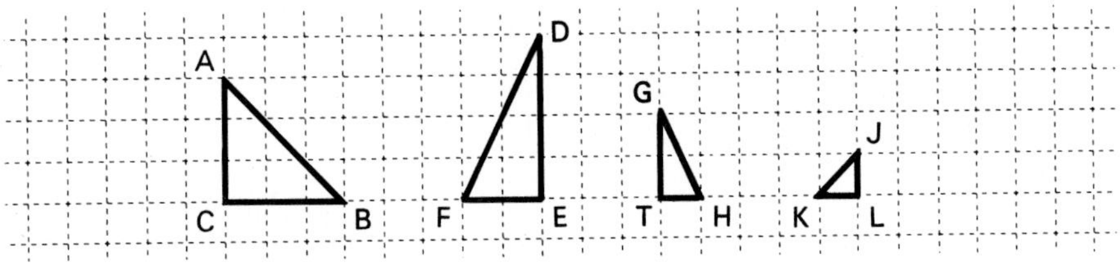

20. Give 5 other names for $\triangle DEF$.

C Answer each question.

21. Are all squares similar?

22. Are all rectangles similar?

23. Are all circles similar?

24. Are all triangles similar?

Use graph paper to do the following.

25. Draw 2 rectangles that are similar.

26. Draw 2 rectangles that are not similar.

27. Draw 2 triangles that are similar.

28. Draw 2 triangles that are not similar.

10.2 Corresponding Angles and Sides

Enlarging or reducing a triangle changes the lengths of the sides, but the measures of the angles remain the same. The symbols $\not)$, $\not\not)$, and $\not\not\not)$ are used to show which angles have the same measure.

△CDE is similar to △FGH.

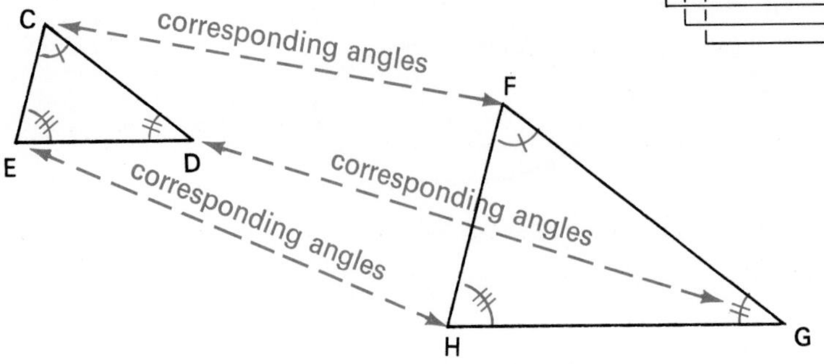

Note: Corresponding angles are listed in the same order when two similar triangles are named.

> In similar triangles, angles that have the same measure are **corresponding angles.**

Example 1: Tell which angles are corresponding angles.

△ABC is similar to △RTS.

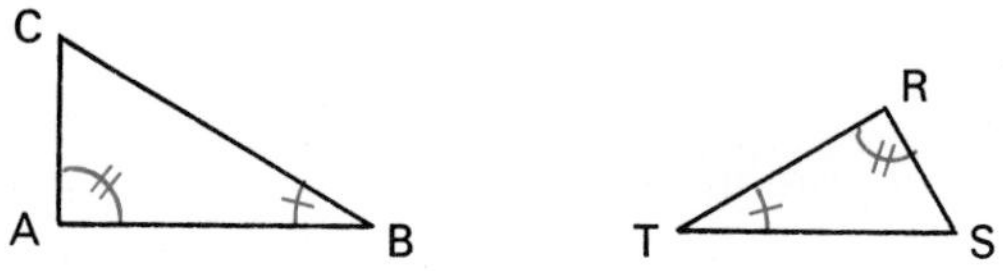

Solution: ∠A and ∠R ← ∠ is the symbol for "angle."

∠B and ∠T

∠C and ∠S ← Notice that when two pairs of angles are marked, the third pair can be left unmarked.

Example 2: Tell which sides are corresponding sides.

△KLM is similar to △XZY.

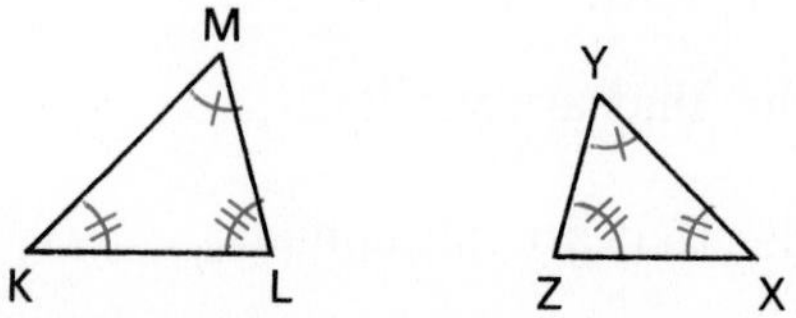

Solution: There are three pairs of corresponding sides.

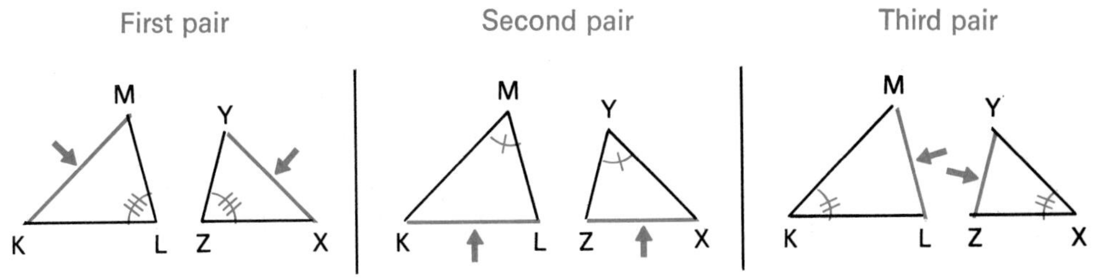

sides KM and XY   sides KL and XZ   sides LM and ZY

> In similar triangles, **corresponding sides** are the sides opposite corresponding angles.

Exercises

A Name the corresponding angles for each pair of similar triangles. (See Example 1.)

1.

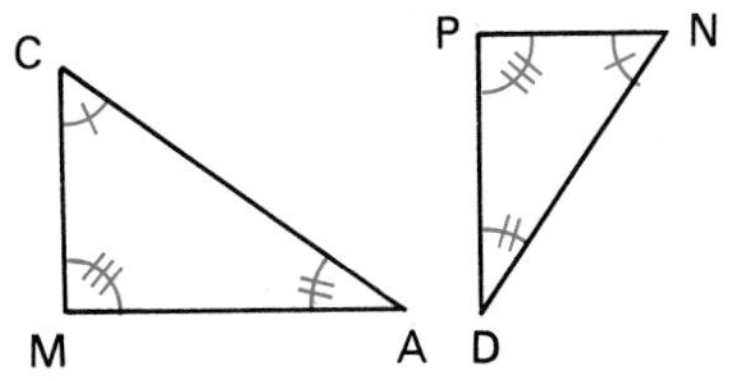

2.

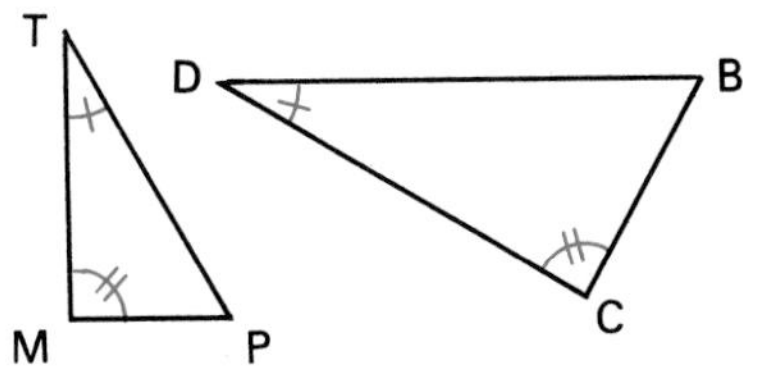

Name the corresponding sides for each pair of similar triangles. (See Example 2.)

3.

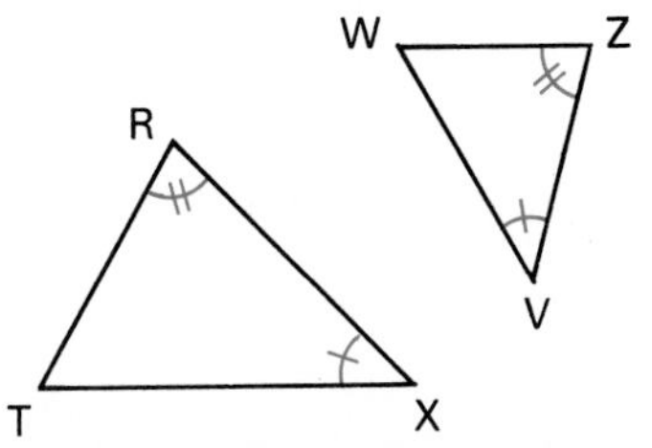

4.

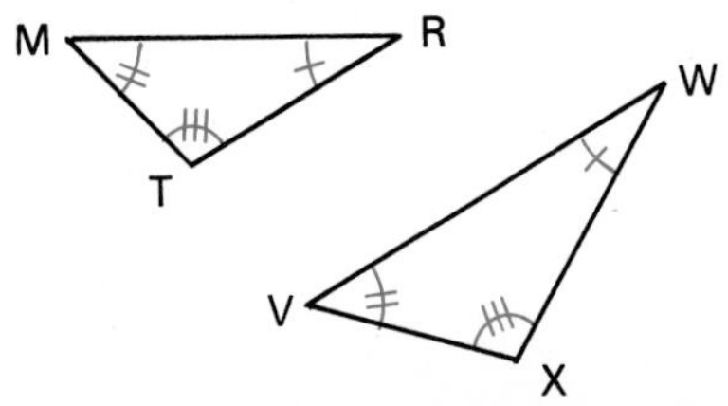

B Name the corresponding angles and sides for each pair of similar triangles.

5.

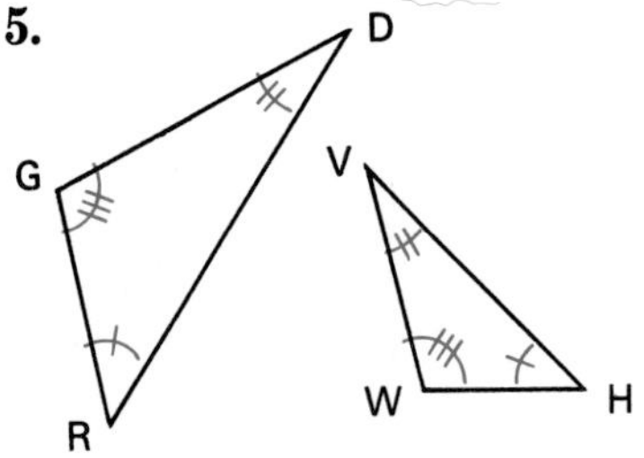

6.

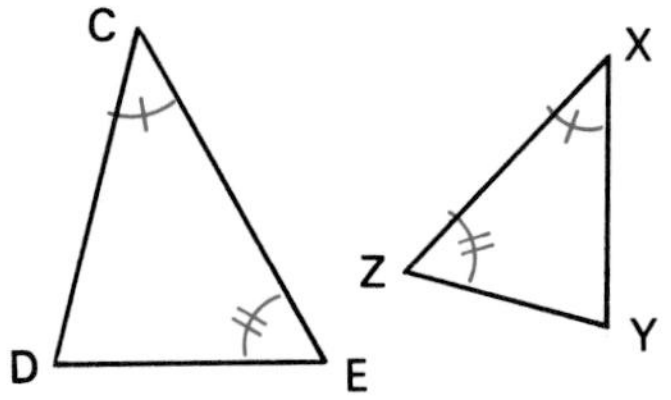

Corresponding angles of the similar triangles are listed. Name the corresponding sides.

7.

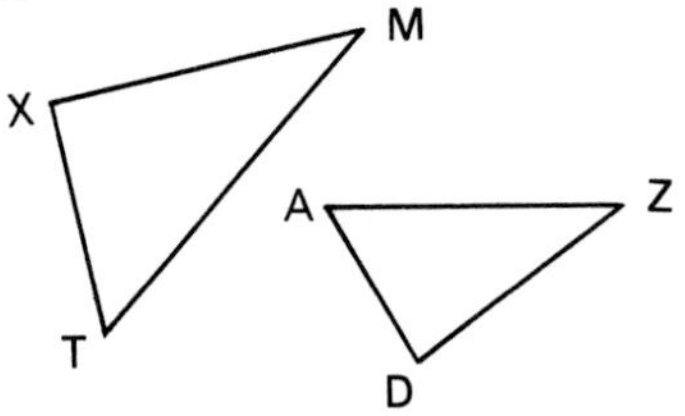

∠X and ∠D

∠M and ∠Z

∠T and ∠A

8.

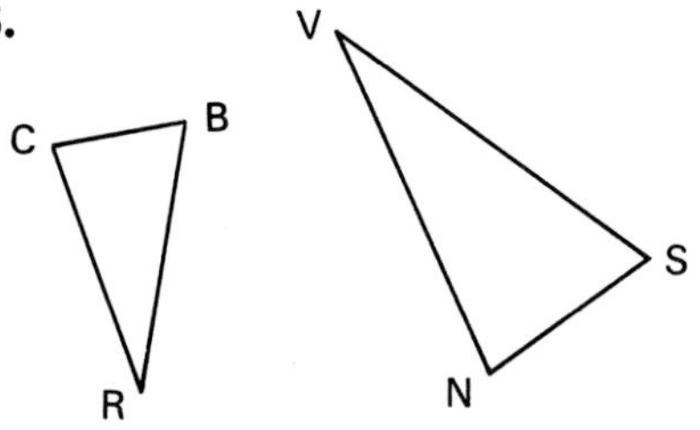

∠R and ∠V

∠B and ∠S

∠C and ∠N

Corresponding sides of the similar triangles are listed. Name the corresponding angles.

9.

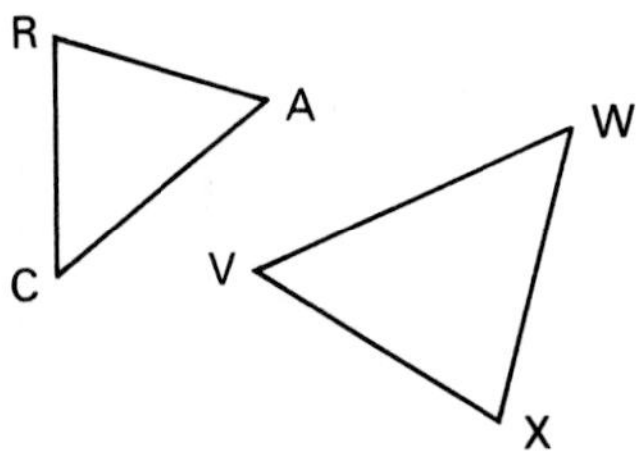

sides AC and VW

sides CR and WX

sides RA and XV

10.

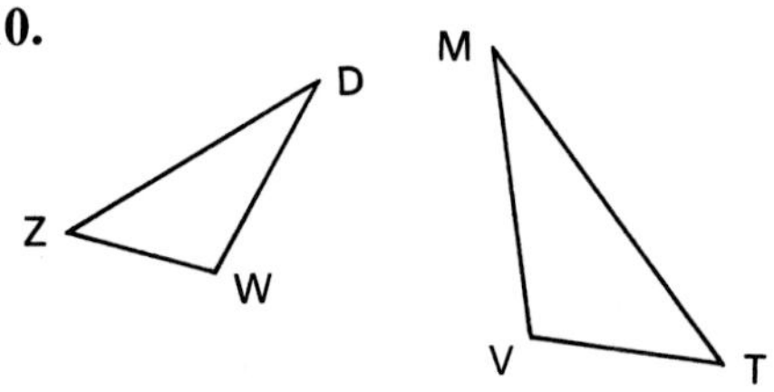

sides DW and MV

sides ZW and TV

sides ZD and TM

Name the corresponding angles and the corresponding sides for each pair of similar triangles.

Example:

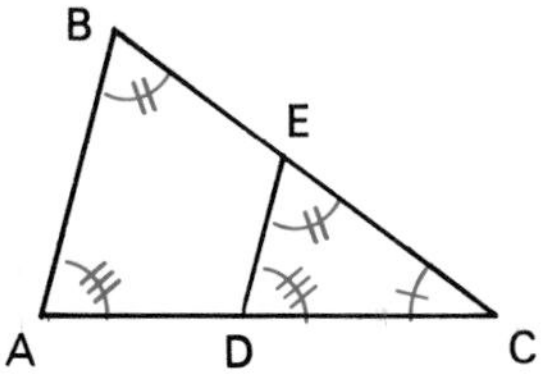

Hint: Think of sliding △DEC off △ABC.

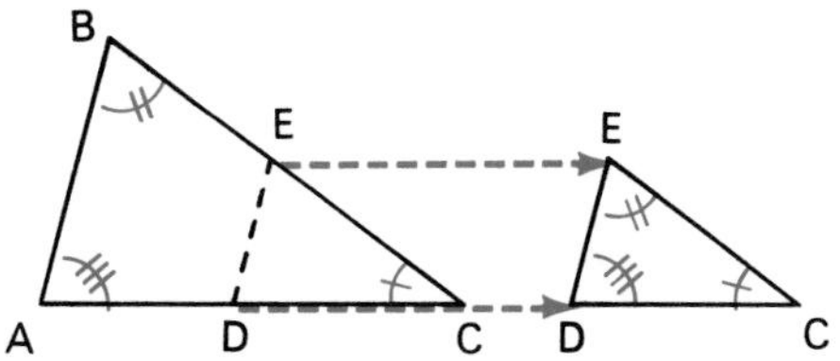

Solution: Corresponding angles

∠A and ∠EDC ← Using three letters shows that we don't mean ∠EDA.

∠B and ∠DEC

∠C is the same for both triangles.
(But we could name it two ways to show what we mean: ∠ACB and ∠DCE.)

Corresponding sides

sides BC and EC

sides AC and DC

sides AB and DE

11.

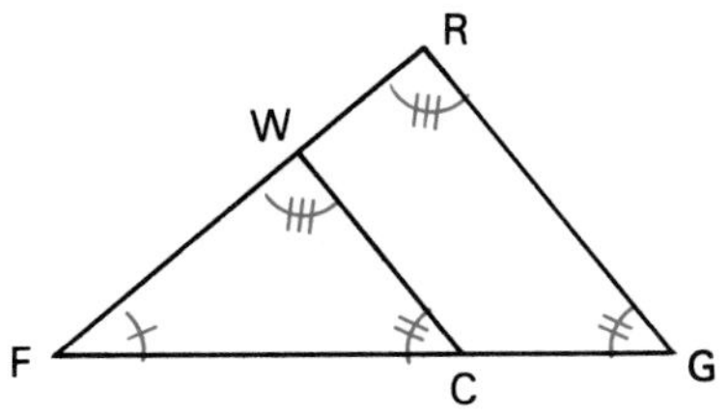

12.

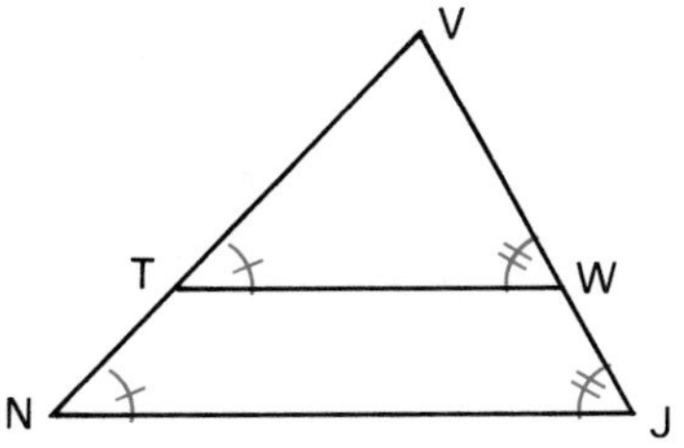

13.

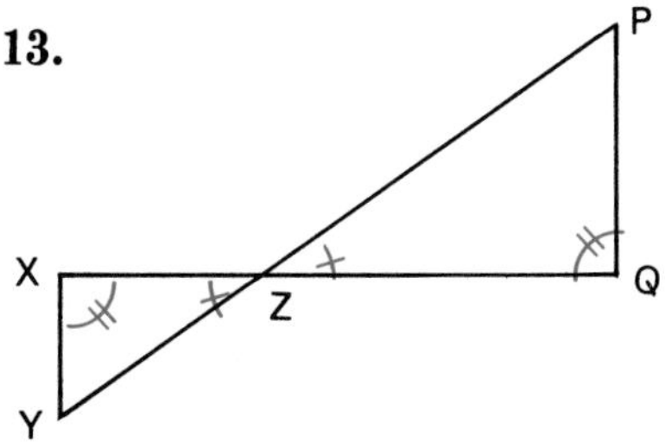

14.

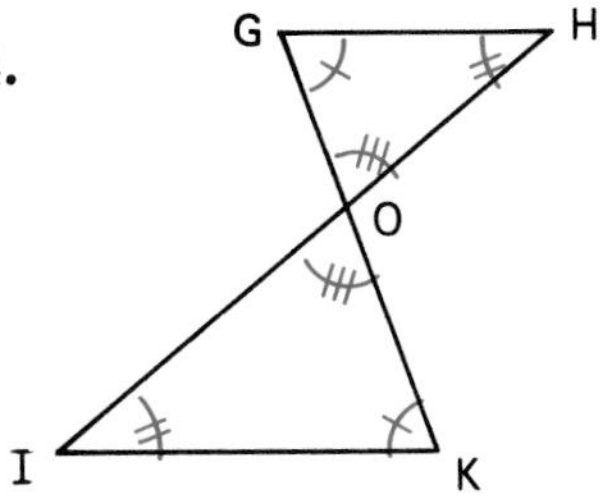

C Give all the pairs of corresponding angles and sides.

15. △PQR is similar to △MTF.

16. △YWZ is similar to △PEG.

17. △DEF is similar to △KLO.

18. △TUV is similar to △ABC.

10.3 Similar Triangles

When a triangle is enlarged or reduced, the ratios of the lengths of corresponding sides are equal. Note that symbols like AB and DE stand for the lengths of the sides.

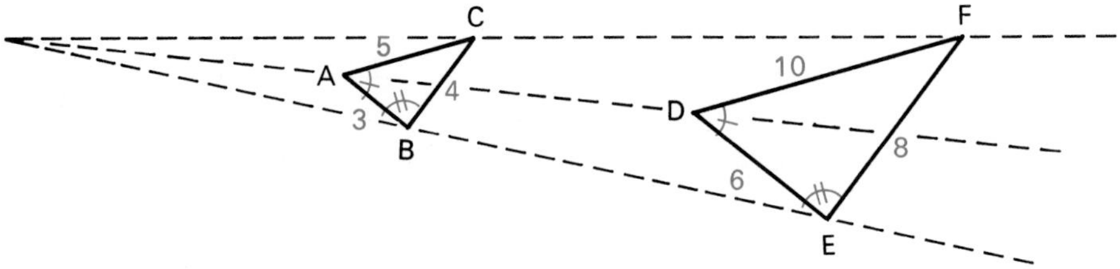

$$\frac{AB}{DE} = \frac{3}{6} = \frac{1}{2} \qquad \frac{BC}{EF} = \frac{4}{8} = \frac{1}{2} \qquad \frac{AC}{DF} = \frac{5}{10} = \frac{1}{2}$$

Note: The numerator of each ratio is from △ABC and the denominator from △DEF.

Since the ratios of the lengths of corresponding sides are equal, the ratios can be expressed as proportions in many different ways.

$$\frac{AB}{DE} = \frac{BC}{EF} \rightarrow \frac{3}{6} = \frac{4}{8} \qquad \frac{BC}{EF} = \frac{AC}{DF} \rightarrow \frac{4}{8} = \frac{5}{10} \qquad \frac{AB}{DE} = \frac{AC}{DF} \rightarrow \frac{3}{6} = \frac{5}{10}$$

We can also choose the numerator of each ratio from △DEF and the denominator from △ABC. In that case, we obtain the following proportions. Notice that these proportions are the same as those above with both sides inverted.

$$\frac{DE}{AB} = \frac{EF}{BC} \rightarrow \frac{6}{3} = \frac{8}{4} \qquad \frac{EF}{BC} = \frac{DF}{AC} \rightarrow \frac{8}{4} = \frac{10}{5} \qquad \frac{DE}{AB} = \frac{DF}{AC} \rightarrow \frac{6}{3} = \frac{10}{5}$$

In similar triangles, corresponding sides are proportional.

Example 1: What letter should replace each question mark?

△RST is similar to △XYZ.

$\frac{s}{y} = \frac{r}{?}$ (x) $\frac{t}{z} = \frac{s}{?}$ (y) $\frac{r}{x} = \frac{t}{?}$ (z)

Example 2: Find the values of x and z.

△ABC is similar to △XYZ.

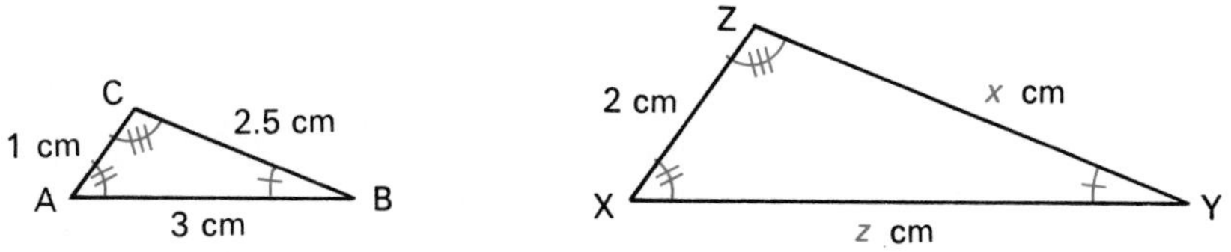

$$\frac{AC}{XZ} = \frac{AB}{XY}$$

$$\frac{1}{2} = \frac{3}{z}$$

$$z = 2 \times 3$$

$$z = 6$$

Check: Are the ratios 3 to 6 and 1 to 2 equivalent? ✓

$$\frac{AC}{XZ} = \frac{BC}{YZ}$$

$$\frac{1}{2} = \frac{2.5}{x}$$

$$x = 2 \times 2.5$$

$$x = 5$$

Check: Are the ratios 2.5 to 5 and 1 to 2 equivalent? ✓

Exercises

A What letter should replace each question mark?

△MNQ is similar to △RST.

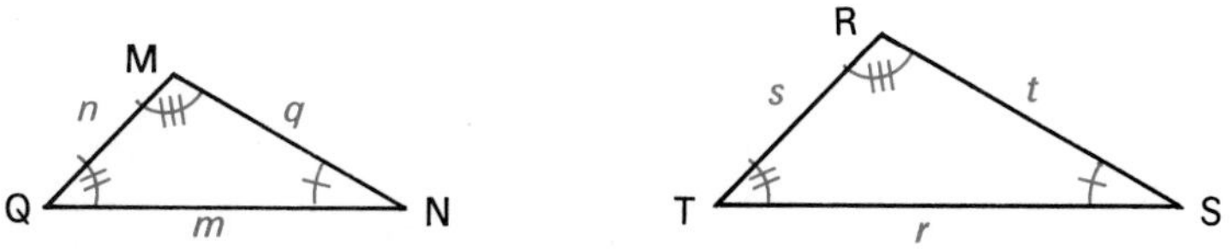

1. $\frac{n}{s} = \frac{q}{?}$
2. $\frac{n}{s} = \frac{m}{?}$
3. $\frac{s}{n} = \frac{t}{?}$
4. $\frac{r}{m} = \frac{?}{n}$
5. $\frac{q}{?} = \frac{m}{r}$
6. $\frac{?}{q} = \frac{s}{n}$

△ABC is similar to △AED.

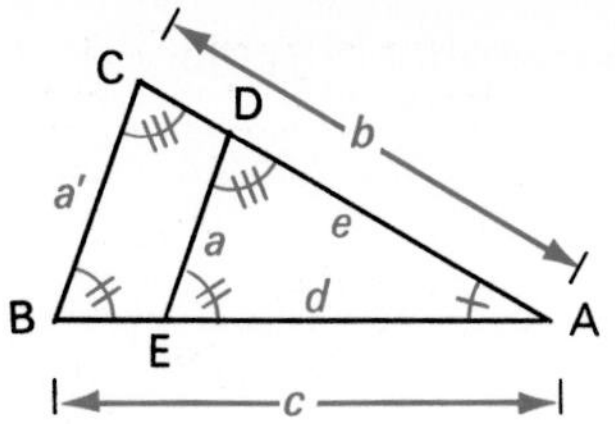

Note: *a′ is read a prime.*

7. $\frac{e}{b} = \frac{d}{?}$ 8. $\frac{a'}{?} = \frac{c}{d}$ 9. $\frac{a}{a'} = \frac{?}{c}$

10. $\frac{b}{?} = \frac{c}{d}$ 11. $\frac{?}{a'} = \frac{d}{c}$ 12. $\frac{d}{c} = \frac{?}{b}$

B Find the values of *x* and *z*.

13. △ABC is similar to △DEF.

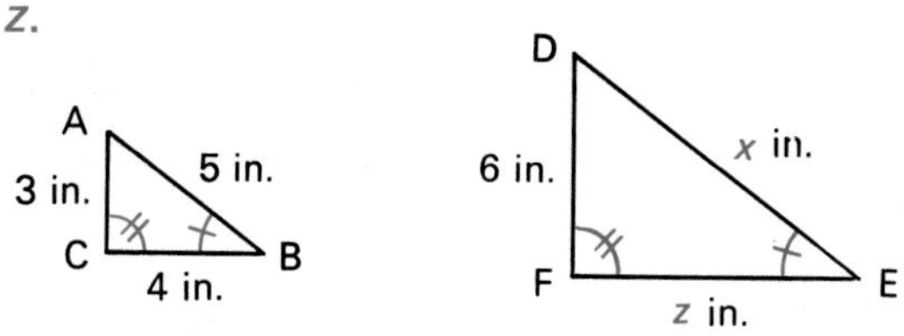

14. △GHI is similar to △JKL.

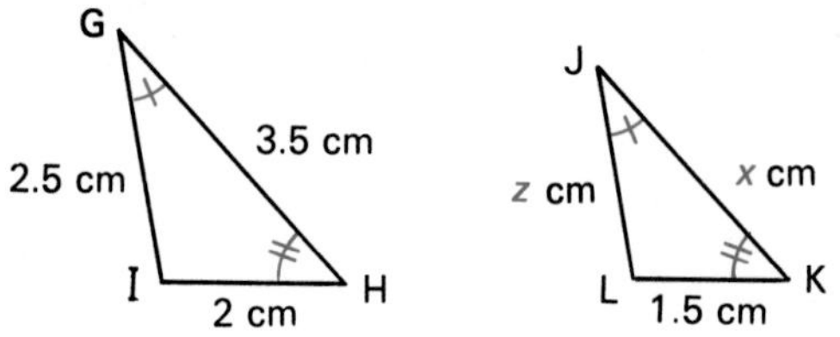

15. △MQN is similar to △PRT.

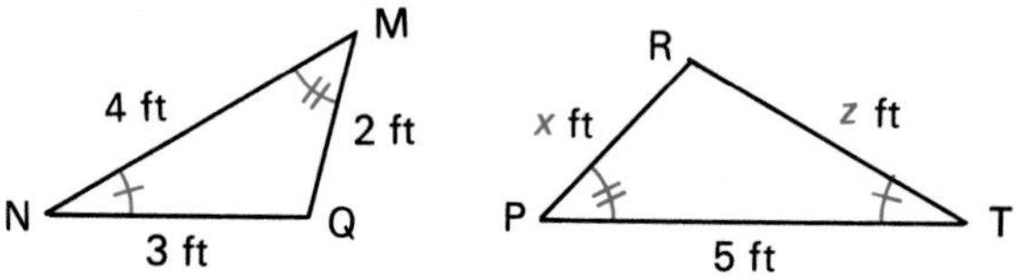

16. △STU is similar to △VWX.

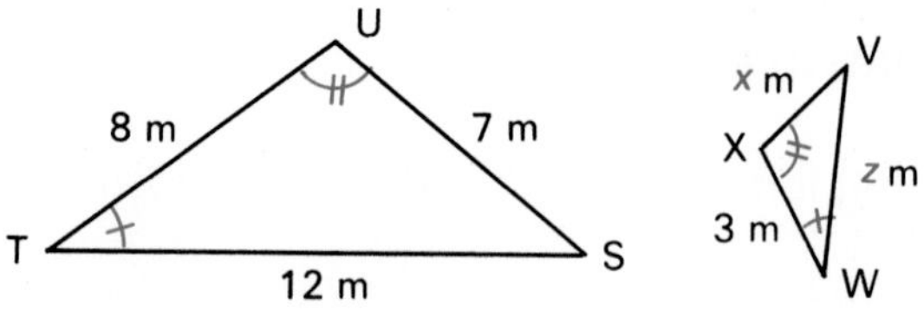

17. △YZA is similar to △BCD.

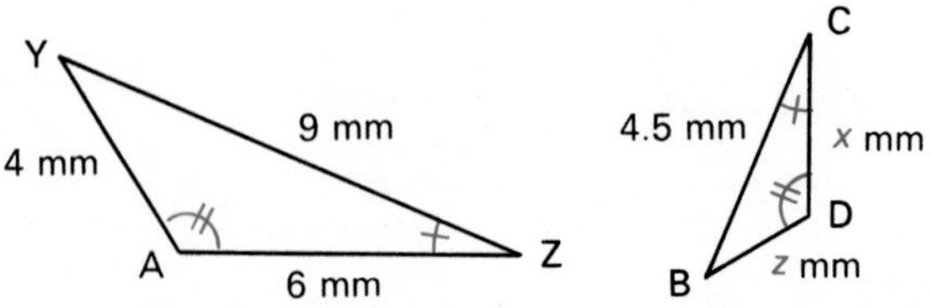

18. △TRE is similar to △TMN.

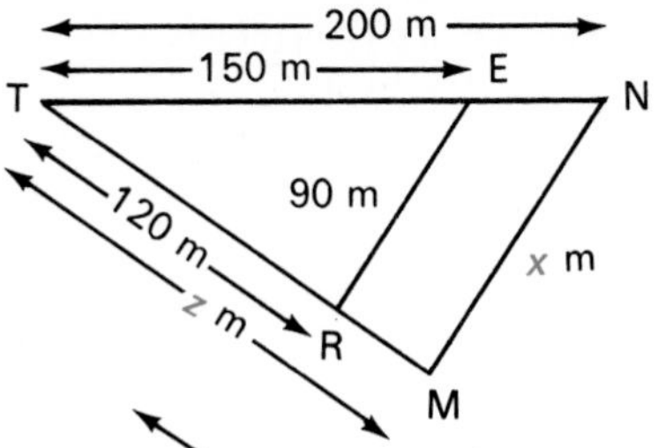

19. △RSA is similar to △CDA.

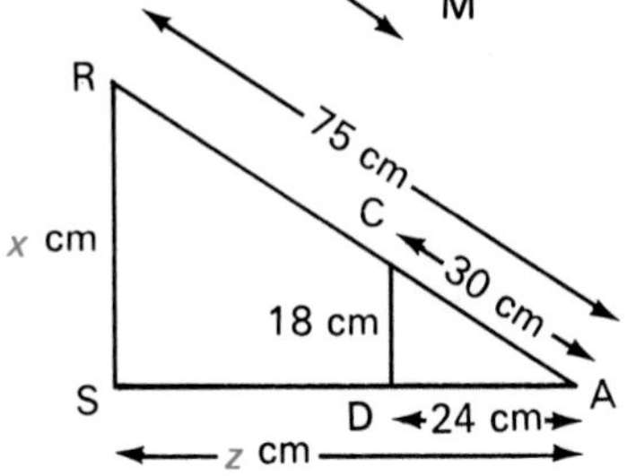

20. △AED is similar to △CEB.

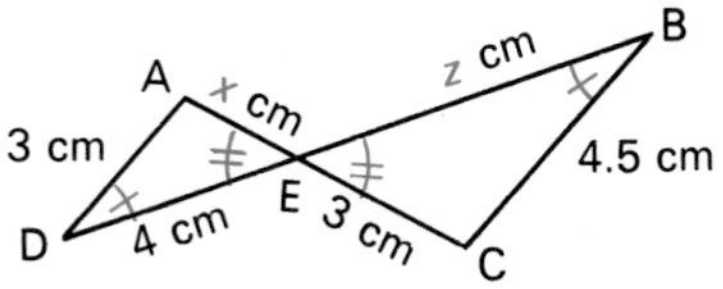

C **21.** △COD is similar to △HOG.

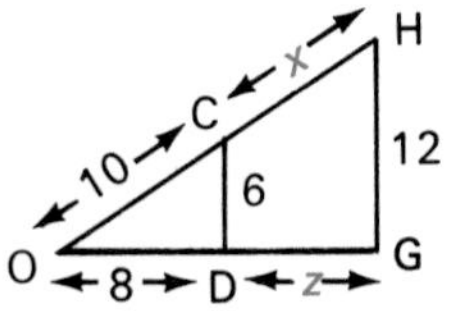

Quick Quiz

Sections 10.1 to 10.3

Are the two figures similar?

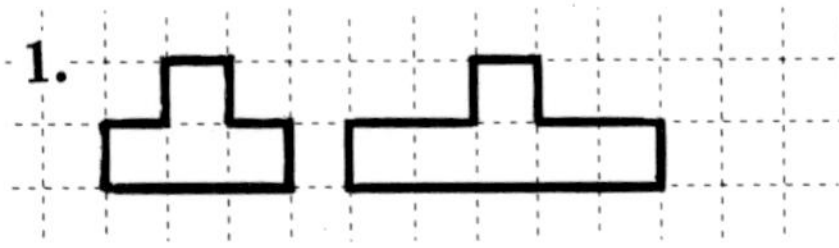

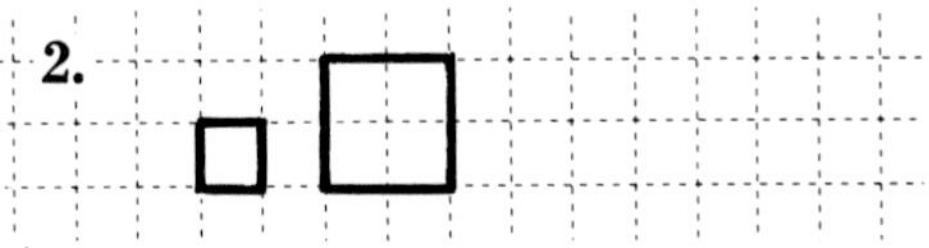

Name the corresponding angles and sides for each pair of similar triangles.

3.

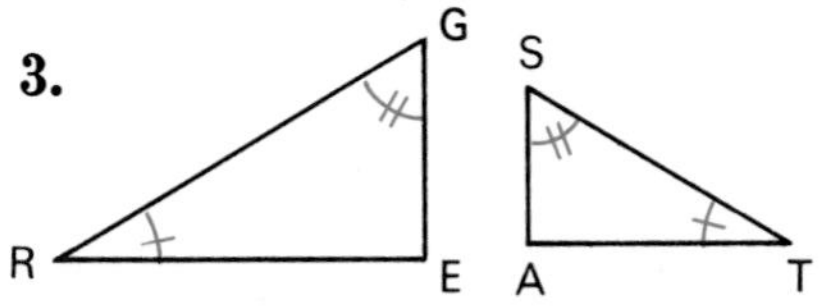

4.

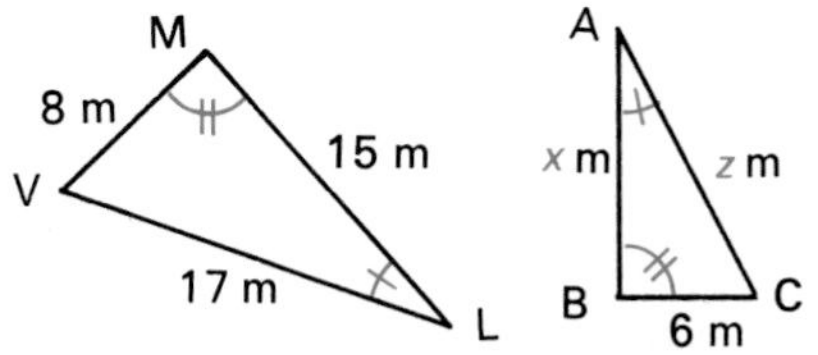

5. Find the values of x and z in Exercise 4.

10.4 Measuring With Similar Triangles

Similar triangles can be used to make indirect measurements.

Example 1: How tall is the pole?

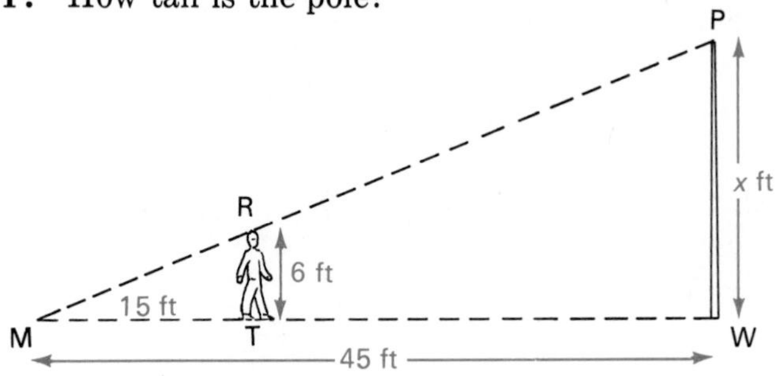

Step 1: △MRT is similar to △MPW.

Step 2: $\dfrac{MT}{MW} = \dfrac{15}{45}$ or $\dfrac{1}{3}$

Step 3: $\dfrac{MT}{MW} = \dfrac{RT}{PW}$ ⇨ $\dfrac{1}{3} = \dfrac{6}{x}$

$x = 3 \times 6$

$x = 18$

Check: Are the ratios 6 to 18 and 1 to 3 equivalent? ✓

So the pole is 18 feet high.

Example 2: How far is it from the post at A to the post at B?

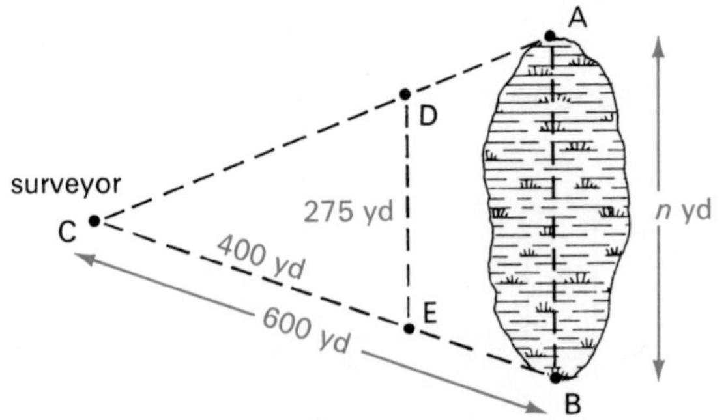

Step 1: Notice the two triangles that are similar.

△ABC is similar to △DEC.

Step 2: Write a proportion that includes the unknown distance.

$$\frac{CE}{CB} = \frac{DE}{AB} \quad \text{or} \quad \frac{400}{600} = \frac{275}{n}$$

Step 3: Solve the proportion.

$$\frac{400}{600} = \frac{275}{n}$$

$$400n = 600 \times 275$$

$$n = \frac{600 \times 275}{400}$$

$$n = 412\frac{1}{2}$$

Check: Are the ratios 275 to $412\frac{1}{2}$ and 400 to 600 equivalent? ✓

So the distance from A to B is $412\frac{1}{2}$ yards.

Exercises

A 1. What is true about the ratios of corresponding sides of similar triangles?

What letter should replace each question mark?

△CDA is similar to △BEA.

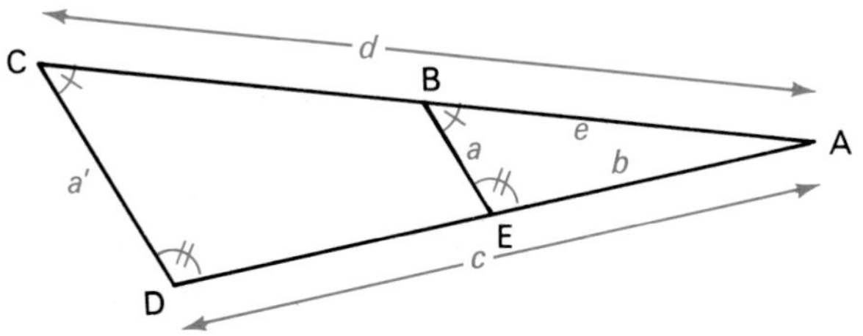

2. $\frac{e}{d} = \frac{b}{?}$
3. $\frac{a}{a'} = \frac{e}{?}$
4. $\frac{c}{b} = \frac{a'}{?}$
5. $\frac{d}{e} = \frac{?}{b}$
6. $\frac{b}{?} = \frac{a}{a'}$
7. $\frac{?}{a} = \frac{d}{e}$

The ratio $\frac{e}{d}$ is $\frac{1}{2}$. What are the following ratios?

8. $\frac{b}{c}$
9. $\frac{a}{a'}$
10. $\frac{d}{e}$
11. $\frac{c}{b}$
12. $\frac{a'}{a}$

B Use similar triangles to solve each problem.

13. The sign and the tree cast shadows as shown. How tall is the tree?

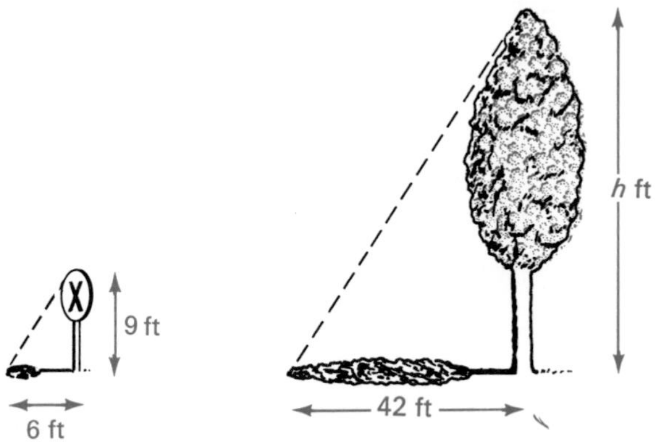

14. How high is the hotel?

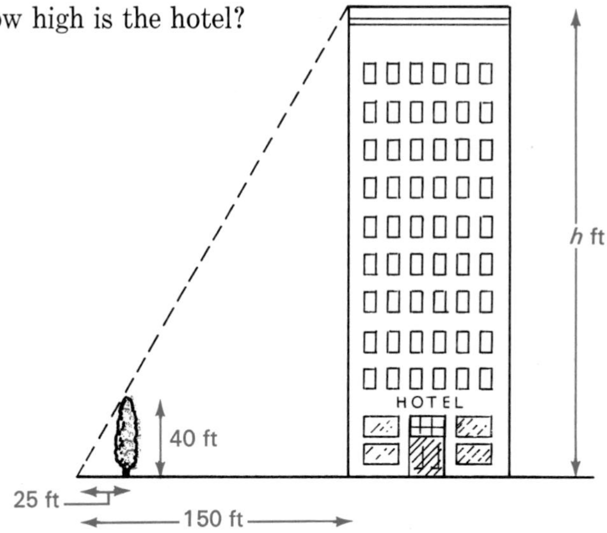

15. What is the length of the fairway?

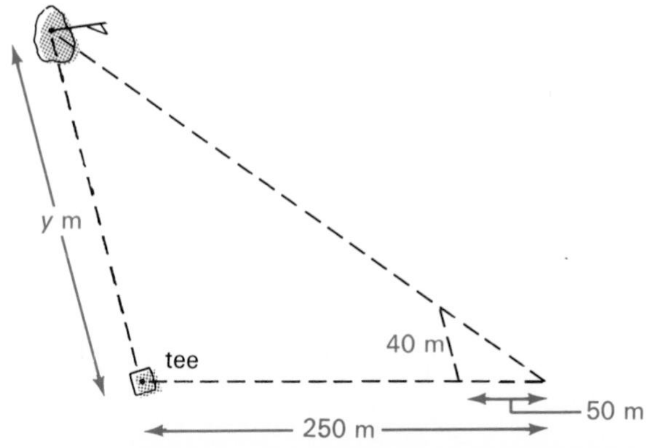

16. How far apart are the lighthouses?

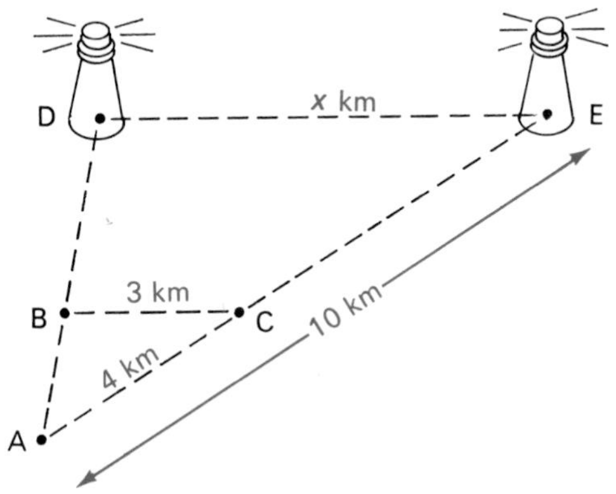

17. Find the height of the flagpole.

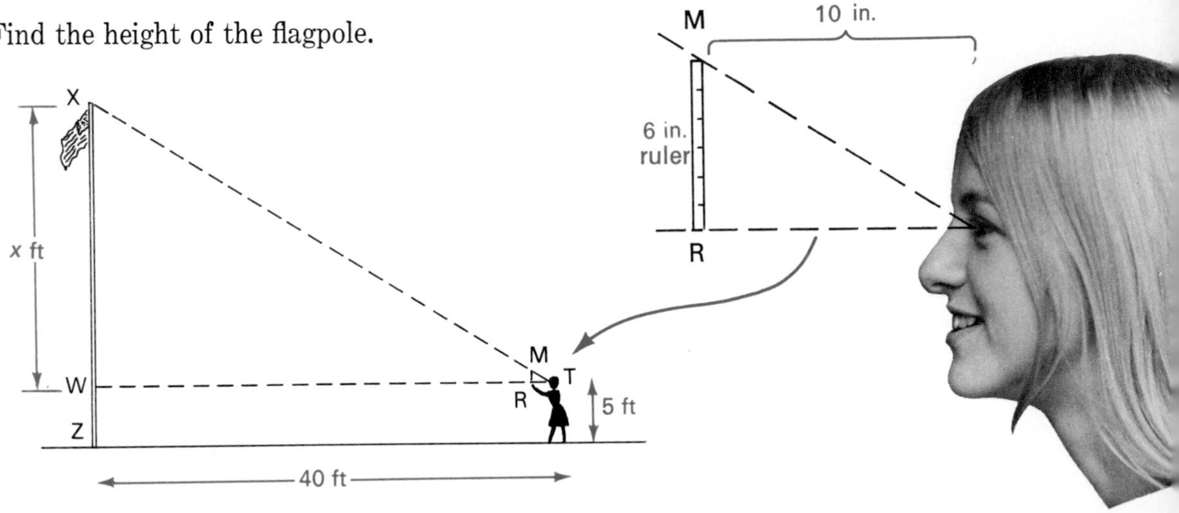

18. Triangles DCE and ABE are similar. Find the width of the lake at AB.

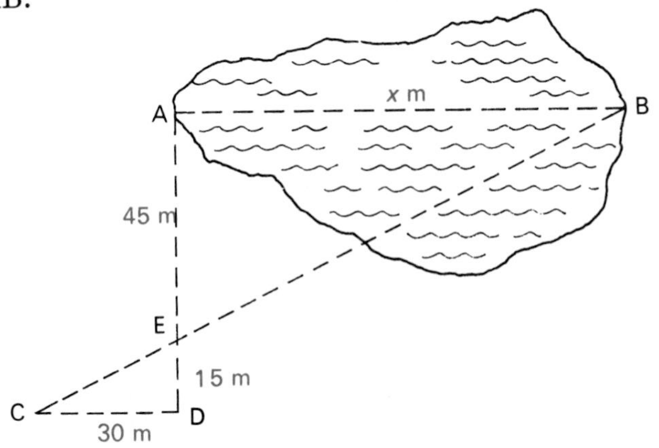

☐C Use a mirror and similar triangles to measure tall objects.

Example: To measure the height of the building, place a mirror a measured distance (10 meters in this case) from the base of the building. Slowly walk toward the mirror until you see the top of the building in the mirror. Measure your distance from the mirror and compute as indicated.

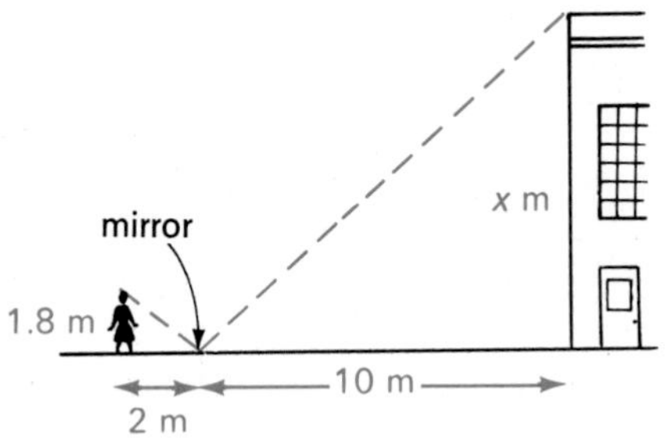

$$\frac{\text{your distance from mirror}}{\text{object's distance from mirror}} = \frac{\text{your eye-level height}}{\text{object's height}} \Rightarrow \frac{2}{10} = \frac{1.8}{x}$$

$$2x = 18$$

$$x = 9$$

The building is 9 meters high.

19. What would be the height of the flagpole if your eye-level height is 5 feet?

20. Use your eye-level height (in inches) and compute the height of the flagpole. (*Note:* It will be necessary to convert 8 ft to inches.)

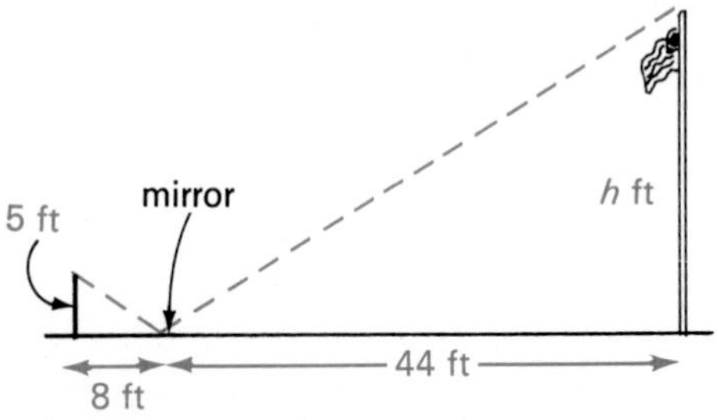

21. Use a mirror to calculate various heights. These might include the height of your classroom, your school building, a tree, and so on.

Similar Triangles in Games

Brent Jones

Courtesy Bally Manufacturing Corp.

In games like pool, miniature golf, air hockey, and many electronic TV games, bank shots can be used. For example, on the miniature golf fairway shown below, you would bank (bounce) the ball off the wall at point B.

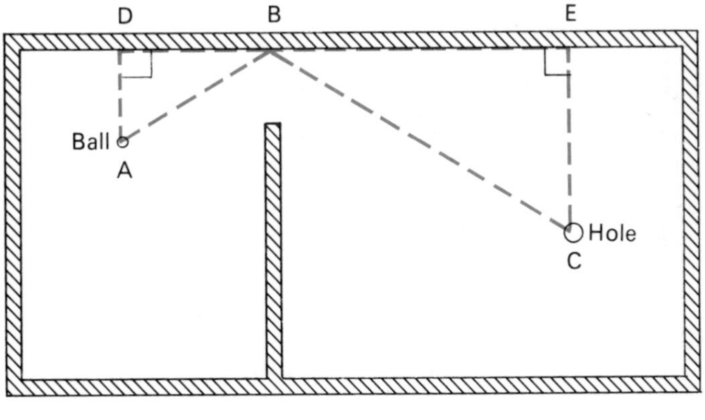

⌟ is the symbol for a right (90°) angle.

There is *only one* point B on the wall. And it is that point where △ABD and △CBE are similar triangles. Notice, therefore, that the angles at which the ball approaches and leaves the wall (angles ABD and CBE) would have the same measure.

Sometimes you can do some quick figuring to find the point where you should bank a shot.

Example: How could you use similar triangles to locate point B in the preceding example?

Step 1: Estimate the distances AD, CE, and DE. Let's say you think:

$$AD = 3 \text{ ft}, CE = 6 \text{ ft}, \text{ and } DE = 15 \text{ ft}.$$

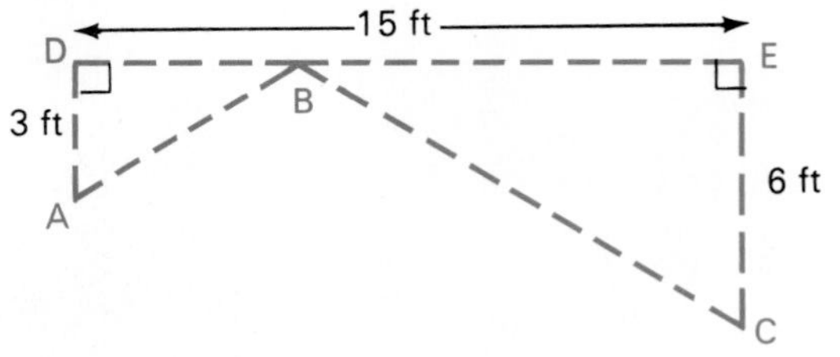

Step 2: Reduce the ratio of the corresponding sides to lowest terms.

$$\frac{AD}{CE} = \frac{3}{6} = \frac{1}{2}$$

Step 3: Find the lengths into which DE must be broken to give the same ratio as found in step 2.

from the ratio in step 2 → $1x + 2x = 15$ ← from the estimate in step 1

$$(1 + 2)x = 15$$

$$3x = 15$$

$$\frac{3x}{3} = \frac{15}{3}$$

$$x = 5$$

So DE must be broken into

$$DB = 1x = 1 \times 5 = 5$$

$$BE = 2x = 2 \times 5 = 10$$

Check: Are the ratios 3 to 6 and 5 to 10 equivalent? ✓

So point B must be 5 ft from point D. Aim at point B.

Exercises

A 1. In the air hockey game below, the puck is at A. Where must the puck be banked to shoot it into the goal at the right?

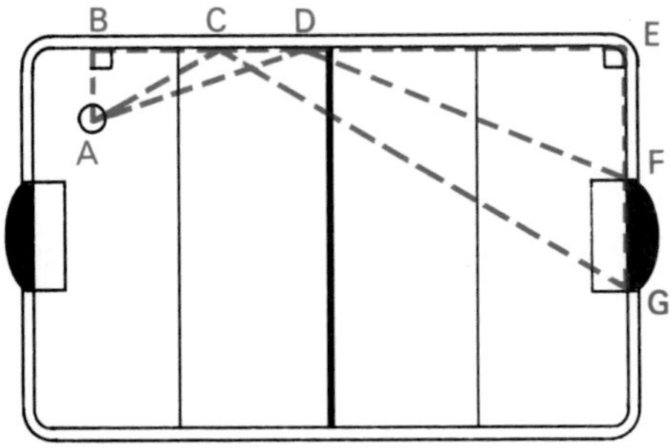

Courtesy Colēco Industries, Inc.

2. Name two pairs of similar triangles above.

Use the pool table shown at right. You want the cue ball at C to bank off the wall at B and hit the eight ball at E.

3. What must be true of $\triangle ACB$ and $\triangle DEB$?

4. What must be true of the angles at which the cue ball approaches and leaves the wall?

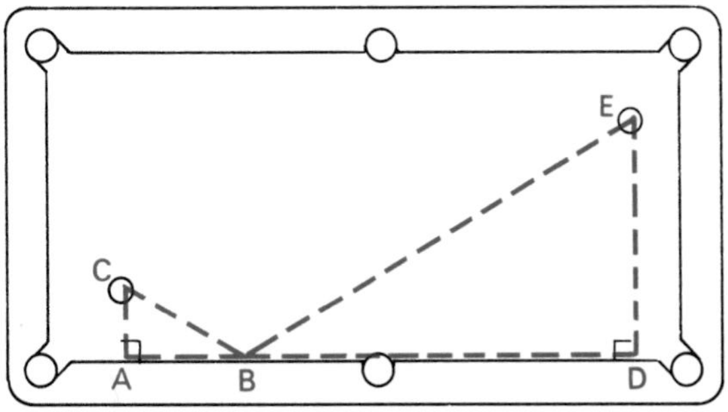

B 5. Let AC = 10 in., DE = 30 in., and AD = 80 in. Find AB and BD.

6. Let AC = 8 in., DE = 32 in., and AD = 75 in. Find AB and BD.

Use the miniature golf fairway shown at right. You want the golf ball at G to bank off the wall at B and go in the hole at H.

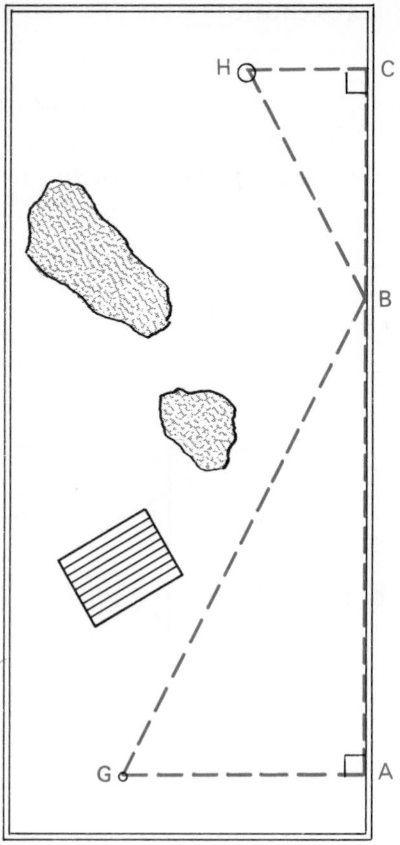

7. What must be true of $\triangle GAB$ and $\triangle HCB$?

8. What must be true of angles ABG and CBH?

9. Let AG = 2 yd, CH = 1 yd, AC = 6 yd. Find AB and BC.

10. Let AG = 2 yd, CH = 1 yd, AC = 5 yd. Find AB and BC.

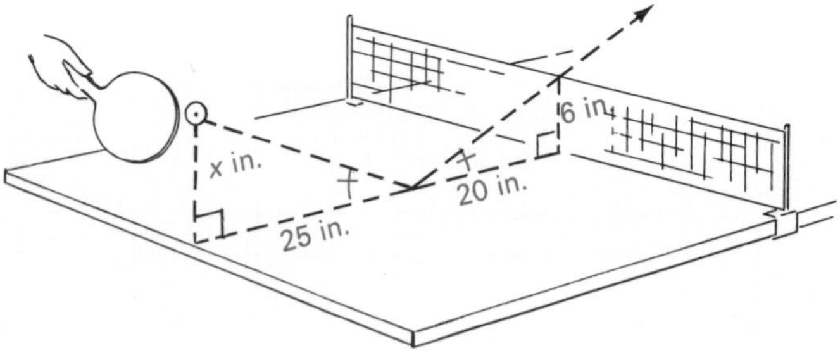

C 11. Suppose you are practicing table tennis. And you want the ball to just clear the net as shown. How high above the table should you serve?

12. If you were playing catch against a wall and threw the ball as shown, how high on the wall would the ball hit?

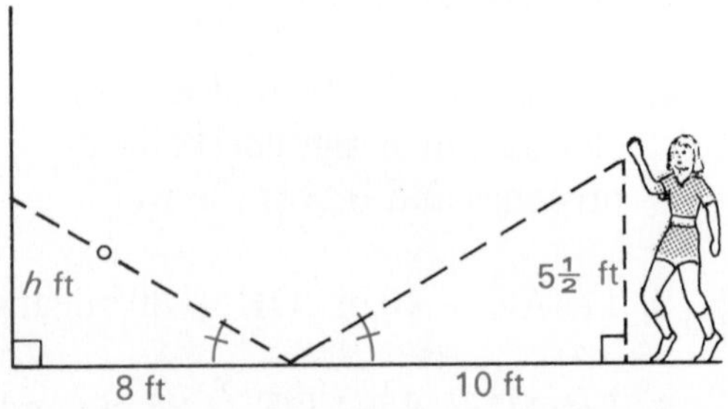

Another Way

Another way to find the point at which to bank a shot follows. Think of flipping (over the wall) the point C, where you want the ball to go. For example,

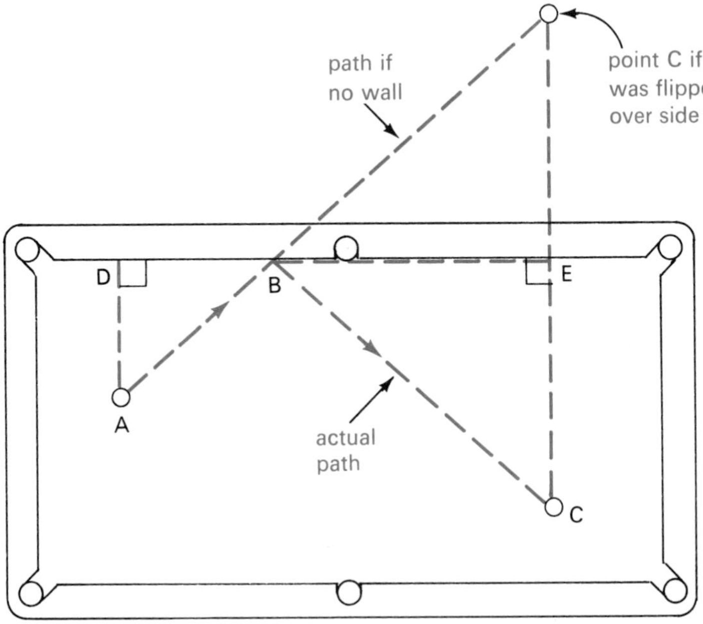

Courtesy Brunswick Corporation

10.6 Maps

A map is a reduced drawing of part of the earth's surface. The amount of reduction or scale is usually given by a ratio. For example, on the following map *1 inch represents 50 miles*. That means the ratio of distances on the map to those on earth is 1 inch to 50 miles.

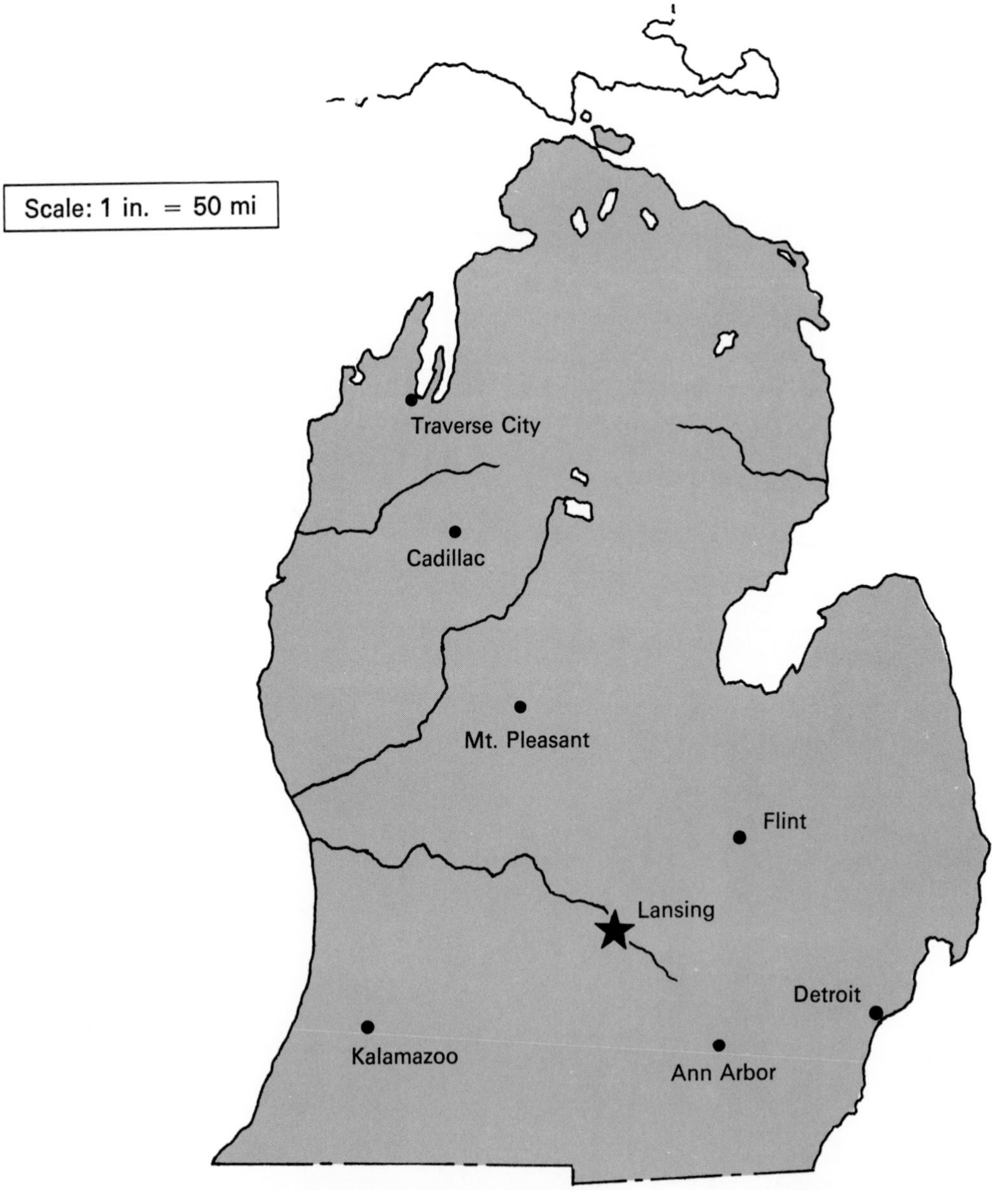

Example: What is the flight distance from Detroit to Kalamazoo?

Step 1: Measure the distance on the map: $2\frac{3}{4}$ inches

Step 2: Use a proportion to find the actual distance d.

$$\frac{1 \text{ in.}}{50 \text{ mi}} = \frac{2\frac{3}{4} \text{ in.}}{d \text{ mi}} \qquad \frac{1}{50} = \frac{2\frac{3}{4}}{d}$$

$$d = 50 \times 2\frac{3}{4}$$

$$d = 137\frac{1}{2}$$

Check: $\frac{1}{50} = \frac{2\frac{3}{4}}{137\frac{1}{2}}$

$137\frac{1}{2}$ $\quad$ $137\frac{1}{2}$ ✓ $\quad$ The ratios are equivalent.

So the flight distance from Detroit to Kalamazoo is $137\frac{1}{2}$ miles.

Exercises

A By using the map on page 336, tell how you could find the distance between each pair of cities given below.

1. Detroit and Mt. Pleasant
2. Flint and Kalamazoo

B Use the map on page 336 to find the flight distance between each pair of cities given below.

3. Mt. Pleasant and Lansing
4. Ann Arbor and Traverse City
5. Ann Arbor and Detroit
6. Cadillac and Kalamazoo

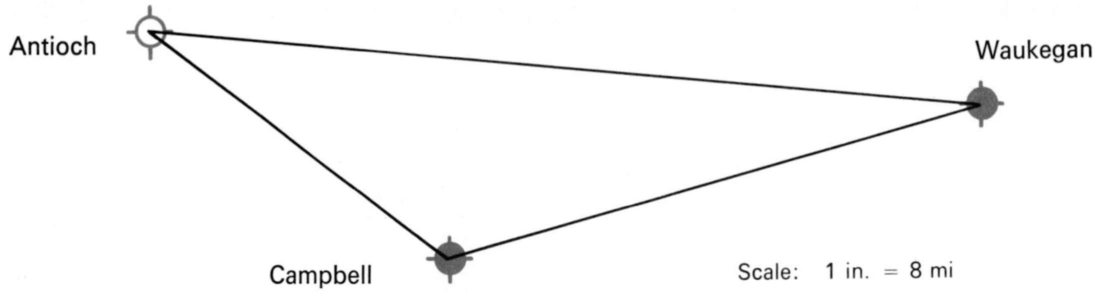

Use the map above to complete the following table.

Flight between	*map distance (in inches)*	*actual distance (in miles)*
7. Campbell and Waukegan		
8. Waukegan and Antioch		
9. Antioch and Campbell		

10. What was the total distance of the trip above?

11. If the plane averaged 120 mph, how long would it take for the trip, allowing 5 minutes for the touchdown at Waukegan and 5 minutes for the touchdown at Antioch?

C Answer the question.

12. The map below is a reduction of the map above. The scale is missing. What should the scale be?

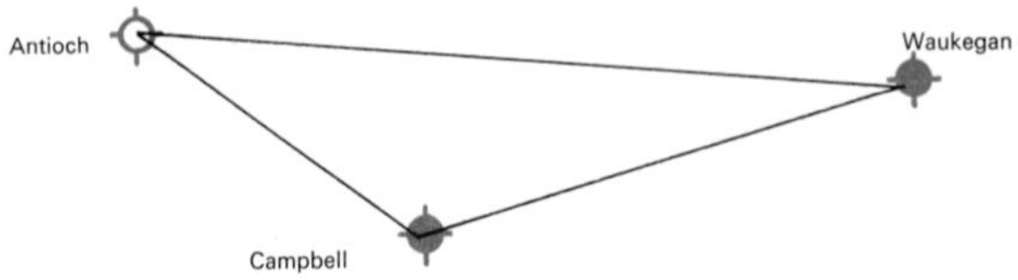

Scale Drawings and Scale Models

10.7

Courtesy Estes Industries, Penrose, Colorado

A map is one kind of *scale drawing*. But scale drawings can be used to show many other things such as floor plans, building designs, machine parts, or car designs. Sometimes three-dimensional *scale models* are made. Each length on the scale drawing or scale model represents a given distance on the actual object.

Example: The model of a building is $12\frac{1}{2}$ inches tall. The scale is 1 inch = 4 feet. What is the height of the actual building?

You can use a proportion to find the actual height.

$$\frac{1 \text{ in.}}{4 \text{ ft}} = \frac{12\frac{1}{2} \text{ in.}}{h \text{ ft}}$$

$$\frac{1}{4} = \frac{12\frac{1}{2}}{h}$$

$$h = 4 \times 12\frac{1}{2}$$

$$h = 50$$

Check:

$$\frac{1}{4} = \frac{12\frac{1}{2}}{50}$$

$$50 \qquad 50 \ \checkmark$$

So the actual building is 50 feet tall.

Exercises

A 1. The length of the scale drawing is 5 cm. What proportion would you use to find the actual length of the building?

2. The height of the scale drawing is 2 cm. What proportion would you use to find the actual height of the building?

B Copy and complete the following. Refer to the scale drawing above. Measure to the nearest 0.5 centimeter.

Measurement	Scale drawing (in cm)	Actual building (in m)
3. Distance between doorways	______	______
4. Width of each window	______	______

Refer to the scale drawing of the car to complete the following. Measure to the nearest 0.5 centimeter.

Measurement	Scale drawing (in cm)	Actual car (in m)
5. Height (roof to ground)	______	______
6. Wheelbase (front-wheel center to rear-wheel center)	______	______
7. Outside diameter of tires	______	______
8. Width of door	______	______
9. Length of antenna	______	______
10. Length of side molding.	______	______

Complete the following table for a model ship that is based on a 1-to-48 reduction from the original. Thus, the scale is 1 in. = 4 ft.

Measurement	Scale model (in inches)	Actual ship (in feet)
11. Length		72 ft
12. Height of mainmast	6 in.	
13. Height of midmast		18 ft
14. Height of mainsail		20 ft

Photri

C Measure the arrow on each photo. Then use your measurement and the scale below the photo to find the corresponding measurement on the real object.

15.

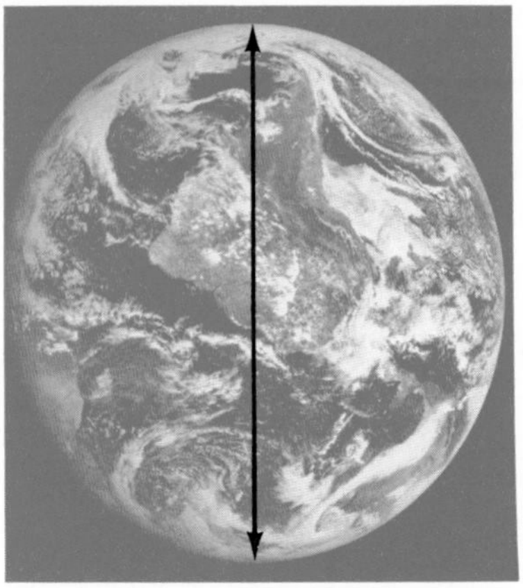

Courtesy NASA

Scale: 1 in. = 4000 mi

16.

Courtesy American Airlines

Scale: 1 cm = 3 m

17.

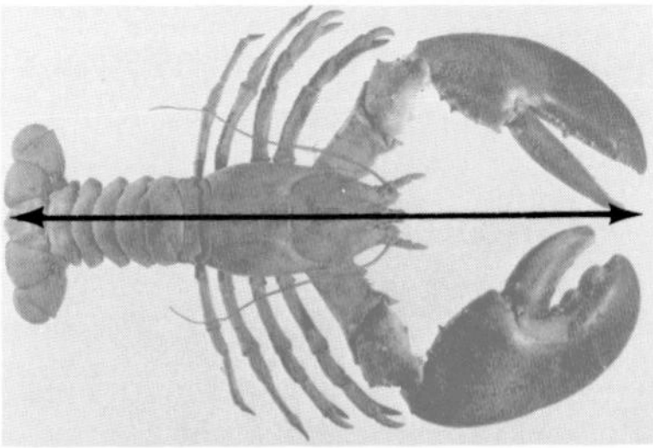

Courtesy Field Museum of Natural History, Chicago

Scale: 1 cm = 5 cm

Activity 1

Bring a map of your state to class. Use the map to do these exercises.

1. What is the scale of the map?

2. Name the states that border your state.

3. Use the map to plan a trip. Then determine the distance you would travel if you really took the trip.

Activity 2

The floor plan of an apartment is shown below. Use the floor plan to do the following exercises.

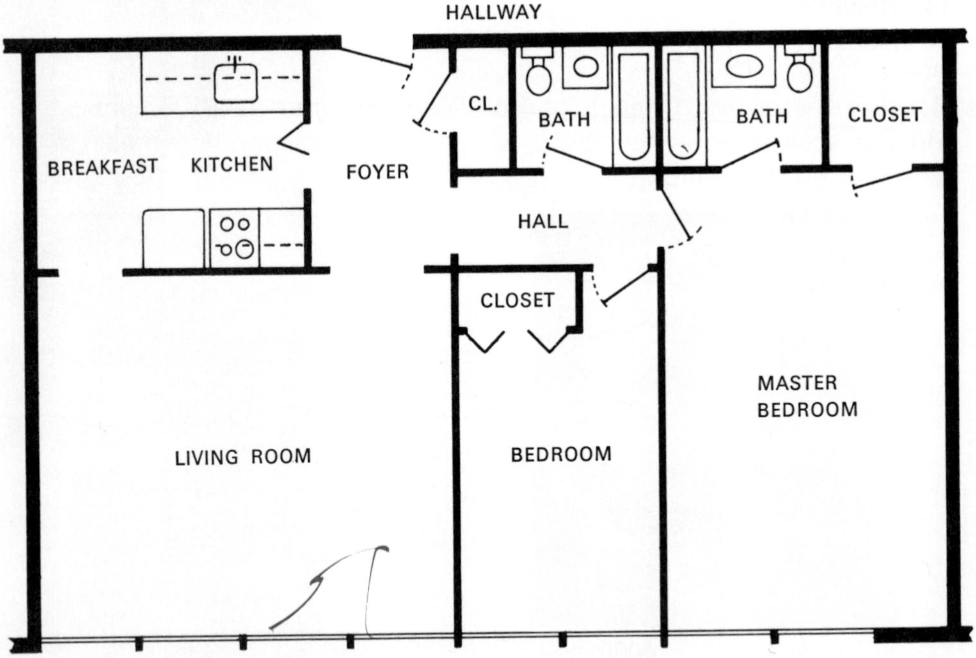

Floor plan scale: 1 inch = 8 feet

1. What are the length and width of the living room? How many square feet of carpeting would be needed to carpet the living room?

2. How many 1-foot-by-1-foot tiles would be needed to tile the master bedroom?

3. Make a floor plan of your room at home. Use the same scale as that shown for the apartment above.

CAREER CORNER

MATH AND PIPELINES

An oil company owns two oil wells. One is located at X and the other at Y. The company wants to connect the two wells by pipeline to a single storage tank T located along the Red River. How far from A should they build the tank so the least amount of pipe is used?

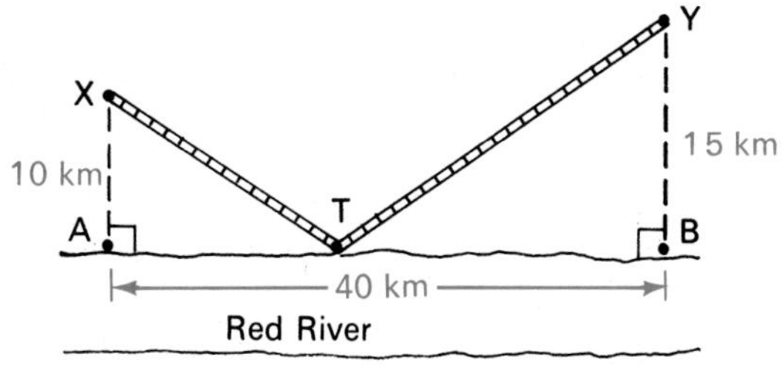

Suppose the distances remained the same, but Y was on the opposite side of riverbank AB. (See drawing below.) Then the shortest distance from X to Y would be on a straight line. You could draw that straight line to locate T.

$\triangle XAT$ is similar to $\triangle YBT$.

So, $\frac{AT}{TB}$ should equal $\frac{AX}{BY}$.

$$\frac{AX}{BY} = \frac{10}{15} = \frac{2}{3}$$

So, use $2x$ and $3x$ for AT and TB and let the sum equal 40.

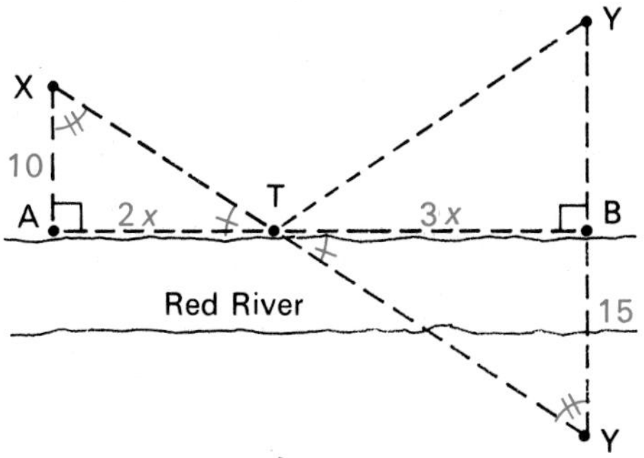

$$2x + 3x = 40$$

$$5x = 40$$

$$\frac{5x}{5} = \frac{40}{5}$$

$$x = 8$$

So, $AT = 2 \times 8 = 16$.

Locate the storage tank 16 km from A.

1. Assume the distance from A to B is 60 km. How far from A should the storage tank be built?

2. Assume the following distances: AX = 20 km, BY = 10 km, and AB = 30 km. How far from A should the storage tank be built?

Terms and Symbols Review

Complete each sentence. Choose from these words.

corresponding *indirect* *proportional* *ratio* *shape* *size*

1. Similar figures have the same ____, but may differ in ____.
2. In similar triangles, ____ angles have the same measure.
3. In similar triangles, corresponding sides are ____.
4. Similar triangles can be used to make ____ measurements.
5. The scale of a map is usually given by a ____.

Chapter 10 Review

10.1 Which pairs of figures are similar?

1. 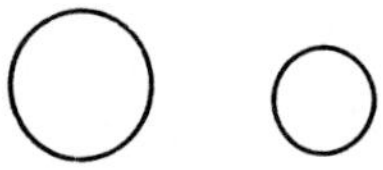

2. 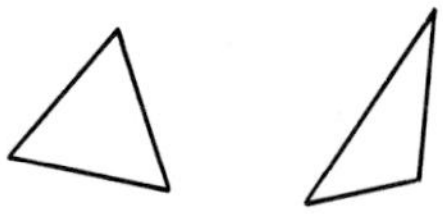

3. 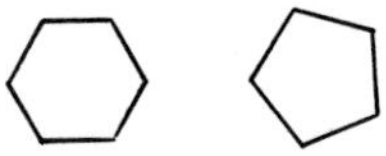

4. 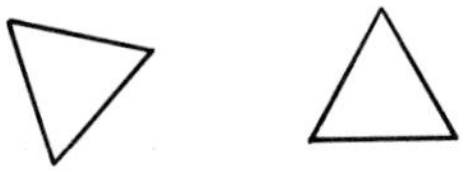

5. 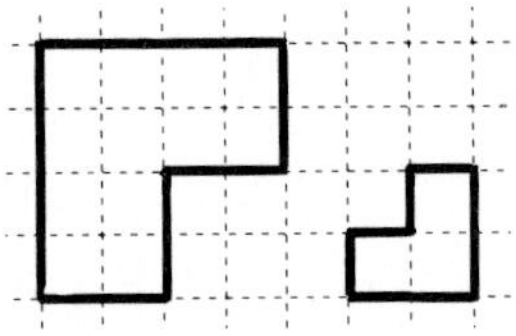

6. 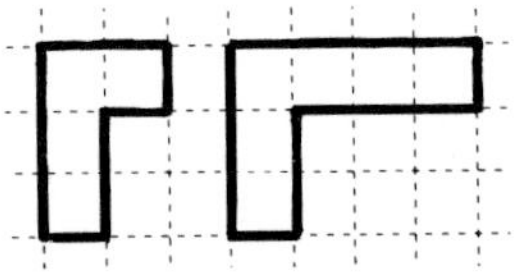

10.2 Name the corresponding angles for each pair of similar triangles.

7. 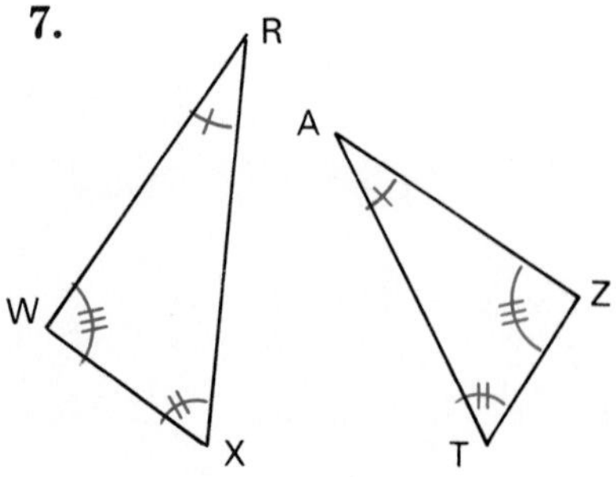

8. 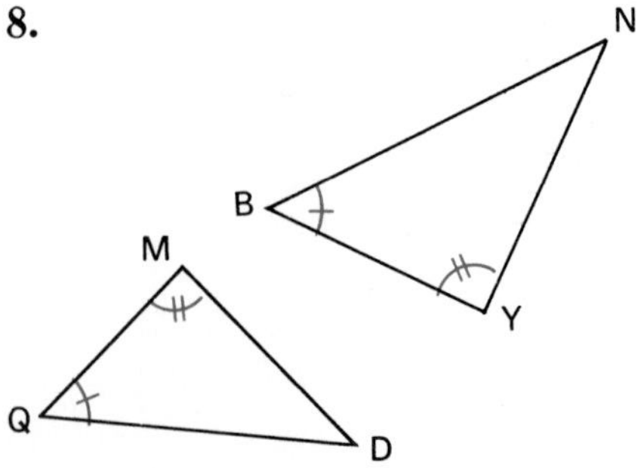

Name the corresponding sides for each pair of similar triangles.

9.

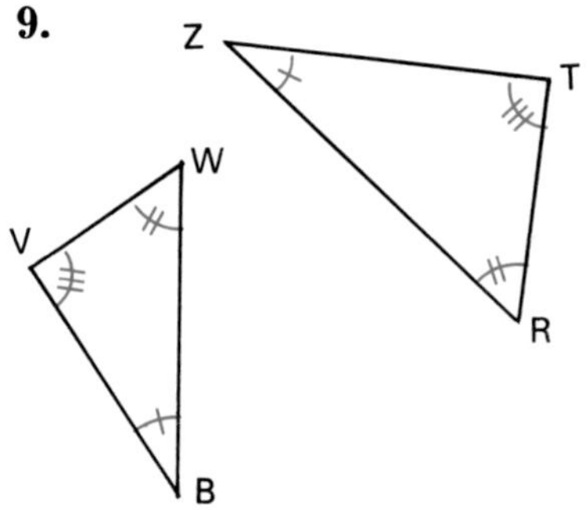

10.

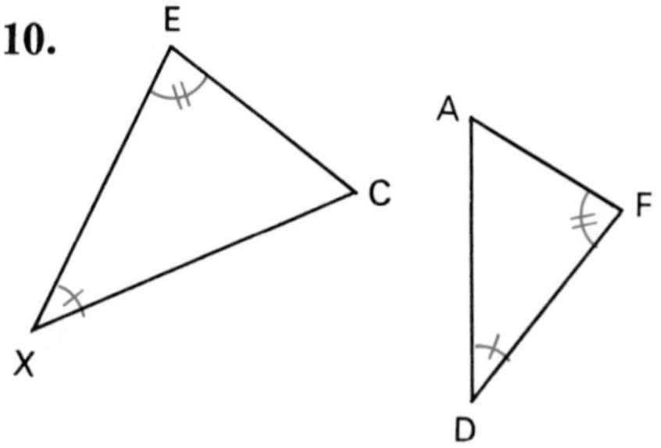

What letter should replace each question mark? 10.3

△RPW is similar to △ZNV.

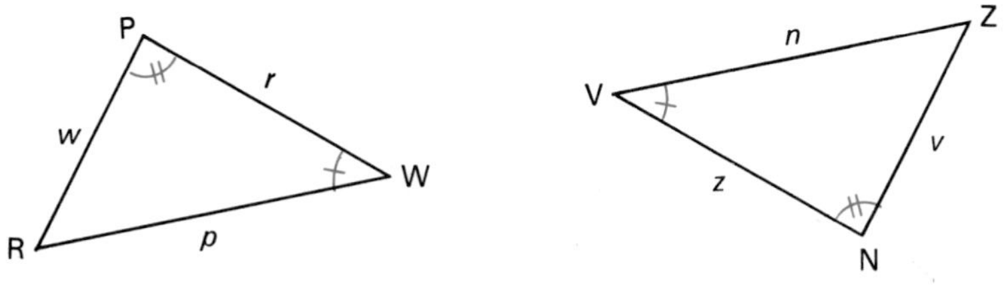

11. $\frac{w}{v} = \frac{p}{?}$ **12.** $\frac{r}{z} = \frac{w}{?}$ **13.** $\frac{p}{n} = \frac{?}{v}$

14. Find the values of x and z.

△ABC is similar to △DEF.

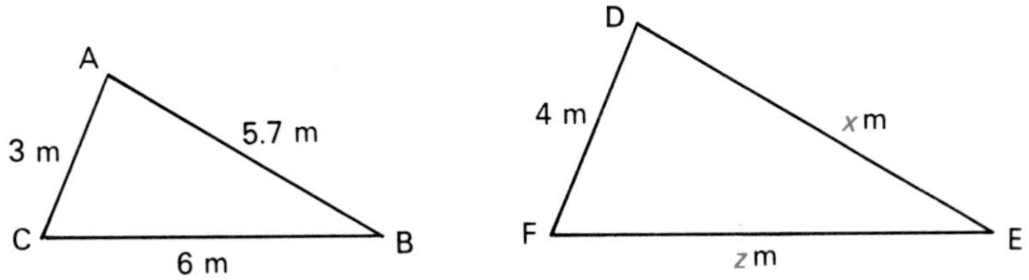

Use similar triangles to solve the problem.

10.4 **15.** What is the height of the tree? (The triangles are similar.)

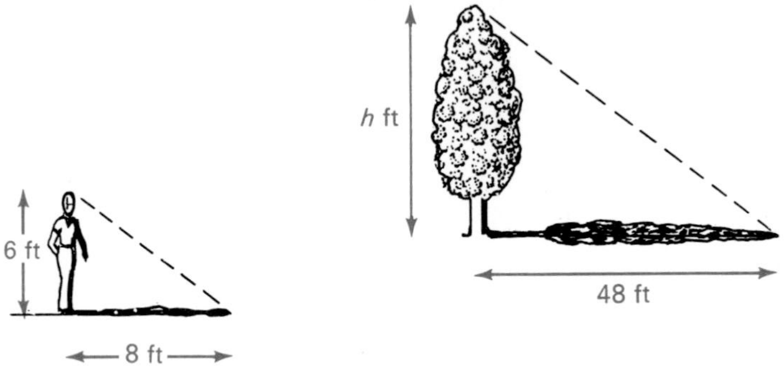

10.5 **16.** You want the cue ball at C to bank off the wall at B and hit the eight ball at E. What is true about △ABC and △DBE?

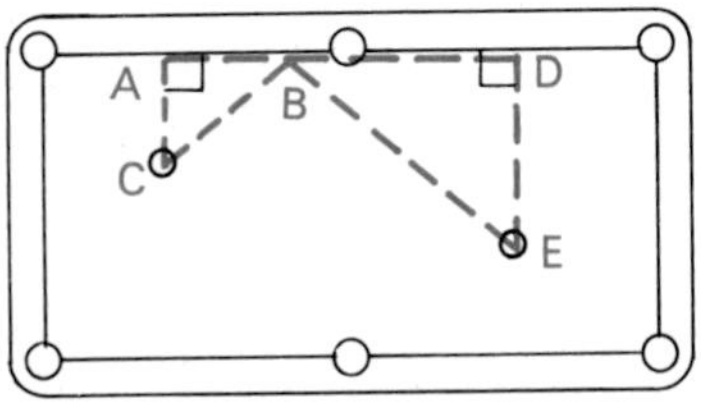

10.6 Use this map to complete the table.

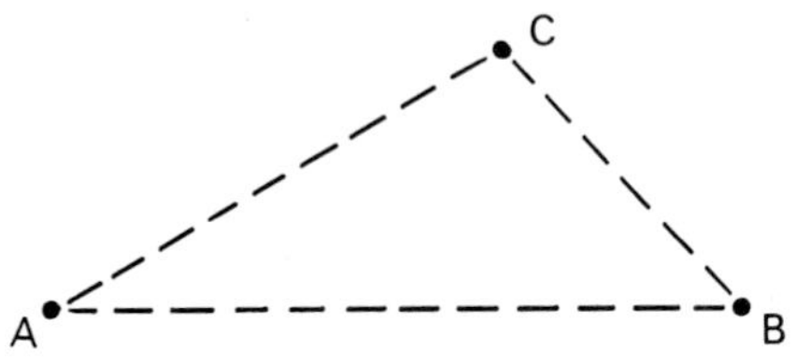

Scale: 1 in. = 12 mi

Distance between	Map distance (in inches)	Actual distance (in miles)
17. A and B		
18. B and C		
19. C and A		

10.7 Use the scale drawing to answer the questions.

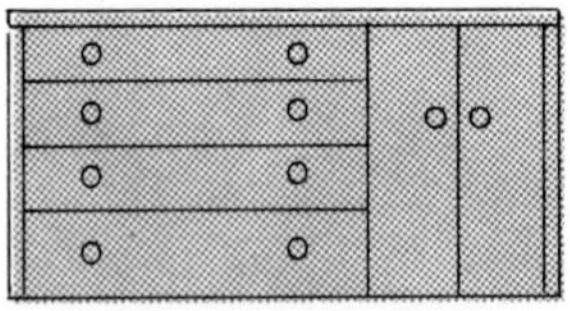

Scale: 1 in. = 2 ft

20. What is the actual width of the cabinet?

21. What is the actual height of the cabinet?

Name the corresponding angles and corresponding sides for each pair of similar triangles.

1.

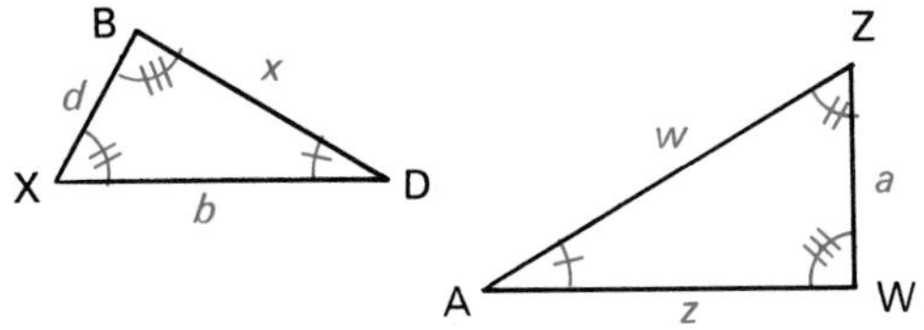

2.

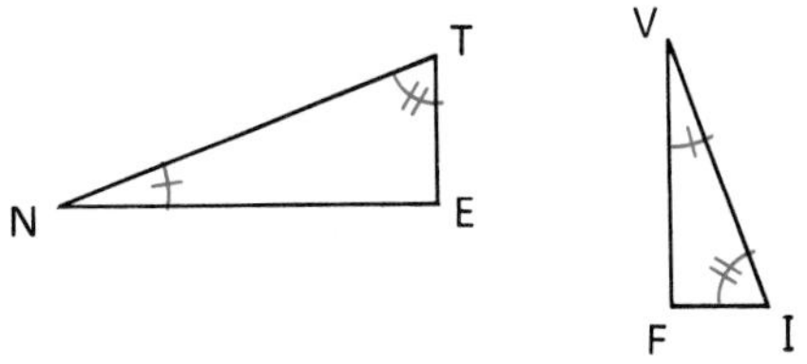

What letter should replace each question mark? Refer to Exercise 1.

3. $\frac{x}{z} = \frac{b}{?}$ **4.** $\frac{d}{a} = \frac{?}{z}$ **5.** $\frac{b}{?} = \frac{d}{a}$

Solve for *x* and *z* in each pair of similar triangles.

6.

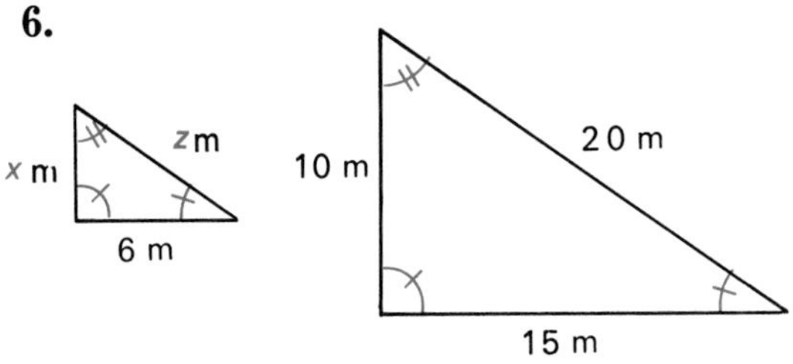

7.

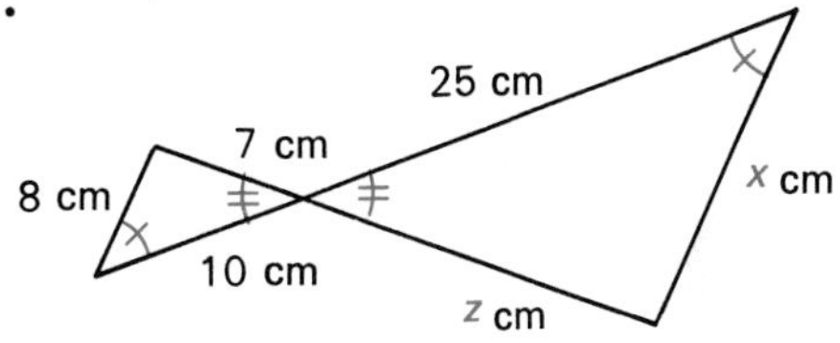

8. What is the actual distance between A and B? Between B and C? Between C and A?

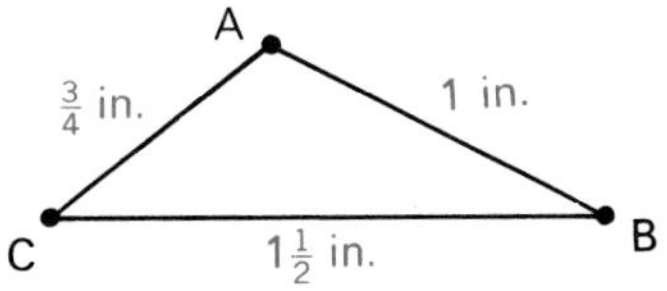

1 inch = 8 mi

9. Find the height of the building. (The triangles are similar.)

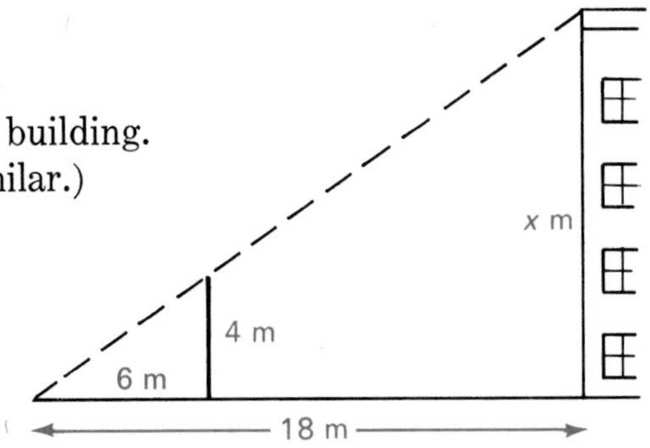

RATE YOURSELF

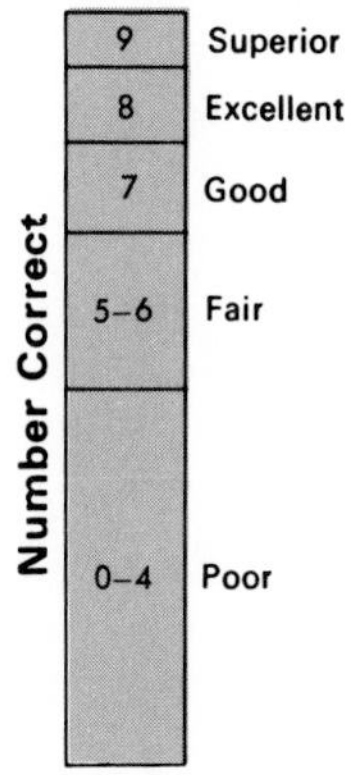

Terms and Symbols Review: Chapters 8–10

Which lettered choice best matches each numbered item?

Ch. 8

1. the point at (0, 0)
2. horizontal axis
3. 2 for the point at (2, $^-3$)
4. positive direction on the y-axis
5. negative direction on the x-axis
6. the graph of ($^-1$, 0)

Ch. 9

7. the ratio of 2 to 5
8. a proportion
9. the ratio of 2 to 100
10. extremes of $\frac{2}{5} = \frac{4}{10}$
11. a cross product for $\frac{2}{5} = \frac{4}{10}$

a. up
b. left
c. point
d. origin
e. x-axis
f. y-axis
g. x-coordinate
h. $\frac{2}{9} = \frac{4}{18}$
i. 2 and 10
j. 5 and 4
k. 2×5
l. 20
m. 2%
n. $\frac{2}{5}$

Ch. 10

Complete each sentence. Choose from these words.

angles *sides* *scale* *similar* *corresponding*

12. ______ figures have the same shape, but may differ in size.
13. In similar triangles, corresponding ______ have the same measure.
14. The ______ of a map is usually given by a ratio.
15. In similar triangles, ______ sides are proportional.

Ch. 8

1. Use the rule to complete the table below.

$y = 2x - 5$

x	−2	−1	0	1	2	3
y						

2. Write the ordered pair for each point on the graph at the right.

a. A **b.** B **c.** C **d.** D

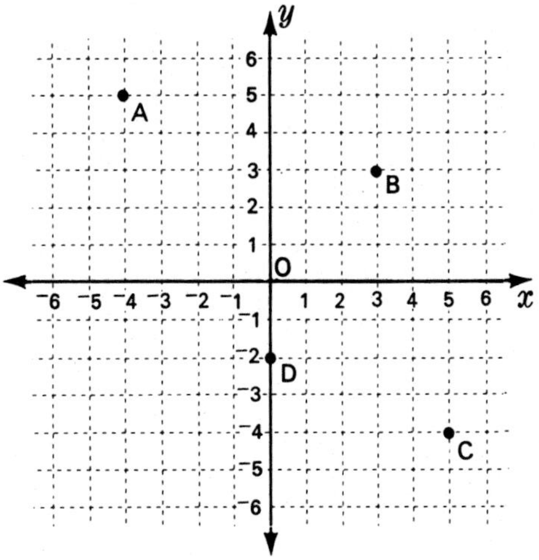

3. Draw a line graph for the table below.

time (hr)	0	1	2	3	4	5	6
temperature (0 °C)	−5	−3	0	1	3	−1	−4

4. Is the set of ordered pairs (1, 3), (1, 4), and (−3, 5) a function?

5. A bus is traveling at a rate (r) of 55 mph. How long (t) will it take the bus to go 165 miles (d)? $r \times t = d$

Copy and graph the following.

6. a slide 5 units down

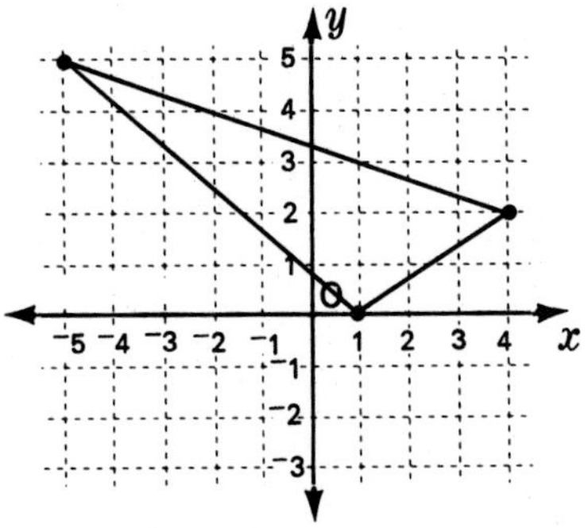

7. a 1-to-2 reduction

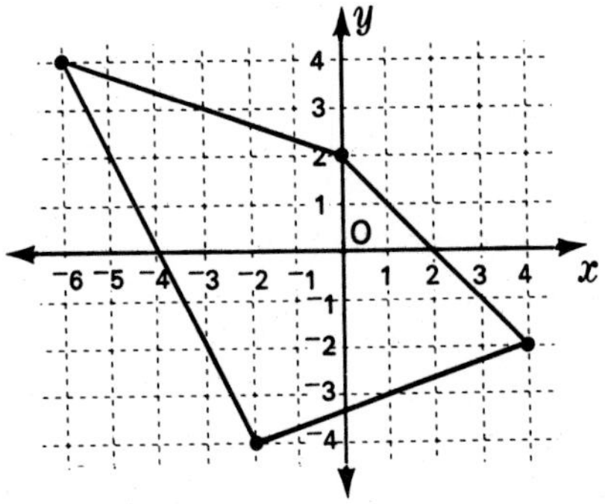

Ch. 9

8. Write the ratio of 12 votes to 5 votes.

9. Write two ratios equivalent to $\frac{5}{7}$.

Solve.

10. $\frac{3}{4} = \frac{n}{24}$

11. $\frac{6}{n} = \frac{60}{37}$

Use a proportion to solve.

12. 1 pound of asparagus serves 3 people. How many pounds will serve 15 people?

Write as **(a)** a fraction or mixed number and **(b)** a decimal.

13. 36%　　**14.** 130%　　**15.** 17.6%　　**16.** $2\frac{1}{2}$%

Express as a per cent.

17. 0.29　　**18.** 3.5　　**19.** $\frac{2}{5}$　　**20.** 9

Solve.

21. What is 20% of 92?

22. 32 is 75% of what?

23. 45 is what per cent of 180?

24. What is $8\frac{1}{2}$% of 100?

25. Morrie averages 14% in tips. How much does he receive in tips on customers' bills of $350?

26. Tell how you would round to estimate 29% of 432.

27. An increase from 32 to 40 is what per cent of increase?

28. A decrease from 20 to 18 is what per cent of decrease?

Ch. 10

29. Name the corresponding sides and the corresponding angles.

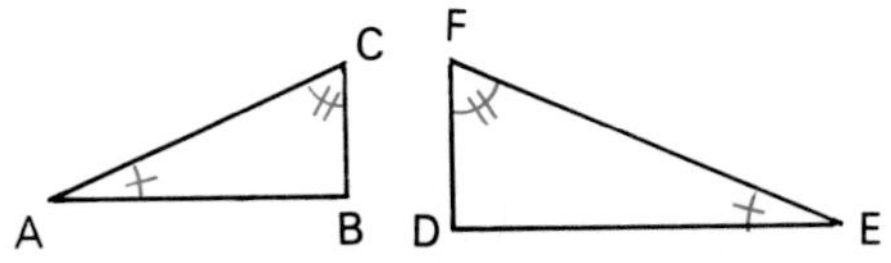

30. Find the values of x and z.

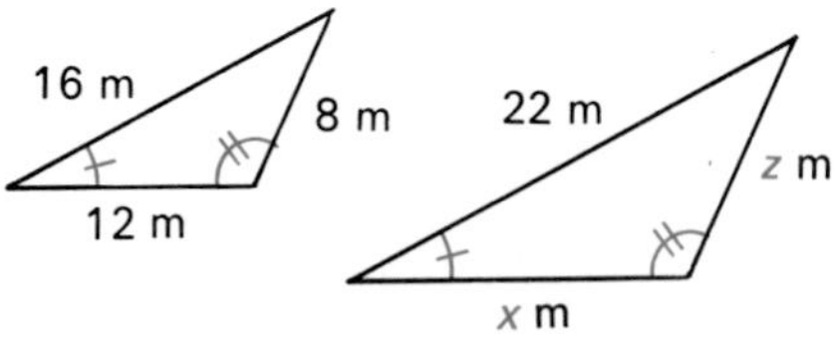

31. What is the height of the pole?

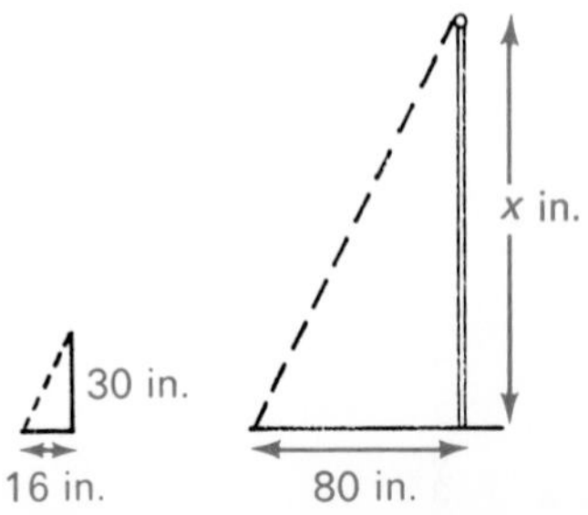

32. Use the scale drawing to find the actual height of the building.

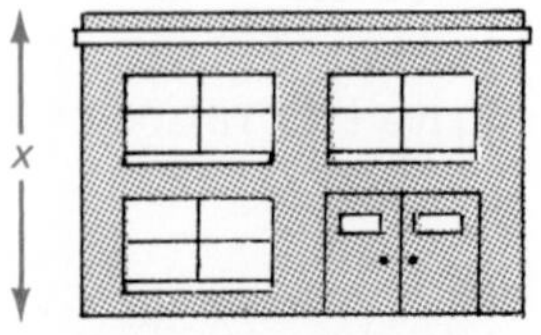

Scale: 1 cm = 3 m

Getting Ready for Chapter 11

Give the opposite of each number. 6.1

1. 3
2. $^-10$
3. 25

Give the absolute value of each number. 6.3

4. 12
5. $^-14$
6. 0

Compute.

7. $\frac{1}{7} + \frac{3}{7}$
8. $\frac{5}{9} - \frac{4}{9}$
9. $\frac{3}{4} + \frac{2}{4}$ — 4.7
10. $\frac{1}{2} - \frac{2}{5}$
11. $\frac{2}{3} + \frac{1}{6}$
12. $\frac{5}{8} - \frac{1}{6}$ — 4.8
13. $1\frac{5}{6} - 1\frac{3}{4}$
14. $2\frac{1}{2} + 1\frac{7}{8}$
15. $3\frac{1}{2} - 2\frac{2}{3}$ — 4.9
16. $0.47 + 0.23$
17. $6.73 - 2.41$
18. $2.537 - 1.72$ — 5.3
19. $^-7 + 6$
20. $7 + {}^-5$
21. $^-8 + {}^-18$ — 6.3
22. $6 - 13$
23. $^-7 - 13$
24. $8 - {}^-26$ — 6.4
25. $6 \div {}^-3$
26. $^-6 \div 3$
27. $^-6 \div {}^-3$ — 7.3

Solve.

28. $a + 8 = 24$
29. $15 = b + 7$ — 6.5
30. $14 = c + {}^-2$
31. $d + {}^-3 = {}^-4$
32. $e - 3 = 6$
33. $27 = f - 15$ — 6.6
34. $7 = g - {}^-10$
35. $h - {}^-6 = {}^-3$

11

11

ADDING AND SUBTRACTING RATIONAL NUMBERS

Earlier, you saw that the numbers called *integers* are just the whole numbers and their opposites.

Integers: $\cdots, {}^-4, {}^-3, {}^-2, {}^-1, 0, 1, 2, 3, 4, \cdots$

Now you will see that other numbers, besides whole numbers, also have opposites. And you will add and subtract with such numbers.

Rational Numbers

11.1

The quotient of two positive integers can be expressed as a *positive fraction.*

$$3 \div 4 = \frac{3}{4} \qquad\qquad 14 \div 9 = \frac{14}{9}$$

Also, the quotient of two negative integers is *positive* and can be expressed as a *positive fraction.*

$$^{-}3 \div {}^{-}4 = \frac{3}{4} \qquad\qquad {}^{-}14 \div {}^{-}9 = \frac{14}{9}$$

If two integers have different signs, their quotient is *negative,* and it can be expressed as a *negative fraction.*

$$^{-}5 \div 2 = \frac{^{-}5}{2} = -\frac{5}{2} \qquad\qquad 5 \div {}^{-}2 = \frac{5}{^{-}2} = -\frac{5}{2}$$

same

So $\boxed{-\frac{5}{2} = \frac{^{-}5}{2} = \frac{5}{^{-}2}}$

A **rational number** is any number that can be named by a fraction whose numerator and denominator are integers. (Of course, the denominator cannot be zero.)

$$1 \div 2 = \frac{1}{2} \qquad 1 = \frac{8}{8} \qquad {}^{-}1\frac{1}{2} = -\frac{3}{2} \qquad 0.7 = \frac{7}{10}$$

$$^{-}1 \div 2 = -\frac{1}{2} \qquad {}^{-}4 = -\frac{4}{1} \qquad 3\frac{1}{5} = \frac{16}{5} \qquad {}^{-}1.25 = -\frac{125}{100}$$

$$3 \div {}^{-}4 = -\frac{3}{4}$$

$$^{-}5 \div {}^{-}2 = \frac{5}{2}$$

Fractions

Integers

Mixed numbers

Decimals

Can be named by fractions.

Rational Numbers

Example 1: How do you read $-\frac{1}{2}$ and $^{-}1.5$?

$-\dfrac{1}{2}$ is read "negative one-half."

$^{-}1.5$ is read "negative one and five-tenths."

You know how to draw a number line that shows positive and negative integers. You can show positive and negative fractions on a number line by naming points between the integer points.

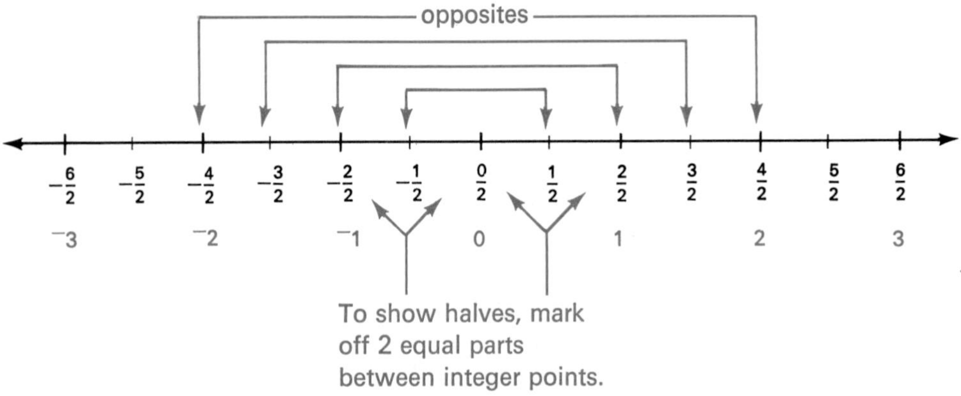

You can draw number lines for thirds, fourths, fifths, and so on, by marking off 3, 4, 5, and so on, equal parts between integer points. The set of all numbers shown on such number lines is called the set of **rational numbers.**

Example 2: What number is the opposite of $\frac{2}{3}$? Of $^{-}1.5$?

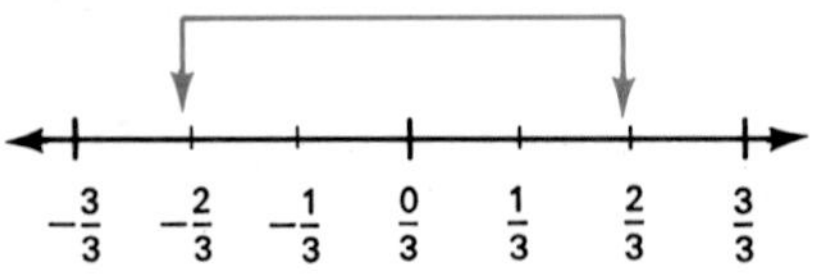

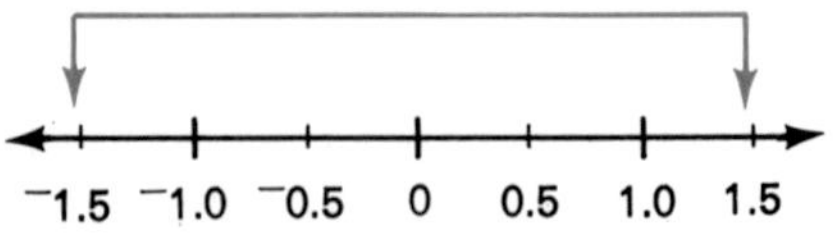

$-\dfrac{2}{3}$ is the opposite of $\dfrac{2}{3}$.

1.5 is the opposite of $^{-}1.5$.

Example 3: Give the absolute values of $\frac{1}{2}$, 2.6, 0, $^-3\frac{2}{5}$, and $^-1.16$.

Number	*Its absolute value*	
$\frac{1}{2}$ or $+\frac{1}{2}$	$\frac{1}{2}$	The absolute value of a positive rational number or 0 is the number itself.
2.6	2.6	
0	0	
$^-3\frac{2}{5}$	$3\frac{2}{5}$	The absolute value of a negative rational number is its opposite.
$^-1.16$	1.16	

Exercises

A Use the terms below to complete the following statements.

rational numbers	*positive*	*fraction*
absolute value	*negative*	*opposites*

1. A rational number is any number that can be named by a ____ whose numerator and denominator are integers.

2. $1\frac{5}{8}$ and $^-1\frac{5}{8}$ are ____ of each other.

3. $1\frac{5}{8}$ is the ____ of $^-1\frac{5}{8}$ and $1\frac{5}{8}$.

4. $\frac{5}{6}$, $^-2$, $^-7\frac{1}{3}$, 0, 9.2, $-\frac{3}{2}$, and $^-2.5$ are ____.

5. The quotient of two integers with different signs can be expressed as a ____ fraction.

6. The quotient of two negative integers can be expressed as a ____ fraction.

7. On a number line, ____ fractions are shown to the left of 0.

B Give the opposite of each number.

8. $-\frac{1}{2}$	**9.** $\frac{3}{4}$	**10.** 0.34	**11.** $^{-}0.57$
12. $\frac{5}{3}$	**13.** $3\frac{1}{2}$	**14.** $^{-}1\frac{2}{3}$	**15.** $^{-}4.795$

Give the absolute value of each number.

16. $-\frac{1}{3}$	**17.** $\frac{3}{8}$	**18.** 0.96	**19.** $^{-}0.34$
20. $\frac{7}{5}$	**21.** $4\frac{1}{6}$	**22.** $^{-}1\frac{3}{4}$	**23.** $^{-}3.159$

Graph the following. Use a separate number line for each exercise.

Example: Graph $-\frac{5}{4}$, $-\frac{1}{4}$, $\frac{3}{4}$, and $\frac{7}{4}$ on a number line.

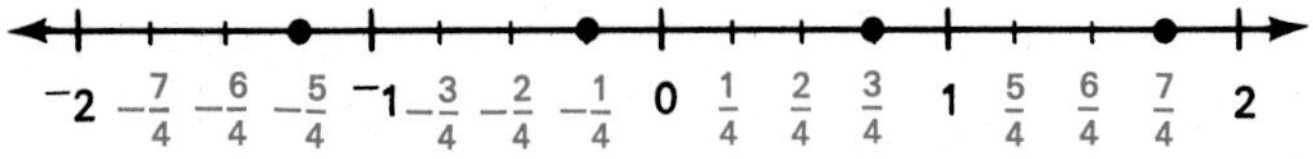

Step 1: Mark off and label integer points.

Step 2: Mark off 4 equal parts between integer points and label them.

Step 3: Graph $-\frac{5}{4}$, $-\frac{1}{4}$, $\frac{3}{4}$, and $\frac{7}{4}$.

24. $-\frac{6}{2}, -\frac{1}{2}, \frac{3}{2}, \frac{5}{2}$

25. $-\frac{4}{3}, -\frac{1}{3}, \frac{1}{3}, \frac{4}{3}$

26. $-\frac{9}{5}, -\frac{3}{5}, \frac{2}{5}, \frac{6}{5}$

27. $-\frac{8}{6}, -\frac{5}{6}, \frac{5}{6}, \frac{10}{6}$

28. $-\frac{11}{8}, -\frac{6}{8}, \frac{5}{8}, \frac{11}{8}$

29. $-\frac{13}{10}, -\frac{5}{10}, \frac{4}{10}, \frac{16}{10}$

C **30.** $-\frac{5}{3}, -\frac{1}{2}, -\frac{1}{3}, \frac{0}{3}, \frac{2}{3}, \frac{4}{2}, \frac{7}{3}$

31. $-\frac{5}{3}, -\frac{3}{4}, -\frac{2}{3}, \frac{0}{4}, \frac{5}{4}, \frac{4}{3}, \frac{6}{4}$

Comparing Fractions 11.2

You can use a number line to compare two rational numbers like $\frac{4}{5}$ and $\frac{2}{3}$.

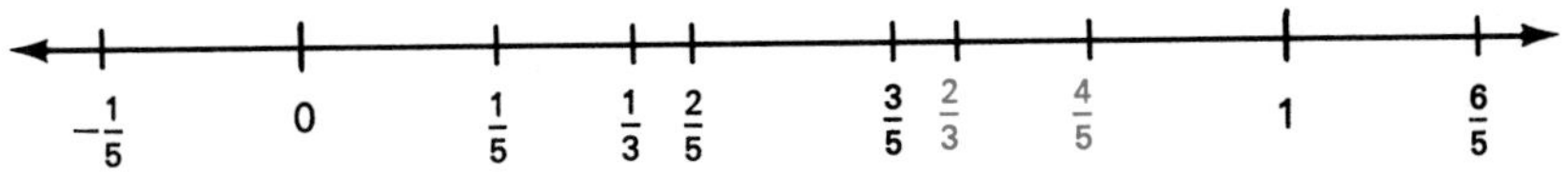

Since $\frac{4}{5}$ is to the right of $\frac{2}{3}$, $\frac{4}{5} > \frac{2}{3}$ or $\frac{2}{3} < \frac{4}{5}$.

An easier way to compare two rational numbers is to rename them so they have the same *positive* denominator. Then compare the numerators.

Example 1: Compare $\frac{4}{5}$ and $\frac{2}{3}$.

$$\frac{4}{5} = \frac{4 \times 3}{5 \times 3} = \frac{12}{15}$$

$$12 > 10, \quad \text{so} \quad \frac{12}{15} > \frac{10}{15}$$

$$\frac{2}{3} = \frac{2 \times 5}{3 \times 5} = \frac{10}{15} \qquad \text{and} \quad \frac{4}{5} > \frac{2}{3}.$$

Example 2: Compare $-\frac{7}{8}$ and $-\frac{5}{6}$.

$$-\frac{7}{8} = \frac{^-7}{8} = \frac{^-7 \times 3}{8 \times 3} = \frac{^-21}{24}$$

Note: To compare negative fractions, think of the numerators as being negative.

$$^-21 < {^-20}, \quad \text{so} \quad \frac{^-21}{24} < \frac{^-20}{24}$$

$$-\frac{5}{6} = \frac{^-5}{6} = \frac{^-5 \times 4}{6 \times 4} = \frac{^-20}{24} \qquad \text{and} \quad -\frac{7}{8} < -\frac{5}{6}.$$

> If two fractions have the same *positive* denominator, the fraction with the greater numerator names the greater number.

Example 3: Compare $\frac{3}{5}$ and $\frac{6}{10}$.

$$\frac{3}{5} = \frac{3 \times 2}{5 \times 2} = \frac{6}{10}, \quad \text{so} \quad \frac{3}{5} = \frac{6}{10}.$$

Exercises

A Tell which fraction in each pair names the greater number.

1. $\frac{5}{12}$ or $\frac{7}{12}$ **2.** $\frac{9}{16}$ or $\frac{3}{16}$ **3.** $-\frac{7}{12}$ or $-\frac{5}{12}$

4. $-\frac{11}{20}$ or $-\frac{9}{20}$ **5.** $-\frac{1}{2}$ or $\frac{1}{2}$ **6.** $-\frac{2}{3}$ or $\frac{3}{4}$

B Should >, <, or = replace ● to make the sentence true?

7. $\frac{4}{9}$ ● $\frac{7}{9}$ **8.** $-\frac{5}{7}$ ● $-\frac{3}{7}$ **9.** $\frac{3}{4}$ ● $-\frac{2}{3}$

10. $\frac{1}{3}$ ● $\frac{1}{2}$ **11.** $\frac{3}{4}$ ● $\frac{5}{2}$ **12.** $\frac{3}{4}$ ● $-\frac{9}{12}$

13. $-\frac{7}{24}$ ● $-\frac{3}{8}$ **14.** $\frac{5}{16}$ ● $-\frac{1}{4}$ **15.** $\frac{5}{8}$ ● $\frac{10}{16}$

16. $-\frac{10}{12}$ ● $-\frac{5}{6}$ **17.** $-\frac{7}{8}$ ● $-\frac{8}{9}$ **18.** $\frac{9}{16}$ ● $\frac{11}{24}$

19. $\frac{7}{4}$ ● $-\frac{5}{3}$ **20.** $\frac{6}{5}$ ● $\frac{5}{4}$ **21.** $-\frac{8}{5}$ ● $\frac{4}{3}$

C Use the shortcut below to find whether the first rational number in each pair is greater than or less than the second one.

Examples: a. $\frac{3}{4}$, $\frac{1}{2}$: $4 \times 1 = 4$; $3 \times 2 = 6$; $6 > 4$, so $\frac{3}{4} > \frac{1}{2}$.

b. $\frac{^-2}{3}$, $\frac{^-5}{8}$: $3 \times {^-5} = {^-15}$; $^-2 \times 8 = {^-16}$; $^-16 < {^-15}$, so $\frac{^-2}{3} < \frac{^-5}{8}$.

22. $\frac{2}{3}$, $\frac{1}{2}$ **23.** $\frac{9}{10}$, $\frac{7}{12}$ **24.** $\frac{3}{4}$, $\frac{4}{5}$

25. $\frac{^-2}{3}$, $\frac{^-3}{4}$ **26.** $\frac{^-5}{12}$, $\frac{^-1}{3}$ **27.** $\frac{^-7}{8}$, $\frac{^-3}{4}$

28. $\frac{4}{5}$, $\frac{^-3}{4}$ **29.** $\frac{^-3}{8}$, $\frac{2}{5}$ **30.** $\frac{5}{6}$, $\frac{^-13}{16}$

Adding and Subtracting With Decimals

Changes in 12-Hour Barometer Readings

Time	Change
6 A.M. Mon.	
	$^-0.25$
6 P.M. Mon.	
	$^-0.18$
6 A.M. Tues.	
	$^+0.35$
6 P.M. Tues.	
	$^+0.12$
6 A.M. Wed.	

Courtesy NOAA

Barometer readings and rainfall amounts are two examples of weather information given with decimals. So weather forecasters must sometimes add and subtract with decimals.

Example 1: Add.

a. $^-0.25$ and $^-0.18$

Both addends have the same sign.

$^-0.25 + {}^-0.18$

Add their absolute values.

$0.25 + 0.18$

Use the sign of the addends.

$^-0.43$

$^-0.25 + {}^-0.18 = {}^-0.43$

b. $^-0.18$ and 0.35

The addends have different signs.

$^-0.18 + 0.35$

Subtract their absolute values.

$0.35 - 0.18$

Use the sign of the addend with the greater absolute value.

$^+0.17$

$^-0.18 + 0.35 = 0.17$

Example 2: Add 0.12 and $^-0.12$.

The Inverse Property of Addition, stated on page 178, can be used for rational numbers that are opposites.

$$0.12 + {}^-0.12 = 0$$

opposites (0.12 and $^-0.12$) sum (0)

Example 3: Subtract $^-0.18$ from 29.72.

$$29.72 - {}^-0.18 = 29.72 + 0.18$$

$$= 29.90$$

To subtract $^-0.18$, add its opposite.

Exercises

A Tell whether each sum is positive, negative, or zero.

1. $1.8 + 4.7$	**2.** ${}^-0.73 + {}^-0.69$	**3.** $1.217 + {}^-1.952$
4. ${}^-27.22 + 14.96$	**5.** $6.251 + {}^-4.213$	**6.** ${}^-8.3 + 8.3$

Tell how to change each subtraction to an addition.

7. $1.6 - 1.9$	**8.** ${}^-4.3 - {}^-5.6$	**9.** $8.27 - {}^-6.28$
10. ${}^-7.234 - 1.732$	**11.** $0.632 - {}^-9.568$	**12.** ${}^-7.35 - 17.58$

B Find each sum or difference.

13. $1.9 + 3.8$	**14.** ${}^-1.6 + {}^-5.9$	**15.** $0.834 + {}^-4.675$
16. ${}^-1.732 + 1.414$	**17.** $6.38 + {}^-6.38$	**18.** ${}^-4.7 + 4.7$
19. $4.9 - 1.6$	**20.** $8.3 - 9.7$	**21.** ${}^-4.65 - 3.78$
22. ${}^-1.752 - 2.869$	**23.** $6.5 - {}^-4.8$	**24.** $7.65 - {}^-10.87$
25. $2.366 + {}^-1.021$	**26.** ${}^-8.65 + 9.52$	**27.** ${}^-4.1 - {}^-2.3$

28. $^{-}8.751 - {}^{-}9.914$ **29.** $0.125 - 0.876$ **30.** $0.35 + 0.75$

31. $^{-}0.165 + {}^{-}0.425$ **32.** $0.438 + {}^{-}5.76$ **33.** $^{-}17.3 - 21.4$

34. $8.6 - {}^{-}2.93$ **35.** $^{-}1.4 - {}^{-}6$ **36.** $^{-}2.371 + 4$

37. $^{-}7.41 + {}^{-}6.9$ **38.** $66.23 + {}^{-}21.1$ **39.** $^{-}1.23 - {}^{-}0.879$

40. $^{-}13 - 11.98$ **41.** $6.28 - {}^{-}29.52$ **42.** $^{-}5.68 + 2.591$

C Solve each problem.

43. The profits of Ace Distributors for January through March are shown at the right. Find the total profit for the three months.

Month	Profit
Jan.	−$795.48
Feb.	$367.42
Mar.	$969.67

44. During one week, Jesse Floyd wrote checks for $20.95 and $16.49. The next week, he made a deposit of $30.00. What was the change in his bank balance for the two weeks?

45. The changes in the Dow Jones stock average for one week are given at the right. Find the change for the week.

Day	Change
Mon.	$^{+}1.76$
Tues.	$^{+}4.38$
Wed.	$^{-}2.69$
Thur.	$^{-}5.99$
Fri.	$^{-}2.78$

46. The level of Oxbow Lake was 1.25 meters above normal in the spring. By late fall, it was 0.78 meter below normal ($^{-}0.78$). What change in water level is given by these two readings?

CONSUMER CORNER

MANAGING PERSONAL FINANCES

If you get an allowance or you work after school, you might be interested in how to manage your finances. The first step toward managing your finances is to keep a record of how you spend your money. One way is to use a chart like the one below.

Courtesy Rockwell International

Day	Item	Income/ expense	Cash on hand
	Balance from last week		18.94
Mon.	Lunch	$^{-}1.26$	17.68
Tues.	Lunch	$^{-}1.34$	16.34
	School supplies	$^{-}1.69$	14.65
	Extra earnings	10.00	24.65
Wed.	Lunch	$^{-}1.58$	23.07
	Record album	$^{-}7.71$	15.36
Thurs.	Lunch	$^{-}1.19$	14.17
	Gift from Aunt Phoebe	10.00	24.17
	Clothing	$^{-}21.73$	2.44
Fri.	Lunch	$^{-}1.25$	1.19
	Paycheck	65.50	66.69
	Toothbrush and comb	$^{-}2.64$	64.05
Sat.	Deposit to savings	$^{-}40.00$	24.05
	Movie	$^{-}4.00$	20.05

Positive numbers show income amounts, and negative numbers show expenses. As each item is listed, its amount is added to the last number in the cash-on-hand column. So the cash-on-hand column tells you how much money you have at any given time.

Activity 1: Keep a record of your income and expenses for two or three weeks.

Activity 2: List each of your expenses for one week under one of the following six areas: Food, Clothing, Entertainment, Personal needs, Savings, and Other. Find the total for each area. Then find what per cent of your total income for the week was spent for each area. (*Example:* If total income was \$60 and total expense for clothing was \$15, then per cent of income spent for clothing was $\frac{15}{60} = .25 = 25\%$.) Do this for each week in Activity 1.

Solving Equations With Decimals

11.4

You can solve equations with decimals the same way you solve equations with integers.

Example 1: Solve $x + 4.7 = {}^{-}3$.

$x + 4.7 = {}^{-}3$

$x + 4.7 + {}^{-}4.7 = {}^{-}3 + {}^{-}4.7$ Add ⁻4.7 to each side.

$x + 0 = {}^{-}7.7$

$x = {}^{-}7.7$

Check: $x + 4.7 = {}^{-}3$

${}^{-}7.7 + 4.7 = {}^{-}3$ Replace x with ⁻7.7.

${}^{-}3 = {}^{-}3$ ✓

Example 2: Solve ${}^{-}3.1 = y - 2.4$.

${}^{-}3.1 = y - 2.4$

${}^{-}3.1 = y + {}^{-}2.4$ Change $y - 2.4$ to $y + {}^{-}2.4$.

${}^{-}3.1 + 2.4 = y + {}^{-}2.4 + 2.4$ Add 2.4 to each side.

${}^{-}0.7 = y + 0$

${}^{-}0.7 = y$

Check: ${}^{-}3.1 = y - 2.4$

${}^{-}3.1 = {}^{-}0.7 - 2.4$ Replace y with ⁻0.7.

${}^{-}3.1 = {}^{-}0.7 + {}^{-}2.4$

${}^{-}3.1 = {}^{-}3.1$ ✓

Exercises

A Tell what the first step would be for solving each equation.

1. $m + 6.7 = 9.4$
2. $n + 1.3 = 8.6$
3. $^-2.4 = t + {}^-3.7$
4. $q + 7.8 = 0$
5. $10.5 = s + {}^-9.1$
6. $11.4 = r + {}^-11.4$

Tell what the first *two* steps would be for solving each equation.

7. $d - 1.5 = 3.6$
8. $e - 2.6 = 1.4$
9. $f - {}^-5.9 = 10$
10. $0 = h - {}^-7.1$
11. $^-8.3 = g - {}^-0.3$
12. $^-0.09 = j - 0.09$

B Solve.

13. $n - 6.3 = 9.5$
14. $n - 7.62 = {}^-6.25$
15. $k + {}^-4.6 = 4.7$
16. $0 = t + {}^-1.5$
17. $6 = h + 2.7$
18. $n - {}^-4.63 = {}^-10$
19. $x - 4.2 = {}^-6.3$
20. $y - 3 = {}^-5.95$
21. $3.4 = m + {}^-0.16$
22. $x + 7.5 = {}^-2.5$
23. $n + 0.75 = {}^-0.26$
24. $y - {}^-4.7 = 9.7$
25. $b - 4.5 = 2.3$
26. $^-0.7 = t - {}^-3.48$
27. $^-5.3 + z = 0.68$
28. $7.1 + x = 4$
29. $^-10.9 = c + {}^-21$
30. $^-25 = {}^-3.75 + y$

C

31. $1.5 - {}^-a = 8.7$
32. $1.6 = {}^-0.77 - {}^-b$
33. $(p + {}^-1.9) + 3.41 = 0$
34. $25.16 = (q + 7.8) + {}^-9.4$
35. $6.15 = {}^-3.5 + k + {}^-1.4$
36. $^-10.76 = {}^-2.5 + m + {}^-17.4$

CONSUMER CORNER

MARKUP AND MARKDOWN

A storekeeper buys an item at the wholesale price and sells the item at the retail price, or sometimes at the sale price.

retail price → p, wholesale price → w, markup → m

$$p = w + m$$

sale price → s, retail price → p, markdown (discount) → d

$$s = p - d$$

Use the formulas above to answer the following:

1. The markup on a record album is \$1.43. If the retail price is \$5.98, what is the wholesale price?

2. The wholesale price of a sleeping bag is \$59.24. If the retail price is \$78.99, what is the markup?

3. A radio is on sale for \$35.98. If the markdown is \$4.01, what is the retail price?

4. The sale price of a ten-speed bicycle is \$169.95. If the markdown is \$84.98, what is the retail price?

Quick Quiz
Sections 11.1 to 11.4

1. $\frac{2}{3}$, $-\frac{7}{5}$, 8, $^-11$, $^-2\frac{3}{4}$, $1\frac{1}{2}$, 0.7, and $^-3.26$ are all ____ numbers.

2. The opposite of $-\frac{3}{4}$ is ____.

3. The absolute value of $^-0.73$ is ____.

Should >, <, or = replace ● to make the sentence true?

4. $\frac{1}{3}$ ● $\frac{2}{3}$ **5.** $-\frac{3}{4}$ ● $-\frac{1}{4}$ **6.** $-\frac{2}{5}$ ● $-\frac{4}{10}$

Compute.

7. $1.8 + {}^-3.5$ **8.** $^-2.6 - {}^-3.15$ **9.** $15.12 - 19.25$

Solve.

10. $x + 7.4 = 8.1$ **11.** $^-10.27 = y - {}^-6.5$

11.5 Adding and Subtracting With Fractions

Example 1: Add $-\frac{1}{4}$ and $-\frac{1}{8}$.

The addends have the same sign.

$$-\frac{1}{4} + \left(-\frac{1}{8}\right)$$

Rename, using the least common denominator.

$$-\frac{2}{8} + \left(-\frac{1}{8}\right)$$

Add the absolute values.

$$\frac{2}{8} + \frac{1}{8}$$

Use the sign of the addends.

$$-\frac{3}{8}$$

$$-\frac{1}{4} + \left(-\frac{1}{8}\right) = -\frac{3}{8}$$

Example 2: Add $\frac{3}{4}$ and $-\frac{1}{2}$.

The addends have different signs.

$$\frac{3}{4} + \left(-\frac{1}{2}\right)$$

Rename, using the least common denominator.

$$\frac{3}{4} + \left(-\frac{2}{4}\right)$$

Subtract the absolute values.

$$\frac{3}{4} - \frac{2}{4}$$

Use the sign of the addend with the greater absolute value.

$$+\frac{1}{4}$$

$$\frac{3}{4} + \left(-\frac{1}{2}\right) = \frac{1}{4}$$

Example 3: Subtract $\frac{5}{6}$ from $\frac{1}{2}$.

$$\frac{1}{2} - \frac{5}{6} = \frac{1}{2} + \left(-\frac{5}{6}\right)$$

Subtracting $\frac{5}{6}$ is the same as adding $-\frac{5}{6}$.

$$= \frac{3}{6} + \left(-\frac{5}{6}\right)$$

$$= -\frac{2}{6}$$

$$= -\frac{1}{3}$$

Simplify.

Exercises

A Tell whether each sum is positive, negative, or zero.

1. $\frac{3}{4} + \frac{2}{3}$ **2.** $\frac{1}{8} + (-\frac{7}{8})$ **3.** $-\frac{1}{4} + (-\frac{3}{8})$

4. $-\frac{5}{6} + 0$ **5.** $-\frac{1}{2} + \frac{1}{4}$ **6.** $\frac{9}{10} + (-\frac{9}{10})$

Tell how to change each subtraction to an addition.

7. $\frac{1}{8} - \frac{7}{8}$ **8.** $-\frac{1}{4} - (-\frac{1}{2})$ **9.** $\frac{1}{2} - (-\frac{3}{8})$

10. $-\frac{1}{6} - \frac{1}{2}$ **11.** $-\frac{2}{3} - (-\frac{1}{2})$ **12.** $\frac{1}{8} - (-\frac{2}{3})$

B Find each sum.

13. $\frac{1}{3} + \frac{1}{2}$ **14.** $\frac{1}{4} + (-\frac{3}{4})$ **15.** $-\frac{7}{10} + \frac{1}{10}$

16. $-\frac{1}{5} + (-\frac{2}{5})$ **17.** $\frac{1}{4} + (-\frac{1}{4})$ **18.** $-\frac{1}{2} + \frac{4}{8}$

19. $-\frac{1}{3} + (-\frac{3}{8})$ **20.** $\frac{1}{4} + (-\frac{7}{8})$ **21.** $-\frac{1}{4} + (-\frac{5}{8})$

22. $\frac{7}{8} + (-\frac{3}{4})$ **23.** $-\frac{1}{2} + \frac{1}{4}$ **24.** $\frac{3}{4} + (-\frac{1}{2})$

Find each difference.

25. $\frac{7}{8} - \frac{3}{8}$ **26.** $\frac{1}{2} - \frac{2}{3}$ **27.** $-\frac{1}{6} - \frac{1}{2}$

28. $\frac{5}{8} - (-\frac{1}{4})$ **29.** $-\frac{3}{5} - (-\frac{1}{5})$ **30.** $-\frac{1}{4} - \frac{1}{2}$

31. $-\frac{1}{2} - (-\frac{7}{8})$ **32.** $\frac{2}{3} - \frac{3}{4}$ **33.** $\frac{1}{2} - \frac{9}{10}$

34. $\frac{1}{2} - (-\frac{1}{4})$ **35.** $-\frac{7}{8} - (-\frac{1}{2})$ **36.** $-\frac{1}{4} - (-\frac{2}{3})$

C Compute.

37. $\frac{5}{12} + (-\frac{5}{8})$ **38.** $-\frac{4}{15} - (-\frac{9}{10})$ **39.** $\frac{5}{9} - \frac{5}{6}$

40. $-\frac{6}{11} + \frac{2}{3}$ **41.** $\frac{9}{14} + (-\frac{3}{4})$ **42.** $\frac{1}{9} - \frac{1}{8}$

43. $(\frac{1}{4} + \frac{1}{8}) + (-\frac{1}{2})$ **44.** $-\frac{3}{5} + (-\frac{2}{3} + \frac{4}{5})$

11.6 Adding and Subtracting With Mixed Numbers

Example 1: Add $^-1\frac{1}{2}$ and $^-1\frac{1}{4}$.

ADDENDS HAVE THE SAME SIGN. $\quad ^-1\frac{1}{2} + {}^-1\frac{1}{4}$

Add their absolute values. $\quad 1\frac{1}{2} + 1\frac{1}{4}$

$$\begin{array}{rcr} 1\frac{1}{2} & \longrightarrow & 1\frac{2}{4} \\ +\,1\frac{1}{4} & \longrightarrow & +\,1\frac{1}{4} \\ \hline & & 2\frac{3}{4} \end{array}$$

Use the sign of the addends. $\quad ^-2\frac{3}{4}$

$$^-1\frac{1}{2} + {}^-1\frac{1}{4} = {}^-2\frac{3}{4}$$

Example 2: Add $^-1\frac{5}{6}$ and $3\frac{1}{6}$.

ADDENDS HAVE DIFFERENT SIGNS. $\quad ^-1\frac{5}{6} + 3\frac{1}{6}$

Subtract their absolute values. $\quad 3\frac{1}{6} - 1\frac{5}{6}$

$$\begin{array}{rcr} 3\frac{1}{6} & \longrightarrow & 2\frac{7}{6} \\ -\,1\frac{5}{6} & \longrightarrow & -\,1\frac{5}{6} \\ \hline & & 1\frac{2}{6} = 1\frac{1}{3} \end{array}$$

Use the sign of the addend with the greater absolute value. $\quad ^+1\frac{1}{3}$

$$^-1\frac{5}{6} + 3\frac{1}{6} = 1\frac{1}{3}$$

Example 3: Subtract $^-1\frac{3}{5}$ from $^-2$.

$$^-2 - {}^-1\frac{3}{5} = {}^-2 + 1\frac{3}{5}$$

Subtracting $^-1\frac{3}{5}$ is the same as adding $1\frac{3}{5}$.

$$= {}^-1\frac{5}{5} + 1\frac{3}{5}$$

$$= -\frac{2}{5}$$

Exercises

A Tell whether each sum is positive, negative, or zero.

1. $1\frac{1}{3} + 2\frac{1}{4}$ **2.** $-\frac{3}{8} + 1\frac{5}{8}$ **3.** $^-2\frac{1}{4} + {}^-1\frac{3}{4}$

4. $2 + {}^-1\frac{3}{4}$ **5.** $^-3\frac{1}{2} + 3\frac{1}{2}$ **6.** $1\frac{3}{5} + {}^-3\frac{1}{5}$

Tell how to change each subtraction to an addition.

7. $1\frac{1}{3} - 2\frac{2}{3}$ **8.** $3\frac{1}{4} - {}^-1\frac{1}{2}$ **9.** $-\frac{1}{3} - {}^-1\frac{5}{6}$

10. $^-2\frac{1}{2} - 1\frac{1}{4}$ **11.** $\frac{3}{4} - {}^-2\frac{1}{8}$ **12.** $^-4 - {}^-2\frac{1}{5}$

B Compute.

13. $1\frac{3}{4} + {}^-1\frac{1}{4}$ **14.** $^-2\frac{1}{3} + {}^-3\frac{2}{3}$ **15.** $3 + {}^-1\frac{3}{5}$

16. $^-1\frac{1}{5} - \frac{2}{5}$ **17.** $3\frac{1}{8} - {}^-1\frac{3}{8}$ **18.** $^-1\frac{5}{6} - {}^-3\frac{1}{6}$

19. $^-5\frac{1}{2} + 1\frac{7}{8}$ **20.** $^-1\frac{3}{4} - 4\frac{1}{2}$ **21.** $^-1\frac{1}{4} + (-\frac{5}{8})$

22. $2\frac{1}{2} - {}^-1\frac{7}{8}$ **23.** $3\frac{1}{2} - 4\frac{9}{10}$ **24.** $^-2\frac{1}{3} + {}^-1\frac{7}{8}$

25. $1\frac{7}{8} + (-\frac{3}{4})$ **26.** $^-3 + 1\frac{4}{5}$ **27.** $^-2 - {}^-1\frac{3}{4}$

28. $^-2\frac{7}{8} + {}^-1\frac{1}{2}$ **29.** $^-7\frac{1}{2} + 3\frac{1}{4}$ **30.** $8\frac{3}{4} + {}^-4\frac{1}{2}$

31. $^-3\frac{1}{4} - (-\frac{2}{3})$ **32.** $^-9\frac{1}{2} + 3\frac{1}{4}$ **33.** $8\frac{1}{2} - {}^-3\frac{1}{4}$

C **34.** $^-6\frac{1}{3} + 5\frac{2}{3} + {}^-8\frac{2}{3}$ **35.** $1\frac{1}{4} + {}^-3\frac{1}{2} + {}^-5\frac{3}{4}$

36. $^-3\frac{1}{2} + {}^-4\frac{1}{8} + 7\frac{5}{8}$ **37.** $^-10\frac{1}{3} + {}^-5\frac{1}{2} + 6\frac{5}{6}$

11.7 Solving Equations With Fractions

Example 1: Solve $y + \frac{5}{8} = \frac{1}{8}$.

$$y + \frac{5}{8} = \frac{1}{8}$$

$$y + \frac{5}{8} + \left(-\frac{5}{8}\right) = \frac{1}{8} + \left(-\frac{5}{8}\right)$$ Add $-\frac{5}{8}$ to each side.

$$y + 0 = -\frac{4}{8}$$

$$y = -\frac{1}{2}$$

Check: $$y + \frac{5}{8} = \frac{1}{8}$$

$$-\frac{1}{2} + \frac{5}{8} = \frac{1}{8}$$ Replace y with $-\frac{1}{2}$.

$$-\frac{4}{8} + \frac{5}{8} = \frac{1}{8}$$

$$\frac{1}{8} = \frac{1}{8} \quad \checkmark$$

Example 2: Solve $-\frac{1}{3} = x - \left(-\frac{1}{4}\right)$.

$$-\frac{1}{3} = x - \left(-\frac{1}{4}\right)$$

$$-\frac{1}{3} = x + \frac{1}{4}$$ Change $x - \left(-\frac{1}{4}\right)$ to $x + \frac{1}{4}$.

$$-\frac{1}{3} + \left(-\frac{1}{4}\right) = x + \frac{1}{4} + \left(-\frac{1}{4}\right)$$ Add $-\frac{1}{4}$ to each side.

$$-\frac{4}{12} + \left(-\frac{3}{12}\right) = x + 0$$

$$-\frac{7}{12} = x$$

Check: $-\frac{1}{3} = x - \left(-\frac{1}{4}\right)$

$-\frac{1}{3} = -\frac{7}{12} - \left(-\frac{1}{4}\right)$ Replace x with $-\frac{7}{12}$.

$-\frac{1}{3} = -\frac{7}{12} + \frac{1}{4}$

$-\frac{1}{3} = -\frac{7}{12} + \frac{3}{12}$

$-\frac{1}{3} = -\frac{4}{12}$

$-\frac{1}{3} = -\frac{1}{3}$ ✓

Exercises

A Tell what should replace each ?.

1. $a - (-\frac{1}{5}) = \frac{4}{5}$

a. $a + ? = \frac{4}{5}$

b. $a + \frac{1}{5} + (-\frac{1}{5}) = \frac{4}{5} + ?$

c. $a + ? = \frac{3}{5}$

d. $a = ?$

2. $b + (-\frac{1}{6}) = -\frac{2}{3}$

a. $b + (-\frac{1}{6}) + ? = -\frac{2}{3} + \frac{1}{6}$

b. $b + 0 = -\frac{?}{6} + \frac{1}{6}$

c. $? = -\frac{3}{6}$

d. $b = ?$

Tell what the first step would be for solving each equation.

3. $n + \frac{3}{4} = \frac{1}{4}$ **4.** $m + \frac{1}{8} = -\frac{5}{8}$ **5.** $-\frac{2}{3} = k + (-\frac{1}{2})$

6. $-\frac{5}{9} = t + (-\frac{1}{9})$ **7.** $x + \frac{3}{7} = -\frac{2}{7}$ **8.** $0 = y + \frac{2}{3}$

Tell what the first *two* steps would be for solving each equation.

9. $b - \frac{1}{4} = \frac{1}{2}$ **10.** $c - \frac{1}{2} = -\frac{5}{8}$ **11.** $\frac{5}{7} = d - (-\frac{4}{7})$

12. $-\frac{1}{3} = f - (-\frac{3}{5})$ **13.** $g - \frac{3}{8} = \frac{1}{4}$ **14.** $0 = h - (-\frac{8}{9})$

B Solve.

15. $a - \frac{1}{3} = \frac{1}{3}$ **16.** $-\frac{5}{6} = c - \frac{5}{6}$ **17.** $b + (-\frac{3}{8}) = \frac{3}{8}$

18. $0 = d + (-\frac{1}{2})$ **19.** $f + \frac{1}{2} = \frac{3}{4}$ **20.** $e - (-\frac{2}{3}) = -\frac{1}{6}$

21. $-\frac{2}{5} = g - \frac{3}{10}$ **22.** $i - \frac{1}{3} = -\frac{2}{9}$ **23.** $-\frac{3}{8} = h + \frac{1}{2}$

24. $j + (-\frac{3}{4}) = -\frac{7}{8}$ **25.** $-\frac{7}{10} = m + \frac{1}{5}$ **26.** $\frac{3}{4} = k - (-\frac{1}{4})$

27. $n - (-\frac{1}{3}) = -\frac{5}{9}$ **28.** $\frac{1}{2} = g - \frac{3}{10}$ **29.** $p + (-\frac{1}{5}) = -\frac{1}{2}$

30. $\frac{1}{4} + r = -\frac{3}{4}$ **31.** $\frac{4}{9} = \frac{2}{3} + s$ **32.** $-\frac{5}{8} = -\frac{1}{4} + t$

Example: Solve $x + 1\frac{1}{5} = {}^-2\frac{3}{5}$.

$$x + 1\frac{1}{5} = {}^-2\frac{3}{5}$$

$$x + 1\frac{1}{5} + {}^-1\frac{1}{5} = {}^-2\frac{3}{5} + {}^-1\frac{1}{5}$$

$$x + 0 = {}^-3\frac{4}{5}$$

$$x = {}^-3\frac{4}{5}$$

Check:

$$x + 1\frac{1}{5} = {}^-2\frac{3}{5}$$

$$^-3\frac{4}{5} + 1\frac{1}{5} = {}^-2\frac{3}{5}$$

$$^-2\frac{3}{5} = {}^-2\frac{3}{5} \checkmark$$

33. $a + 3\frac{1}{3} = {}^-7\frac{1}{3}$ **34.** $b - 1\frac{5}{8} = {}^-2\frac{1}{8}$ **35.** $4\frac{1}{5} = c - {}^-5\frac{4}{5}$

36. $^-3\frac{2}{3} = d - 1\frac{1}{4}$ **37.** $3\frac{1}{2} = e - 5\frac{1}{4}$ **38.** $f - {}^-2\frac{3}{4} = 1\frac{2}{3}$

C **39.** $g + 2\frac{1}{8} = 1\frac{5}{6}$ **40.** $h - 8\frac{2}{3} = {}^-10\frac{4}{5}$ **41.** $4\frac{2}{9} = i - 2\frac{3}{8}$

42. $^-5\frac{1}{3} = j + 3\frac{4}{7}$ **43.** $k + 10\frac{5}{6} = {}^-4\frac{1}{15}$ **44.** $16\frac{1}{4} = t + 12\frac{5}{11}$

Using Equations to Solve Problems

Now we can write equations with rational numbers to help solve problems.

Example 1: Mary's earned run average this year was 2.44. This was a change of $^-0.52$ from last year. What was her earned run average last year?

Let x = average last year.

last year's average → x; change → $^-0.52$; this year's average → 2.44

$$x + {}^-0.52 = 2.44$$

$$x + {}^-0.52 + 0.52 = 2.44 + 0.52$$

$$x + 0 = 2.96$$

$$x = 2.96$$

Check: Does an earned run average of 2.96 followed by a $^-0.52$ change give an earned run average of 2.44? ✓

Her earned run average last year was 2.96.

Terry McKoy/The Picture Cube

Terry McKoy/The Picture Cube

Example 2: A club at Mary's school sells booster buttons. Last year, the club made a profit of $16\frac{3}{4}$¢ on each button sold. This year the profit was $15\frac{1}{2}$¢ for each button. What was the change in profit from last year to this year?

Let c = change in profit.

last year's profit → $16\frac{3}{4}$; change → c; this year's profit → $15\frac{1}{2}$

$$16\frac{3}{4} + c = 15\frac{1}{2}$$

$$c + 16\frac{3}{4} = 15\frac{1}{2}$$

$$c + 16\frac{3}{4} + {}^{-}16\frac{3}{4} = 15\frac{1}{2} + {}^{-}16\frac{3}{4}$$

$$c + 0 = 15\frac{2}{4} + {}^{-}16\frac{3}{4}$$

$$c = {}^{-}1\frac{1}{4}$$

Check: Does going from a profit of $16\frac{3}{4}$¢ to $15\frac{1}{2}$¢ give a change in profit of $^{-}1\frac{1}{4}$¢? ✓

The change in profit was $^{-}1\frac{1}{4}$¢. Or we can say this year the club made $1\frac{1}{4}$¢ less on each button than it did last year.

Exercises

A Refer to the problem below to answer each question.

Problem: Ms. Willis drove her car from Hilltown to Pine City. Her car used $\frac{1}{4}$ of a tank of gas for the trip. If the gas tank was $\frac{3}{8}$ full when Ms. Willis got to Pine City, how full was the tank before she left Hilltown?

1. What should x represent?

a. how full the tank was after getting to Pine City

b. how much gas was used on the trip

c. how full the tank was before leaving Hilltown

2. Which number represents the amount of gas used?

a. $\frac{3}{8}$ b. $-\frac{1}{4}$ c. $-\frac{3}{8}$

3. Which number represents the amount of gas left at the end of the trip?

a. $\frac{3}{8}$ b. $-\frac{1}{4}$ c. $-\frac{3}{8}$

4. Which equation could you use to help solve the problem?

a. $\frac{3}{8} + x = -\frac{1}{4}$ b. $x + (-\frac{1}{4}) = \frac{3}{8}$ c. $-\frac{1}{4} + \frac{3}{8} = x$

B Solve each problem by using an equation. (Use negative numbers whenever they fit.)

5. This morning the barometer reading was 29.96 inches. Now it is 29.82 inches. What was the change in readings?

6. Ms. Anderson's car has a 40-liter gas tank. If it took 33.7 liters of gas to fill the tank, how much gas was in the tank before it was filled?

7. Yesterday Juan's body temperature was 101.6 °F. Today his temperature is 98.9 °F. What was the change in his temperature readings from yesterday to today?

8. A smoke detector sells for \$27.85. If you use a refund coupon from the company that makes the detector, the cost is only \$22.85. How much is the refund?

9. Sam is a wrestler. On Wednesday he weighed $\frac{3}{4}$ lb over the limit for his weight class. On Friday he weighed $\frac{1}{2}$ lb under the limit. What was his change in weight from Wednesday to Friday?

10. Mary's chemistry lab is $\frac{3}{4}$ hour long. If she takes $\frac{1}{4}$ hour to read about an experiment, how much time does she have to do the experiment?

M. Wannemacher/Taurus Photos

11. At one time during a rainstorm, the water level of a river was $\frac{2}{3}$ ft below the flood line. Three hours later, it was $\frac{1}{2}$ ft above the flood line. What change in the water level is given by these two measurements?

12. At the beginning of February, the inflation rate for the year was $\frac{1}{2}$ per cent. By the end of February the rate rose to $\frac{7}{8}$ per cent. What was the change in the inflation rate during February?

13. The sale price of a certain record is \$4.99. This is \$0.98 less than the regular price of the record. How much would you pay for the record at the regular price?

14. Mr. Conway lives in Cedar City. He drove to Oakville, which is 12.8 miles from Cedar City. If the mileage reading was 18,945.7 after he got to Oakville, what was the reading before he left Cedar City?

15. Last fall a small maple tree was $5\frac{1}{2}$ ft tall. This fall the tree was $6\frac{2}{3}$ ft tall. What was the change in the height of the tree from last fall to this fall?

16. Last year a cherry tree produced $2\frac{1}{2}$ bushels of cherries. This year the same tree produced $2\frac{1}{4}$ bushels. What was the change in number of bushels produced from last year to this year?

C 17. In April the balance of a charge account was $^{-}$\$157.49. In May the balance was $^{-}$\$193.34. What was the change in the balance from April to May?

18. Stan borrowed some money and agreed to decrease his debt by \$3.25 each month. After one month, his balance was $^{-}$\$22.14. How much money did Stan borrow?

19. Between January 1 and November 24 of the same year, the prime lending rate of a large New York bank increased by $3\frac{3}{4}$ per cent. The rate on November 24 was $11\frac{1}{2}$ per cent. What was the rate on January 1?

20. The price of a share of stock was $24\frac{1}{4}$ dollars at the beginning of the day. At the end of the day, the price was $22\frac{1}{2}$ dollars. What was the change in the price for the day?

CAREER CORNER

BOOKKEEPING

Bookkeeping workers keep the records of businesses in an up-to-date and systematic way. They also make up forms that show all amounts taken in and paid out during certain periods.

High-school graduates who have taken business math, bookkeeping, and accounting courses meet the minimum requirements for most bookkeeping jobs. But some employers prefer that applicants also have taken business courses in a community or business college.

A bookkeeping worker might have to find the sum below. The numbers in parentheses are negative. Find the sum.

Account 07359
Monday, Jan. 5, 1981

Received from Acme Tool	\$ 1253.75
Received from Harper Welding	576.67
Paid to Phaeton Steel	(2175.00)
Received from Raycon Fabricators	3411.05
Paid to Wilco Aluminum	(575.50)
Total	

Courtesy NCR

RATS!

Players Two

Equipment An ordinary deck of 52 playing cards

Black cards (clubs and spades) stand for positive integers, and red cards (hearts and diamonds) stand for negative integers as follows:

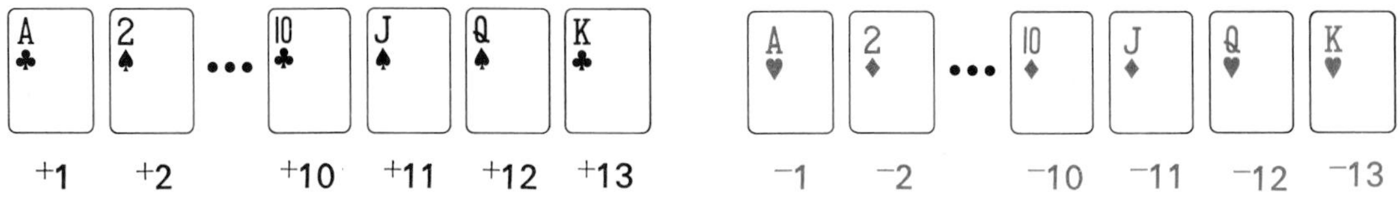

Setup The deck of cards is placed facedown on a table. This becomes the draw pile.

Play START: Each player takes two cards from the draw pile.

OBJECT: The cards in your hand make a rational number. One card is the numerator of a fraction, and the other is the denominator. You want to make the greatest number you can with the cards.

Mary Elenz Tranter Photographics

Example: You draw the 3 of diamonds and the 9 of clubs. There are two ways you can play the cards.

$= \frac{^-3}{9} = -\frac{1}{3}$

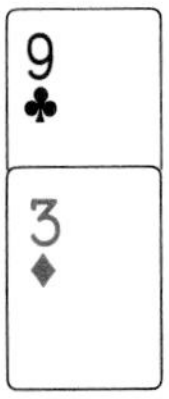

$= \frac{9}{^-3} = ^-3$

$-\frac{1}{3} > {}^-3$, so you would place your cards on the table as shown on the left above.

WINNING THE HAND: Once the cards have been placed on the table, they cannot be changed. The player whose cards make the greater number wins the hand and picks up all four cards. The cards are placed in the player's point pile.

Example:

Player A:

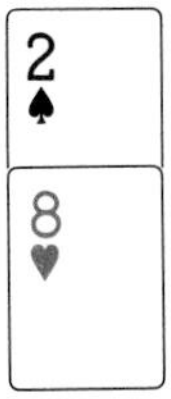

Player B:

$-\frac{1}{4} > -\frac{1}{3}$, so player A wins the hand.

STARTING A NEW HAND: Each player takes two more cards from the draw pile. The winner of the last hand draws first.

End of game

The game is over when there are no cards left in the draw pile and the last four cards have been played.

Tie hand

In case of a tie (when both players' cards make the same number), the cards are left on the table. A new hand is played. The winner of the new hand picks up all the cards on the table. If the game ends before a tie can be broken, the cards stay on the table and are not counted in either player's score.

RATS!

You can take a win from the other player if the player won the hand but you think he/she could have made a greater number with his/her cards. (For example, the play was $\frac{6}{7}$ instead of $\frac{7}{6}$.) You must say "RATS!" before the cards are picked up from the table. If you are right, you get the cards. If you are wrong, the other player gets the cards and you must give the other player 2 points (1 picture card or 2 other cards) from your point pile (or as soon as your point pile has the points if it is empty).

Scoring

Each picture card (jack, queen, king) counts 2 points. All other cards count 1 point each. Your score is the total number of points in your point pile. High score wins.

Terms and Symbols Review

True or False?

1. $\frac{5}{6}$, $^-2$, $^-7\frac{1}{3}$, 0, 9.2, $-\frac{3}{2}$, and $^-2.5$ are rational numbers.
2. $-\frac{1}{4}$ is the opposite of $\frac{1}{4}$.
3. $^-3.61$ is the absolute value of $^-3.61$.
4. The graph of $-\frac{1}{3}$ is a point on a number line between 0 and 1.
5. $^-1 \div {}^-2$ can be expressed as $-\frac{1}{2}$.
6. Subtracting $^-2.1$ is the same as adding $^-2.1$.
7. $\frac{5}{8} + (-\frac{7}{8})$ is a negative sum.
8. $^-1\frac{1}{4} + 3\frac{3}{4}$ is a negative sum.

Chapter 11 Review

11.1 Give the opposite of each number.

1. $\frac{1}{3}$ **2.** $^-0.58$ **3.** $1\frac{2}{5}$ **4.** $-\frac{9}{10}$

Give the absolute value of each number.

5. 10.49 **6.** $^-0.68$ **7.** $-\frac{4}{9}$ **8.** $1\frac{3}{4}$

11.2 Should $>$, $<$, or $=$ replace ● to make the sentence true?

9. $\frac{3}{7}$ ● $\frac{5}{7}$ **10.** $\frac{3}{4}$ ● $\frac{7}{8}$ **11.** $\frac{3}{4}$ ● $-\frac{2}{3}$

12. $-\frac{5}{6}$ ● $\frac{2}{3}$ **13.** $-\frac{5}{8}$ ● $-\frac{1}{2}$ **14.** $-\frac{7}{8}$ ● $\frac{14}{16}$

11.3 Find each sum or difference.

15. $^-5.9 + 3.7$ **16.** $^-4.2 + {}^-1.9$ **17.** $6.38 + {}^-2.69$

18. $^-1.732 - 4.12$ **19.** $^-5.7 - {}^-5.2$ **20.** $8.3 - {}^-9.6$

Solve. 11.4

21. $t - 2.4 = 1.6$ **22.** $v + 1.7 = 10.1$ **23.** $^-1.6 = w - ^-3.1$

24. $x + ^-1.31 = ^-5.7$ **25.** $y + 1.9 = 0$ **26.** $^-2.4 = z + 3.35$

Find each sum or difference.

27. $-\frac{1}{8} + \frac{3}{8}$ **28.** $\frac{3}{4} + (-\frac{1}{8})$ **29.** $-\frac{1}{2} + (-\frac{1}{3})$ 11.5

30. $\frac{1}{4} - \frac{2}{3}$ **31.** $-\frac{1}{2} - \frac{1}{4}$ **32.** $-\frac{3}{8} - (-\frac{3}{4})$

33. $^-1\frac{3}{8} + 1\frac{5}{8}$ **34.** $3 + ^-1\frac{1}{2}$ **35.** $^-2\frac{3}{4} + ^-1\frac{2}{3}$ 11.6

36. $^-2\frac{3}{5} - 1\frac{2}{5}$ **37.** $\frac{3}{4} - ^-1\frac{1}{8}$ **38.** $^-1\frac{3}{4} - ^-2\frac{1}{4}$

Solve. 11.7

39. $n + \frac{3}{4} = \frac{1}{4}$ **40.** $p - \frac{3}{8} = -\frac{5}{8}$ **41.** $\frac{1}{2} = q + (-\frac{3}{4})$

42. $\frac{2}{3} = r - (-\frac{5}{6})$ **43.** $s + \frac{3}{8} = -\frac{1}{4}$ **44.** $\frac{1}{3} = t + (-\frac{1}{2})$

Solve each problem by using an equation. 11.8

45. At 8:00 A.M. a water cooler contained $\frac{3}{4}$ gallon of water. At 10:00 A.M. there was $\frac{1}{8}$ gallon of water in the cooler. How much water was used from 8:00 A.M. to 10:00 A.M.?

46. This morning the barometer reading was 30.16. This was a change of $^-0.13$ from last night. What was the reading last night?

Chapter 11 Test

1. Give the absolute value of $5\frac{1}{3}$.

2. Give the opposite of ${}^{-}7.03$.

Find each sum or difference.

3. $-\frac{3}{4} + \frac{1}{8}$

4. $\frac{7}{8} + (-\frac{1}{2})$

5. $1\frac{1}{2} + (-\frac{5}{8})$

6. ${}^{-}3\frac{1}{2} + {}^{-}4\frac{1}{2}$

7. ${}^{-}3.75 + 4.29$

8. ${}^{-}8.79 + {}^{-}6.75$

9. $-\frac{4}{5} - \frac{1}{10}$

10. $\frac{1}{4} - (-\frac{5}{8})$

11. ${}^{-}1\frac{2}{5} - {}^{-}2\frac{1}{3}$

12. $6.7 - 9.6$

13. ${}^{-}8.9 - 5.2$

14. $1.42 - {}^{-}6.75$

15. $4 + {}^{-}1\frac{2}{3}$

16. $-\frac{1}{2} + (-\frac{1}{5})$

17. ${}^{-}1\frac{3}{8} - {}^{-}1\frac{1}{4}$

Solve.

18. $z + \frac{1}{5} = -\frac{3}{5}$

19. $x + {}^{-}7.2 = 5.3$

20. $c - 3.2 = {}^{-}5.7$

21. $\frac{3}{4} + f = -\frac{5}{8}$

22. $-\frac{7}{8} + m = 0$

23. ${}^{-}4.2 = a + {}^{-}7.3$

24. $k - (-\frac{1}{2}) = -\frac{5}{6}$

25. $\frac{3}{4} = h - \frac{5}{8}$

26. $b - 6.9 = 8.3$

27. $\frac{1}{4} = y - \frac{1}{2}$

RATE YOURSELF

Number Correct	
28–29	Superior
25–27	Excellent
21–24	Good
15–20	Fair
0–14	Poor

Solve each problem by using an equation.

28. This year's sales for Zee Company were down \$1.7 million from last year's sales. If this year's sales were \$30.5 million, what were last year's sales?

29. On the first day of a canoe trip, the average speed was $2\frac{1}{2}$ miles per hour. On the second day, the average was $1\frac{3}{4}$ miles per hour. What was the change in average speed from the first day to the second day?

Find each product or quotient.

1. $\frac{1}{8} \times \frac{3}{2}$	**2.** $\frac{3}{4} \times \frac{5}{12}$	**3.** $\frac{2}{3} \times \frac{9}{16}$	4.2
4. $4\frac{1}{2} \times 3$	**5.** $\frac{1}{2} \times 2\frac{2}{3}$	**6.** $2\frac{1}{2} \times 1\frac{2}{3}$	4.5
7. $\frac{1}{8} \div \frac{2}{3}$	**8.** $\frac{3}{5} \div \frac{9}{16}$	**9.** $1\frac{1}{2} \div 2\frac{3}{8}$	4.6
10. 4.3×2.1	**11.** 75.3×0.001	**12.** 3.14×65	5.4
13. $0.196 \div 14$	**14.** $4.791 \div 3$	**15.** $0.042 \div 6$	5.5
16. $0.1917 \div 14.2$	**17.** $9 \div 2.25$	**18.** $10.24 \div 3.2$	5.6
19. $8 \times {}^{-}7$	**20.** ${}^{-}7 \times 8$	**21.** ${}^{-}14 \times 9$	7.1
22. ${}^{-}14 \times {}^{-}4$	**23.** ${}^{-}7 \times {}^{-}4 \times 2$	**24.** $8 \times {}^{-}7 \times 5$	7.2
25. ${}^{-}21 \div 7$	**26.** ${}^{-}42 \div {}^{-}6$	**27.** $84 \div {}^{-}12$	7.3

Solve each equation.

28. $2n = {}^{-}10$	**29.** ${}^{-}35 = {}^{-}5k$	7.4
30. $\frac{n}{4} = {}^{-}8$	**31.** $17 = \frac{x}{{}^{-}9}$	7.5
32. $17 = {}^{-}2x - 3$	**33.** $\frac{z}{6} + 5 = {}^{-}12$	7.8
34. $n - 9.5 = {}^{-}1.3$	**35.** ${}^{-}6.1 = t + {}^{-}4.6$	11.4
36. $x - \frac{3}{8} = -\frac{1}{8}$	**37.** $n + \frac{7}{12} = -\frac{11}{12}$	11.7

Find each value.

38. 10^2	**39.** 10^4	**40.** 10^3	3.8
41. $25 + 10 \div 5$	**42.** $(25 + 10) \div 5$		1.2

43. Which of the following fractions are equal to $\frac{{}^{-}2}{5}$? 11.1

a. $\frac{2}{5}$ **b.** $\frac{2}{{}^{-}5}$ **c.** $\frac{{}^{-}2}{{}^{-}5}$ **d.** $-\frac{2}{5}$

44. Use the formula $t = \frac{d}{r}$ to find how far a skier going 58 feet per second travels in $3\frac{1}{2}$ seconds. 1.9

12

12 MULTIPLYING AND DIVIDING RATIONAL NUMBERS

Keith Gunnar/Tom Stack & Associates

Air temperature changes about $^-2.5\ ^\circ C$ for every $^+300$ meter change in altitude. So the change that might be expected in climbing from sea level to the top of a mountain 4833.6 meters high is given by this expression.

$$\frac{4833.6}{300} \times {}^-2.5$$

To multiply or divide rational numbers, just multiply or divide as you would fractions, mixed numbers, or decimals. Then take care of the sign as you would with integers.

Multiplying and Dividing With Decimals

12.1

For rational numbers expressed using decimals, first multiply or divide the decimals. Then find the sign of the product as you would for integers.

If two factors have

a. the *same sign*, the product is *positive*.

b. *different signs*, the product is *negative*.

Example 1: Find each product.

a.

same sign, so product is positive

$$\begin{array}{r} ^{-}4.32 \\ \times\, ^{-}1.4 \\ \hline 1728 \\ 432 \\ \hline 6.048 \end{array}$$

b.

different signs, so product is negative

$$\begin{array}{r} ^{-}8.25 \\ \times\, 3.7 \\ \hline 5775 \\ 2475 \\ \hline ^{-}30.525 \end{array}$$

A similar pattern exists for division.

If the divisor and dividend have

a. the *same sign*, the quotient is *positive*.

b. *different signs*, the quotient is *negative*.

Example 2: Find each quotient.

a.

positive quotient because the signs are the same

$$\begin{array}{r} 64 \\ ^{-}0.08\overline{)\,^{-}5.12} \\ 48 \\ \hline 32 \\ 32 \\ \hline 0 \end{array}$$

b.

negative quotient because the signs are different

$$\begin{array}{r} ^{-}8 \\ ^{-}0.23\overline{)\,1.84} \\ 1\,84 \\ \hline 0 \end{array}$$

Exercises

A Tell whether each product or quotient is positive or negative.

1. 123×4.7	**2.** $^-4.3 \times 7.2$	**3.** $8.6 \times {}^-4.9$
4. $^-2.37 \times {}^-6.67$	**5.** $6 \times {}^-1.672$	**6.** $^-9.125 \times {}^-8$
7. $927 \div 7.8$	**8.** $628 \div {}^-4.8$	**9.** $^-9.63 \div 0.037$
10. $^-0.69 \div {}^-0.03$	**11.** $^-8.84 \div 1.25$	**12.** $^-1.98 \div {}^-9$

B Find each product or quotient.

13. 1.7×4.6	**14.** $^-1.65 \times 46.9$	**15.** $0.125 \times {}^-48.9$
16. $^-8.6 \times {}^-9.2$	**17.** $0.25 \times {}^-1.95$	**18.** $^-6.75 \times 2.57$
19. $^-2.95 \times {}^-4.2$	**20.** $1.732 \times {}^-5$	**21.** $^-1.414 \times 6$
22. 6.2×4.7	**23.** $8.8 \times {}^-6.75$	**24.** $^-9.99 \times {}^-0.55$
25. $3.19 \div 2.9$	**26.** $^-0.498 \div 8.3$	**27.** $9.99 \div {}^-2.7$
28. $^-13.69 \div {}^-0.37$	**29.** $^-0.1794 \div 0.26$	**30.** $19.69 \div 0.11$
31. $855 \div {}^-9.5$	**32.** $184.8 \div {}^-0.77$	**33.** $^-9.90 \div {}^-2.2$
34. $158.1 \div 9.3$	**35.** $^-23.8 \div {}^-1.4$	**36.** $0.304 \div {}^-0.16$

Use multiplication or division to answer each question.

37. The height of a weather balloon is changing $^-4.5$ feet per second (ft/sec). What will the change in height be after 15 seconds?

38. The temperature of a gas is to be lowered from 0 °C to $^-37.5$ °C in three stages. If the degree drop is the same in each stage, what will be the temperature of the gas after the first stage?

39. The level of the city reservoir is changing $^-1.75$ feet per day, At this rate, what will be the change for a 5-day period?

40. The depth of an oil well is to be $^-3680$ feet (3680 feet below sea level). The drilling is now 68% complete. At what depth are they now drilling?

Find each value.

41. $1.7 \times {}^{-}2.8 \times 8.3$

42. $1.26 \times 0.3 \times {}^{-}0.3$

43. $6.5 \div {}^{-}1.3 \times 4.6$

44. $8.7 \div {}^{-}2.9 \times {}^{-}9.7$

45. $1.4 \times {}^{-}1.6 \div 0.56$

46. $1.96 \div {}^{-}0.2 \times 0.7$

47. $1.44 \times {}^{-}0.9 + {}^{-}12.6$

48. ${}^{-}1.728 \div {}^{-}1.44 + {}^{-}12$

49. $7.2 + 8.3 \times {}^{-}6.1$

50. ${}^{-}11.8 + 4.4 \div 1.1$

51. ${}^{-}12.9 - 6.2 \div 3.1$

52. ${}^{-}8.7 - 4.5 \times 3.6$

53. $3.36 \div 6.72 - {}^{-}5.14$

54. ${}^{-}6.94 \times 5.81 - 2.32$

55. $1.6 + 7.1 \div {}^{-}0.5$

56. ${}^{-}0.8 - 1.7 \times 0.09$

57. $(1.6 + 7.1) \div {}^{-}0.5$

58. $({}^{-}0.8 - 1.7) \times 0.09$

C 59. $0.\overline{3} \times 2$

60. $0.\overline{3} \times 3$

61. $0.\overline{3} \times 4$

62. $0.\overline{3} \times 5$

63. Are multiples of repeating decimals also repeating decimals?

For some outdoor activities, it is wise to keep in mind that air temperature changes about ${}^{-}2.5$ °C for every ${}^{+}300$ meter change in altitude.

64. A sky diver is to leave the plane at an altitude of 2700 meters. About what will the temperature at that altitude be if the temperature on the ground is 10 °C?

65. Mt. Whitney, in California, is about 4400 meters high. If the temperature is 3 °C at the 3500 meter level, about what is it at the top?

Ray Cottingham

12.2 Solving Equations With Decimals

Authenticated News International

The fish in the tank shown here eat a total of 13.4 pounds of food daily. They are fed 4 times a day. About how many pounds of food do they eat at each feeding?

The following equation can be used to solve this problem, where n is the number of pounds per feeding.

$$4n = 13.4$$

Example 1: Solve $4n = 13.4$.

$$4n = 13.4$$

$$\frac{4n}{4} = \frac{13.4}{4} \quad \text{Divide each side by 4.}$$

$$n = 3.35$$

Check: $4n = 13.4$

$$4(3.35) = 13.4$$

$$13.4 = 13.4 \checkmark$$

So the fish eat about 3.35 pounds at each feeding.

Exercises

[A] To solve each equation, what would you do on each side?

1. $4.1n = 25.42$

2. $\frac{m}{^-3.6} = 4$

3. $\frac{x}{6} = 3.29$

4. $^-6.8 = 4m$

5. $\frac{t}{^-3.7} = {}^-8.3$

6. $7.2 = {}^-3x$

7. $\frac{m}{^-4} = 8.7$

8. $7.3m = 6.7$

B Solve.

9. $\frac{x}{6.3} = 5$	**10.** $3.9x = 1.95$	**11.** $\frac{m}{7.2} = {}^{-}8$
12. $3.7 = \frac{x}{4}$	**13.** $6m = 3.6$	**14.** $27.4 = {}^{-}2x$
15. ${}^{-}1.7x = 6.8$	**16.** $\frac{x}{9} = {}^{-}3.3$	**17.** $\frac{m}{{}^{-}6.7} = 4.2$
18. $4.5 = \frac{x}{{}^{-}5}$	**19.** ${}^{-}2.7x = {}^{-}7.29$	**20.** ${}^{-}3.6 = {}^{-}3b$
21. $\frac{t}{{}^{-}4.3} = {}^{-}4.7$	**22.** ${}^{-}5t = {}^{-}5.3$	**23.** ${}^{-}0.16x = {}^{-}1.44$

Write and solve an equation for each problem.

24. The product of a number and ${}^{-}3.6$ is 9. What is the number?

25. When a number is divided by ${}^{-}0.05$, the quotient is 10. What is the number?

A. Devaney, Inc.

26. A capsule of Brand A cold remedy weighs 0.62 grams. How much do 100 capsules weigh?

27. The total weight of the capsules in a bottle is 64.8 grams. If each capsule weighs 0.9 grams, how many capsules are in the bottle?

28. What would be the weight of 36 of the capsules in Exercise 27?

29. A company's profit-and-loss statement for 3 months shows a balance of ${}^{-}\$2169.15$. What was the monthly average?

30. If the temperature changed ${}^{-}8.25$ °C in 3 hours, what was the average change per hour?

C **31.** An airplane is flying at 8000 feet altitude. The pilot is told to change altitude at the rate of ${}^{-}400$ feet per minute for the next 15 minutes. What will the plane's altitude be after 15 minutes?

32. Jay's Auto Sales has a cash reserve of \$10,500. This week, subtracting expenses from income gives ${}^{-}\$750$ (a loss of \$750). In how many weeks will the reserve be gone if this continues?

12.3 Multiplying and Dividing With Fractions

For rational numbers expressed using fractions, multiply or divide the fractions and then find the sign as you would for integers.

Examples: Find each product or quotient.

1. $-\frac{3}{8} \times \left(-\frac{3}{4}\right)$

$\frac{3}{8} \times \frac{3}{4} = \frac{9}{32}$ Multiply fractions.

same sign, so product is positive

$-\frac{3}{8} \times \left(-\frac{3}{4}\right) = \frac{9}{32}$

2. $\frac{3}{4} \div \left(-\frac{1}{2}\right)$

$\frac{3}{4} \div \frac{1}{2} = \frac{3}{\not{4}_{2}} \times \frac{\not{2}^{1}}{1}$ Divide fractions.

$= \frac{3}{2}$

$= 1\frac{1}{2}$

different signs, so quotient is negative

$\frac{3}{4} \div \left(-\frac{1}{2}\right) = -1\frac{1}{2}$

3. $-\frac{2}{3} \div 6$

$\frac{2}{3} \div 6 = \frac{2}{3} \div \frac{6}{1}$ Write a whole number as a fraction with denominator 1.

$= \frac{\not{2}^{1}}{3} \times \frac{1}{\not{6}_{3}}$

$= \frac{1}{9}$

different signs, so quotient is negative

$-\frac{2}{3} \div 6 = -\frac{1}{9}$

Exercises

A Tell whether each product or quotient is positive or negative.

1. $\frac{3}{4} \times \frac{1}{2}$ **2.** $\frac{3}{8}\left(-\frac{1}{6}\right)$ **3.** $-\frac{3}{8} \times \frac{6}{7}$

4. $-\frac{2}{3}\left(-\frac{2}{5}\right)$ **5.** $4\left(\frac{3}{7}\right)$ **6.** $-\frac{4}{5}(7)$

7. $\frac{2}{3} \div \frac{1}{2}$

8. $\frac{7}{8} \div (-\frac{3}{5})$

9. $-\frac{3}{8} \div \frac{1}{2}$

10. $-\frac{5}{8} \div (-\frac{2}{3})$

11. $^{-}4 \div \frac{3}{4}$

12. $\frac{2}{3} \div {}^{-}10$

13. $\frac{1}{3}(\frac{2}{7})(-\frac{1}{5})$

14. $\frac{1}{2}(-\frac{2}{3})(-\frac{1}{5})$

15. $-\frac{2}{5}(\frac{1}{4} \times \frac{2}{3})$

B Find each product or quotient.

16. $\frac{2}{3} \times \frac{1}{5}$

17. $-\frac{2}{3} \times \frac{7}{8}$

18. $\frac{3}{5}(-\frac{7}{9})$

19. $\frac{5}{9} \div (-\frac{1}{6})$

20. $-\frac{1}{2} \div \frac{1}{4}$

21. $-\frac{1}{5}(^{-}35)$

22. $\frac{4}{7} \div (-\frac{2}{3})$

23. $49(-\frac{3}{7})$

24. $-\frac{5}{6}(-\frac{3}{4})$

25. $63 \div \frac{21}{25}$

26. $\frac{5}{7}(^{-}84)$

27. $^{-}18 \div \frac{6}{7}$

28. $\frac{3}{4} \div \frac{1}{2}$

29. $-\frac{7}{8} \div \frac{2}{3}$

30. $\frac{4}{5} \div (-\frac{3}{4})$

31. $-\frac{1}{2}(-\frac{2}{3})$

32. $^{-}28 \div (-\frac{7}{8})$

33. $-\frac{4}{5}(\frac{7}{8})$

34. $^{-}52(\frac{3}{4})$

35. $\frac{5}{6}(\frac{3}{10})$

36. $\frac{1}{3}(\frac{2}{7})(-\frac{1}{5})$

37. $-\frac{2}{5}(\frac{1}{4} \times \frac{2}{3})$

38. $\frac{1}{2}(-\frac{2}{3})(-\frac{1}{5})$

39. $\frac{3}{5}(-\frac{7}{9})(-\frac{3}{7})$

Find each value.

40. $-\frac{3}{5} + \frac{4}{5} \times (-\frac{2}{7})$

41. $-\frac{8}{3} + (-\frac{4}{5}) \div \frac{3}{8}$

42. $\frac{1}{6} \times \frac{3}{10} + \frac{1}{5}$

43. $\frac{1}{6} \times (\frac{3}{10} + \frac{1}{5})$

44. $\frac{3}{7} - \frac{4}{5} \div (-\frac{2}{15})$

45. $\frac{9}{16} \times \frac{1}{4} - \frac{3}{32}$

C Determine if the following are true.

46. $\frac{3}{4} \times (-\frac{2}{3}) = -\frac{2}{3} \times \frac{3}{4}$

47. $^{-}1.2 \times 4.3 = 4.3 \times {}^{-}1.2$

48. $9(\frac{2}{3} \times \frac{5}{6}) = (9 \times \frac{2}{3})\frac{5}{6}$

49. $(1.2 \times 2.3)3 = 1.2(2.3 \times 3)$

50. $-\frac{3}{8} \times 1 = -\frac{3}{8}$

51. $1 \times {}^{-}7.5 = {}^{-}7.5$

Use your answers for Exercises 46–51 to answer the following.

52. Do you think multiplication of rational numbers is commutative?

53. Do you think multiplication of rational numbers is associative?

54. Name the identity number for multiplication of rational numbers.

12.4

Multiplying and Dividing With Mixed Numbers

For rational numbers expressed as mixed numbers, first multiply or divide. Then find the sign of the result as you would for integers.

Examples: Find each product or quotient.

1. $1\frac{1}{4} \times \frac{2}{3}$

$\frac{5}{\not{4}_2} \times \frac{\not{2}^1}{3} = \frac{5}{6}$

Write a mixed number as a fraction. Then multiply or divide.

same sign, so product is positive

$1\frac{1}{4} \times \frac{2}{3} = \frac{5}{6}$

2. $1\frac{1}{4} \div {}^-2\frac{2}{3}$

$\frac{5}{4} \div \frac{8}{3} = \frac{5}{4} \times \frac{3}{8}$

$= \frac{15}{32}$

different signs, so quotient is negative

$1\frac{1}{4} \div {}^-2\frac{2}{3} = {}^-\frac{15}{32}$

3. ${}^-4\frac{1}{3} \times 4$

$4\frac{1}{3} \times 4 = \frac{13}{3} \times \frac{4}{1}$ Write a whole number as a fraction with denominator 1.

$= \frac{52}{3}$

$= 17\frac{1}{3}$

different signs, so product is negative

${}^-4\frac{1}{3} \times 4 = {}^-17\frac{1}{3}$

Exercises

A Tell whether each product or quotient is positive or negative.

1. $7\frac{5}{8} \times \frac{3}{4}$ **2.** $\frac{2}{5}({}^-5\frac{1}{4})$ **3.** ${}^-2\frac{1}{2} \times 4\frac{2}{3}$

4. ${}^-6\frac{7}{8}({}^-1\frac{2}{5})$ **5.** ${}^-3\frac{4}{5}(\frac{1}{3})$ **6.** $4(8\frac{3}{16})$

7. $9\frac{3}{5} \div {}^-1\frac{1}{4}$ **8.** $-\frac{2}{3} \div {}^-5\frac{3}{5}$ **9.** $7\frac{1}{5} \div {}^-1\frac{1}{2}$

10. $12\frac{2}{3} \div 4\frac{1}{2}$ **11.** ${}^-27\frac{3}{10} \div 6$ **12.** ${}^-9\frac{7}{10} \div (-\frac{2}{3})$

13. $({}^-1\frac{1}{2})({}^-1\frac{2}{3})({}^-1\frac{4}{5})$ **14.** $2 \times 1\frac{2}{5} \times {}^-1\frac{7}{10}$ **15.** $({}^-3\frac{1}{2})(6\frac{2}{3})({}^-5)$

B Find each product or quotient.

16. $^-3\frac{1}{8} \times \frac{3}{4}$
17. $4\frac{1}{2} \div (-\frac{1}{2})$
18. $4\frac{1}{2} \times \frac{2}{3}$
19. $^-3\frac{1}{2}(-\frac{2}{3})$
20. $^-4\frac{1}{4} \div \frac{2}{3}$
21. $2\frac{1}{4}(-\frac{4}{5})$
22. $^-5\frac{1}{2} \times {}^-2\frac{1}{4}$
23. $^-4\frac{1}{2} \div 3\frac{1}{4}$
24. $5\frac{2}{3} \times {}^-9$
25. $3\frac{1}{7} \div 2$
26. $4\frac{1}{2} \times {}^-1\frac{1}{2}$
27. $^-1\frac{1}{2} \times 3\frac{3}{4}$
28. $^-5\frac{1}{2} \div 2\frac{1}{4}$
29. $\frac{7}{8}({}^-3\frac{1}{7})$
30. $^-2\frac{1}{2} \div {}^-1\frac{1}{4}$
31. $-\frac{7}{8} \div 3\frac{2}{3}$
32. $^-6\frac{3}{4} \div \frac{7}{16}$
33. $1\frac{1}{4} \div (-\frac{2}{3})$
34. $-\frac{3}{4} \times {}^-1\frac{7}{8}$
35. $3\frac{1}{2} \div {}^-2\frac{1}{4}$
36. $-\frac{3}{8} \div 4\frac{1}{2}$
37. $^-3\frac{1}{4} \times 2\frac{1}{2}$
38. $^-4\frac{3}{4} \div 8$
39. $^-7({}^-3\frac{5}{14})$
40. $({}^-2\frac{2}{5})(1\frac{2}{3})({}^-6\frac{1}{2})$
41. $(4\frac{3}{4})(5\frac{1}{5})({}^-3\frac{2}{3})$

Find each value.

42. $9\frac{1}{2} \div 2\frac{1}{2} \times {}^-4\frac{3}{5}$
43. $6\frac{2}{5} \div 3\frac{2}{3} \times {}^-5\frac{1}{2}$

C 44. $\frac{1}{2}(7\frac{9}{10}) + \frac{1}{2}({}^-3\frac{3}{10})$
45. $({}^-2\frac{3}{10} \times 8\frac{1}{10}) + (\frac{7}{10} \times 8\frac{1}{10})$
46. $({}^-4\frac{3}{5})(6\frac{1}{2}) + ({}^-4\frac{3}{5})(9\frac{1}{4})$
47. $(3\frac{1}{2} \times {}^-1\frac{1}{4}) - (3\frac{1}{2} \times {}^-5\frac{1}{4})$

Use multiplication or division to answer each question.

48. If the temperature changed $^-1\frac{3}{4}$ °F every hour for $3\frac{1}{2}$ hours, what was the total change?

49. If the temperature changed $^-12\frac{1}{2}$ °F in $7\frac{1}{2}$ hours, what was the average change per hour?

50. The Royster Corporation wants to increase sales \$$3\frac{3}{4}$ million. How long will it take to do this if sales increase \$$1\frac{1}{4}$ million per year?

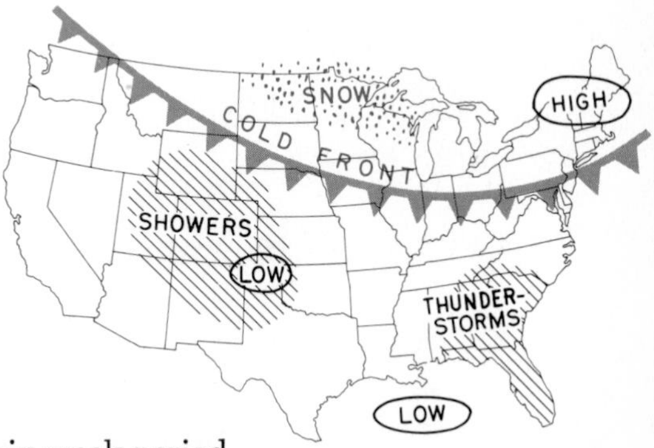

51. Mrs. Wilson's weight changed $^-18\frac{3}{4}$ pounds over a six-week period. What was her average weekly weight change?

52. Steel production changed an average of $-\frac{3}{4}$ ton a day for 5 days. What was the total change for this period?

CONSUMER CORNER

Stock Reports

A person who buys shares of a company's stock is buying part ownership in the company. Shares are usually bought and sold through a *stock market* (a group of people, called brokers, whose business is buying and selling stock for others). Many newspapers print daily reports of stock prices. Part of such a report is shown below.

The first column lists some companies. The *Volume* column tells how many of each company's shares were bought and sold that day. The columns labeled *High* and *Low* give the highest and lowest prices paid for a share of the company's stock during the day. (All amounts are in dollars and fractions of a dollar.)

	Volume	High	Low	Close	Chg.
Dictaphone	450,700	26	25	25 ⅝	+5 ⅜
SearsRoeb	333,100	20 ⅛	19 ⅞	20 ⅛	....
TexacoInc	247,700	24 ⅛	23 ⅜	23 ⅝	− ⅛
Boeing	240,200	73 ½	71 ¾	72 ⅛	+ ⅝
HarrisCp	205,500	30 ⅝	29 ¾	30	−1
Exxon	194,200	49 ⅜	48 ½	48 ½	− ½
USSteel	191,900	21 ⅝	21 ½	21 ½	+ ⅛
Chrysler	187,100	8 ⅝	8 ⅜	8 ⅜	....

The *Close* column tells the price of a share at the end of the day. The amount in the *Chg.* column shows how much the closing price of a share went up or down from the closing price of the previous day.

What does the *Chg.* column of the report above tell you about the price of a share of each of the following stocks?

1. Dictaphone **2.** Exxon **3.** Chrysler

Quick Quiz

Sections 12.1 to 12.4

Find each product or quotient.

1. $2.3 \times {}^{-}1.7$ **2.** ${}^{-}4\frac{1}{4} \times {}^{-}2$ **3.** $3.42 \times {}^{-}6$

4. $425 \div {}^{-}1.7$ **5.** ${}^{-}6.39 \div {}^{-}3$ **6.** ${}^{-}12.42 \div {}^{-}0.06$

7. ${}^{-}7 \div \frac{7}{8}$ **8.** $-\frac{2}{3} \times (-\frac{4}{5})$ **9.** $21(-\frac{3}{7})$

10. $\frac{7}{3} \div (-\frac{2}{3})$ **11.** ${}^{-}7\frac{1}{2} \times {}^{-}2\frac{1}{4}$ **12.** $-\frac{3}{4}(2\frac{1}{3})$

13. $5 \div {}^{-}1\frac{1}{2}$ **14.** ${}^{-}6\frac{2}{3} \div \frac{4}{3}$ **15.** $9\frac{1}{2} \div {}^{-}3$

Solve.

16. ${}^{-}2x = 16.2$ **17.** $\frac{n}{3.2} = {}^{-}10$ **18.** ${}^{-}4.6 = {}^{-}18.4a$

Reciprocals

Reciprocals are two numbers whose product is 1.

Example 1: Find the reciprocal of $\frac{2}{3}$.

$$\frac{2}{3} \times \frac{3}{2} = 1$$

So $\frac{2}{3}$ and $\frac{3}{2}$ are reciprocals.

To find the reciprocal of a fraction, invert the fraction.

Example 2: Find the reciprocal of $-\frac{3}{5}$.

$$-\frac{3}{5} \times \left(-\frac{5}{3}\right) = 1$$

So $-\frac{3}{5}$ and $-\frac{5}{3}$ are reciprocals.

The reciprocal of a negative number is negative.

Example 3: Find the reciprocals of **(a)** 6 and **(b)** $3\frac{1}{2}$.

a. $6 = \frac{6}{1}$

$$\frac{6}{1} \times \frac{1}{6} = 1$$

So 6 and $\frac{1}{6}$ are reciprocals.

b. $3\frac{1}{2} = \frac{7}{2}$

$$\frac{7}{2} \times \frac{2}{7} = 1$$

So $3\frac{1}{2}$ and $\frac{2}{7}$ are reciprocals.

To find the reciprocal of an integer or a mixed number, write the number as a fraction and invert.

Example 4: Does 0 have a reciprocal?

You can express 0 as $\frac{0}{1}$. If you invert $\frac{0}{1}$, you get $\frac{1}{0}$. But you know that you can never divide by 0. So 0 has no reciprocal.

Exercises

A Name the reciprocal, if any.

1. $\frac{3}{5}$ **2.** $\frac{5}{3}$ **3.** $-\frac{4}{7}$ **4.** $-\frac{7}{4}$

5. 7 **6.** $\frac{1}{7}$ **7.** $^-9$ **8.** 0

Find the product.

9. $\frac{7}{8} \times \frac{8}{7}$ **10.** $-\frac{3}{4} \times (-\frac{4}{3})$ **11.** $\frac{5}{1} \times \frac{1}{5}$

12. $-\frac{1}{6} \times (-\frac{6}{1})$ **13.** $\frac{19}{4} \times \frac{4}{19}$ **14.** $-\frac{21}{5} \times (-\frac{5}{21})$

B Name the reciprocal.

15. $\frac{1}{2}$ **16.** $^-11$ **17.** $-\frac{4}{13}$ **18.** $-\frac{1}{10}$

19. 17 **20.** $\frac{5}{12}$ **21.** $-\frac{13}{3}$ **22.** $\frac{12}{5}$

23. $5\frac{1}{2}$ **24.** $^-7\frac{1}{3}$ **25.** $^-6\frac{3}{10}$ **26.** $4\frac{7}{8}$

27. $12\frac{3}{4}$ **28.** $^-11\frac{4}{5}$ **29.** 1 **30.** $^-1$

C **31.** What positive integer is its own reciprocal? (See Exercise 29.)

32. What negative integer is its own reciprocal? (See Exercise 30.)

Find the product.

33. 0.4×2.5 **34.** 0.625×1.6

Name the reciprocal in decimal form. (See Exercises 33 and 34.)

35. 0.625 **36.** 2.5 **37.** 0.4 **38.** 1.6

39. Find the reciprocal of 0.8 in decimal form.

Solving Equations With Fractions

Example 1: Solve $\frac{2}{3}x = -\frac{5}{9}$.

$$\frac{2}{3}x = -\frac{5}{9}$$

$$\frac{2}{3}x \div \frac{2}{3} = -\frac{5}{9} \div \frac{2}{3}$$ Divide each side by $\frac{2}{3}$.

Dividing by $\frac{2}{3}$ undoes multiplying by $\frac{2}{3}$.

$$x = -\frac{5}{\cancel{9}_{3}} \times \frac{\cancel{3}^{1}}{2}$$

$$x = -\frac{5}{6}$$

Check:

$$\frac{2}{3}x = -\frac{5}{9}$$

$$\frac{\cancel{2}^{1}}{3}\left(-\frac{5}{\cancel{6}_{3}}\right) = -\frac{5}{9}$$ Replace x with $-\frac{5}{6}$.

$$-\frac{5}{9} = -\frac{5}{9} \checkmark$$

Shortcut: To divide by a number, you can multiply by its reciprocal.

Example 2: Use the shortcut to solve $\frac{2}{3}x = -\frac{5}{9}$.

$$\frac{2}{3}x = -\frac{5}{9}$$

$$\frac{3}{2} \times \frac{2}{3}x = \frac{\cancel{3}^{1}}{2} \times \left(-\frac{5}{\cancel{9}_{3}}\right)$$ Multiply each side by $\frac{3}{2}$.

$$1x = -\frac{5}{6}$$ This step is usually not written.

$$x = -\frac{5}{6}$$

Check: Same as in Example 1.

Example 3: Solve $\frac{n}{8} = -\frac{3}{5}$.

$$\frac{n}{8} = -\frac{3}{5}$$

$$\frac{n}{8} \times 8 = -\frac{3}{5} \times 8$$

$$n = -\frac{3}{5} \times \frac{8}{1}$$

$$n = -\frac{24}{5}$$

$$n = {}^{-}4\frac{4}{5}$$

Check:

$$\frac{n}{8} = -\frac{3}{5}$$

$$\frac{{}^{-}4\frac{4}{5}}{8} = -\frac{3}{5}$$

$$-\frac{24}{5} \div \frac{8}{1} = -\frac{3}{5}$$

$$-\frac{\overset{3}{\cancel{24}}}{5} \times \frac{1}{\underset{1}{\cancel{8}}} = -\frac{3}{5}$$

$$-\frac{3}{5} = -\frac{3}{5} \checkmark$$

Exercises

A To solve each equation, what would you do on each side?

1. $\frac{2}{3}x = -\frac{3}{5}$
2. $\frac{3}{14} = -\frac{1}{2}n$
3. $-\frac{3}{10}x = {}^{-}7$
4. $\frac{4}{5} = {}^{-}5y$
5. $-\frac{5}{6}m = \frac{4}{9}$
6. $-\frac{4}{9} = -\frac{3}{8}x$
7. $\frac{x}{3} = -\frac{4}{5}$
8. $\frac{5}{8} = \frac{a}{{}^{-}6}$
9. $\frac{x}{{}^{-}6} = -\frac{3}{2}$

B Solve.

10. $\frac{4}{5}n = \frac{16}{25}$
11. $-\frac{2}{5} = -\frac{8}{15}t$
12. $\frac{x}{6} = -\frac{13}{4}$
13. $\frac{7}{4} = \frac{a}{4}$
14. $\frac{n}{{}^{-}9} = -\frac{11}{3}$
15. $\frac{4}{7}r = {}^{-}5$
16. $\frac{6}{5}n = \frac{12}{10}$
17. $-\frac{7}{3}r = \frac{7}{10}$
18. $\frac{11}{4} = -\frac{11}{2}x$
19. $\frac{n}{{}^{-}3} = 18$
20. $-\frac{3}{5} = \frac{3}{5}s$
21. $-\frac{10}{63} = \frac{a}{3}$
22. $\frac{n}{3} = -\frac{2}{5}$
23. $12 = -\frac{2}{3}p$
24. $-\frac{13}{20}y = -\frac{39}{100}$
25. $-\frac{1}{3} = {}^{-}5t$
26. $\frac{d}{{}^{-}19} = -\frac{1}{38}$
27. $-\frac{9}{10} = {}^{-}4p$
28. $\frac{15}{2} = {}^{-}3x$
29. $\frac{2}{5} = \frac{m}{{}^{-}3}$
30. ${}^{-}36 = \frac{9}{7}r$

31. $\frac{c}{5} = -\frac{38}{15}$ **32.** $21n = -\frac{84}{7}$ **33.** $\frac{9}{7} = \frac{d}{^-56}$

34. $\frac{a}{^-13} = -\frac{13}{169}$ **35.** $0 = \frac{10}{3}x$ **36.** $^-16r = \frac{80}{11}$

Write and solve an equation for each problem.

37. The product of a number and $-\frac{4}{5}$ is $^-12$. What is the number?

38. The product of a number and $\frac{7}{2}$ is $^-14$. What is the number?

39. When a number is divided by 6, the quotient is $-\frac{2}{3}$. What is the number?

40. When a number is divided by $^-3$, the quotient is $\frac{5}{12}$. What is the number?

C Solve.

Example: Solve $\frac{1}{5}n = {^-3}\frac{1}{3}$.

$$\frac{1}{5}n = {^-3}\frac{1}{3}$$

$$5 \times \frac{1}{5}n = 5 \times {^-3}\frac{1}{3}$$

$$n = {^-16}\frac{2}{3}$$

Check:

$$\frac{1}{5}n = {^-3}\frac{1}{3}$$

$$\frac{1}{5}\left({^-16}\frac{2}{3}\right) = {^-3}\frac{1}{3}$$

$$\frac{1}{\cancel{5}_1}\left(-\frac{\cancel{50}^{10}}{3}\right) = {^-3}\frac{1}{3}$$

$${^-3}\frac{1}{3} = {^-3}\frac{1}{3} \checkmark$$

41. $-\frac{2}{5}m = {^-4}\frac{1}{2}$ **42.** ${^-3}\frac{1}{2} = 6n$

43. $6\frac{3}{4} = {^-1}\frac{1}{2}x$ **44.** ${^-3}\frac{2}{3}a = {^-3}\frac{2}{3}$

45. ${^-4}\frac{1}{2} = \frac{x}{8}$ **46.** $\frac{x}{3} = {^-5}\frac{1}{3}$

Use the formula $d = rt$ to solve each problem.

47. A diving sphere can move up or down in the water at a rate of $4\frac{1}{2}$ feet per second. At that rate, how long will it take to descend 3150 feet?

48. How long would it take the diving sphere in Exercise 47 to rise 405 feet?

Courtesy NOAA

CAREER CORNER

MATH IN BUILDING TRADES

Carpenters, plumbers, cement workers, plasterers, and many other workers are employed in the building trades. Such workers must often use mathematics in their work.

1. *Plumber:* How many 18-inch lengths of pipe can be cut from three 8-foot lengths of pipe?

2. *Carpenter:* A window opening $3\frac{1}{2}$ feet wide is to be placed in the center of a 12-foot wall. How far from each end of the wall should the opening be?

3. *Plasterer:* About 200 pounds of lime are needed to make enough plaster to cover 45 square yards of wall with a finish coat $\frac{1}{8}$ inch thick. About how much lime is needed to finish 819 square yards of wall?

4. *Cement worker:* Steel bars are used to strengthen parts of concrete buildings. A concrete wall is to have two vertical reinforcing bars at each end and two additional bars every 8 inches of its length. How many reinforcing bars are needed if the wall is 18 feet long?

John D. Firestone & Associates, Inc.

C. E. Pefley

Equations With Two Operations

12.7

The George Washington Bridge has two end spans of equal length and a center span 0.68 mile long. The overall length of the bridge is 0.9 mile. How long is each end span?

Authenticated News International

If n is the length in miles of each end span, then

$$2n + 0.68 = 0.9.$$

Example 1: Solve $2n + 0.68 = 0.9$.

$$2n + 0.68 = 0.9$$
$$2n + 0.68 + {}^{-}0.68 = 0.9 + {}^{-}0.68$$
$$2n + 0 = 0.22$$
$$2n = 0.22$$
$$\frac{2n}{2} = \frac{0.22}{2}$$
$$n = 0.11$$

So each end span of the bridge above is 0.11 mile long.

Check:
$$2n + 0.68 = 0.9$$
$$2(0.11) + 0.68 = 0.9$$
$$0.22 + 0.68 = 0.9$$
$$0.9 = 0.9 \checkmark$$

Example 2: Solve $-\frac{1}{3} = \frac{n}{2} + \frac{2}{3}$.

$$-\frac{1}{3} = \frac{n}{2} + \frac{2}{3}$$
$$-\frac{1}{3} + \left(-\frac{2}{3}\right) = \frac{n}{2} + \frac{2}{3} + \left(-\frac{2}{3}\right)$$
$$-\frac{3}{3} = \frac{n}{2} + 0$$
$$^{-}1 = \frac{n}{2}$$
$$^{-}1 \times 2 = \frac{n}{2} \times 2$$
$$^{-}2 = n$$

Check:
$$-\frac{1}{3} = \frac{n}{2} + \frac{2}{3}$$
$$-\frac{1}{3} = \frac{^{-}2}{2} + \frac{2}{3}$$
$$-\frac{1}{3} = {}^{-}1 + \frac{2}{3}$$
$$-\frac{1}{3} = -\frac{3}{3} + \frac{2}{3}$$
$$-\frac{1}{3} = -\frac{1}{3} \checkmark$$

Exercises

A The main steps in the solution of each given equation are shown. Tell how each equation can be found from the equation on its left.

1. $2.6m + 0.4 = {}^-6.1$	$2.6m = {}^-6.5$	$m = {}^-2.5$	
2. $-\frac{7}{8} = \frac{4x}{3}$	$-\frac{21}{8} = 4x$	$-\frac{21}{32} = x$	
3. $3.6t - 2.4 = 10.2$	$3.6t + {}^-2.4 = 10.2$	$3.6t = 12.6$	$t = 3.5$
4. $\frac{m}{3} + \frac{7}{9} = \frac{1}{3}$	$\frac{m}{3} = -\frac{4}{9}$	$m = -\frac{12}{9}$	$m = {}^-1\frac{1}{3}$
5. ${}^-8 = -\frac{2}{5}n + \frac{6}{5}$	$-\frac{46}{5} = -\frac{2}{5}n$	$23 = n$	
6. $\frac{x - {}^-3}{4} = 1.2$	$x - {}^-3 = 4.8$	$x + 3 = 4.8$	$x = 1.8$

B Solve.

7. $2.7m + 0.4 = 5.8$ **8.** $3.2k - 4.7 = 4.9$ **9.** $-\frac{14}{5} = \frac{a}{3} - \frac{4}{5}$

10. $\frac{2}{3}n + \frac{5}{6} = \frac{1}{6}$ **11.** $\frac{3x}{{}^-4} = 1.8$ **12.** ${}^-2 = \frac{a}{3} - \frac{3}{5}$

13. ${}^-3y - \frac{3}{4} = \frac{5}{8}$ **14.** $2 = \frac{1}{3}x - 1$ **15.** $\frac{3}{5}b - (-\frac{1}{4}) = \frac{2}{3}$

16. $\frac{2x}{{}^-7} = 6.4$ **17.** $\frac{k}{4} + 1.5 = {}^-2.7$ **18.** $\frac{x - {}^-2.6}{5.2} = 7.3$

19. $\frac{y}{6} - 1.5 = {}^-7.2$ **20.** $\frac{3}{5}r + \frac{3}{5} = \frac{7}{10}$ **21.** ${}^-7.6 = \frac{5x}{4.1}$

22. $3.4k - {}^-4.7 = {}^-8.9$ **23.** $\frac{6}{7}d + \frac{2}{5} = \frac{8}{20}$ **24.** ${}^-7n + \frac{2}{15} = \frac{5}{6}$

25. $5m + {}^-2.6 = 3.7$ **26.** $\frac{t}{1.9} + 2 = {}^-1.3$ **27.** $\frac{a}{3} + (-\frac{4}{7}) = \frac{11}{14}$

28. $\frac{4x}{3} = {}^-6.9$ **29.** $-\frac{5}{9} = \frac{2}{3}a + \frac{1}{9}$ **30.** $\frac{x + 4.5}{{}^-3.2} = {}^-7.3$

31. $\frac{7}{12} = 6n - \frac{5}{12}$ **32.** $\frac{t}{{}^-4} - 1.5 = 2.7$ **33.** $-\frac{7}{2}r + \frac{5}{4} = \frac{31}{8}$

C Use the formula $9C = 5F - 160$ to complete the table. Give each result as a fraction, mixed number, or whole number.

	34.	**35.**	**36.**	**37.**	**38.**	**39.**	**40.**	**41.**	**42.**
°C	0	$^-10$	$^-11.4$	$^-17.77$	$^-17.78$	$^-23$	$^-40$	$^-41$	$^-100$
°F									

43. At what temperature are the Fahrenheit and Celsius thermometer readings the same? (See the table above.) Below what temperature are the Fahrenheit readings less than the equivalent Celsius readings? Above what temperature are they more?

Solve.

44. $3x + 1\frac{3}{4} = {}^-5\frac{1}{4}$ **45.** $2k - 1\frac{1}{2} = 4\frac{1}{3}$ **46.** $\frac{^-4x}{3} = {}^-1\frac{2}{3}$

47. $\frac{m}{3} + \frac{3}{8} = 4\frac{1}{2}$ **48.** $\frac{x-3}{4} = {}^-1\frac{2}{3}$ **49.** $3x - ({}^-\frac{2}{3}) = 4\frac{1}{2}$

50. $\frac{2x}{3} = {}^-1\frac{2}{3}$ **51.** $5x - 1\frac{2}{3} = {}^-7\frac{1}{2}$ **52.** $\frac{t+4}{^-7} = 1\frac{2}{3}$

53. $2k - 1\frac{2}{3} = {}^-5\frac{1}{2}$ **54.** $3x + 1\frac{2}{3} = {}^-2\frac{1}{2}$ **55.** $\frac{y}{3} - 1\frac{2}{3} = {}^-5\frac{1}{3}$

Quick Quiz
Sections 12.5 to 12.7

Name the reciprocal.

1. $\frac{2}{5}$ **2.** $-\frac{7}{8}$ **3.** 17 **4.** $^-4\frac{1}{2}$

Solve.

5. $\frac{x}{5} = -\frac{3}{16}$ **6.** $-\frac{6}{7} = \frac{n}{^-2}$

7. $^-4t = \frac{12}{13}$ **8.** $\frac{4}{5} = \frac{3}{10}r$

9. $2m + 1.2 = {}^-5.6$ **10.** $\frac{n}{^-3} + \frac{2}{3} = -\frac{5}{2}$

12.8 Using Formulas to Solve Problems

The number of kilowatt-hours you use determines what you pay for electricity.

$$1000k = tw$$

(kilowatt-hours → k; time in hours → t; watts → w)

Example 1: How many kilowatt-hours are used to run a 200-watt TV for 28 hours?

$$1000k = tw$$

$$1000k = 28 \times 200$$

$$\frac{1000k}{1000} = \frac{5600}{1000}$$

$$k = 5.6$$

Check: Is 1000×5.6 equal to 28×200? ✓

So 5.6 kilowatt-hours are used.

The approximate horsepower rating of an electric motor is determined by this formula.

$$h = \frac{w}{750}$$

(horsepower → h; watts → w)

Example 2: How many watts are used by a 2-horsepower lawn mower?

Courtesy Black & Decker

$$h = \frac{w}{750}$$

$$2 = \frac{w}{750}$$

$$2 \times 750 = \frac{w}{750} \times 750$$

$$1500 = w$$

Check: Is $1500 \div 750$ equal to 2? ✓

So the lawn mower uses 1500 watts.

There are many different ways to find the horsepower rating for an automobile. Here is one way.

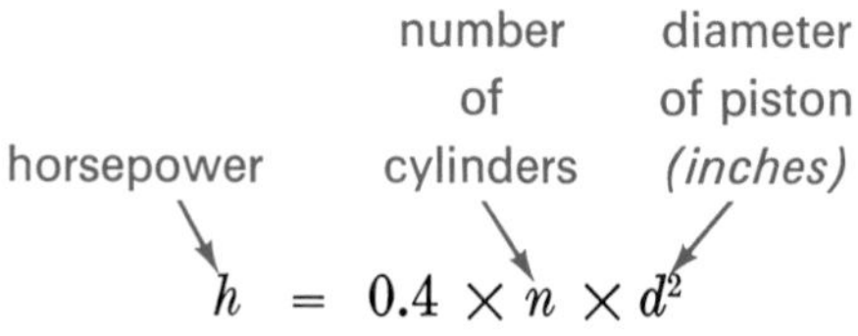

$$h = 0.4 \times n \times d^2$$

Example 3: Find the horsepower of a 6-cylinder engine that has a 3.5-inch piston diameter.

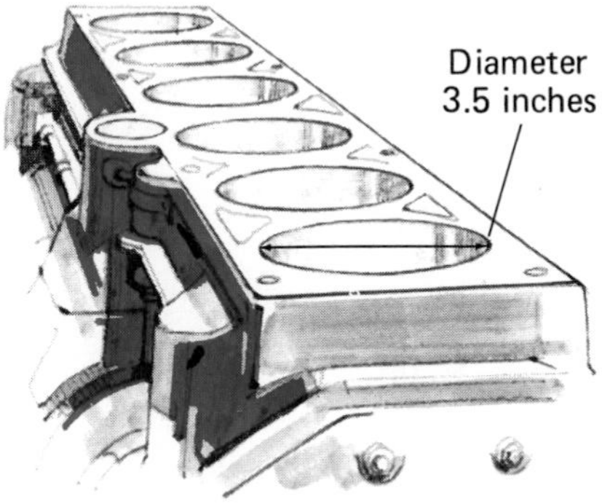

$$\begin{aligned} h &= 0.4 \times n \times d^2 \\ &= 0.4 \times 6 \times (3.5)^2 \\ &= 0.4 \times 6 \times 12.25 \\ &= 29.4 \end{aligned}$$

Check: In this case, check by redoing your arithmetic. ✓

So the horsepower is 29.4.

Exercises

A **1.** If your radio uses 2 kilowatt-hours of electricity a month and electricity costs $0.045 per kilowatt-hour, how can you find how much it costs to run the radio each month?

2. If you know that your 18-watt radio used 1 kilowatt-hour of electricity last month, how can you use the formula from Example 1 to find how many hours it was on last month?

3. If you know that your television set was on 50 hours last month and that it used 8.5 kilowatt-hours of electricity, how can you use the formula from Example 1 to tell how many watts it uses?

4. Which formula would you use to find the horsepower rating of a 750-watt vacuum-cleaner motor?

5. Which formula would you use to find the horsepower rating of a 4-cylinder engine with a 3-inch piston diameter?

B Use the kilowatt-hour formula from Example 1 to complete this table.

	Appliance	t	w	k
6.	Hot comb	3	400	
7.	Iron	12	1100	
8.	Radio	50	15	
9.	Sewing machine		80	2.24
10.	Toaster		1100	11.22
11.	Refrigerator		250	25.00
12.	Electric range	2.5	12,000	
13.	Hair dryer	20		15.00

14. At $0.045 per kilowatt-hour, how much does it cost to run the hot comb in Exercise 6? The radio in Exercise 8? The toaster in Exercise 10?

15. How long must you use the sewing machine in Exercise 9 to use 1 kilowatt-hour of electricity?

16. At $0.04 per kilowatt-hour, how much can you save by using a 60-watt bulb instead of a 100-watt bulb for 600 hours?

Use the horsepower formula from Example 2 to complete this table.

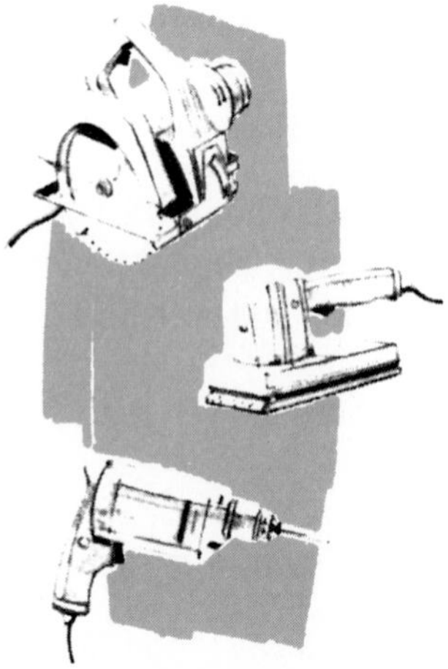

	Appliance	w	h
17.	Power saw	1500	
18.	Trash compactor		$\frac{1}{3}$
19.	Power sander	1000	
20.	Furnace fan	375	
21.	Power drill		$\frac{1}{5}$
22.	Vacuum cleaner	1250	

Use the horsepower formula from Example 3 to complete this table.

	Car	*n*	*d*	*h*
23.	A	6	4.00	
24.	B		4.00	51.2
25.	C	8	3.75	
26.	D	4	3.25	
27.	E		4.25	57.8

Courtesy Chevrolet Motor Division, General Motors Corporation

C Stopping distance is the distance the car travels after you notice an obstacle and decide to stop. It depends on your speed. This formula applies to an alert driver whose car has good brakes and is on dry pavement.

stopping distance (*feet*) → d; speed (*mph*) → s

$$d = 1.1s + 0.05s^2$$

Example: Find the stopping distance at 20 mph.

$$\begin{aligned} d &= 1.1s + 0.05s^2 \\ &= (1.1 \times 20) + (0.05 \times 20^2) \\ &= (1.1 \times 20) + (0.05 \times 400) \\ &= 22 + 20 \\ &= 42 \end{aligned}$$

The stopping distance is 42 feet.

28. Use the formula to complete this table.

Speed s	10	20	30	40	50	60	70	80
Stopping distance d		42						

29. Is the stopping distance at 40 mph double or more than double the stopping distance at 20 mph?

30. Find the difference between the stopping distances for 10 and 20 mph. For 20 and 30 mph. For 30 and 40 mph. Is there a pattern to the differences? Does the rest of the table follow the pattern?

12.9 Scientific Notation

To talk about the distance to a star and the size of an atom, scientists need very large and very small numbers. Written out in full, these numbers would be hard to work with. But powers of ten can be used to write them in a form that is easier to use.

Courtesy Hale Observatories

You already know what positive exponents mean. The pattern they follow for powers of 10 is shown and extended below.

Yerkes Observatory, University of Chicago

Each time the *exponent* is decreased by 1, the *value* is divided by 10.

This pattern can be continued to give meaning to 10^0 and to negative exponents.

power of ten	value
10^4	10000
10^3	1000
10^2	100
10^1	10
10^0	1
10^{-1}	0.1
10^{-2}	0.01
10^{-3}	0.001
10^{-4}	0.0001

> A number is expressed in **scientific notation** by writing it as a number between 1 and 10 multiplied by a power of 10.

Example 1: Express 6000 and 0.03 in scientific notation.

a number between 1 and 10 → ; ← a power of 10

$$6000 = 6 \times 1000 = 6 \times 10^3$$

$$0.03 = 3 \times 0.01 = 3 \times 10^{-2}$$

Example 2: Express 61,000 and 0.00327 in scientific notation.

First, move the decimal point so it follows the first nonzero digit.	⇨	Then multiply by the power of 10 that gives back the original number.
6 1000		6.1×10^4
Move the decimal point left 4 places. (This multiplies the number by 10^{-4}.)	⇨	To undo this, multiply by 10^4.
0.003 27		3.27×10^{-3}
Move the decimal point right 3 places. (This multiplies the number by 10^3.)	⇨	To undo this, multiply by 10^{-3}.

Example 3: Express 351.6, 0.0085, 0.0135, and 4065 in scientific notation.

Number	Move decimal point	Multiply by	Scientific notation
351.6	left 2	10^2	3.516×10^2
0.0085	right 3	10^{-3}	8.5×10^{-3}
0.0135	right 2	10^{-2}	1.35×10^{-2}
4065	left 3	10^3	4.065×10^3

Exercises

A What exponent should replace each n?

1. $50 = 5 \times 10^n$ **2.** $500 = 5 \times 10^n$ **3.** $5000 = 5 \times 10^n$

4. $3000 = 3 \times 10^n$ **5.** $60 = 6 \times 10^n$ **6.** $400 = 4 \times 10^n$

7. $0.2 = 2 \times 10^n$ **8.** $0.02 = 2 \times 10^n$ **9.** $0.002 = 2 \times 10^n$

10. $0.004 = 4 \times 10^n$ **11.** $0.7 = 7 \times 10^n$ **12.** $0.06 = 6 \times 10^n$

13. $800 = 8 \times 10^n$ **14.** $0.008 = 8 \times 10^n$ **15.** $80 = 8 \times 10^n$

16. To undo moving the decimal point left 8 places, multiply by (10^8, 10^{-8}).

17. You would multiply by 10^{-6} to undo moving the decimal point (*left, right*) 6 places.

[B] Express each number in scientific notation.

18. 3142	**19.** 34.21	**20.** 546,204
21. 59,603	**22.** 541.2	**23.** 608
24. 0.0134	**25.** 0.00142	**26.** 0.123
27. 0.25	**28.** 0.0004	**29.** 0.0304

Express each measurement using scientific notation.

30. Astronomers use the light-year to measure distance. A light-year is about 6,000,000,000,000 miles.

31. The earth's atmosphere contains about 1 200 000 000 000 000 000 kilograms of oxygen.

32. One micrometer (or micron) is 0.000 001 meter.

33. The distance between the sun and the planet Pluto varies from about 2,760,000,000 miles to about 4,600,000,000 miles.

[C] **34.** In living tissue, a typical cell is about 0.000 003 meter long; its volume is about 0.000 000 000 000 000 006 cubic meter.

35. A molecule of oxygen weighs 0.000 000 000 000 000 000 000 05 gram.

Googol

Googol is defined in the cartoon. The word was invented about forty years ago when mathematician Edward Kasner asked his nine-year-old nephew to think of a name for this number.

Now *googol* and *googolplex* are both in the dictionary. A googolplex is 1 followed by a googol of zeros.

1. Write 1 googol in scientific notation.

2. Write 1 googolplex as a power of 10.

Terms and Symbols Review

1. The product of 1.32 and $^{-}5.7$ is (*positive, negative*).

2. The quotient of 5.382 and 8 is (*positive, negative*).

3. The product of $^{-}2\frac{1}{2}$ and $^{-}4\frac{7}{8}$ is (*positive, negative*).

4. The quotient of $\frac{4}{5}$ and $-\frac{2}{3}$ is (*positive, negative*).

5. To divide by $-\frac{3}{4}$, you can multiply by its (*opposite, reciprocal*).

6. 10^{-3} has a value of (*1000, 0.001, 0.0001*).

7. In scientific notation, 7300 is written (73×10^2, 7.3×10^3, 7.3×1000).

8. In scientific notation, 0.006 is written (6×10^{-3}, $6 \div 1000$, 6×10^3).

Chapter 12 Review

Find each product or quotient. 12.1

1. $4.27 \times {}^{-}1.8$
2. $^{-}0.24 \times {}^{-}3.5$
3. $^{-}7 \times 5.2$
4. $^{-}4.44 \div 1.2$
5. $^{-}73.8 \div {}^{-}6$
6. $123 \div {}^{-}0.3$

Solve. 12.2

7. $\frac{n}{4.3} = {}^{-}2$
8. $^{-}4.3x = 24.08$
9. $^{-}5.6 = \frac{a}{4}$
10. $\frac{m}{^{-}6} = 8.7$
11. $^{-}2.7d = 1.62$
12. $7r = {}^{-}12.6$

Find each product or quotient.

13. $-\frac{4}{5} \times \frac{3}{7}$
14. $-\frac{2}{3} \times (-\frac{7}{8})$
15. $-\frac{5}{9} \times \frac{3}{5}$ 12.3
16. $-\frac{2}{3} \div \frac{7}{8}$
17. $\frac{1}{4} \div (-\frac{1}{3})$
18. $-\frac{4}{7} \div 2$
19. $^{-}3\frac{1}{7} \times (-\frac{3}{4})$
20. $3\frac{1}{2} \div {}^{-}2$
21. $^{-}2\frac{1}{4} \times 4\frac{1}{2}$ 12.4
22. $^{-}6\frac{1}{2} \div \frac{1}{8}$
23. $^{-}4\frac{1}{3} \div {}^{-}3\frac{1}{4}$
24. $7 \div {}^{-}1\frac{3}{4}$

12.5 Name the reciprocal, if any.

25. $\frac{7}{11}$ **26.** $-\frac{4}{9}$ **27.** $5\frac{2}{3}$

28. 14 **29.** 0 **30.** $^{-}1\frac{3}{4}$

Solve.

12.6

31. $\frac{x}{^{-}4} = \frac{3}{8}$ **32.** $-\frac{3}{5} = \frac{2}{15}r$ **33.** $-\frac{6}{25} = \frac{d}{5}$

34. $-\frac{3}{8}a = -\frac{3}{4}$ **35.** $\frac{5}{8}p = -\frac{25}{64}$ **36.** $-\frac{6}{11} = 3c$

12.7

37. $\frac{t-3}{6} = -\frac{1}{3}$ **38.** $\frac{n}{3} - \frac{1}{2} = -\frac{5}{6}$ **39.** $0.6x + 8.1 = 5.1$

40. $\frac{3x}{^{-}4} = -\frac{5}{8}$ **41.** $^{-}3.6t - 2.4 = 1.02$ **42.** $\frac{x - {}^{-}5.2}{3.7} = {}^{-}3.6$

12.8 Solve each problem.

43. Use the formula $k = \frac{tw}{1000}$ to find how long it takes a 25-watt appliance to use 8 kilowatt-hours of electricity.

44. Use the formula $h = \frac{w}{750}$ to find the number of watts used by a 3-horsepower motor.

12.9 Express in scientific notation.

45. 300.2 **46.** 58.6 **47.** 934,000

48. 0.673 **49.** 0.009842 **50.** 0.01

Chapter 12 Test

Find each product or quotient.

1. $\frac{3}{4}(-\frac{2}{3})$

2. $-\frac{3}{8} \times \frac{7}{8}$

3. $1\frac{1}{4} \times {}^{-}2\frac{1}{2}$

4. ${}^{-}2\frac{3}{4} \times {}^{-}1\frac{7}{8}$

5. 8.13×4.5

6. ${}^{-}8.2 \times {}^{-}7.3$

7. $\frac{2}{3} \div \frac{7}{8}$

8. $\frac{1}{4} \div (-\frac{9}{10})$

9. $-\frac{1}{2} \div \frac{5}{8}$

10. ${}^{-}1\frac{1}{2} \div {}^{-}2\frac{5}{6}$

11. $9.57 \div {}^{-}2.9$

12. ${}^{-}19.46 \div {}^{-}1.39$

13. $-\frac{2}{3} \div 1\frac{1}{3}$

14. $4 \times {}^{-}6\frac{1}{2}$

15. $-\frac{7}{8} \div 4$

16. $-\frac{3}{17} \times {}^{-}5\frac{2}{3}$

17. $\frac{7}{9} \times \frac{9}{7}$

18. $12 \times \frac{1}{12}$

Solve each equation.

19. $9x = \frac{2}{3}$

20. $5.2x = {}^{-}7.8$

21. $\frac{x}{6.2} = {}^{-}7.3$

22. $\frac{x}{{}^{-}8} = -\frac{2}{3}$

23. $3x + \frac{2}{3} = \frac{1}{2}$

24. $\frac{3x}{4} = -\frac{2}{3}$

25. $\frac{x + {}^{-}3.2}{5.7} = {}^{-}6.5$

26. $3.14x - 5.7 = 10.942$

Solve each problem.

27. From the formula $k = \frac{tw}{1000}$, find the number of watts used by a bulb that burns 36 kilowatt-hours of electricity in 24 hours.

28. From the formula $h = \frac{w}{750}$, find the horsepower rating of a 3300-watt motor.

Express in scientific notation.

29. 67,300

30. 980.4

31. 0.00036

RATE YOURSELF

Number Correct	
30–31	Superior
27–29	Excellent
23–26	Good
16–22	Fair
0–15	Poor

CONSUMER CORNER

AIR CONDITIONING

Air conditioners are rated by the amount of heat they can remove each hour. The rating is in *British thermal units per hour* (BTU/hr).

An air conditioner for cooling just one room of a house is usually rated between 5000 BTU/hr and 8500 BTU/hr. The number of BTU/hr needed depends on such things as the climate, the size of the room, the location of the room in the house, and the materials the house is made of.

Air conditioners are also rated by how much electricity they use to do their cooling. This rating is called the *energy efficiency ratio* (EER). The EER of an air conditioner is found by dividing its BTU/hr rating by the electrical power, in *watts*, needed to run it. (An air conditioner with an EER of less than 8 is not very efficient.)

Complete the chart. Give each EER to the nearest tenth.

	BTU/hr	watts	EER	
	5000	575	8.7	← $\frac{5000}{575} \approx 8.7$
1.	5100	649		
2.	5300	655.5		
3.	7000	862.5		
4.	8500	862.5		

To find the cost of operating an air conditioner for a certain number of hours, you can use this formula:

time in hours → t; watts → w

$$\text{cost} = tew \times 10^{-3}$$

cost of electricity per kilowatt-hour → e

Example: What does it cost to run a 690-watt air conditioner for 100 hours if electricity costs 5 cents a kilowatt-hour?

$$\text{cost} = 100 \times 0.05 \times 690 \times 10^{-3}$$

$$= 3.45 \qquad \text{The cost is \$3.45.}$$

If electricity costs 6 cents a kilowatt-hour, find the cost (to the nearest cent) of running each air conditioner in Exercises 1–4 above for 100 hours.

Find the value.

1. 5^2	**2.** 11^2	**3.** 21^2	3.8
4. $^-7 \times {}^-7$	**5.** $^-1 \times {}^-1$	**6.** $^-10 \times {}^-10$	7.1
7. $\frac{1}{2} \times \frac{1}{2}$	**8.** $\frac{2}{3} \times \frac{2}{3}$	**9.** $\frac{9}{10} \times \frac{9}{10}$	4.2
10. 0.3×0.3	**11.** 0.7×0.7	**12.** 1.2×1.2	5.4

Express each fraction in lowest terms. 4.3

13. $\frac{8}{100}$ **14.** $\frac{10}{25}$ **15.** $\frac{12}{16}$

Express each decimal as a fraction. 5.1

16. 0.9 **17.** 0.03 **18.** 1.1

Solve each equation.

19. $x + 16 = 25$ **20.** $x + 141 = 315$ 6.5

21. $y - 15 = 70$ **22.** $z - 81 = 200$ 6.6

23. The formula for the perimeter of a rectangle is $p = 2l + 2w$. Find the perimeter of a rectangle if $l = 7$ and $w = 5$. 1.9

13

A. Devaney, Inc.

13

SQUARE ROOTS

Each of the four types of storms (tornado, hurricane, thunderstorm, and cyclone) covers the ground in a roughly circular pattern. Using pictures from weather satellites or radar, weather forecasters can estimate the diameter of a storm. Then with the formula below they can estimate how long the storm will last.

$$t = \sqrt{\frac{d^3}{216}}$$

time the storm will last in hours (t)

diameter of storm in miles (d)

After you substitute for *d* above, you must find a square root to solve for *t*. In this chapter, you will learn how to find square roots and how to solve problems involving square roots.

What Are Square Roots?

13.1

You have 81 one-foot-square patio stones. You want to build a square patio and need to find the length of each side.

Zefa

Suppose you call each side s. Then

$$s \times s = 81$$

or

$$s^2 = 81.$$

You know $\begin{cases} 9 \times 9 = 81. \\ ^-9 \times {}^-9 = 81. \end{cases}$

We say: 9 and $^-9$ are **square roots** of 81.

We write: $\sqrt{81} = 9$ and $^-\sqrt{81} = {}^-9$.

The positive square root of 81 is 9.

The negative square root of 81 is $^-9$.

Every positive number has two square roots—one positive, the other negative. Zero has only one square root: $\sqrt{0} = 0$.

> The symbol $\sqrt{}$ is used for the non-negative square root of a number, while $^-\sqrt{}$ is used for the negative square root.

Now we know that the patio mentioned above must be 9 feet on each side. (Since we are dealing with a length, we can disregard the negative square root.)

Example 1: Find two solutions for $a^2 = 16$.

Since $4 \times 4 = 16$

and $^-4 \times {}^-4 = 16$,

the solutions are 4 and $^-4$.

Example 2: Find $\sqrt{400}$ and $^-\sqrt{400}$.

$\sqrt{400}$ is the positive number that gives 400 when squared.

Since $20^2 = 400$, we write $\sqrt{400} = 20$.

$^-\sqrt{400}$ is the negative number that gives 400 when squared.

Since $(^-20)^2 = 400$, we write $^-\sqrt{400} = {}^-20$.

Exercises

A Solve. Find two solutions for each equation if possible.

1. $x^2 = 1$
2. $y^2 = 9$
3. $z^2 = 25$
4. $z^2 = 36$
5. $w^2 = 4$
6. $a^2 = 0$
7. $b^2 = 16$
8. $c^2 = 49$
9. $m^2 = 64$
10. $k^2 = 100$
11. $n^2 = 81$
12. $p^2 = 400$

B Find each square root.

13. $\sqrt{4}$
14. $\sqrt{9}$
15. $^-\sqrt{4}$
16. $^-\sqrt{9}$
17. $\sqrt{36}$
18. $\sqrt{25}$
19. $^-\sqrt{49}$
20. $^-\sqrt{16}$
21. $\sqrt{64}$
22. $\sqrt{100}$
23. $^-\sqrt{25}$
24. $^-\sqrt{36}$
25. $\sqrt{81}$
26. $\sqrt{121}$
27. $\sqrt{144}$

C

28. $\sqrt{196}$
29. $^-\sqrt{196}$
30. $\sqrt{225}$
31. $\sqrt{256}$
32. $^-\sqrt{289}$
33. $^-\sqrt{324}$

Approximate Square Roots

13.2

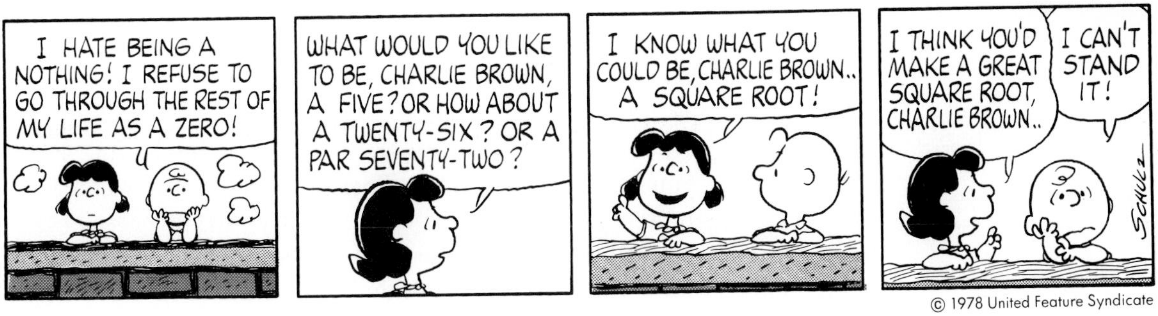

You already know the square roots of many square numbers.

$$1^2 = 1, \quad \text{so } \sqrt{1} = 1.$$

$$2^2 = 4, \quad \text{so } \sqrt{4} = 2.$$

$$3^2 = 9, \quad \text{so } \sqrt{9} = 3.$$

$$\vdots \qquad \qquad \vdots$$

(↑ square numbers)

Suppose you want to find the square root of a whole number that is not a square number. The following table gives a hint as to how you might begin.

$$\sqrt{1} = 1$$

$$\left.\begin{array}{l} \sqrt{2} = ? \\ \sqrt{3} = ? \end{array}\right\} \text{between 1 and 2}$$

$$\sqrt{4} = 2$$

$$\left.\begin{array}{l} \sqrt{5} = ? \\ \sqrt{6} = ? \\ \sqrt{7} = ? \\ \sqrt{8} = ? \end{array}\right\} \text{between 2 and 3}$$

$$\sqrt{9} = 3$$

$$\vdots$$

Suppose you want to estimate $\sqrt{3}$. You know 3 is between 1 and 4, and $\sqrt{3}$ is between $\sqrt{1}$ and $\sqrt{4}$. So $\sqrt{3}$ is between 1 and 2. Since 3 is closer to 4 than to 1, you might estimate $\sqrt{3}$ to be 1.6 or 1.7.

If $\sqrt{3} = 1.6$, then $(1.6)^2$ should equal 3. But $(1.6)^2 = 2.56$. If $\sqrt{3} = 1.7$, then $(1.7)^2$ should equal 3. But $(1.7)^2 = 2.89$.

Therefore, both 1.6 and 1.7 are too small as an estimate for $\sqrt{3}$. If you try 1.8, you find $(1.8)^2 = 3.24$. Therefore, $\sqrt{3}$ is between 1.7 and 1.8. You could continue to estimate $\sqrt{3}$ by this process. But there are better methods, and these have been used to compute approximate square roots for tables like the one on page 422. The table also lists the squares of the whole numbers 1–150.

Example 1: Use the table of square roots to find an approximation for $\sqrt{29}$.

n	n^2	$\sqrt{n}$
26	676	5.10
27	729	5.20
28	784	5.29
29	841	5.39

Find 29 in the n-column.

Read $\sqrt{29}$ in the $\sqrt{n}$-column.

Example 2: Use the table of squares to find 48^2.

n	n^2	$\sqrt{n}$
46	2,116	6.78
47	2,209	6.86
48	2,304	6.93

Find 48 in the n-column.

Read 48^2 in the n^2-column.

Exercises

A Tell how to use the table to find the following.

1. $\sqrt{7}$
2. $\sqrt{79}$
3. $\sqrt{142}$
4. 15^2
5. 87^2
6. 119^2

B Use the table to find the following.

7. $\sqrt{18}$
8. $\sqrt{42}$
9. $\sqrt{94}$
10. $\sqrt{110}$
11. $\sqrt{128}$
12. $\sqrt{149}$
13. 14^2
14. 37^2
15. 69^2
16. 86^2
17. 108^2
18. 134^2
19. $\sqrt{29}$
20. 71^2
21. $\sqrt{63}$
22. 92^2
23. $\sqrt{122}$
24. 146^2

(a) Find each square root in the table. **(b)** Then square that approximation.

Example:

(**a**) $\sqrt{12} \approx 3.46$

(**b**) $(3.46)^2 = 3.46 \times 3.46$

$= 11.9716$

25. $\sqrt{2}$
26. $\sqrt{3}$
27. $\sqrt{15}$
28. $\sqrt{41}$
29. $\sqrt{56}$
30. $\sqrt{75}$

C Square each approximation given for $\sqrt{2}$ below to see how close the result is to 2.

31. $\sqrt{2} \approx 1.414$
32. $\sqrt{2} \approx 1.4142$
33. $\sqrt{2} \approx 1.41421$
34. $\sqrt{2} \approx 1.414213$
35. If you square the following decimal, do you think you will get exactly 2? $\sqrt{2} \approx 1.41421356237309504880$3

TABLE OF SQUARES AND SQUARE ROOTS

n	n^2	$\sqrt{n}$	n	n^2	$\sqrt{n}$	n	n^2	$\sqrt{n}$
1	1	1.00	**51**	2,601	7.14	**101**	10,201	10.05
2	4	1.41	**52**	2,704	7.21	**102**	10,404	10.10
3	9	1.73	**53**	2,809	7.28	**103**	10,609	10.15
4	16	2.00	**54**	2,916	7.35	**104**	10,816	10.20
5	25	2.24	**55**	3,025	7.42	**105**	11,025	10.25
6	36	2.45	**56**	3,136	7.48	**106**	11,236	10.30
7	49	2.65	**57**	3,249	7.55	**107**	11,449	10.34
8	64	2.83	**58**	3,364	7.62	**108**	11,664	10.39
9	81	3.00	**59**	3,481	7.68	**109**	11,881	10.44
10	100	3.16	**60**	3,600	7.75	**110**	12,100	10.49
11	121	3.32	**61**	3,721	7.81	**111**	12,321	10.54
12	144	3.46	**62**	3,844	7.87	**112**	12,544	10.58
13	169	3.61	**63**	3,969	7.94	**113**	12,769	10.63
14	196	3.74	**64**	4,096	8.00	**114**	12,996	10.68
15	225	3.87	**65**	4,225	8.06	**115**	13,225	10.72
16	256	4.00	**66**	4,356	8.12	**116**	13,456	10.77
17	289	4.12	**67**	4,489	8.19	**117**	13,689	10.82
18	324	4.24	**68**	4,624	8.25	**118**	13,924	10.86
19	361	4.36	**69**	4,761	8.31	**119**	14,161	10.91
20	400	4.47	**70**	4,900	8.37	**120**	14,400	10.95
21	441	4.58	**71**	5,041	8.43	**121**	14,641	11.00
22	484	4.69	**72**	5,184	8.49	**122**	14,884	11.05
23	529	4.80	**73**	5,329	8.54	**123**	15,129	11.09
24	576	4.90	**74**	5,476	8.60	**124**	15,376	11.14
25	625	5.00	**75**	5,625	8.66	**125**	15,625	11.18
26	676	5.10	**76**	5,776	8.72	**126**	15,876	11.22
27	729	5.20	**77**	5,929	8.77	**127**	16,129	11.27
28	784	5.29	**78**	6,084	8.83	**128**	16,384	11.31
29	841	5.39	**79**	6,241	8.89	**129**	16,641	11.36
30	900	5.48	**80**	6,400	8.94	**130**	16,900	11.40
31	961	5.57	**81**	6,561	9.00	**131**	17,161	11.45
32	1,024	5.66	**82**	6,724	9.06	**132**	17,424	11.49
33	1,089	5.74	**83**	6,889	9.11	**133**	17,689	11.53
34	1,156	5.83	**84**	7,056	9.17	**134**	17,956	11.58
35	1,225	5.92	**85**	7,225	9.22	**135**	18,225	11.62
36	1,296	6.00	**86**	7,396	9.27	**136**	18,496	11.66
37	1,369	6.08	**87**	7,569	9.33	**137**	18,769	11.70
38	1,444	6.16	**88**	7,744	9.38	**138**	19,044	11.75
39	1,521	6.24	**89**	7,921	9.43	**139**	19,321	11.79
40	1,600	6.32	**90**	8,100	9.49	**140**	19,600	11.83
41	1,681	6.40	**91**	8,281	9.54	**141**	19,881	11.87
42	1,764	6.48	**92**	8,464	9.59	**142**	20,164	11.92
43	1,849	6.56	**93**	8,649	9.64	**143**	20,449	11.96
44	1,936	6.63	**94**	8,836	9.70	**144**	20,736	12.00
45	2,025	6.71	**95**	9,025	9.75	**145**	21,025	12.04
46	2,116	6.78	**96**	9,216	9.80	**146**	21,316	12.08
47	2,209	6.86	**97**	9,409	9.85	**147**	21,609	12.12
48	2,304	6.93	**98**	9,604	9.90	**148**	21,904	12.17
49	2,401	7.00	**99**	9,801	9.95	**149**	22,201	12.21
50	2,500	7.07	**100**	10,000	10.00	**150**	22,500	12.25

Extending the Square-Root Table

13.3

The table on page 422 lists the square roots of numbers from 1–150. Often you need to know the square root of a number larger than 150. In some such cases you can use the n^2-column.

Example 1: Find $\sqrt{400}$.

n	n^2	$\sqrt{n}$
19	361	4.36
20	400	4.47
21	441	4.58

400 is given in the n^2-column of the table.

$$400 = 20^2$$

$$\sqrt{400} = 20$$

In many cases, however, you will not find the given number in either the n-column or the n^2-column. In these cases, another method is sometimes useful.

The following examples suggest an important property.

$$\sqrt{100} = 10 = 5 \times 2$$

$$\sqrt{25 \times 4} = \sqrt{25} \times \sqrt{4}$$

$$\sqrt{144} = 12 = 3 \times 4$$

$$\sqrt{9 \times 16} = \sqrt{9} \times \sqrt{16}$$

For positive numbers a and b,

$$\sqrt{ab} = \sqrt{a} \times \sqrt{b}.$$

Example 2: Find $\sqrt{400}$ by using the property just stated.

$$\sqrt{400} = \sqrt{4 \times 100} = \sqrt{4} \times \sqrt{100} = 2 \times 10 = 20$$

or

$$\sqrt{400} = \sqrt{16 \times 25} = \sqrt{16} \times \sqrt{25} = 4 \times 5 = 20$$

Example 3: Find $\sqrt{160}$ by using the table on page 422.

160 is not in the n-column or the n^2-column. But 160 can be named as the product of two numbers, each less than 150.

$\sqrt{160} = \sqrt{16 \times 10}$	Find the largest square-number factor.
$= \sqrt{16} \times \sqrt{10}$	Both numbers are in the n-column.
$\approx 4 \times 3.16$	Find $\sqrt{10}$ in the table
≈ 12.64	

Exercises

A Find each square root in the table.

1. $\sqrt{169}$ 2. $\sqrt{196}$ 3. $\sqrt{576}$ 4. $\sqrt{484}$

5. $\sqrt{841}$ 6. $\sqrt{1296}$ 7. $\sqrt{2601}$ 8. $\sqrt{3969}$

B Name each square root as a product of two square roots, one of which has the largest possible square number under the square-root sign.

Example: $\sqrt{200} = \sqrt{100} \times \sqrt{2}$

9. $\sqrt{18}$ 10. $\sqrt{32}$ 11. $\sqrt{75}$ 12. $\sqrt{72}$

13. $\sqrt{300}$ 14. $\sqrt{2100}$ 15. $\sqrt{99}$ 16. $\sqrt{999}$

17. $\sqrt{810}$ 18. $\sqrt{250}$ 19. $\sqrt{360}$ 20. $\sqrt{1440}$

Name each square root as the product of a whole number and a square root. *Hint:* Use your answers from Exercises 9–20.

Example: $\sqrt{200} = \sqrt{100} \times \sqrt{2}$

$= 10 \times \sqrt{2}$

21. $\sqrt{18}$ 22. $\sqrt{32}$ 23. $\sqrt{75}$ 24. $\sqrt{72}$

25. $\sqrt{300}$ 26. $\sqrt{2100}$ 27. $\sqrt{99}$ 28. $\sqrt{999}$

29. $\sqrt{810}$ 30. $\sqrt{250}$ 31. $\sqrt{360}$ 32. $\sqrt{1440}$

Find each square root. Use the table on page 422.

33. $\sqrt{640}$ **34.** $\sqrt{250}$ **35.** $\sqrt{1000}$ **36.** $\sqrt{750}$

37. $\sqrt{1500}$ **38.** $\sqrt{500}$ **39.** $\sqrt{189}$ **40.** $\sqrt{204}$

41. $\sqrt{700}$ **42.** $\sqrt{550}$ **43.** $\sqrt{168}$ **44.** $\sqrt{175}$

45. $\sqrt{490}$ **46.** $\sqrt{280}$ **47.** $\sqrt{630}$ **48.** $\sqrt{240}$

C Compute.

Examples: **a.** $\sqrt{144 + 25} = \sqrt{169}$ **b.** $\sqrt{144} + \sqrt{25} = 12 + 5$

$= 13$ $= 17$

49. $\sqrt{16 + 9}$ **50.** $\sqrt{16} + \sqrt{9}$ **51.** $\sqrt{64 + 36}$ **52.** $\sqrt{64} + \sqrt{36}$

53. Compare answers for Exercises 49 and 50 and for Exercises 51 and 52. Is $\sqrt{a + b}$ equal to $\sqrt{a} + \sqrt{b}$?

Compute.

54. $\sqrt{25 - 9}$ **55.** $\sqrt{25} - \sqrt{9}$ **56.** $\sqrt{100 - 36}$ **57.** $\sqrt{100} - \sqrt{36}$

58. Is $\sqrt{a - b}$ equal to $\sqrt{a} - \sqrt{b}$?

Quick Quiz
Sections 13.1 to 13.3

Find each square root.

1. $\sqrt{25}$ **2.** $\sqrt{49}$ **3.** $\sqrt{81}$

Find two solutions for each equation.

4. $x^2 = 36$ **5.** $m^2 = 100$ **6.** $y^2 = 9$

Use the table on page 422 to find the following.

7. $\sqrt{11}$ **8.** 23^2 **9.** $\sqrt{139}$

Using the table on page 422, find each square root.

10. $\sqrt{300}$ **11.** $\sqrt{360}$ **12.** $\sqrt{162}$

13.4

Square Roots of Rational Numbers

You know that whole numbers have square roots. Now you will see that rational numbers also have square roots.

Example 1: Find $\sqrt{\frac{4}{9}}$.

Here are two ways to do it.

$$\sqrt{\frac{4}{9}} = \sqrt{\frac{2}{3} \times \frac{2}{3}} = \frac{2}{3}$$

$$\sqrt{\frac{4}{9}} = \frac{\sqrt{4}}{\sqrt{9}} = \frac{2}{3}$$

For positive numbers a and b,

$$\sqrt{\frac{a}{b}} = \frac{\sqrt{a}}{\sqrt{b}}.$$

Example 2: Find $\sqrt{0.64}$.

Here are two ways to do it.

$$\sqrt{0.64} = \sqrt{0.8 \times 0.8} = 0.8$$

$$\sqrt{0.64} = \sqrt{\frac{64}{100}} = \frac{\sqrt{64}}{\sqrt{100}} = \frac{8}{10} \text{ or } \frac{4}{5} \text{ or } 0.8$$

Exercises

A Name as the square of a fraction. Example: $\frac{4}{100} = (\frac{2}{10})^2$

1. $\frac{16}{100}$
2. $\frac{9}{36}$
3. $\frac{1}{4}$
4. $\frac{16}{25}$
5. $\frac{64}{81}$
6. $\frac{25}{100}$
7. $\frac{49}{64}$
8. $\frac{9}{16}$

Name as a fraction. Example: $0.08 = \frac{8}{100}$

9. 0.09 **10.** 0.81 **11.** 0.16 **12.** 0.04

13. 0.25 **14.** 0.36 **15.** 0.01 **16.** 0.0025

[B] Find each square root as a fraction.

17. $\sqrt{\frac{9}{25}}$ **18.** $\sqrt{\frac{16}{49}}$ **19.** $\sqrt{\frac{25}{64}}$ **20.** $\sqrt{\frac{64}{81}}$

21. $\sqrt{\frac{1}{4}}$ **22.** $\sqrt{\frac{49}{100}}$ **23.** $\sqrt{\frac{9}{16}}$ **24.** $\sqrt{\frac{81}{100}}$

Find each square root as a decimal.

25. $\sqrt{0.09}$ **26.** $\sqrt{0.81}$ **27.** $\sqrt{0.04}$ **28.** $\sqrt{0.25}$

29. $\sqrt{0.36}$ **30.** $\sqrt{0.01}$ **31.** $\sqrt{0.0036}$ **32.** $\sqrt{1.44}$

[C] Find each square root.

Examples:

a. $\sqrt{\frac{2}{9}} = \frac{\sqrt{2}}{\sqrt{9}}$

$\approx \frac{1.41}{3}$ ← from table

≈ 0.47

b. $\sqrt{\frac{5}{8}} = \sqrt{\frac{5 \times 2}{8 \times 2}}$ ← Multiply both numerator and denominator to make the denominator a square number.

$= \sqrt{\frac{10}{16}}$

$= \frac{\sqrt{10}}{\sqrt{16}}$

$\approx \frac{3.16}{4}$ ← from table

≈ 0.79

33. $\sqrt{\frac{5}{16}}$ **34.** $\sqrt{\frac{7}{25}}$ **35.** $\sqrt{\frac{11}{100}}$ **36.** $\sqrt{\frac{5}{36}}$

37. $\sqrt{\frac{1}{2}}$ **38.** $\sqrt{\frac{3}{10}}$ **39.** $\sqrt{\frac{7}{8}}$ **40.** $\sqrt{\frac{3}{50}}$

13.5 Square Roots and Equations

To solve some practical problems you have to solve equations like $x^2 = 36$. You already know that this equation has two solutions—one positive and the other negative.

$$x^2 = 36$$

positive solution

$$x = \sqrt{36}$$
$$= 6$$

negative solution

$$x = {}^{-}\sqrt{36}$$
$$= {}^{-}6$$

In practical problems you are usually interested only in a distance or an amount, and not a direction, so the negative solution does not apply.

Example 1: Find the positive solution of $x^2 = 16$.

$$x^2 = 16$$
$$\sqrt{x^2} = \sqrt{16}$$
$$x = 4$$

Take the square root of each side. (The square root of x^2 is x. The positive square root of 16 is $\sqrt{16}$ or 4.)

Example 2: Find the positive solution of $x^2 = 21$.

$$x^2 = 21$$

$$\sqrt{x^2} = \sqrt{21}$$ Take the square root of each side.

$$x \approx 4.58$$ Use the table.

Example 3: Find the positive solution of $x^2 + 5 = 81$.

$$x^2 + 5 = 81$$

$$x^2 + 5 + {}^{-}5 = 81 + {}^{-}5$$ Add $^{-}5$ to each side.

$$x^2 = 76$$

$$\sqrt{x^2} = \sqrt{76}$$ Take the square root of each side.

$$x \approx 8.72$$ Use the table.

Exercises

A How would you find the positive solution of each equation?

1. $x^2 = 25$ **2.** $x^2 = 30$ **3.** $x^2 + 9 = 90$

4. $x^2 - 5 = 59$ **5.** $x^2 + 2 = 10$ **6.** $x^2 - 4 = 14$

B Find the positive solution of each equation.

7. $x^2 = 9$ **8.** $x^2 = 27$ **9.** $x^2 = 42$

10. $x^2 + 5 = 30$ **11.** $x^2 + 9 = 42$ **12.** $x^2 + 16 = 25$

13. $x^2 - 4 = 60$ **14.** $x^2 - 9 = 81$ **15.** $x^2 - 25 = 144$

If an airplane is h miles above the earth, it is approximately d miles from the horizon. The relationship between h and d can be expressed by the following formula.

$$d = \sqrt{8000h}$$

Example: If an airplane is 5 miles high, what is the distance to the horizon?

$$d = \sqrt{8000h}$$
$$= \sqrt{8000 \times 5}$$
$$= \sqrt{40000}$$
$$= 200$$ It is 200 miles to the horizon.

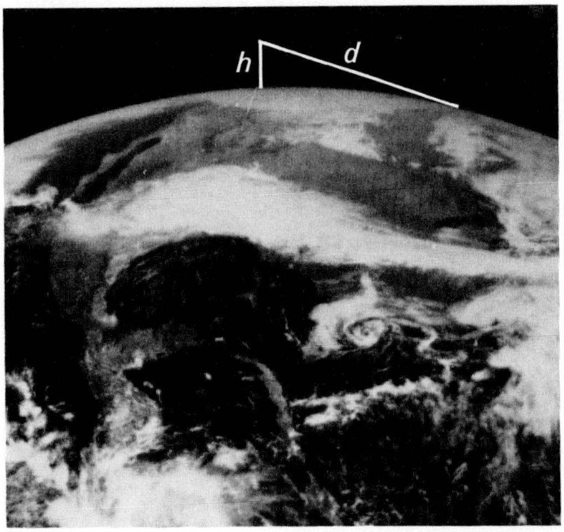

Courtesy NASA

Use the formula above. Copy and complete.

	Altitude	*Distance to horizon*
16.	1 mile	
18.	2 miles	
20.	3 miles	

	Altitude	*Distance to horizon*
17.	$1\frac{1}{4}$ miles	
19.	$2\frac{1}{2}$ miles	
21.	3.2 miles	

C Solve each equation.

Example:

$$\sqrt{x} = 5.1$$
$$(\sqrt{x})^2 = (5.1)^2 \quad \text{Square each side.}$$
$$x = 26.01$$

22. $\sqrt{x} = 6$ **23.** $\sqrt{y} = 6.2$ **24.** $\sqrt{r} = \frac{4}{7}$

25. $\sqrt{k} = 49$ **26.** $\sqrt{r} = 25$ **27.** $\sqrt{t} = 128$

Example:

$$\sqrt{x+3} = 5$$
$$(\sqrt{x+3})^2 = 5^2 \quad \text{Square each side.}$$
$$x + 3 = 25$$
$$x + 3 + {}^-3 = 25 + {}^-3$$
$$x = 22$$

28. $\sqrt{x+7} = 4$ **29.** $\sqrt{x+5} = 9$ **30.** $\sqrt{x+11} = 15$

31. $\sqrt{x-7} = 7$ **32.** $\sqrt{x-4} = 6$ **33.** $\sqrt{x-9} = 14$

Meeting Halley's Comet

Courtesy NASA

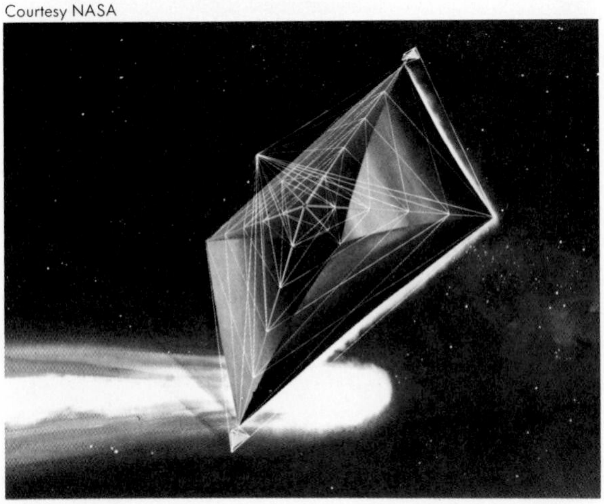

The National Aeronautics and Space Administration is studying plans to launch an unmanned spacecraft to meet with Halley's Comet when it next approaches the sun in 1986. A giant square sail, having an area of 640 000 square meters, would be used to propel the spacecraft by means of sunlight. What would be the length of a side of the sail?

The Pythagorean Property 13.6

As you probably know, a **right triangle** has one 90° angle (called a *right angle*).

The right triangle shown here has sides that are 5, 4, and 3 units long. If a square is drawn on each side as shown, then it is easy to see that the square of the longest side is equal to the sum of the squares of the other two sides.

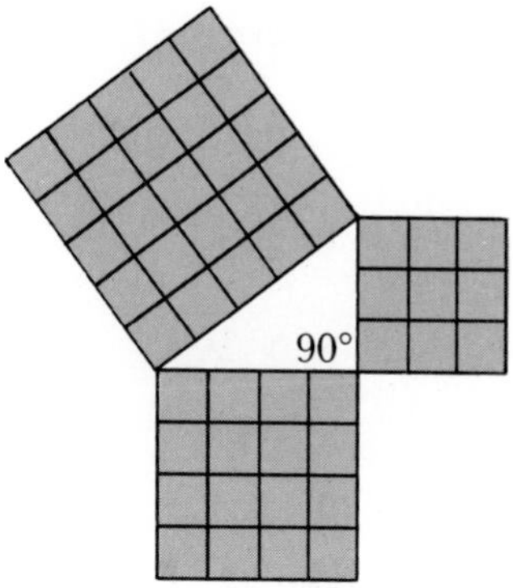

25 square units → 25, 16 square units → 16, 9 square units → 9

$$25 = 16 + 9$$

$$5^2 = 4^2 + 3^2$$

This illustrates an important property of right triangles.

> **Pythagorean Property**
>
> In a right triangle, the square of the hypotenuse is equal to the sum of the squares of the other two sides. (*Note:* The hypotenuse is the side opposite the right angle, and it is always the longest side.)

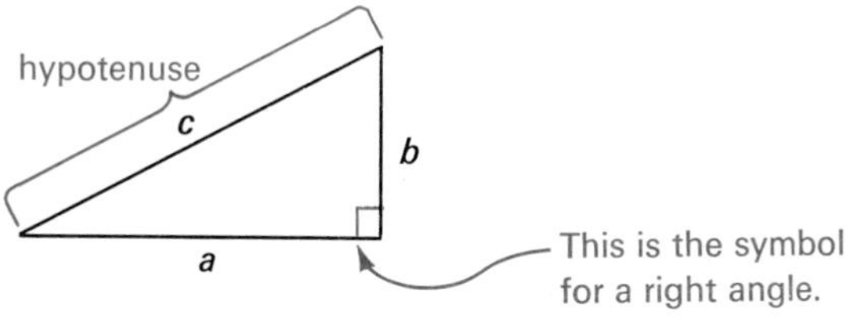

$$c^2 = a^2 + b^2$$

This property can be used to find the third side of a right triangle when the other two sides are known.

Example 1: Find the length c of the hypotenuse.

$$c^2 = a^2 + b^2$$
$$c^2 = 8^2 + 6^2$$
$$c^2 = 64 + 36$$
$$c^2 = 100$$
$$\sqrt{c^2} = \sqrt{100}$$
$$c = 10$$

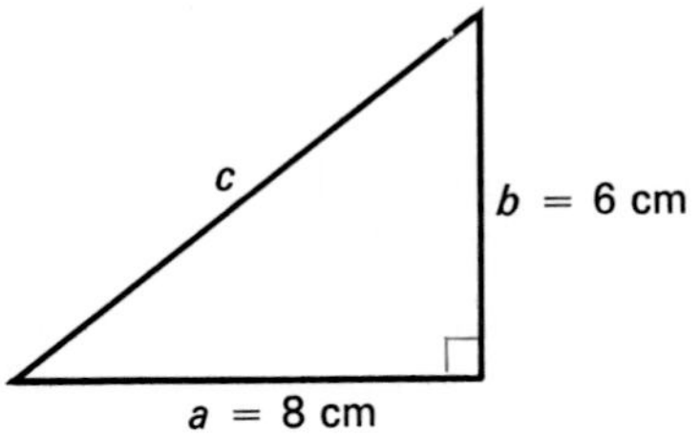

The hypotenuse is 10 cm long.

Example 2: Find the length a of the side.

Hint: Use the table on page 422 to find 25^2 and 24^2.

$$c^2 = a^2 + b^2$$
$$25^2 = a^2 + 24^2$$
$$625 = a^2 + 576$$
$$625 + {}^-576 = a^2 + 576 + {}^-576$$
$$49 = a^2$$
$$\sqrt{49} = \sqrt{a^2}$$
$$7 = a$$

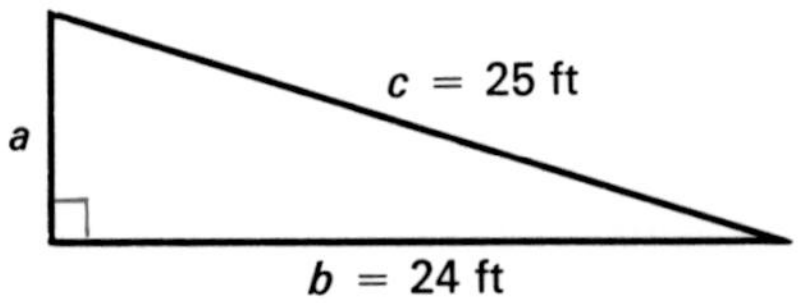

The side is 7 ft long.

Example 3: Find the length b of the side.

$$c^2 = a^2 + b^2$$
$$17^2 = 15^2 + b^2$$
$$289 = 225 + b^2$$
$${}^-225 + 289 = {}^-225 + 225 + b^2$$
$$64 = b^2$$
$$\sqrt{64} = \sqrt{b^2}$$
$$8 = b$$

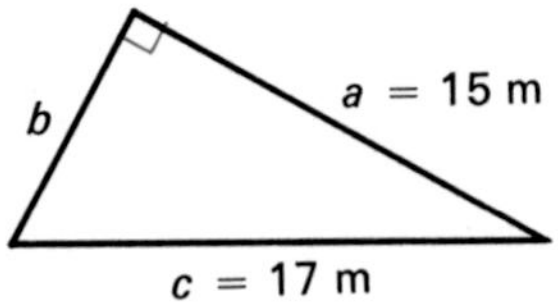

The side is 8 m long.

Exercises

A What equation can you use to find the unknown side in each triangle?

1.

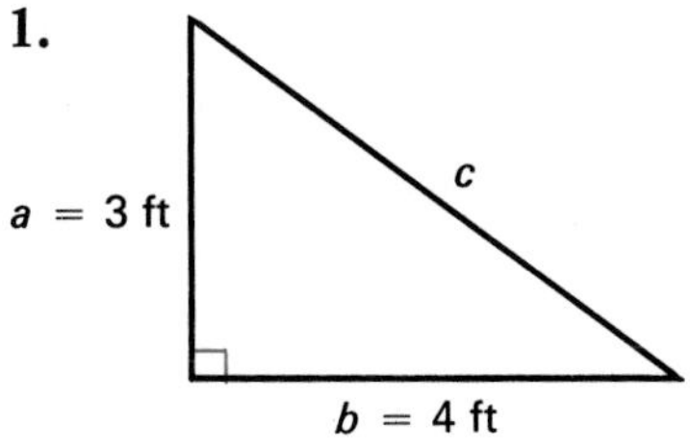

2.

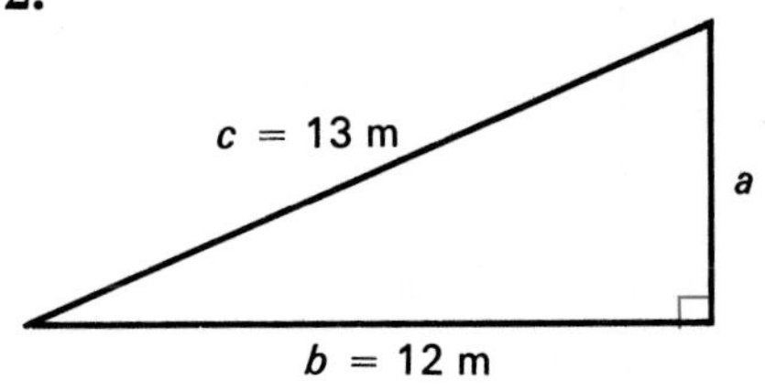

How would you solve each equation?

3. $25 = 9 + b^2$ **4.** $100 = a^2 + 64$ **5.** $c^2 = 144 + 25$

6. $5^2 = 3^2 + b^2$ **7.** $10^2 = a^2 + 8^2$ **8.** $c^2 = 12^2 + 5^2$

B Use the right triangle below to help you find each unknown side in the tables.

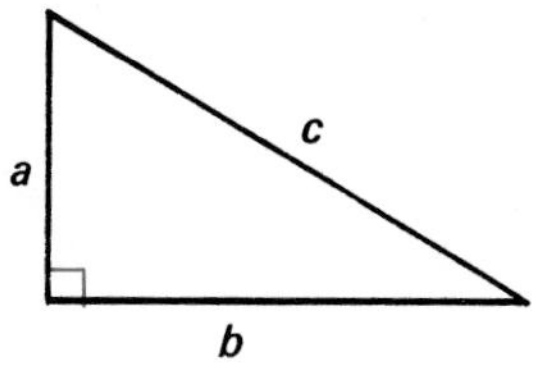

	a	b	c
9.	3	4	___
11.	15	8	___
13.	___	24	25
15.	___	40	41
17.	63	___	65
19.	21	___	29

	a	b	c
10.	5	12	___
12.	24	7	___
14.	___	20	29
16.	___	60	61
18.	45	___	53
20.	8	___	17

Determine if each triangle is a right triangle.

Examples:

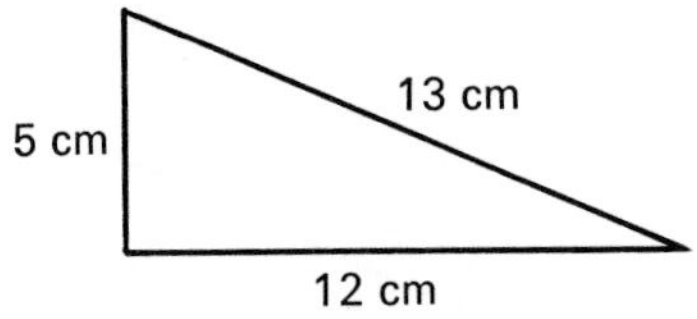

$13^2 = 5^2 + 12^2$

$169 = 25 + 144$

$169 = 169$ True

Yes, it is a right triangle.

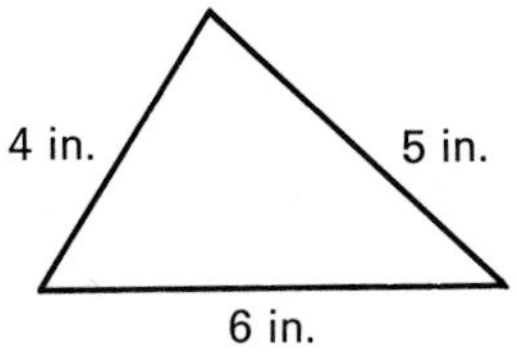

$6^2 = 5^2 + 4^2$

$36 = 25 + 16$

$36 = 41$ False

No, it is not a right triangle.

21.

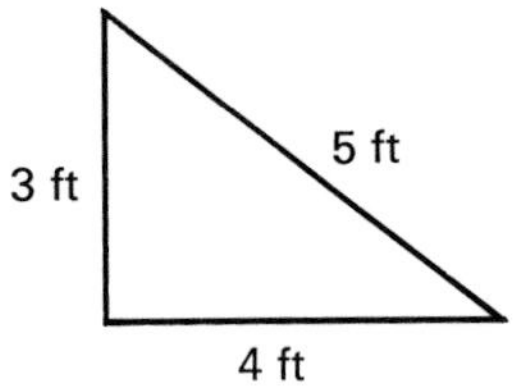

22.

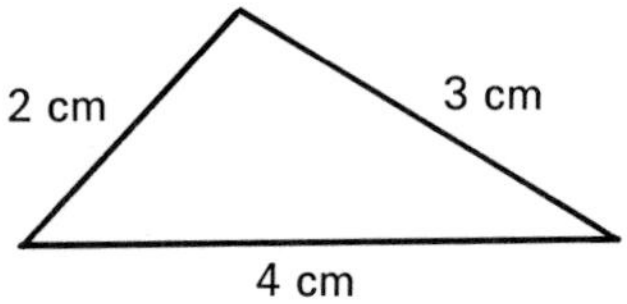

23.

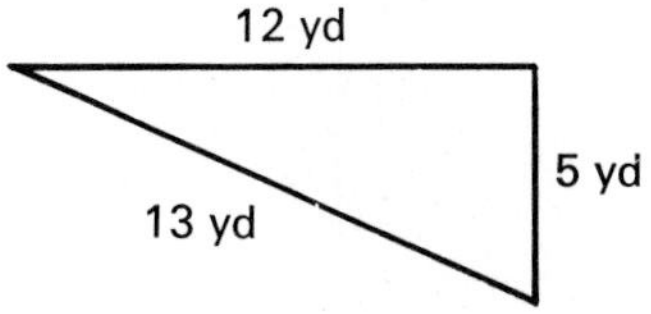

24.

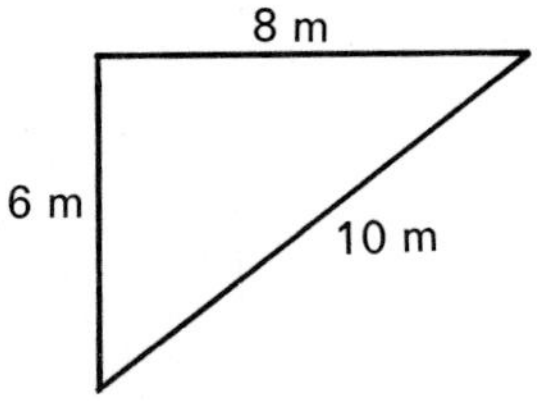

C **25.**

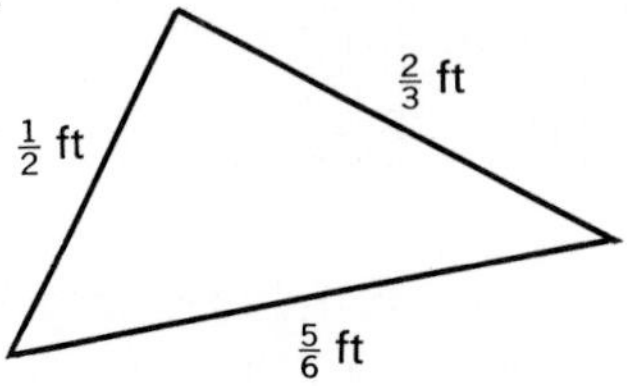

26.

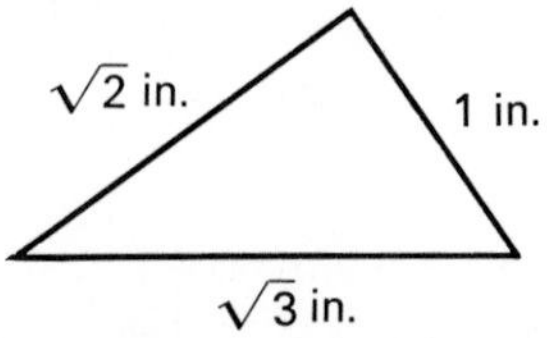

Quick Quiz
Sections 13.4 to 13.6

Find each square root as a fraction.

1. $\sqrt{\frac{4}{49}}$ **2.** $\sqrt{\frac{25}{81}}$ **3.** $\sqrt{\frac{1}{100}}$

Find each square root as a decimal.

4. $\sqrt{0.16}$ **5.** $\sqrt{0.49}$ **6.** $\sqrt{0.09}$

Find the positive solution of each equation.

7. $x^2 = 25$ **8.** $x^2 - 4 = 32$ **9.** $x^2 - 9 = 72$

Use the right triangle to help you find each unknown side in the following.

	a	b	c
10.	9	12	___
11.	12	___	13
12.	___	8	10

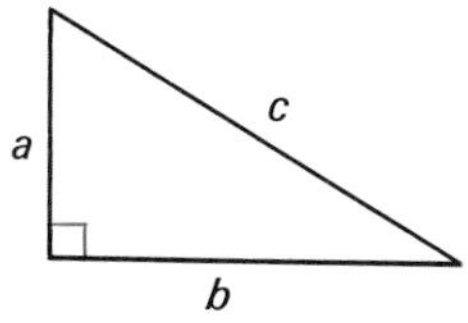

In a Pig's Sty!

H. Armstrong Roberts

A farmer has 250 pigs to sell. How can the pigs be arranged in 8 pens so the farmer can instantly deliver any number of pigs from 1 to 250 by simply opening the right gate or gates and herding the pigs out?

13.7 Using the Pythagorean Property

The Pythagorean Property can be used in solving many practical problems.

Example 1: How far is it from point D to point E?

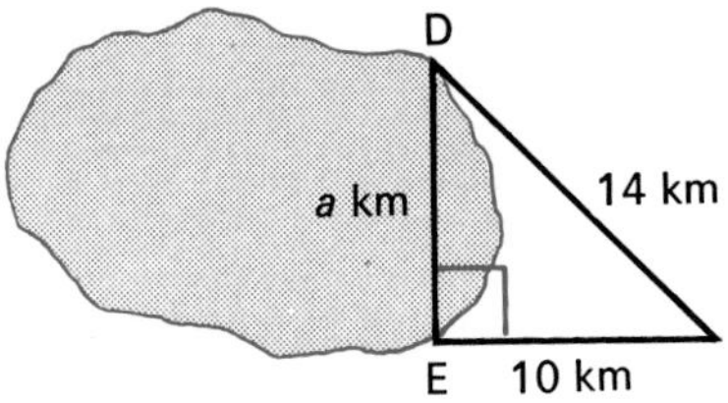

$$c^2 = a^2 + b^2$$
$$14^2 = a^2 + 10^2$$
$$196 = a^2 + 100$$
$$196 + {}^{-}100 = a^2 + 100 + {}^{-}100$$
$$96 = a^2$$
$$\sqrt{96} = \sqrt{a^2}$$
$$9.80 \approx a$$

Check: Is 14^2 approximately equal to $(9.8)^2 + 10^2$? ✓

So it is about 9.8 kilometers from D to E.

Example 2: A telephone pole is to be braced by a wire as shown. How high up on the pole should the wire be fastened?

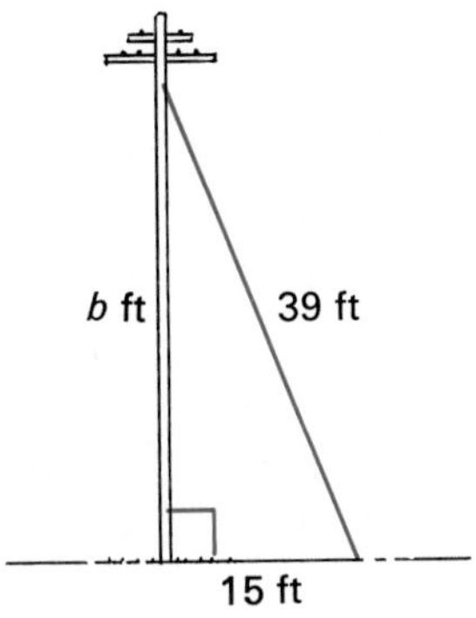

$$c^2 = a^2 + b^2$$
$$39^2 = 15^2 + b^2$$
$$1521 = 225 + b^2$$
$${}^{-}225 + 1521 = {}^{-}225 + 225 + b^2$$
$$1296 = b^2$$
$$\sqrt{1296} = \sqrt{b^2}$$
$$36 = b$$

Check: Is 39^2 equal to $15^2 + 36^2$? ✓

So the wire should be fastened 36 feet above the ground.

Exercises

A What equation would you use to find the unknown side in each right triangle?

1.

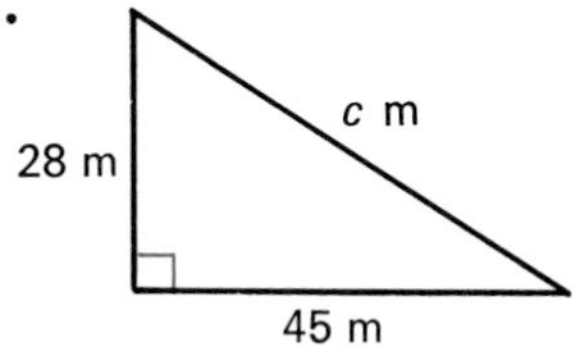

2.

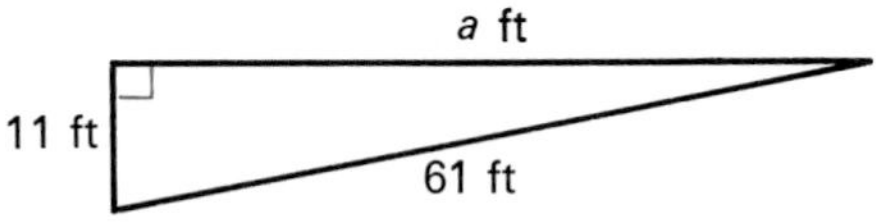

3.

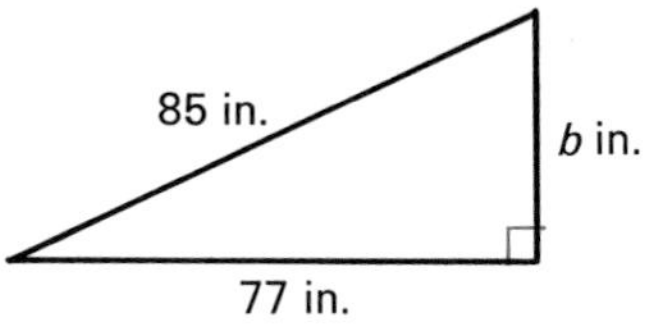

4.

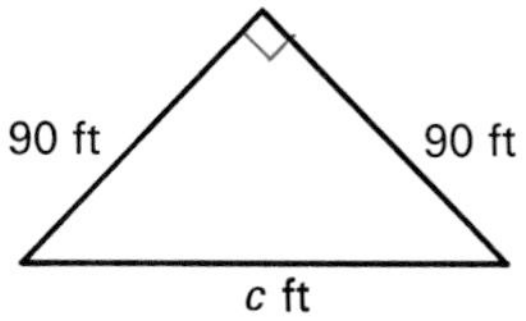

B Solve each problem.

5. When Joe had let out 100 yards of kite string, Rita was directly beneath the kite. If Joe is 80 yards from Rita, how high is the kite?

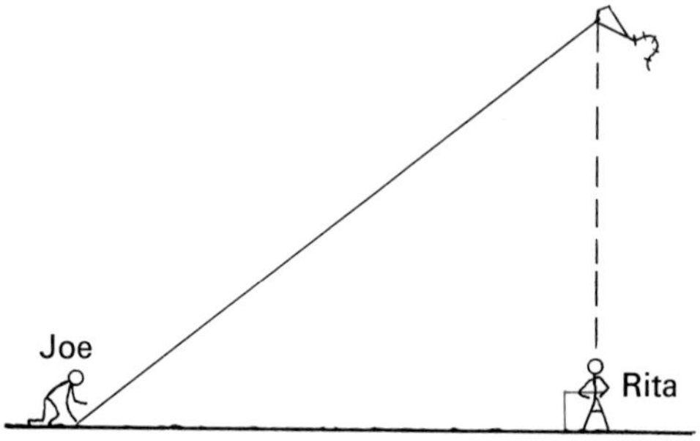

6. On a baseball diamond, it is 90 feet between bases. How far is it from home plate to second base?

7. On a softball diamond, it is 60 feet between bases. How far is it from home plate to second base?

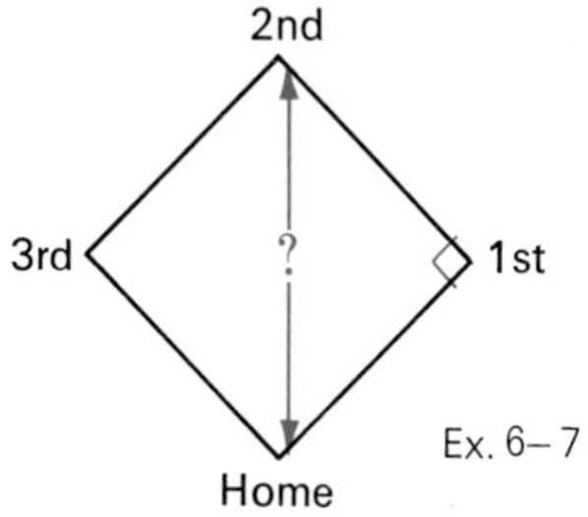

Ex. 6–7

8. What is the height of the TV screen shown at the right?

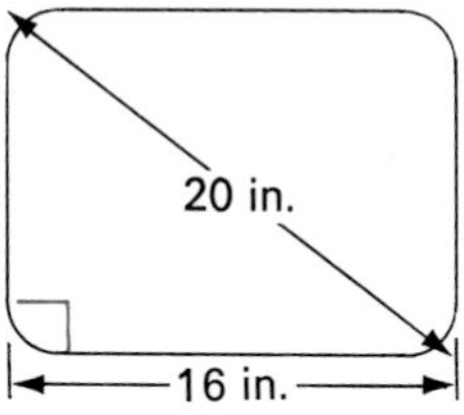

9. The bottom of a 12-foot ladder is placed 3 feet from a building. How high up on the building will the ladder reach?

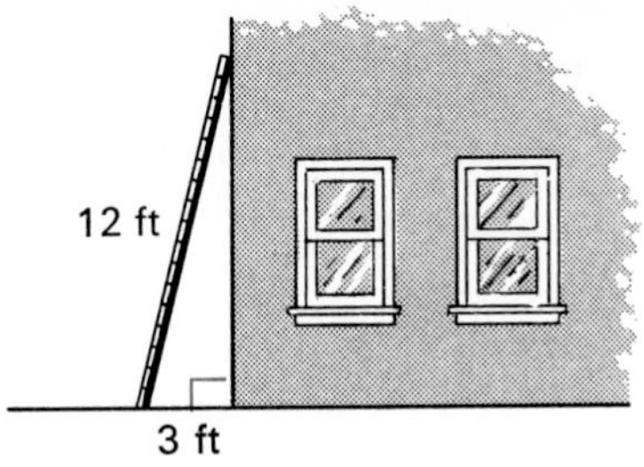

10. A ship left port and sailed 5 miles west and then 8 miles south. How far was the ship from the port?

11. A ramp must rise 4 feet over a horizontal distance of 10 feet. What must be the length of the ramp?

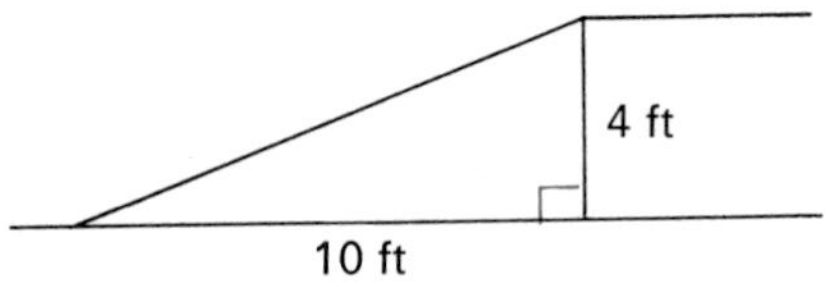

12. The roof of a house is to be built as shown. How long should each rafter be?

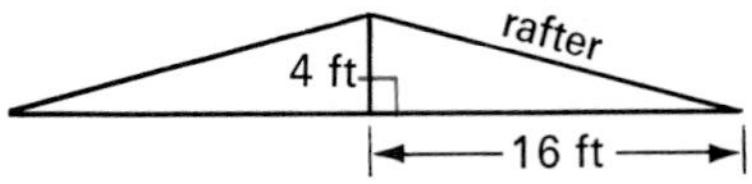

C Solve each problem.

Example: The lighthouse at Bernice Point is 16 miles from the lighthouse at Leigh Sound. The point at which the radio beams from these lighthouses make right angles is the same distance from each. What is that distance?

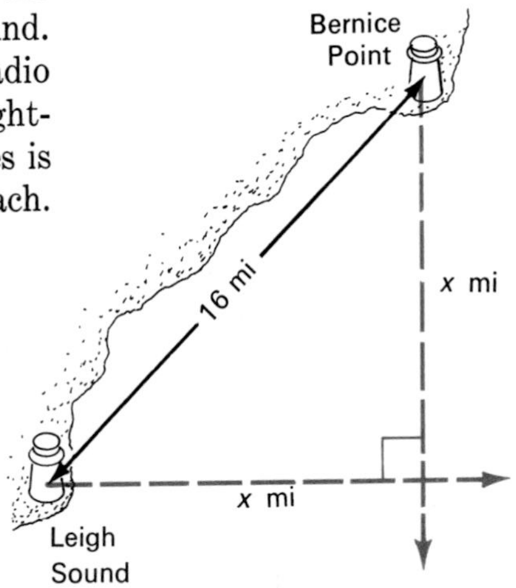

$$x^2 + x^2 = 16^2$$
$$2x^2 = 256$$
$$\frac{2x^2}{2} = \frac{256}{2}$$
$$x^2 = 128$$
$$\sqrt{x^2} = \sqrt{128}$$
$$x \approx 11.31$$

The point is about 11.31 miles from each lighthouse.

13. How far is point A from each corner of the square window?

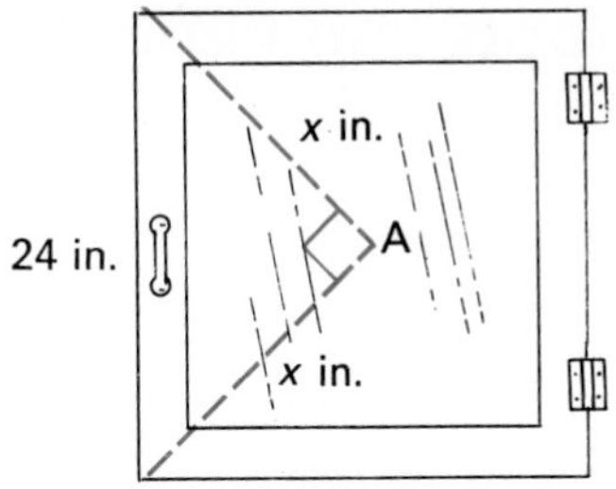

14. If the diagonal of a square is 18 inches long, what is the length of each side?

15. It is 100 meters from one corner of a square parking lot to the opposite corner. What are the dimensions of the parking lot?

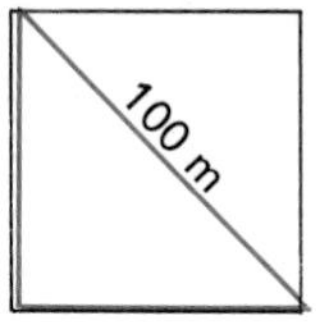

16. The brace for the square gate shown is 44 inches long. What are the dimensions of the gate?

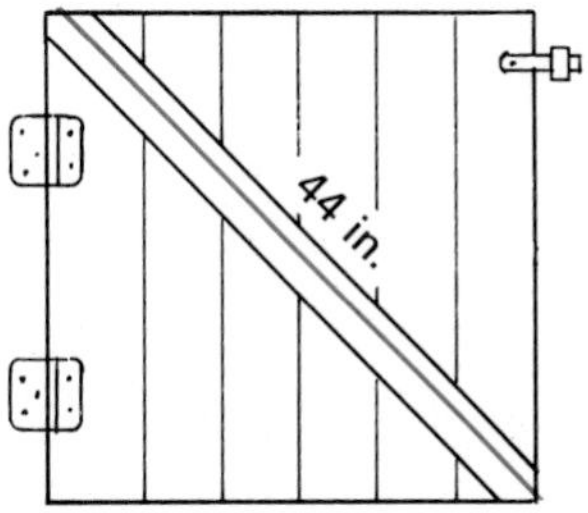

CHECKING RIGHT ANGLES

activities

Builders and surveyors often use the following procedure to check that corners are square (form right angles).

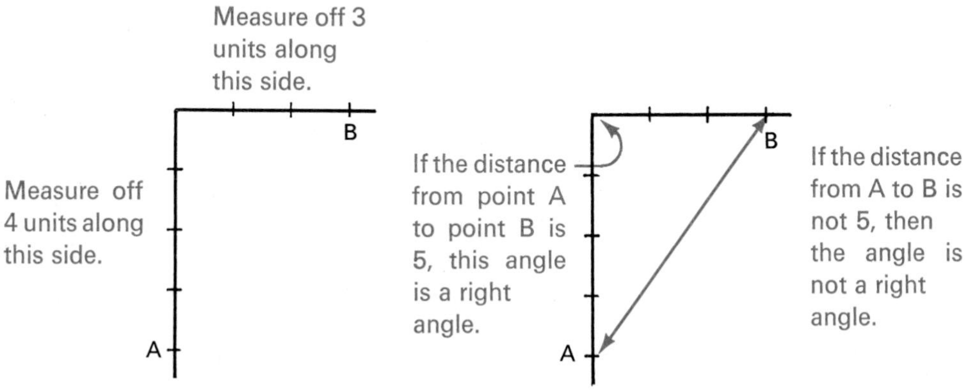

For greater accuracy, multiples of 3, 4, and 5 (such as 6, 8, 10; 12, 16, 20; and so on) are used. Use the above procedure to check the corners of your classroom, a fence, or a tabletop.

13.8 Square Roots and Formulas

To use some formulas, you have to find square roots. Remember the formula from page 416?

time the storm will last in hours → $t = \sqrt{\dfrac{d^3}{216}}$ ← diameter of storm in miles

Example 1: How long will a storm last if its diameter is 12 miles?

$$t = \sqrt{\frac{d^3}{216}}$$

$$= \sqrt{\frac{12^3}{216}}$$

$$= \sqrt{\frac{12 \times 12 \times 12}{36 \times 6}}$$

$$= \sqrt{\frac{\overset{2}{\cancel{12}} \times \overset{2}{\cancel{12}} \times \overset{2}{\cancel{12}}}{\underset{1}{\cancel{6}} \times \underset{1}{\cancel{6}} \times \underset{1}{\cancel{6}}}}$$

$$= \sqrt{8}$$

$$\approx 2.83$$

The storm will last about 2.83 hours.

Example 2: The formula for the area of a circle is $A = \pi r^2$. Find the radius of a circle if its area is 6.28 m^2. Use 3.14 for π.

$$A = \pi r^2$$

$$6.28 = 3.14 r^2$$

$$\frac{6.28}{3.14} = \frac{3.14 r^2}{3.14}$$

$$2 = r^2$$

$$\sqrt{2} = \sqrt{r^2}$$

$$1.41 \approx r$$

The radius is about 1.41 m.

Exercises

A **1.** In the formula in Example 1, what does each letter stand for?

2. In Example 2, how would you check the solution 1.41?

B Solve these problems from various kinds of occupations. Use 3.14 for π.

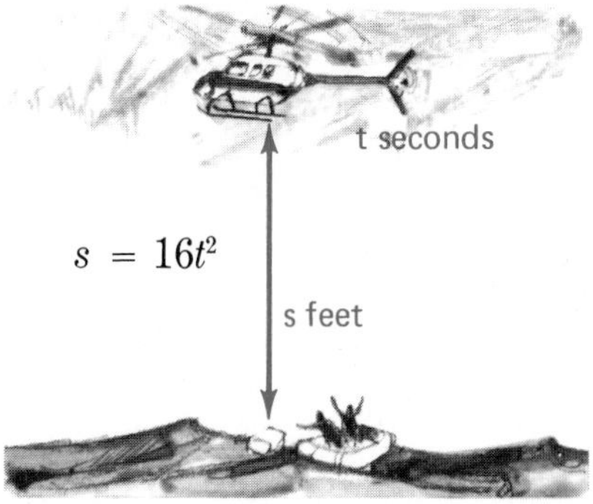

3. *Weather forecaster:* How long will a storm last if its diameter is 18 miles?

4. *Tinsmith:* Find the radius of a sheet-metal circle with an area of 28.26 cm^2.

5. *Rescue worker:* A helicopter dropped a survival kit from an altitude of 1024 feet. How long did it take to hit the water?

6. *Pilot:* If a plane's altitude h is $\frac{1}{2}$ mile, how many miles d is it to the horizon? Use $d = \sqrt{8000h}$.

7. *Tinsmith:* A sheet-metal cylinder is to have a volume V of 15,700 cm^3 and a height h of 50 cm. What is its radius r? Use $V = \pi r^2 h$.

8. *Plumber:* A drain pipe is to have a circular cross-sectional area A of 50.24 cm^2. What must its diameter d be? Use $A = \frac{1}{4}\pi d^2$.

Ex. 9

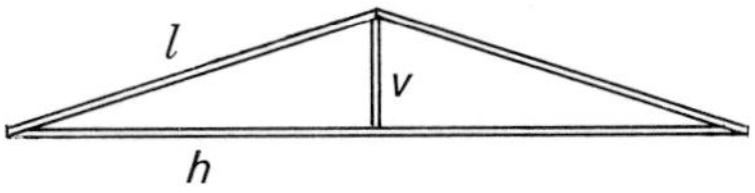

9. *Carpenter:* Find the length l of a rafter where the horizontal run h is 12 feet and the vertical rise v is 4 feet. Use $l = \sqrt{h^2 + v^2}$.

Ex. 10

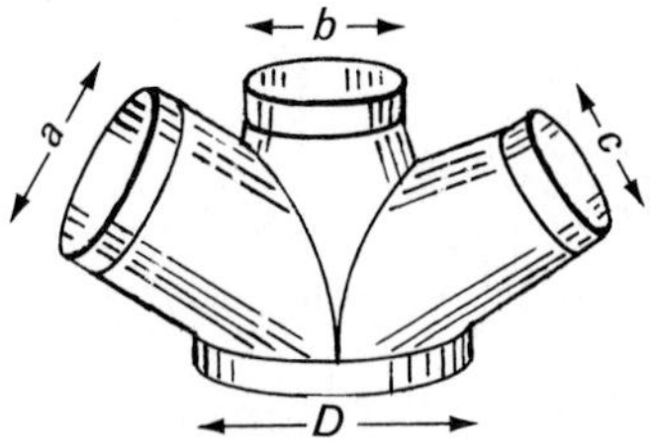

10. *Air-conditioning technician:* Find the diameter D of the main air duct if it feeds three branch ducts with diameters of 8 inches, 7 inches, and 6 inches. Use $D = \sqrt{a^2 + b^2 + c^2}$.

C **11.** *Electrician:* The resistance R of a certain 55-watt lamp is 220 ohms. What current I does it require? Use $I = \sqrt{\frac{P}{R}}$, where I is the current in amperes, P is the number of watts, and R is the resistance in ohms.

activities → USING A CALCULATOR FOR SQUARE ROOTS

Square roots can be found with a calculator.

Suppose you want to find $\sqrt{1090}$. You know $30^2 = 900$. So $\sqrt{1090} > 30$. Suppose you make a guess of 32. (Actually, any guess will do.)

(1) Divide 1090 by 32.

Press: 1090 [÷] 32 [=]

Display: 34.0625 (Do not clear the calculator.)

(2) Average your guess with the result of step 1.

Press: [+] 32 [÷] 2 [=]

Display: 33.03125 ← If the calculator has a memory, store this result in the memory and recall in steps 3 and 4. If not, record the result on paper.

(3) Divide 1090 by the result of step 2.

Press: 1090 [÷] 33.03125 [=]

Display: 32.999053 (Do not clear.)

(4) Average the results of steps 2 and 3.

Press: [+] 33.03125 [÷] 2 [=]

Display: 33.015151

Notice that the first three digits in the averages from steps 2 and 4 match. So

$\sqrt{1090} \approx 33.0$, correct to the tenths place.

You could continue to divide and average until the last two averages agree to as many decimal places as you like.

Use the method above to find each square root, correct to the tenths place. If the calculator has a square root key, use it to check your results.

1. $\sqrt{93}$ **2.** $\sqrt{168}$ **3.** $\sqrt{264}$ **4.** $\sqrt{193}$ **5.** $\sqrt{48}$

6. $\sqrt{761}$ **7.** $\sqrt{1020}$ **8.** $\sqrt{1500}$ **9.** $\sqrt{2601}$ **10.** $\sqrt{1387}$

Terms and Symbols Review

Use the terms or symbols to correctly complete the sentences.

square root	*Pythagorean Property*	$\sqrt{}$
hypotenuse	$-\sqrt{}$	

1. Every positive number has a positive and a negative ______.
2. The symbol ______ is used for the nonnegative square root of a number.
3. In a right triangle, the ______ is the side opposite the right angle.
4. The symbol ______ is used for the negative square root of a number.
5. The ______ states that $c^2 = a^2 + b^2$, where c is the hypotenuse and a and b are the other sides of a right triangle.

Chapter 13 Review

Find two solutions for each equation. 13.1

1. $a^2 = 9$ 2. $b^2 = 25$ 3. $c^2 = 16$

4. $x^2 = 36$ 5. $y^2 = 49$ 6. $z^2 = 81$

Use the table on page 422 to find the following. 13.2

7. $\sqrt{2}$ 8. $\sqrt{3}$ 9. $\sqrt{7}$

10. $\sqrt{15}$ 11. $\sqrt{26}$ 12. $\sqrt{89}$

13. $\sqrt{21}$ 14. $\sqrt{45}$ 15. $\sqrt{96}$

16. 27^2 17. 52^2 18. 119^2

Find each square root by using the table on page 422. 13.3

19. $\sqrt{200}$ 20. $\sqrt{490}$ 21. $\sqrt{600}$

22. $\sqrt{180}$ 23. $\sqrt{360}$ 24. $\sqrt{1700}$

13.4 Find each square root as a fraction or decimal, as given.

25. $\sqrt{\frac{1}{4}}$ **26.** $\sqrt{\frac{4}{9}}$ **27.** $\sqrt{\frac{49}{100}}$

28. $\sqrt{0.49}$ **29.** $\sqrt{0.36}$ **30.** $\sqrt{1.21}$

13.5 Find the positive solution of each equation.

31. $x^2 + 5 = 54$ **32.** $x^2 - 4 = 21$

33. $x^2 + 6 = 40$ **34.** $x^2 - 12 = 28$

13.6 Use the right triangle below to help you complete the following.

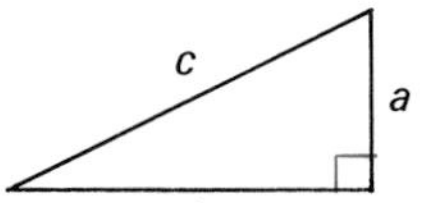

35. $a = 8, b = 15, c =$ _____ **36.** $a = 3, c = 5, b =$ _____

37. $b = 24, c = 25, a =$ _____ **38.** $c = 53, b = 28, a =$ _____

13.7 Solve each problem.

Ex. 39

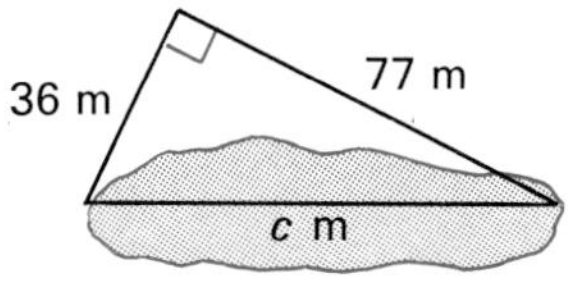

39. What is the length of the pond shown at the right?

Ex. 40

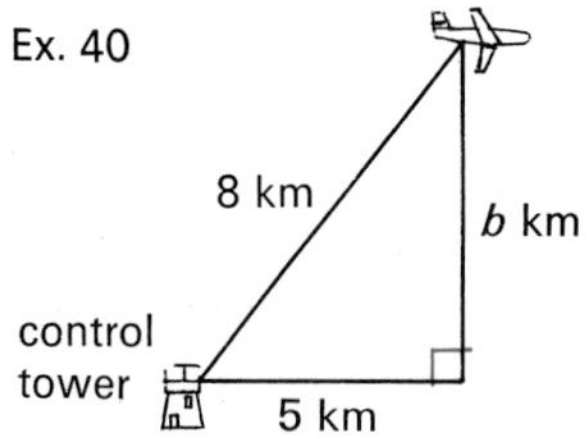

40. What is the height b of the airplane?

13.8 **41.** A ball is dropped from the top of a cliff that is 64 feet tall. How long will it take the ball to reach the foot of the cliff? Use the formula $s = 16t^2$, where s is the distance in feet and t is the time in seconds.

Chapter 13 Test

Find each square root as a whole number, fraction, or decimal, as given.

1. $\sqrt{36}$ **2.** $\sqrt{81}$ **3.** $\sqrt{\frac{4}{9}}$

4. $\sqrt{\frac{16}{25}}$ **5.** $\sqrt{0.64}$ **6.** $\sqrt{0.81}$

Find each square root by using the table on page 422.

7. $\sqrt{5}$ **8.** $\sqrt{8}$ **9.** $\sqrt{12}$

10. $\sqrt{288}$ **11.** $\sqrt{250}$ **12.** $\sqrt{700}$

Find the positive solution of each equation.

13. $x^2 = 25$ **14.** $x^2 = 37$ **15.** $x^2 + 5 = 41$

16. $x^2 - 9 = 40$ **17.** $x^2 - 7 = 16$ **18.** $x^2 + 9 = 41$

Use the Pythagorean Property to solve the following.

19. A 26-foot cable is used to brace an antenna. The cable is anchored 10 feet from the foot of the antenna. How tall is the antenna?

Ex. 19

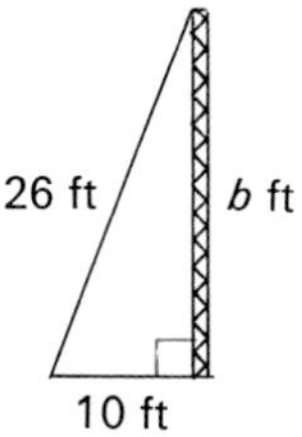

Ex. 20

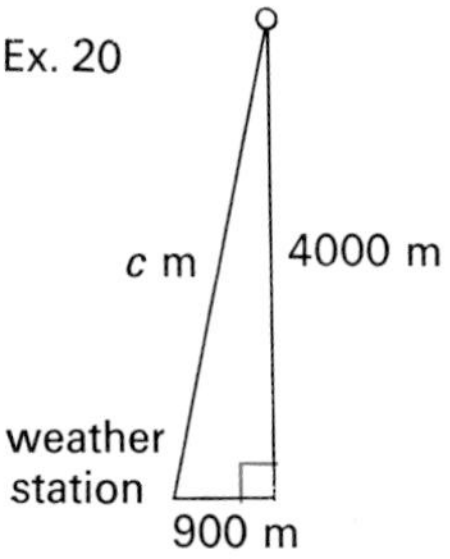

20. A weather balloon is 4000 meters high and directly over a point 900 meters from the weather station. How far is the balloon from the station?

21. The area of a circle is 28.26 square meters. What is the radius of the circle? Use $A = \pi r^2$ and use 3.14 for π.

RATE YOURSELF

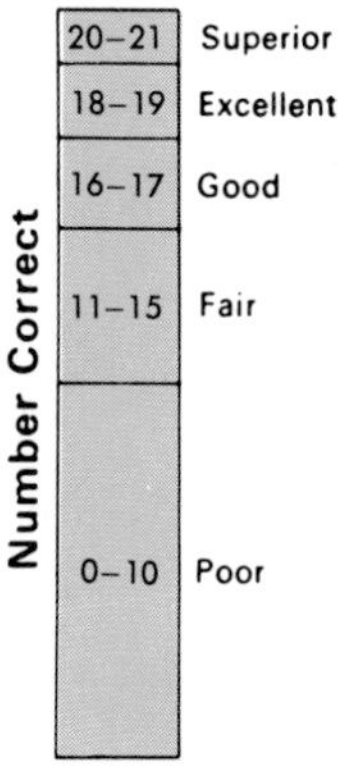

CAREER CORNER

MATH AND POLICE WORK

You can determine the speed that a car was traveling by measuring the skid marks.

If all four tires skid and the car comes to a stop without hitting another object, you can use these formulas.

Dry concrete-road

$s = \sqrt{24d}$

s ← speed (mph); d ← distance (ft) car skidded

Wet concrete-road

$s = \sqrt{12d}$

s ← speed (mph); d ← distance (ft) car skidded

Example: A car skidded to a stop on a dry concrete-road. The skid marks were 48 feet long. How fast was the car traveling?

$$\begin{aligned} s &= \sqrt{24d} \\ &= \sqrt{24 \times 48} \\ &= \sqrt{24 \times 24 \times 2} \\ &= 24\sqrt{2} \\ &\approx 33.84 \text{ or } 34 \end{aligned}$$

34 mph

Solve these problems.

1. A car skidded to a stop on a dry concrete-road. The skid marks were 120 feet long. How fast was the car traveling?

2. A car skidded to a stop on a wet concrete-road. It left skid marks that were 96 feet long. How fast was the car traveling?

Getting Ready for Chapter 14

Express the following using exponents. 3.8

1. $n \times n \times n \times n$ **2.** $a \times a$

3. $y \times y \times y$ **4.** $b \times b \times b \times b \times b$

What number should replace each ? 3.4

5. $8(3 + 2) = (8 \times 3) + (? \times 2)$

6. $(4 \times 7) + (4 \times 8) = 4(? + 8)$

Compute.

7. $^-11 + {}^-6$ **8.** $^-9 + 7$ 6.3

9. $^-1.1 + {}^-3.6$ **10.** $4.6 + {}^-2.7$ 11.3

11. $13 - {}^-7$ **12.** $^-16 - 9$ 6.4

13. $\frac{1}{4} + (-\frac{1}{2})$ **14.** $-\frac{7}{8} + (-\frac{1}{4})$ 11.5

15. $(^-8)(7)$ **16.** $(16)(^-8)$ 7.1

17. $(^-4)(^-8)$ **18.** $(^-3)(^-9)$ 7.2

19. $(^-7.2)(0.2)$ **20.** $(^-3.4)(^-0.5)$ 12.1

21. $\frac{1}{2} \times {}^-6$ **22.** $-\frac{3}{4} \times 8 \times \frac{1}{2}$ 12.3

23. $\frac{^-8}{^-2}$ **24.** $\frac{16}{^-8}$ 7.3

Express each fraction in lowest terms. 4.3

25. $\frac{15}{20}$ **26.** $\frac{20}{30}$ **27.** $\frac{18}{24}$

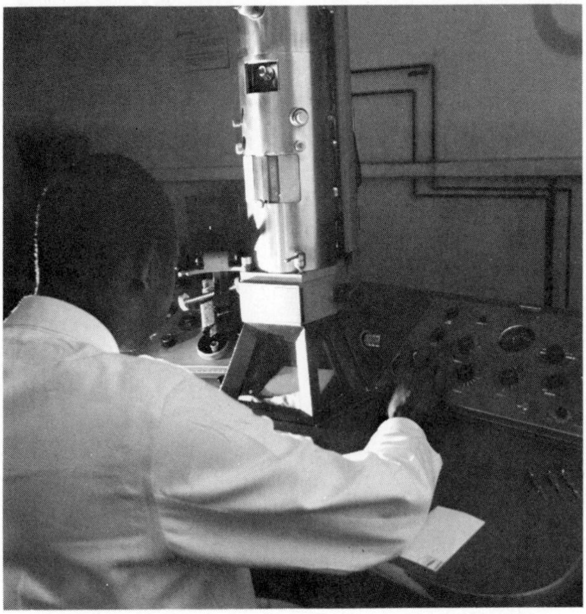

Courtesy Rush Presbyterian St. Luke's

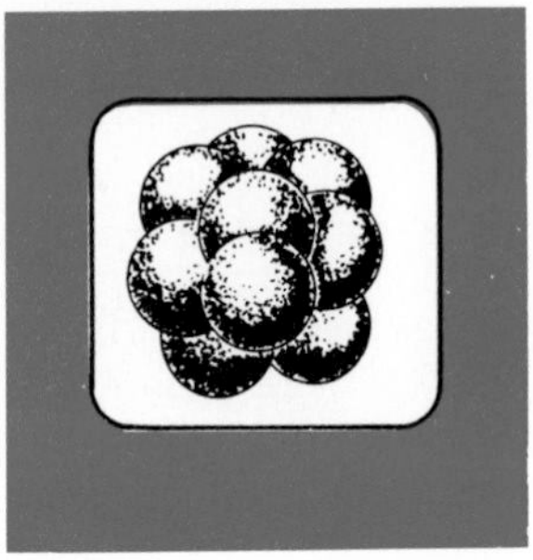

14 USING ALGEBRA

All living things are made up of *cells.* The cube is a common shape for plant cells, while the sphere is a common shape for animal cells.

Scientists who study living things might have to find the volume of a cell or its surface area. They could use the following formulas.

Volume of cube $= s^3$ Volume of sphere $= \frac{4}{3}\pi r^3$

Surface area of cube $= 6s^2$ Surface area of sphere $= 4\pi r^2$

The right-hand side of each formula is a **polynomial.** In this chapter, you will learn more about polynomials, including how to add, subtract, multiply, and divide polynomials. Also, you'll use algebra to solve more problems.

More About Solving Problems

Earlier you solved problems that could be translated into equations with one operation. The following problems translate into equations that involve more steps.

Example 1: A punch is made from ginger ale and orange juice. Twice as much orange juice is used as ginger ale. How much of each do you need for 6 quarts of punch?

Let x = amount of ginger ale.

Then $2x$ = amount of orange juice.

amount of ginger ale → x; amount of orange juice → $2x$; total amount of punch → 6

$$x + 2x = 6$$
$$3x = 6$$
$$\frac{3x}{3} = \frac{6}{3}$$
$$x = 2 \quad \text{2 quarts of ginger ale}$$
$$2x = 4 \quad \text{4 quarts of orange juice}$$

Check:
- Is 4 quarts of orange juice twice as much as 2 quarts of ginger ale? ✓
- Do 4 quarts of orange juice and 2 quarts of ginger ale give 6 quarts of punch? ✓

Example 2: The sum of two consecutive integers is $^{-}19$. What are the integers?

Let n = some integer.

Then $n + 1$ = next integer.

some integer → n; next integer → $n + 1$; sum → $^{-}19$

$$n + n + 1 = {}^{-}19$$
$$2n + 1 = {}^{-}19$$
$$2n + 1 + {}^{-}1 = {}^{-}19 + {}^{-}1$$
$$2n + 0 = {}^{-}20$$
$$2n = {}^{-}20$$
$$\frac{2n}{2} = \frac{{}^{-}20}{2}$$
$$n = {}^{-}10 \quad \text{One integer is } {}^{-}10.$$
$$n + 1 = {}^{-}9 \quad \text{The next integer is } {}^{-}9.$$

Check:
- Are $^{-}9$ and $^{-}10$ consecutive integers? ✓
- Is the sum of $^{-}9$ and $^{-}10$ equal to $^{-}19$? ✓

Exercises

A

1. If n names an integer, how would you name the next two integers?

2. If n names an even integer, name the next even integer.

3. If n names an odd integer, name the next two odd integers.

B Give an equation for each problem. Then solve the problem.

4. One number is three times a second number. Their sum is 28. What are the numbers?

5. The sum of two consecutive integers is 65. What are the integers?

6. The sum of two consecutive even integers is 34. What are the integers?

7. To make dark orange paint, you mix red and yellow paint. You use 5 times as much red as yellow paint. How much of each should you mix to make 18 quarts of dark orange paint?

8. The sum of two consecutive integers is $^-31$. What are the integers?

9. The sum of three consecutive integers is $^-57$. What are the integers?

10. One number is 3 more than another. Their sum is $^-47$. What are the numbers?

11. The perimeter of a triangle is 24 inches. Two sides are the same length. The third side is 3 inches longer than each of the other two. How long is each side?

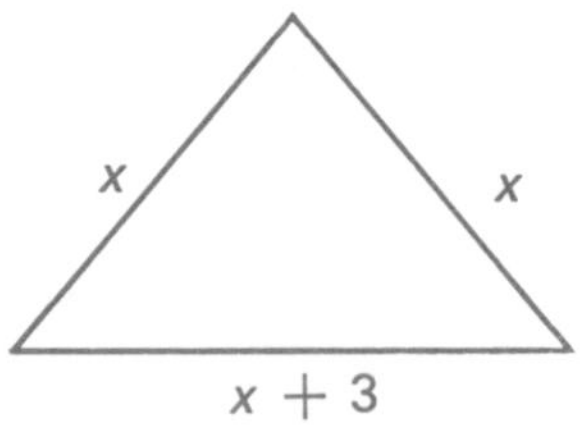

12. The sum of two numbers is 6. One number is 3 times the other. What are the numbers?

13. Joanne paid \$15 for 2 books. One book cost \$3 more than the other. How much did she pay for each book?

14. One number is $2\frac{1}{2}$ more than 4 times a second number. The sum of the two numbers is $37\frac{1}{2}$. What are the numbers?

15. A 124-centimeter board is to be cut into 3 pieces. Two of the pieces should be the same length. The third piece should be 5.5 centimeters longer than each of the other two. How long should each piece be?

16. A football field is 40 feet longer than twice its width. Its perimeter is 1040 feet. Find its dimensions.

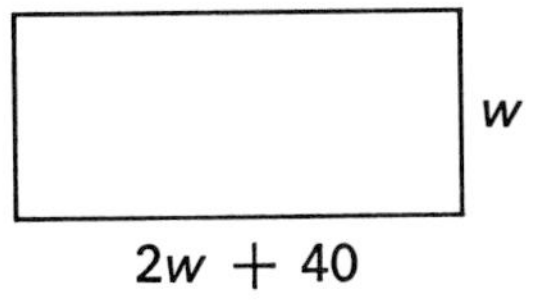

C **Example:** A store owner took a group of 20 students to an amusement park as a reward for being on the honor roll. Tickets for students under 14 years of age cost \$8, and the other tickets cost \$10. If the store owner spent \$190 on tickets, how many of each kind of ticket were bought?

	number	value
\$10 tickets	x	$10x$
\$ 8 tickets	$20 - x$	$8(20 - x)$

Courtesy Marriott's Great America®

$$10x + 8(20 - x) = 190$$

$$10x + 160 - 8x = 190$$

$$2x + 160 + ^{-}160 = 190 + ^{-}160$$

$$\frac{2x}{2} = \frac{30}{2}$$

$x = 15$ ◀ 10-dollar tickets

$20 - x = 5$ ◀ 8-dollar tickets

17. Martha sold 38 albums for a total of \$130. Some albums sold for \$3, and the others for \$4. How many of each were sold?

18. Twenty-five sacks were placed in a carton. Some weighed 3 pounds, the others 5 pounds. They weighed a total of 89 pounds. How many of each were in the carton?

19. Bill has \$2.25 in dimes and quarters. He has twice as many dimes as quarters. How many of each does he have? *Hint:* Change \$2.25 to 225¢.

14.2 Problems With Too Much or Too Little Information

Sometimes in solving problems, you find that not all the given information is needed. At other times, not enough information has been given to solve the problem.

Example 1: Marylou is 16 years old, and her sister Carrie is 13 years old. Marylou weighs 108 pounds, and Carrie weighs 96 pounds. How much more does Marylou weigh than Carrie?

You are asked to find how much more Marylou weighs than Carrie. So the information about their ages is not needed.

Example 2: A car traveled from Arlington to Lyons at an average speed of 55 miles per hour. How long did the trip take?

In this case, not enough information is given. You need to know the distance from Arlington to Lyons before you can find how long the trip took.

Exercises

A For each problem, tell **(a)** what you are to find and **(b)** whether the problem gives too little, just enough, or too much information for solving the problem.

1. Frank earns $3.25 per hour at his part-time job. How much did he earn last month?

2. Marsha sells macrame belts at $5.00 apiece. Each belt costs her $1.27 in materials. The belts range in width from $1\frac{1}{2}$ inches to 2 inches. How much profit does Marsha make on each belt she sells?

3. A camera costs $189, and a wide-angle lens for the camera costs $78. How much do both the camera and the wide-angle lens cost?

4. At 7 A.M. the temperature was $^{-}2°$. By noon the temperature had risen $10°$. During that period a total of 1.5 inches of precipitation fell. What was the temperature at noon?

B **5–8.** Solve each problem in Exercises 1–4, if possible.

Solve each problem, if possible.

9. A checking account had a balance of \$270. A month later the balance was $^-$\$70. What was the change in balance?

10. Sally drove a total of 740 miles on her vacation. Her car used a total of 37 gallons of gasoline. The trip lasted 8 days and cost her a total of \$480. How many miles per gallon of gasoline did her car average on the trip?

11. A carpenter sawed two pieces off a board 60 inches long. One piece was $25\frac{1}{2}$ inches long, and the other piece was $16\frac{1}{4}$ inches long. How long was the remaining piece?

12. A tinsmith cut a small circular disk from a 50-centimeter square piece of metal. How much metal was left over?

13. A salesperson in a department store receives a 5% commission on all merchandise she sells. Last month she sold \$8200 worth of merchandise. She also receives a regular salary of \$400 per month, and she received a bonus of \$200 for selling the most merchandise for the month. How much was her commission for last month?

14. Jerry bought a new watch that cost \$119. He also had to pay a sales tax and an excise tax. What was the total cost of the watch?

Photo Trends

15. The regular price of a coat was \$79, but it was marked down 20% from the regular price. How much would you save by buying the coat on sale?

16. A diver descended from the surface of a lake to the bottom of the lake in $8\frac{1}{2}$ minutes. What was the rate of descent?

C **17.** Paul's car has a 13-gallon tank. The car had traveled 206 miles since the last fill-up, and it took 9.8 gallons of gas to fill the tank. How much did it cost to fill the tank?

18. An apartment rents for \$225 per month. The utilities cost an average of \$41 per month, and the garage rent is \$25 per month. What is the yearly cost of living in this apartment, including the utilities and the garage rent?

14.3 What Is a Polynomial?

Each of the following is a monomial.

$17 \qquad x \qquad {}^-3y^3 \qquad xy \qquad 8abc^2 \qquad \sqrt{2}$

Note: In monomials like ${}^-3y^3$, the exponent applies only to the variable that precedes it. So ${}^-3y^3 = {}^-3yyy$, and $8abc^2 = 8abcc$.

> A monomial is a number, a variable, or a product of a number and one or more variables.

The following expressions are not monomials. The first is the sum of two monomials. The second is the sum of three monomials.

$x^2 + 2 \qquad 7x^2 + {}^-3x + {}^-5$ ◀ Usually written $7x^2 - 3x - 5$

The expressions above are called polynomials.

> A polynomial is a monomial or the sum of two or more monomials.

Each monomial in a polynomial is called a **term** of the polynomial. Polynomials are named according to how many terms they have. (A polynomial with more than three terms is usually just called a polynomial.)

Monomials (1 term)	**Binomials** (2 terms)	**Trinomials** (3 terms)
$2x^3$	$4x^3 - 3x$	$3x^3 + {}^-2x + \sqrt{5}$
$-\frac{1}{2}$	$7x + 6$	$\frac{1}{2}y^2 + 2y - 4$

When two or more monomials have the same variables with equal exponents for the same variables, the monomials are called **like terms.** Otherwise, the monomials are **unlike terms.** (Remember that $x = x^1$.)

Like terms

$3x$ and ${}^-7x$

$\frac{1}{2}xy^2$ and $7xy^2$

$3x^3y^2$ and $\frac{3}{4}x^3y^2$

◀ same variables with equal exponents

Unlike terms

${}^-4y$ and $8z$ ◀ different variables

$3x^2$ and $4x$

$6xy^2$ and $8x^2y$

◀ same variables but different exponents

Exercises

A Which are monomials?

1. 2 **2.** $\frac{2}{3}x + 1$ **3.** $^{-}7z^2$ **4.** $x + y$

5. xy **6.** $y^3 + 2y - 1$ **7.** $\sqrt{7}$ **8.** a^2bc

9. Can a polynomial have one term?

10. Is a monomial also a polynomial?

Identify each polynomial as a monomial, binomial, or trinomial.

11. $x^3 + 2$ **12.** $\frac{1}{2}x^2$ **13.** $xy^3 + x^3y + xy$

14. $\sqrt{2}x$ **15.** $x + \sqrt{2}$ **16.** $\frac{3}{4}x^2 + \frac{1}{2}$

B Identify each pair of terms as like terms or unlike terms.

17. $7x, 8x$ **18.** $8z, {}^{-}2z$ **19.** $\frac{1}{2}xyy, 2xyy$

20. $\frac{1}{2}xy^2, 2xy^2$ **21.** $^{-}7xxy, 9xyy$ **22.** $^{-}7x^2y, 9xy^2$

23. $4w, {}^{-}8wz$ **24.** $-\frac{2}{3}x^3y, x^2y^2$ **25.** $8yz, {}^{-}4xz$

26. abc, a^2bc **27.** $3x^2y^2, \frac{1}{2}x^2y^2$ **28.** $2, 2x$

29. $^{-}7x^2, 3x^4$ **30.** $^{-}10s^2t^2, 12s^2t^2$ **31.** $3xy, 4yz$

32. $3xy, 4yx$ **33.** $5mn^2p^2, \frac{1}{2}mn^2p^2$ **34.** abc, cba

Rewrite each polynomial as a sum of monomials.

Example: $7x - 3 = 7x + {}^{-}3$

35. $2x - 5$ **36.** $^{-}6y - 1$ **37.** $x^2 - 3x + 2$

38. $^{-}2x^2 - 5x$ **39.** $8y^3 - y$ **40.** $^{-}2x^3 - 5x^2 - 7x$

C Numbers can be expressed in polynomial form, using powers of 10.

Number	Expanded form	Polynomial form
38	$30 + 8$	$3(10^1) + 8$
392	$300 + 90 + 2$	$3(10^2) + 9(10^1) + 2$

Express each number in polynomial form.

41. 79 **42.** 82 **43.** 467 **44.** 896 **45.** 1972

14.4 Combining Like Terms

When you replace each variable in a polynomial with a number, the polynomial names a specific number. Then you can *evaluate the polynomial.*

Suppose you evaluate the polynomials $2x + 3x$ and $5x$ for several different replacements.

	$2x + 3x$	Value	$5x$	Value
Replace x with 2.	$2(2) + 3(2)$	10	$5(2)$	10
Replace x with 1.	$2(1) + 3(1)$	5	$5(1)$	5
Replace x with 0.	$2(0) + 3(0)$	0	$5(0)$	0

The polynomials $2x + 3x$ and $5x$ will always give equal values for each replacement of the variable. Such polynomials are called **equivalent expressions.**

By using the distributive property, you can change some polynomials to simpler equivalent expressions.

Examples: 1. $9a + {}^-3a = (9 + {}^-3)a = 6a$

2. ${}^-7x^2 + 2x^2 + 1 = ({}^-7 + 2)x^2 + 1 = {}^-5x^2 + 1$

Notice that only like terms can be combined.

Examples: Simplify.

Notice that subtraction is rewritten as an addition of the opposite.

3. $7x - 8x = (7 + {}^-8)x = {}^-1x$ or ${}^-x$

4. $4xy^2 - 6xy^2 - 2xy^2 = (4 + {}^-6 + {}^-2)xy^2 = {}^-4xy^2$

5. $\underbrace{\tfrac{1}{2}y^3 + (-\tfrac{3}{4})y^2 + \tfrac{1}{2}y^2}_{\text{like terms}} = \tfrac{1}{2}y^3 + (-\tfrac{3}{4} + \tfrac{1}{2})y^2 = \tfrac{1}{2}y^3 + (-\tfrac{1}{4})y^2$

Sometimes it is convenient to rewrite a polynomial in column form. For example, $7x - 3x + 4x$ can be written as

$$\begin{array}{r} 7x \\ {}^-3x \\ \underline{4x} \\ 8x. \end{array}$$

Exercises

A What are the missing numbers?

1. $2x + 4x = (2 + 4)x = \_\_\_x$

2. $6y + {}^{-}10y = (6 + {}^{-}10)y = \_\_\_y$

3. $\_\_\_z - 9z = (6 + {}^{-}9)z = {}^{-}3z$

4. $\frac{1}{3}x + \frac{1}{4}x = (\frac{1}{3} + \_\_\_)x = \frac{7}{12}x$

5. $2x + 5x - 9x = (2 + 5 + {}^{-}9)x = \_\_\_x$

6. $9y + {}^{-}8y + {}^{-}y = (9 + \_\_\_ + {}^{-}1)y = 0y$ or 0

7. $1.2x + 2.9x = (1.2 + \_\_\_)x = 4.1x$

8. Which expression is equivalent to $6y + {}^{-}4y$?

   a. $6y + {}^{-}4$ **b.** $2y$ **c.** ${}^{-}2y$ **d.** 2

9. Choose all expressions that are equivalent to $10y$.

   a. $8y + 2$ **b.** $7y + 3y$ **c.** $12y + {}^{-}2y$ **d.** $10y - 1$

10. Choose all expressions that are equivalent to $7y$.

   a. $(5 + 2)y$ **b.** $7y - 1$ **c.** $(10 - 3)y$ **d.** $5y + 2y$

   e. $10y - 3y$ **f.** $6y + y$ **g.** $(4 + 3)y$ **h.** $(8 - 1)y$

B Evaluate each pair of expressions for $x = 0$, $x = 1$, and $x = 2$. Then write *Yes* or *No* to tell if the expressions are equivalent.

11. $5x + 2, 7x$

12. $5x + 2x, 7x$

13. $3x^2 + x^2, 4x^4$

14. $3x^2 + x^2, 4x^2$

15. $2x - 6x, {}^{-}4x$

16. $3x^2 - 2x^2, x^2$

17. ${}^{-}x + {}^{-}x, {}^{-}2x$

18. $x + x^2, 2x^2$

Simplify.

19. $8x + 3x$

20. $^{-}4x^2 + {}^{-}6x^2$

21. $^{-}7y + 4y$

22. $2m - 5m$

23. $^{-}9y^2 + {}^{-}3y^2$

24. $11xy - 12xy$

25. $14m^2n + {}^{-}6m^2n$

26. $26m^3 - 13m^3$

27. $12y^2 + {}^{-}16y^2 + 8y$

28. $41x + {}^{-}12x + 12$

29. $^{-}18n + 30n + 10$

30. $26m + {}^{-}59m$

31. $^{-}8y - 7y + 11y$

32. $20z + {}^{-}10z + 9z$

33. $6x^2 + 10x^2 + {}^{-}8x^2$

34. $14xy + {}^{-}19xy + {}^{-}13xy$

35. $1.8x + 6.4x$

36. $-\frac{1}{3}z + (-\frac{2}{3})z$

37. $\frac{7}{10}m^2 + (-\frac{1}{5})m^2$

38. $^{-}3.3y^2 + 2.2y^2$

Add.

39. $\begin{array}{r} 11x \\ ^{-}10x \\ 9x \\ \underline{^{-}3x} \end{array}$

40. $\begin{array}{r} 1.8x \\ ^{-}2.3x \\ 4.4x \\ \underline{1.5x} \end{array}$

41. $\begin{array}{r} 14ab \\ ^{-}16ab \\ ^{-}9ab \\ \underline{8ab} \end{array}$

42. $\begin{array}{r} 7.5y \\ 2.5y \\ ^{-}1.5y \\ \underline{^{-}2.8y} \end{array}$

C 43. $\begin{array}{r} 1\frac{1}{2}z \\ ^{-}2\frac{1}{2}z \\ \underline{^{-}7z} \end{array}$

44. $\begin{array}{r} ^{-}6\frac{3}{4}m \\ ^{-}1\frac{1}{2}m \\ \underline{2\frac{1}{4}m} \end{array}$

45. $\begin{array}{r} ^{-}3\frac{3}{8}a \\ 1\frac{1}{8}a \\ \underline{^{-}2\frac{1}{4}a} \end{array}$

46. $\begin{array}{r} 5\frac{5}{12}x^2 \\ ^{-}3\frac{1}{2}x^2 \\ \underline{^{-}2\frac{1}{6}x^2} \end{array}$

Find the perimeter of each rectangle.

47.

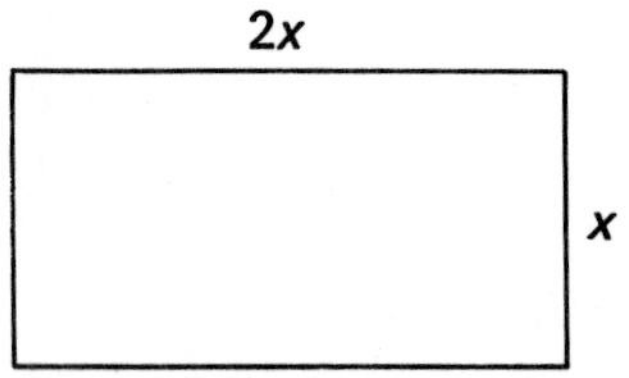

48.

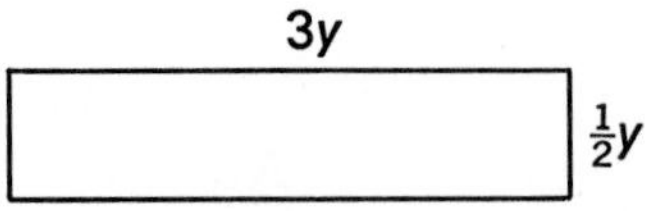

49. Find a monomial for the perimeter of a rectangle where the length is 5 times the width w.

50. Find a monomial for the perimeter of a rectangle where the width is one-half of the length x.

Multiplying Monomials

You know that a^2 means $a \times a$ and a^3 means $a \times a \times a$.

$$\text{So } a^2 \cdot a^3 = \overbrace{(a \cdot a)}^{\text{2 factors}} \cdot \overbrace{(a \cdot a \cdot a)}^{\text{3 factors}}$$ ◀ The · can be used for ×.

$$= a \cdot a \cdot a \cdot a \cdot a$$ ◀ 2 + 3 factors

$$= a^5.$$

This example suggests a shortcut we can use when multiplying certain monomials that involve exponents.

Examples: **1.** $x^3 \cdot x^4 = x^{3+4}$ ← The steps in red can be left out.

$= x^7$

2. $y \cdot y^5 = y^{1+5}$ ◀ Note that $y = y^1$.

$= y^6$

Often a monomial contains both a **constant** (a specific number) and a variable. Notice how such monomials are multiplied.

Examples: **3.** $3x^2 \cdot 5x^4 = (3 \cdot 5) \cdot (x^2 \cdot x^4)$ ◀ Rearrange the factors.

$= 15x^6$ ◀ Multiply the constants. Then multiply the variables.

4. $(^-3x^2)(2x)(^-4x^3) = (^-3)(2)(^-4) \cdot x^2 \cdot x \cdot x^3$

$= 24x^6$

5. $(^-6x^2)(3y)(2x) = (^-6)(3)(2) \cdot x^2 \cdot x \cdot y$

$= {}^-36x^3y$

> To multiply monomials containing constants, rearrange the factors so the constants are together and the variables are together. Multiply the constants. Multiply like variables by adding their exponents.

Exercises

A 1. Which expression is equivalent to $(x^3)(x^2)$?

a. x^6 b. x^5 c. $2x^5$ d. $2x^6$

2. Which expression is equivalent to $(3x)(2x^2)$?

a. $5x^2$ b. $5x^3$ c. $6x^2$ d. $6x^3$

Replace each ? with the correct exponent.

3. $10^2 \times 10^4 = 10^?$

4. $(2^3)(2^4) = 2^?$

5. $5^2 \times 5^5 = 5^?$

6. $10^2 \times 10^3 \times 10^4 = 10^?$

7. $(^-6)^3 \times (^-6)^3 = (^-6)^?$

8. $7 \cdot x^2 \cdot x^3 = 7x^?$

9. $(2x) \cdot (3x^5) = 6x^?$

10. $(3m)(5m^3) = 15m^?$

11. $(3y)(4y) = 12y^?$

12. $(2x)(3x)(4x) = 24x^?$

B Multiply.

13. $a^5 \cdot a^2$

14. $x^2 \cdot x$

15. $y^5 \cdot y^9$

16. $m^6 \cdot m^2$

17. $(2x)3$

18. $(8y^3)(2)$

19. $6(^-5x^2)$

20. $(^-7)(^-5m)$

21. $(x^3)(^-4x)$

22. $(^-2c)(^-3c)$

23. $(10x)(20x)$

24. $(7x^2)(3y)$

25. $(3m^2)(^-2m^2)(2)$

26. $(6x)(^-2x)(\frac{1}{2}x)$

27. $(\frac{1}{4}z)(8z^3)(-\frac{1}{2}z^2)$

28. $(^-2a)(^-2a)(^-2a)$

29. $(21x)(-\frac{3}{7}x^2)(2x^3)$

30. $(^-7x^3)(4y^2)(^-5x^2)$

31. $(0.2cd)(0.01c^2)(10d^3)$

32. $(^-5m)(13m^2)(0.001n^3)$

C 33. $(\frac{1}{4}x^2)(12x)(-\frac{2}{3}y^2)$

34. $(^-6x)(-\frac{2}{3}x^3)(7y^2)$

35. $(a^2)^3$

36. $(b^2)^4$

37. $(3x^3)^2$

38. $(^-2y^2)^3$

39. $(7m)(^-2m)^4$

40. $(x^3)^4(^-7x^2)^5$

Quick Quiz
Sections 14.1 to 14.5

1. Todd bought 2 records for \$10. One cost \$2 more than the other. How much did he pay for each record?

Identify each pair of terms as *like terms* or *unlike terms.*

2. $8xy^2, {}^-7x^2y$
3. $3x^2y^3, {}^-5x^2y^3$
4. ${}^-6y, 4z$

Simplify.

5. $9y + 2y$
6. ${}^-17a + {}^-3a$
7. $12n + {}^-15n$
8. ${}^-12ab + 18ab + 8ab$
9. $5y^2 + {}^-10y^2 + {}^-7y^2$

Multiply.

10. $m^3 \cdot m^3$
11. $x \cdot x^4$
12. $3(5m^2)$
13. $({}^-4n)(4n^2)$
14. $(2x^3)(8x^4)$
15. $(4x)({}^-8x)$

What's the Catch?

A group on a photograph safari traveled 60 km through swamp and forest, 5 times as far through swamp as through forest. They traveled twice as many kilometers through swamp as the number of crocodiles they saw, and the number of crocodiles they saw was equal to the number of chimpanzees they saw. How far did they travel altogether?

M.A. Geissinger/Van Cleve Photography

Dr. G.J. Chafaris

14.6 Multiplying a Binomial by a Monomial

When you multiply a binomial by a monomial, you can use the distributive property. Remember that the distributive property can be stated as

$$a(b + c) = a \cdot b + a \cdot c$$

or

$$(b + c)a = b \cdot a + c \cdot a.$$

This can also be illustrated with areas of rectangles.

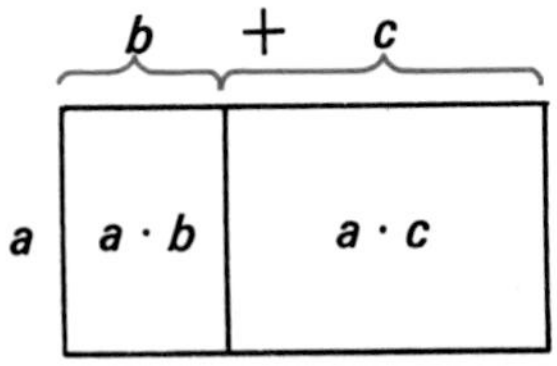

Total area = width × length = $a(b + c)$.

Total area = sum of 2 smaller areas = $a \cdot b + a \cdot c$.

The following examples show how the distributive property is used to multiply a binomial by a monomial.

Examples:

1. $x^2(x + 2) = x^2 \cdot x + x^2 \cdot 2$

$= x^3 + 2x^2$

2. $^{-}2z(z^3 + 2z^2) = {}^{-}2z \cdot z^3 + {}^{-}2z \cdot 2z^2$

$= {}^{-}2z^4 + {}^{-}4z^3$ or ${}^{-}2z^4 - 4z^3$

3. $(5xy - y^2)2xy = 5xy \cdot 2xy - y^2 \cdot 2xy$

$= 10x^2y^2 - 2xy^3$

When multiplying a binomial by a monomial, you can also arrange the work as follows.

$$\begin{array}{r} 10x^2 + 3x \\ 8x \\ \hline 80x^3 + 24x^2 \end{array}$$

Multiply each term of the binomial by the monomial.

Exercises

A Match each expression in Column A with an equivalent expression in Column B.

A	B
1. $3x(x + 1)$	**a.** $3x^3 - x^2$
2. $3x(x^2 + x)$	**b.** $3x^3 + 3x^2$
3. $x^2(3x - 1)$	**c.** $3x^2 + 9x$
4. $3x(x + 3)$	**d.** $3x^2 + 3x$

5. Which expressions are equivalent to $x^4 - 4x^2$?

a. $x(x^3 - 4x)$ **b.** $x^2(x^2 - 4)$ **c.** $x(x^4 - 4x^2)$ **d.** $x(x^3 - 4x^2)$

6. Which expressions are equivalent to $8x^3 + 4x$?

a. $4x(2x^2 + 1)$ **b.** $8x(x^2 + 1)$ **c.** $x(8x^2 + 4)$ **d.** $2(4x^3 + 2x)$

Replace each ? with the correct number.

7. $2x(3x + 4) = 6x^2 + ?x$

8. $9y(2y - 4) = ?y^2 - 36y$

9. $m(m + z) = m^? + mz$

10. $6y(y - 3) = 6y^2 - ?y$

B Multiply.

11. $b^3(9ab + a^2)$

12. $2a^2(7a + 4b)$

13. $^-3x(3x - 5y)$

14. $5ab(3b^3 + a^2)$

15. $^-3a(5a + 7b)$

16. $10r(^-4r - 7)$

17. $(9x^2 + 3y)2xy$

18. $(8abc + c)c^3$

19. $(11rs + {}^-8s)10s^2$

20. $(12x^2y^3z + 8xyz)3z$

21. $\frac{1}{2}m(8m + 5)$

22. $\frac{2}{3}y(12y^2 + 6y)$

23. $0.1x(6.8x + 3)$

24. $0.01y(3.8y + 6)$

C **25.** $m^3(3m^2 + 3m + 1)$

26. $2y(y^3 + 5y^2 + 3)$

27. $^-7y(11y^2 + {}^-4xy + {}^-7y)$

28. $x^4(x^3 + x^2 + x + 1)$

CAREER CORNER

FORMULAS AT WORK

Formulas are often used by many kinds of workers. Sometimes the right side of a formula is a polynomial, as in the following examples.

Courtesy Snips Magazine, Inc./ Donald Rich

A metalworker wants to figure the surface area S of a metal container that is shaped like a cylinder. The formula is

radius of base — height

$$S = 2\pi r^2 + 2\pi rh.$$

$\pi \approx 3.14$

A builder may have to figure the force with which water pushes on a window in an aquarium. The formula for the force F in pounds is

$$F = 31h^2w + 62dhw.$$

d = depth, in feet, of window below surface of water

h = height, in feet

w = width, in feet

H. Armstrong Roberts

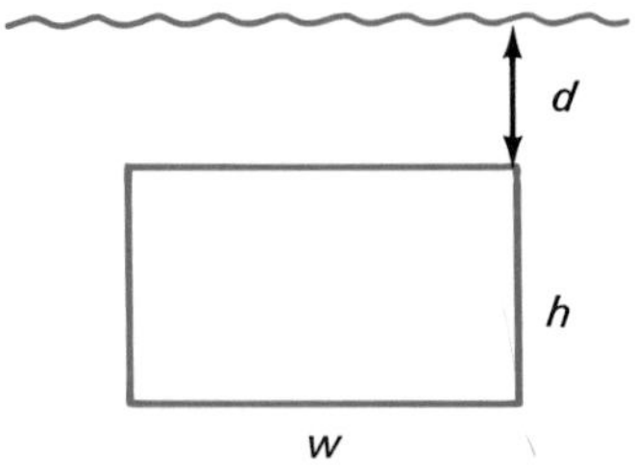

1. Find the surface area of a metal cylinder if $r = 12$ cm and $h = 25$ cm. Use 3.14 for π.

2. Find the force on an aquarium window that is 2 feet below the water surface if the window is 5 feet wide by 4 feet high.

Multiplying Binomials

To find the product of 13 and 25, you could use the following method.

$$\begin{array}{rrrl} & 10 + & 3 & \\ & 20 + & 5 & \\ \hline & 50 + & 15 & \leftarrow 5(10+3) \\ 200 + & 60 & & \leftarrow 20(10+3) \\ \hline 200 + & 110 + & 15 & = 325 \end{array}$$

A similar method can be used to find the product of two binomials. For example, the product of $x + 3$ and $2x^2 + 5x$ can be found as shown below.

Example 1:

Like terms are placed in a column, then added.

$$\begin{array}{rrrl} & x + & 3 & \\ & 2x^2 + & 5x & \\ \hline & 5x^2 + & 15x & \leftarrow 5x(x+3) \\ 2x^3 + & 6x^2 & & \leftarrow 2x^2(x+3) \\ \hline 2x^3 + & 11x^2 + & 15x & \end{array}$$

> To multiply one binomial by another, you must multiply each term of the first by each term of the second.

The multiplication in Example 1 can also be written as follows. Notice how the distributive property is used.

Example 2:

$$(x+3)(2x^2+5x) = (x+3)2x^2 + (x+3)5x$$

Use the distributive property once.

$$= x \cdot 2x^2 + 3 \cdot 2x^2 + x \cdot 5x + 3 \cdot 5x$$

Use the distributive property two more times.

$$= 2x^3 + 6x^2 + 5x^2 + 15x$$

Combine like terms when possible.

$$= 2x^3 + 11x^2 + 15x$$

The product of two binomials can be illustrated with areas of rectangles.

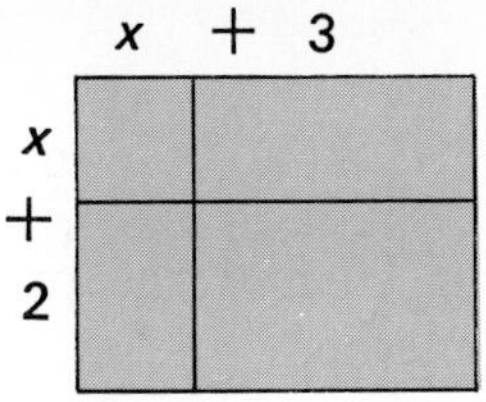

Example 3: Multiply $x + 3$ by $x + 2$.

Total area = length × width $= (x + 3)(x + 2)$.

Total area = sum of 4 smaller areas $= x^2 + 3x + 2x + 6$

$$= x^2 + 5x + 6.$$

Example 4: Multiply $n + 4$ by $n - 6$.

$$\begin{aligned}(n + 4)(n - 6) &= (n + 4)(n + {}^{-}6)\\ &= (n + 4)n + (n + 4) \cdot {}^{-}6\\ &= n^2 + 4n + {}^{-}6n + {}^{-}24\\ &= n^2 + {}^{-}2n + {}^{-}24\\ &= n^2 - 2n - 24\end{aligned}$$

Exercises

A Replace each ? with the correct number or variable.

1. $(x + 3)(x + 4) = (x + 3)? + (x + 3)4$

2. $(y + 5)(y^2 + 6) = (y + 5)y^2 + (y + 5)?$

3.
$$\begin{array}{r} 7x + 3 \\ 2x + 5 \\ \hline 35x + 15 \\ 14x^2 + 6x \phantom{{}+15} \\ \hline 14x^2 + ?x + 15 \end{array}$$

4.
$$\begin{array}{r} y + 6 \\ y^2 - 3 \\ \hline {}^{-}3y + ? \\ y^3 + 6y^2 \phantom{{}+{}^{-}3y+{}^{-}18} \\ \hline y^3 + 6y^2 + {}^{-}3y + {}^{-}18 \text{ or} \\ y^3 + 6y^2 - 3y - 18 \phantom{\text{ or}} \end{array}$$

Think $y^2 + {}^{-}3$.

Tell the area of each small rectangle A, B, C, and D. Then tell the total area of the large rectangle.

5.

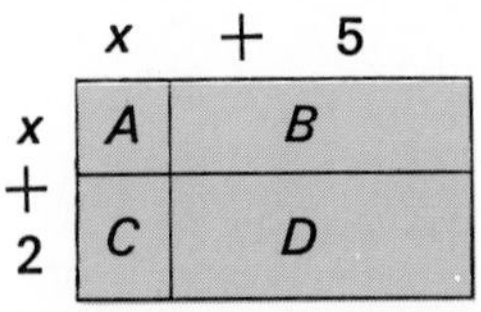

$(x + 5)(x + 2) =$ ____

6.

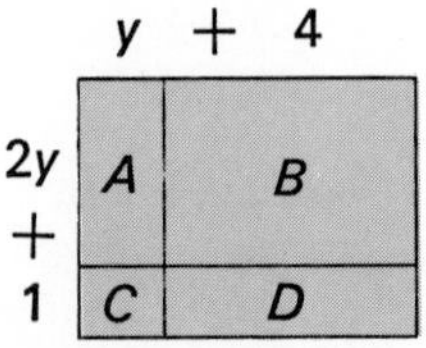

$(y + 4)(2y + 1) =$ ____

[B] Find each product.

7. $(x + 2)(x + 5)$

8. $(y + 1)(y + 6)$

9. $(x^2 + 1)(x + 4)$

10. $(y + 3)(y^2 + 6)$

11. $(2y + 1)(y + 6)$

12. $(3x + 1)(x + 3)$

13. $(xy + 1)(x - 3)$

14. $(4m - 1)(m + 3)$

15. $(3x - 5y)(2x + 6y)$

16. $(7x - 2y)(2x - 3y)$

17. $(2x^2 + 3y)(5x^2 - 2y)$

18. $(4y - 2)(3y + 1)$

19. $(4m^2 - 1)(4m^2 - 1)$

20. $(^-5a + 1)(^-3a - 2)$

21. $(\frac{1}{2}x + 2)(\frac{1}{2}x + 4)$

22. $(\frac{3}{4}y + 1)(\frac{1}{4}y + 2)$

23. $(1.1m + 3)(0.3m + 6)$

24. $(2.8c + 1)(1.5c + 1)$

[C] A shortcut for finding the product of two binomials is simply to add up the products of four pairs of terms.

① *First terms* of the binomials

② *Outside terms* of the binomials

③ *Inside terms* of the binomials

④ *Last terms* of the binomials

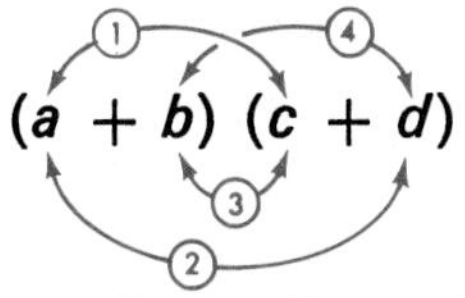

① ② ③ ④

$ac + ad + bc + bd$

This method for multiplying two binomials is called the FOIL method. Use the FOIL method to find each product below.

25. $(x + 5)(x + 2)$

26. $(y + 3)(y + 3)$

27. $(2x + 1)(3x + 4)$

28. $(m + 5)(4m + 2)$

29. $(x^2 + 4)(2x + 3)$

30. $(3y^2 + 1)(2y^2 + 1)$

14.8 Adding Polynomials

When you add two or more polynomials, you simply combine like terms.

Example 1: Add $6a + 9$ and $5a + 7$.

like terms

$$(6a + 9) + (5a + 7) = 11a + 16$$

like terms

If you want to, you can first rearrange the terms so that like terms are next to each other.

Example 2: Add $9x^2 + 12$ and ${}^-3x^2 + x + {}^-4$.

$$\begin{aligned}(9x^2 + 12) + ({}^-3x^2 + x + {}^-4) &= \underbrace{9x^2 + {}^-3x^2} + x + \underbrace{12 + {}^-4}\\ &= 6x^2 + x + 8\end{aligned}$$

In some cases, you might find the method in the next example helpful. Notice how like terms are arranged in columns. And each polynomial is expressed as a sum of monomials.

Example 3: Add $4x^2 - 6x + 2$ and ${}^-7x^2 + x + 5$.

$$\begin{array}{r} 4x^2 + {}^-6x + 2 \\ {}^-7x^2 + \quad x + 5 \\ \hline {}^-3x^2 + {}^-5x + 7 \end{array} \quad \text{or} \quad {}^-3x^2 - 5x + 7$$

Notice how $4x^2 - 6x + 2$ was changed.

Example 4: Add $3x^2 - 3xy - 2$, $16y^2 - 3 - 9xy$, and $xy + 4x^2 - 1$.

$$\begin{array}{rrrr} & 3x^2 + & {}^-3xy + & {}^-2 \\ 16y^2 & + & {}^-9xy + & {}^-3 \\ & 4x^2 + & xy + & {}^-1 \\ \hline 16y^2 + & 7x^2 + & {}^-11xy + & {}^-6 \end{array}$$

or $16y^2 + 7x^2 - 11xy - 6$

Express each polynomial as a sum and rearrange the terms, placing like terms in columns.

Exercises

A Replace each ? with the correct number.

1. $(7a + 4) + (5a + 6) = ? \cdot a + 10$

2. $(4x^2 + {}^-1) + (8x^2 + {}^-6) = 12x^2 + ?$

3. $(11y^2 + {}^-10y + 2) + (8y + {}^-5) = ? \cdot y^2 + {}^-2y + {}^-3$

4. $(4xy + {}^-2y^2 + 3x^2) + (6xy + 5y^2 + x^2) = 10xy + 3y^2 + ? \cdot x^2$

B Add.

5. $(2x + 6) + (3x + 3)$

6. $(9m + 3) + ({}^-7m + {}^-6)$

7. $({}^-4y + {}^-2) + (7y + 1)$

8. $(14w + 3) + ({}^-17w + 8)$

9. $(9a + 7b) + (4a + 9b)$

10. $(x^2 + {}^-8) + ({}^-x^2 + 8)$

11. $(2a + 3b + 3c) + ({}^-1b + 2a + 4c)$

12. $(9y + 8z + {}^-3) + ({}^-9y + {}^-8z + 3)$

13. $(m - n + p) + (m - n + p)$

14. $(y^2 + 3y + 7) + (4y - 9 + 4y^2)$

15. $(7x^2y + 8) + ({}^-9xy + 16)$

16. $(3mn - 4m) + (4m^2n + 8m)$

17. $(\frac{1}{2}a + 3) + (\frac{1}{2}a + {}^-2)$

18. $(\frac{2}{3}y - 1) + (-\frac{1}{3}y + 3)$

19. $(-\frac{2}{5}x + \frac{1}{10}) + (-\frac{2}{5}x + \frac{3}{10})$

20. $(\frac{5}{8}b + \frac{1}{6}) + (\frac{7}{8}b + \frac{1}{4})$

21. $(1.3m + {}^-1.8) + (0.8m + {}^-1.3)$

22. $({}^-2.4m + {}^-1.7) + (3.4m + 1.9)$

23.
$$\begin{array}{rcrcr} 12x^2 &+& 14x &+& {}^-5 \\ 8x^2 &+& {}^-5x &+& 1 \\ \underline{{}^-2x^2} &\underline{+}& \underline{8x} &\underline{+}& \underline{7} \end{array}$$

24.
$$\begin{array}{rcrcr} {}^-6y^2 &+& {}^-8y &+& {}^-5 \\ 2y^2 &+& 3y &+& 1 \\ \underline{{}^-7y^2} &\underline{+}& \underline{{}^-7y} &\underline{+}& \underline{{}^-6} \end{array}$$

C **25.**
$$\begin{array}{rcrcr} 5 &+& 4y &+& y^2 \\ 8y &+& 3y^2 &+& 1 \\ \underline{{}^-6y} &\underline{+}& \underline{{}^-5} &\underline{+}& \underline{7y^2} \end{array}$$

26.
$$\begin{array}{rcrcr} {}^-6xy &+& 3 &+& y^2 \\ 2y^2 &+& 5xy &+& 1 \\ \underline{y^2} &\underline{+}& \underline{{}^-7} &\underline{+}& \underline{8y} \end{array}$$

27. $(y^4 + 8y - 6y^3 + 5) + (7y + 8y^2 + 3y^4 - 2)$

28. $(6a + 2a^3 + 7 - a^2) + (a^3 + 7a^2 - 6a + 1)$

14.9 Subtracting Polynomials

You know that to subtract an integer, you add its opposite. For example,

$$8 - {}^{-}5 = 8 + 5.$$

Remember that the sum of an integer and its opposite is 0.

$$7 + {}^{-}7 = 0 \qquad\qquad {}^{-}19 + 19 = 0$$

Now consider $2x^2 + 3x$ and ${}^{-}2x^2 + {}^{-}3x$. Notice that the sum of these two polynomials is 0.

$$\begin{aligned}(2x^2 + 3x) + ({}^{-}2x^2 + {}^{-}3x) &= 2x^2 + {}^{-}2x^2 + 3x + {}^{-}3x \\ &= 0 + 0 \\ &= 0\end{aligned}$$

Therefore, $2x^2 + 3x$ and ${}^{-}2x^2 + {}^{-}3x$ are *opposites.*

> The sum of a polynomial and its opposite is 0.

Example 1: Show that ${}^{-}5y^2 + 7y$ and $5y^2 + {}^{-}7y$ are opposites.

$$\begin{aligned}({}^{-}5y^2 + 7y) + (5y^2 + {}^{-}7y) &= {}^{-}5y^2 + 5y^2 + 7y + {}^{-}7y \\ &= 0 + 0 \\ &= 0\end{aligned}$$

The example above suggests a way for finding the opposite of a polynomial.

> To find the opposite of a polynomial, change the sign of *each* term of the polynomial.

Example 2: Find the opposite of each polynomial.

a. ${}^{-}3x^3 + {}^{-}5x^2 + 4$

The opposite is

$3x^3 + 5x^2 + {}^{-}4.$

b. $7y^2 - 5y + 3$

The opposite is

${}^{-}7y^2 + 5y - 3.$

You can use the same method to subtract polynomials as you used to subtract integers.

To subtract a polynomial, you add its opposite.

Example 3: Subtract.

a.

$$\begin{array}{r} 12x^2 + 5x + 3 \\ \underline{-(^-5x^2 + {}^-2x + 1)} \end{array} \quad \Rightarrow \quad \begin{array}{r} 12x^2 + 5x + 3 \\ \underline{+(5x^2 + 2x + {}^-1)} \\ 17x^2 + 7x + 2 \end{array}$$

b. $(9y^2 - 2y + 1) - (3y^2 - y + 5)$

$= (9y^2 - 2y + 1) + (^-3y^2 + y - 5)$

$= 6y^2 - y - 4$

Exercises

A Find the opposite of each polynomial.

1. $7x$ **2.** ^-5y **3.** $2x + 1$

4. $^-7y + 3$ **5.** $9y^2 + 2y + 3$ **6.** $^-7a^2 + 5a + 4$

Replace each ? with the correct term.

7. $3x - {}^-2x = 3x + ?$ **8.** $^-9y - 3y = {}^-9y + ?$

9. $(3a + 1) - (2a + {}^-3) = (3a + 1) + (? + 3)$

10. $(^-x + 4) - (^-3x + 1) = (^-x + 4) + (? + {}^-1)$

B Subtract.

11. $14a - {}^-5a$ **12.** $^-12y - 3y$

13. $^-9a - {}^-3a$ **14.** $16m - {}^-3m$

15. $(3x + 1) - (^-5x + 2)$ **16.** $(2a + 4) - (3a + 5)$

17. $(11a + {}^-6) - (a + {}^-5)$ **18.** $(5m + 4) - (^-5m + {}^-6)$

19. $(10y - 7) - (3y - 2)$ **20.** $(^-3y^2 - 6) - (5y^2 + 4)$

21. $(^-15z^2 - 7) - (^-8z^2 - 14)$ **22.** $(13m - 19) - (^-17m + 8)$

23. $\begin{array}{r} 11m^2 + 10m + 8 \\ -(9m^2 + {}^-6m + 5) \\ \hline \end{array}$

24. $\begin{array}{r} {}^-21y^2 + 13y + {}^-9 \\ -({}^-8y^2 - 8y - 3) \\ \hline \end{array}$

25. $\begin{array}{r} 9x^2 + 8x + 5 \\ -(3x^2 - 3x - 7) \\ \hline \end{array}$

26. $\begin{array}{r} 13m^2 + {}^-7m + {}^-8 \\ -({}^-9m^2 + {}^-4m + 12) \\ \hline \end{array}$

27. $\begin{array}{r} {}^-14a^2 + 13a + {}^-9 \\ -({}^-7a^2 + {}^-9a + 8) \\ \hline \end{array}$

28. $\begin{array}{r} 20x^2 + 19x + 12 \\ -(x^2 + {}^-5x + 10) \\ \hline \end{array}$

C **29.** $({}^-7y + 8y^2 + {}^-10) - (12 + {}^-5y + 2y^2)$

30. $(5y + 2y^2 + {}^-3) - ({}^-9 + 3y + 2y^2)$

31. $\begin{array}{r} 17a + 13 + a^3 + {}^-a^2 \\ -(15 + {}^-2a^3 + a^2 + {}^-3a) \\ \hline \end{array}$

32. $\begin{array}{r} {}^-25 + 10a + a^2 + {}^-14a^3 \\ -(18a^3 + 7a^2 + {}^-8a + 12) \\ \hline \end{array}$

Simplify.

33. $(7x + {}^-3) + ({}^-3x + 1) - (5x + {}^-4)$

34. $({}^-4x^2 + 3x) + (6x + {}^-2x^2) - (3x + 7x^2)$

35. $({}^-9x^2 + 3x + {}^-2) + (9x^2 + {}^-6x + 1) - ({}^-8x^2 + {}^-5x + 3)$

36. $(6x^2 + 3) + (x + {}^-6) - ({}^-5x^2 + {}^-3x)$

Can You Solve It?

Dividing by a Monomial

14.10

When you divide monomials, you often use exponents. For example,

$$\frac{x^6}{x^4} = \frac{x \cdot x \cdot x \cdot x \cdot x \cdot x}{x \cdot x \cdot x \cdot x} = x^2. \qquad \textit{Shortcut: } \frac{x^6}{x^4} = x^{6-4} = x^2$$

Notice how the shortcut above can be used to help find the quotient of two monomials. Remember that you can check a division problem by multiplying the quotient by the divisor. The result should equal the dividend.

Examples:

1. $\frac{x^5}{x^2} = x^{5-2} = x^3$ *Check:* $x^3 \cdot x^2 = x^5$ ✓

2. $\frac{\overset{3}{\cancel{15}}x^4}{\underset{1}{\cancel{5}}x^2} = 3x^{4-2} = 3x^2$ *Check:* $3x^2 \cdot 5x^2 = 15x^4$ ✓

3. $\frac{\overset{-4}{\cancel{-48}}m^3n^2}{\underset{1}{\cancel{12}}mn} = {}^-4m^{3-1}n^{2-1} = {}^-4m^2n$ *Check:* ${}^-4m^2n \cdot 12mn = {}^-48m^3n^2$ ✓

> To divide monomials containing constants, divide the constants. Divide like variables by subtracting their exponents.

When you divide a polynomial by a monomial, you must divide each term of the polynomial by the monomial.

Examples:

4. $\frac{20x^3 + 4x^2}{2x} = \frac{20x^3}{2x} + \frac{4x^2}{2x} = 10x^2 + 2x$

5. $\frac{6x^3 + 12x^2 + 18x}{3x} = \frac{6x^3}{3x} + \frac{12x^2}{3x} + \frac{18x}{3x} = 2x^2 + 4x + 6$

Exercises

A Replace each ? with the correct number or expression.

1. $\frac{x^6}{x^3} = x^?$

2. $\frac{y^7}{y^4} = y^?$

3. $\frac{m^5}{m} = m^?$

4. $\frac{25x^2}{5} = ?x^2$

5. $\frac{12x^2}{3x} = ?x$

6. $\frac{16mn^2}{8mn} = ?n$

7. $\frac{8x^2 + 8x}{4x} = \frac{8x^2}{4x} + \frac{8x}{?}$
$= 2x + 2$

8. $\frac{21x^3 + 14x^2}{7x} = \frac{21x^3}{7x} + \frac{?}{7x}$
$= 3x^2 + 2x$

B Divide.

9. $\frac{y^6}{y^4}$

10. $\frac{x^7}{x^3}$

11. $\frac{m^3}{m^3}$

12. $\frac{a^3}{a^2}$

13. $\frac{10x^2}{5}$

14. $\frac{12m^3}{4}$

15. $\frac{16x^4}{4x}$

16. $\frac{20x^3}{5x^2}$

17. $\frac{36y^5}{4y^3}$

18. $\frac{18c^9}{9c^7}$

19. $\frac{27a^2b^3c^5}{^-9ab^2c^4}$

20. $\frac{^-16x^3y^2}{4xy}$

21. $\frac{12a^2 + 6a}{3}$

22. $\frac{18x^2 + 9y^2}{9}$

23. $\frac{c^5 + c^2}{c}$

24. $\frac{24c^3 + 12c^2}{2c}$

25. $\frac{18x^2 - 16x - 24}{2}$

26. $\frac{25y^2 - 10y + 15}{5}$

27. $\frac{^-36x^3y^2 - 18x^2y^2 + 24xy}{6xy}$

28. $\frac{100x^3 + 50x^2 + 20x}{10x}$

C **29.** Use $\frac{n^4}{n^2} = n^2$. Let $n = 2$. Substitute and find the powers. Then divide on the left side. Does a true equation result?

30. Repeat Exercise 29, but this time let $n = {^-3}$.

31. Repeat Exercise 29, but this time let $n = 0$.

32. Which statement is more precise, **(a)** $\frac{n^4}{n^2} = n^2$ or **(b)** $\frac{n^4}{n^2} = n^2$ if $n \neq 0$? Why?

Terms and Symbols Review

Complete each sentence. Choose from these words.

monomial *binomial* *trinomial* *like* *unlike*

1. A polynomial with 3 terms is called a ____.
2. When terms have the same variables with equal exponents, the terms are called ____ terms.
3. A polynomial is a ____ or the sum of two or more monomials.
4. A polynomial with 2 terms is called a ____.

Chapter 14 Review

Give an equation for the problem. Then solve the problem. 14.1

1. George paid \$40 for two sweaters. One cost \$12 more than the other. How much did each sweater cost?

Solve if possible. 14.2

2. On a trip the Wheats traveled 153 miles in 3 hours. They had to pay \$3.40 in tolls and used 9.2 gallons of gasoline. What was their average speed for the trip?

Which pairs of monomials are like terms? 14.3

3. $3x^2y$, $^-6xy^2$
4. $\frac{1}{2}x^3y$, $\frac{2}{3}x^3y$
5. $9x$, ^-7y
6. ^-3y, ^-10y

Add. 14.4

7. $^-7y + 14y$
8. $3m + {}^-16m$
9. $9xy^2 + {}^-11xy^2$
10. $^-6x + {}^-10x + 7x$

14.5 **Multiply.**

11. $x^3 \cdot x^5$

12. $y \cdot y^4$

13. $(^-3x^2)(2x^2)$

14. $(^-4m)(^-9m^3)$

14.6 **15.** $2x(^-5x + 1)$

16. $(8y + 4)(^-3y)$

17. $(3x - 4)(5x^2)$

18. $8m(^-4m + ^-2)$

14.7 **19.** $(3x + 2)(2x + 4)$

20. $(5y + ^-2)(2y + ^-3)$

21. $(^-8z + 5)(^-3z + 4)$

22. $(7m - 2)(m - 6)$

14.8 **Add.**

23. $(6x + 3) + (5x + 7)$

24. $(^-8m + 5) + (^-3m + 7)$

25. $(^-3x^2 + 7x + 1) + (8x^2 - 8x + 10)$

26.
$$\begin{array}{r} 13x^2 + ^-25x + 12 \\ \underline{^-11x^2 + \quad 9x + \ \ 8} \end{array}$$

27.
$$\begin{array}{r} ^-14y^2 + 7y + \ \ 1 \\ \underline{^-10y \ \ + 8 \ \ + ^-3y^2} \end{array}$$

14.9 **Subtract.**

28. $12a - ^-5a$

29. $^-10y - 8y$

30.
$$\begin{array}{r} 9b + ^-7 \\ \underline{-(2b + ^-3)} \end{array}$$

31.
$$\begin{array}{r} 3m^2 + ^-8m + 5 \\ \underline{-(2m^2 + ^-2m + 1)} \end{array}$$

14.10 **Divide.**

32. $\dfrac{24m^2}{8}$

33. $\dfrac{^-36x}{12x}$

34. $\dfrac{^-48y^3}{8y}$

35. $\dfrac{27x^3 + 12x^2 + 21x}{3x}$

36. $\dfrac{10y^3 + ^-5y^2 + ^-15y}{^-5y}$

Chapter 14 Test

Give an equation for the problem. Then solve the problem.

1. Alana earned \$120 last week at two different jobs. She earned \$20 more at the first job than at the second job. How much did she earn at each job?

Add.

2. ${}^{-}16y^2 + 7y^2$

3. ${}^{-}8a + {}^{-}7a + {}^{-}2a$

4. $\begin{array}{r} 9y + {}^{-}8 \\ \underline{{}^{-}2y + 4} \end{array}$

5. $\begin{array}{r} 16x^2 + 10x + {}^{-}5 \\ \underline{3x^2 + {}^{-}7x + 4} \end{array}$

Multiply.

6. $a^2 \cdot a^6$

7. $({}^{-}3m^3)(7m^2)$

8. $5x(4x + {}^{-}7)$

9. $({}^{-}9y^2 + 3y)({}^{-}2y)$

10. $(y + 7)(y + 2)$

11. $(3x - 4)(2x + 1)$

Subtract.

12. $14y - {}^{-}3y$

13. $({}^{-}7x + 6) - (5x + {}^{-}3)$

Divide.

14. $\dfrac{25x^3}{5x}$

15. $\dfrac{{}^{-}54m^5}{{}^{-}6m^2}$

16. $\dfrac{18a^3 + {}^{-}12a^2 + 15a}{3a}$

RATE YOURSELF

Number Correct	
16	Superior
14–15	Excellent
12–13	Good
9–11	Fair
0–8	Poor

CAREER CORNER

GOING TO COLLEGE?

Many careers require a college education. To prepare for college, you may have to take two or more years of high-school math. Below are some recommendations of the Mathematical Association of America and the National Council of Teachers of Mathematics.

For each college program listed, the recommended number of years of high-school math is indicated.

Reprinted with permission from *The Math in High School . . . you'll need for college*, The Mathematical Association of America, 1978

Agriculture:	
Agricultural economics	3
Entomology	3
Environmental sciences	4
Food sciences	3
Forestry	3
Genetics	3
Landscape architecture	3
Plant pathology	3
Rural sociology	3
Wildlife ecology	3
Other areas of agriculture	2
Architecture	3
Art	2
Business:	
Accounting	3
Economics	4
Management	4
Communications	2
Education:	
Elementary	3
Child development and preschool	3
Engineering	4
History	2
Language and Literature	2
Law	3
Life sciences:	
Bacteriology	4
Biochemistry	4
Biology	4
Linguistics	3
Mathematical sciences:	
Mathematics	4
Statistics	4
Actuarial sciences	4
Computer science	4
Medicine:	
Allied medicine	3
Dental hygiene	3
Dentistry	4
Medical technology	4
Nursing	3
Optometry	4
Medicine: (continued)	
Physical therapy	3
Pre-medicine	4
Public health	3
Music	2
Pharmacy	4
Philosophy	2
Physical sciences:	
Astronomy	4
Chemistry	4
Geology	4
Physics	4
Social sciences:	
Anthropology	2
Asian studies	2
Black studies	3
Geography	3
Political science	3
Psychology	4
Social welfare	2
Sociology	3
Theater	2

This is what a certain number of years of high-school math means.

1 year	First year of *algebra*
2 years	One year of *geometry*
3 years	Second year of *algebra*
4 years	One year of *precalculus mathematics*

You may not have a career in mind right now. But by taking enough high-school math, you'll have more career choices open to you later. And you won't have to take remedial courses in college.

Getting Ready for Chapter 15

For each number, give **(a)** the hundreds digit, **(b)** the tens digit, and **(c)** the ones digit.

1. 3278 **2.** 378 **3.** $25

Put each set of numbers in order from smallest to largest.

4. 15, 36, 10, 25, 9, 16, 2, 5, 36, 25

5. 296, 525, 609, 610, 436, 525, 508, 423, 312, 213

6. 3.7, 6.8, 2.8, 1.7, 2.1, 5.2, 3.9, 3.3, 9.3, 4.8

Add.

7. 8, 34, 52, 28, 6, 16, 11, 44, 1

8. 5, 19, 12, 18, 0, 18, 14, 26

9. 40, 250, 119, 640, 19, 91, 447, 124

Compute.

10. $\frac{1}{2} \times \frac{1}{3}$ **11.** $\frac{2}{5} \times \frac{1}{5}$ **12.** $\frac{5}{12} \times \frac{4}{5}$ 4.2

13. $\frac{1}{2} + \frac{1}{4}$ **14.** $\frac{1}{6} + \frac{1}{3}$ **15.** $\frac{5}{12} + \frac{1}{3}$ 4.8

16. $0.4 + 0.5$ **17.** $0.25 + 0.8$ **18.** $0.58 + 0.33$ 5.3

19. $18.99 + $19.99 + $20.95 + $14.98 + $15.00 + $6.00

20. 0.7×0.6 **21.** 0.95×0.3 **22.** 0.5×0.75 5.4

23. $135 \div 6$ **24.** $4125 \div 12$ **25.** $100.10 ÷ 10 5.5

Write as decimals.

26. $\frac{1}{4}$ **27.** $\frac{3}{8}$ **28.** $\frac{42}{200}$ 5.5

15 STATISTICS AND PROBABILITY

Statistics and *probability* are two closely related branches of mathematics. As branches of mathematics go, both are rather new.

This chapter begins by looking at *statistics*—the mathematics of organizing and studying sets of numerical facts.

The chapter ends by taking a look at *probability*—the mathematics of chance.

15.1 Frequency Tables

Rita asked 30 classmates how many times they had been to a movie in the last two months. These were the answers:

4, 0, 1, 3, 2, 3, 1, 3, 5, 4, 7, 3, 1, 0, 4,
2, 3, 4, 3, 1, 5, 3, 2, 3, 4, 3, 2, 1, 4, 0

You can usually get a better understanding of a set of numerical facts (like those above) by organizing them in some way. Here's what Rita did. She found the **range** of the answers by finding the lowest answer and the highest answer.

low answer → 0–7 ← high answer

range

Then she made a table that shows how many times each answer was given. This is called a **frequency table.**

Example: Make a frequency table, using Rita's information.

Number of movies	Tally	Number of classmates
0	𝍷𝍷𝍷	3
1	𝍸	5
2	𝍷𝍷𝍷𝍷	4
3	𝍸 𝍷𝍷𝍷𝍷	9
4	𝍸 𝍷	6
5	𝍷𝍷	2
6		0
7	𝍷	1
	Total	30

Count the number of times each answer occurred.

3 classmates answered 0.

No classmates answered 6.

Exercises

A True or False?

1. Making a frequency table is one way to organize information.

2. The range of 6, 5, 9, 8 is 5–9.

Use the set of numbers below to complete the frequency table at the right.

4, 5, 5, 6, 6, 5, 8, 4

	Number	Tally	Frequency
	4	||	2
3.	5	|||	?
4.	6	?	2
5.	?		0
6.	8	|	?
		Total	8

B Find the range.

7. 8, 7, 5, 8, 9, 8, 8, 7, 8, 7, 6

8. 5, 3, 0, 1, 3, 3, 4, 5, 0, 3, 1

9. 19, 21, 20, 17, 18, 21, 17, 18, 21, 17

10. 39, 36, 40, 36, 38, 37, 39, 36, 40, 36

Make a frequency table for the set of numbers in each exercise.

11. Exercise 7 **12.** Exercise 8 **13.** Exercise 9 **14.** Exercise 10

15. *Ratings of a new food product by 50 tasters:* 0, $^{-}2$, 1, 1, $^{-}1$, 2, $^{-}1$, 1, 0, 1, 2, $^{-}2$, 0, 0, 1, 0, 1, 1, 0, 2, 1, 0, 2, 0, 1, 2, $^{-}1$, 0, 1, 0, 1, 0, 0, 0, 1, 0, 2, 1, 0, 1, 0, 1, 2, 1, 1, 2, $^{-}2$, $^{-}1$, $^{-}1$, 0 (*Note:* Each rating is given as $^{-}2$, $^{-}1$, 0, 1, or 2, with *$^{-}2$* meaning "terrible" and *2* meaning "excellent.")

16. *Results of tossing a die (singular of dice) 50 times:* 5, 3, 4, 1, 1, 1, 5, 3, 6, 1, 2, 2, 1, 5, 5, 2, 6, 4, 2, 3, 4, 5, 3, 3, 5, 1, 4, 3, 2, 1, 1, 6, 2, 5, 5, 3, 4, 4, 3, 2, 5, 1, 1, 6, 1, 6, 4, 2, 6, 2

Courtesy Chrysler-Plymouth

17. *Miles-per-gallon ratings of 50 four-cylinder cars:* 26, 24, 22, 22, 22, 24, 24, 21, 20, 22, 25, 28, 20, 20, 24, 24, 24, 23, 26, 26, 20, 28, 23, 23, 26, 20, 21, 23, 24, 20, 28, 22, 22, 21, 28, 24, 21, 25, 20, 21, 25, 25, 20, 20, 20, 23, 26, 22, 21, 24

18. *Test scores of 50 students:* 89, 83, 90, 84, 86, 86, 85, 83, 85, 87, 83, 85, 87, 90, 84, 87, 83, 83, 89, 88, 87, 90, 85, 86, 84, 85, 87, 89, 84, 86, 86, 88, 84, 84, 86, 86, 85, 86, 87, 87, 86, 89, 90, 86, 88, 84, 84, 87, 84, 84

C Sometimes the numbers in a set are spread out, and each number appears only once or just a few times. To make the frequency table compact and easy to read, the numbers are *grouped*.

Example: *Number of hours per week 20 students with jobs work:* 25, 30, 12, 20, 40, 15, 23, 24, 24, 20, 35, 35, 28, 30, 26, 31, 19, 25, 11, 28

Count the numbers in each group.

Hours per week	Tally	Number of students
11–16	|||	3
17–22		
23–28		
29–34		
35–40		
	Total	

There are 3 numbers in the 11–16 group (12, 15, and 11).

19. Copy and complete the frequency table above.

Make a frequency table, using the given groups.

20. *40 test scores:* 87, 43, 78, 75, 87, 93, 68, 58, 59, 86, 40, 80, 68, 92, 90, 60, 65, 73, 78, 71, 64, 62, 85, 68, 71, 57, 88, 99, 82, 71, 85, 79, 80, 85, 73, 73, 87, 76, 73, 77

Groups: 40–49, 50–59, 60–69, 70–79, 80–89, 90–99

21. *50 numbers:* 61, 94, 64, 87, 90, 11, 60, 28, 30, 43, 22, 25, 71, 18, 32, 4, 34, 49, 55, 41, 20, 36, 65, 59, 37, 4, 81, 16, 48, 92, 96, 34, 67, 90, 65, 26, 99, 94, 39, 67, 63, 48, 59, 35, 72, 80, 75, 39, 65, 82

Groups: 4–19, 20–35, 36–51, 52–67, 68–83, 84–99

22. *50 numbers:* 0.9, 6.6, 5.4, 4.6, 7.2, 7.4, 7.6, 2.3, 3.3, 5.7, 6.7, 3.0, 1.8, 0.5, 4.6, 9.8, 6.5, 9.1, 1.3, 4.8, 7.8, 7.7, 1.4, 5.0, 1.1, 3.4, 7.5, 6.5, 0.4, 0.3, 7.6, 6.3, 4.1, 2.7, 6.7, 3.2, 2.2, 0.3, 4.5, 4.5, 1.8, 1.0, 0.5, 3.5, 1.3, 1.4, 5.2, 1.7, 2.1, 2.0

Groups: 0.3–1.8, 1.9–3.4, 3.5–5.0, 5.1–6.6, 6.7–8.2, 8.3–9.8

15.2 Bar Graphs

Mr. Davis made a frequency table showing the grades of the 24 students in his pre-algebra class.

Grade	Tally	Number of students
A	卌 |||	8
B	卌 卌 ||	12
C	|||	3
D	|	1
F		0
Total		24

This information can also be shown in a **bar graph.** The bars on the graph are all the same width. The heights of the bars represent the frequencies of the grades.

Example 1: How many students received an A in math?

The bar over the "A" column has a height of 8.

Eight students received a grade of A.

Example 2: What grade was the most frequently received?

The bar over the "B" column is the highest.

The grade most frequently received was B.

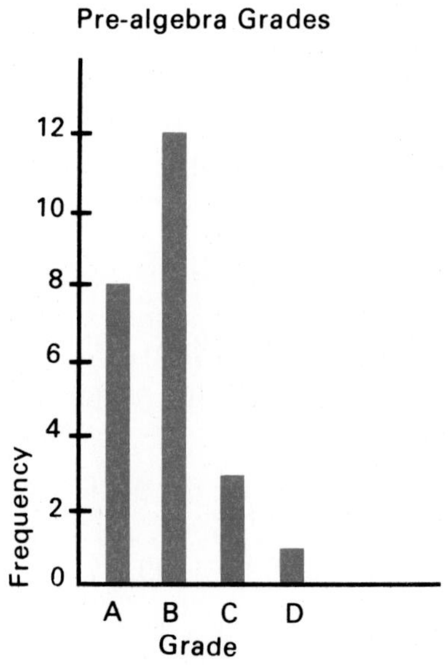

The item that occurs most frequently in a set is called the **mode** of the set. The mode of this set is B.

A bar graph that shows frequency and uses only numbers is called a **histogram.** A histogram has no spaces between the bars.

This histogram shows the frequencies with which students received certain scores on a 25-point quiz.

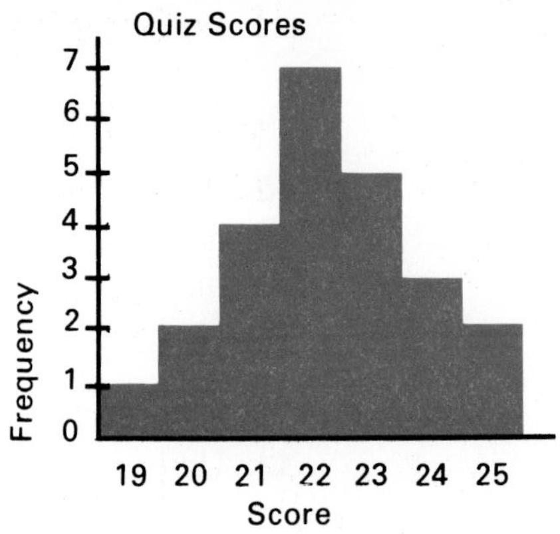

Example 3: What is the mode?

The highest bar is over the 22.

The mode is 22.

Example 4: How many students received scores over 22?

Five students received scores of 23, 3 received scores of 24, and 2 received scores of 25.

$5 + 3 + 2 = 10$

Ten students received scores over 22.

Exercises

A Use the bar graph at the right for Exercises 1–8.

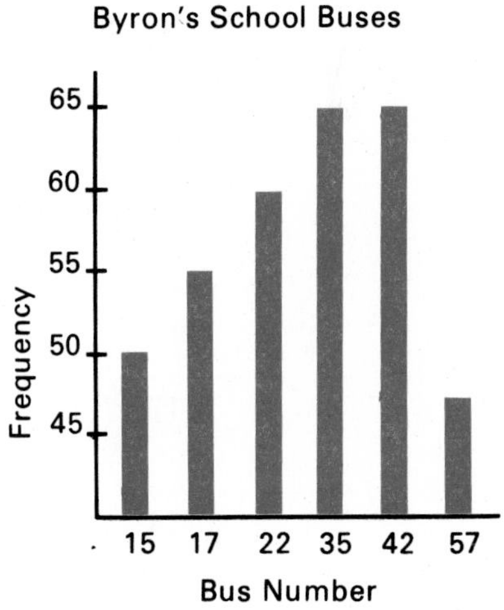

1. What is the mode?
2. Which bus brings the least number of students?
3. Which bus brings 50 students?
4. Which bus brings 60 students?
5. Which two buses bring the same number of students?
6. Which bus brings fewer than 50 students?
7. The maximum number of students allowed on each bus is 66. Which buses cannot hold 10 extra students?
8. Give two reasons why this graph is not a histogram.

B Use the histogram at the right for Exercises 9–14.

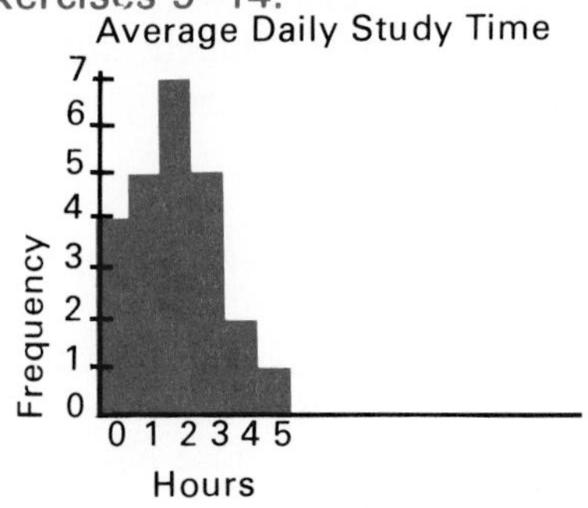

9. What is the mode?

10. What average number of hours a day is spent in study by the least number of students?

11. How many students study an average of 3 hours a day?

12. How many students study an average of 2 hours a day?

13. How many students average less than 2 hours of study a day?

14. How many students average more than 2 hours of study a day?

Make a graph for each frequency table.

15.

Favorite class	Tally	Number of students
Math	|||	3
Science	||	2
History	|||	3
English	||||	4
Phys ed	卌 |||	8
Art/music	||||	4

16.

Height (cm)	Tally	Number of students
145			1
150					3
155	卌		6
160	卌 |||	8
165						4
170				2

C Make a frequency table and a graph for the numbers in each exercise.

17. *Test scores of 24 students:* 96, 88, 84, 84, 72, 76, 88, 92, 96, 80, 76, 92, 88, 88, 84, 92, 84, 88, 76, 88, 84, 88, 88, 84

18. *Results of rolling a die 30 times:* 1, 6, 5, 6, 4, 2, 1, 6, 4, 6, 5, 3, 2, 6, 4, 5, 2, 1, 1, 3, 5, 6, 5, 4, 5, 6, 3, 3, 1, 4

The Median

15.3

Artstreet

The median of a major roadway is the grassy or paved strip in the middle. The **median** of a set of numbers is the number in the middle when the numbers are listed in order.

Example 1: Find the median of these test scores: 80, 90, 85, 75, 80.

Put the numbers in order.

2 numbers: 75, 80 — 80 — 2 numbers: 85, 90

75, 80, 80, 85, 90

Find the middle number.

median (middle number): 80

If there is an even number of scores or numbers, there are two middle numbers. To find the median, add the two middle numbers, and then divide by 2.

Example 2: Find the median of 12, 4, 1, 16, 9, 13.

Put the numbers in order. (3 numbers, 3 numbers) 1, 4, 9, 12, 13, 16

Find the two middle numbers. 9, 12 — 2 middle numbers

Add, and divide by 2. $\frac{9 + 12}{2} = \frac{21}{2} = 10.5$ ← median

Exercises

A

1. The number in the middle of a set of numbers listed in order is called the ____.
2. If there are two middle numbers, add them and divide by ____ to find the median.
3. The median for 1, 3, 4, 7, 7 is ____.
4. The median for 2, 4, 6, 8 is ____.

B Find the median.

5. 1, 5, 7, 9, 11
6. 2, 4, 6, 8, 10
7. 7, 10, 14, 15
8. 8, 9, 11, 13
9. 11, 14, 23, 27, 28, 34, 36
10. 31, 35, 38, 42, 42, 45, 46, 53, 54

11. 71, 73, 78, 78,
83, 84, 86, 87,
89, 93, 99, 99

12. 54, 55, 57, 58,
61, 63, 65, 68,
72, 77, 79

13. 5, 9, 8, 6, 1, 7, 4

14. 12, 13, 6, 7, 3, 0, 5

15. 4.2, 8.9, 6.1, 1.8, 0.5, 3.4

16. 3.1, 6.9, 4.3, 3.4, 7.1, 6.3

17. 144, 221, 320, 320, 183, 128,
32, 121, 330, 371, 364, 274

18. 534, 198, 165, 91, 258, 410,
174, 543, 521, 567, 321, 207

19. 19, 24, 9, 12, 36, 59, 33,
56, 10, 38, 11, 29, 10, 19,
15, 18, 9, 4

20. 32, 82, 53, 80, 80, 62, 75,
61, 64, 36, 78, 84, 37, 75,
64, 80, 58, 36

21. 2:12 (2 minutes, 12 seconds), 4:01, 3:23, 2:46, 1:03, 1:01, 1:46,
1:32, 1:06, 3:21, 2:35, 2:33, 5:25

22. 1:17 (1 minute, 17 seconds), 2:18, 2:25, 1:46, 3:14, 5:16, 4:39,
3:23, 2:18, 1:11, 4:16, 5:00, 3:06

C The median can be found by using a frequency table.

Example:

Number	Frequency
1	3
2	2
3	4
4	5
5	4
6	3
Total	21

(Frequencies 3, 2, 4 and the first 1 of the 5: 10 numbers)

5 { 1, 1, 3 — The middle number is a 4.

(The last 3 of the 5 and frequencies 4, 3: 10 numbers)

The median is 4.

Make a frequency table and then find the median. Use the set in

23. Exercise 7, page 482

24. Exercise 8, page 482

25. Exercise 17, page 482

26. Exercise 18, page 483

15.4 The Mean

Suppose someone asked you to find the average of *four* bowling scores. You probably would add the scores and then divide the sum by 4. In statistics, your answer is called the **mean.**

Most averages in sports are means, but other numbers are also called "averages." Many times an "average salary" is the median. A shirt manufacturer may call the size worn by the most people (the mode) the "average shirt size."

Example 1: A bowler's scores for 4 games were 143, 156, 148, and 133. Find the mean score.

Add the scores. $143 + 156 + 148 + 133 = 580$

Divide by the number of scores. $\frac{580}{4} = 145$ ← mean

Example 2: Find the mean: 1.4, 3.9, 3.7, 2.5.

$$\begin{array}{r} 1.4 \\ 3.9 \\ 3.7 \\ +\ 2.5 \\ \hline 11.5 \end{array} \qquad \begin{array}{r} 2.875 \\ 4\overline{)11.500} \\ 8 \\ \hline 3\,5 \\ 3\,2 \\ \hline 30 \\ 28 \\ \hline 20 \end{array}$$

Carry the division out only far enough to give a sensible answer, usually to the same decimal place as (or one more place than) the numbers in the set. In this case 2.88 or 2.9 will do.

If you know the mean and the number of items in the set, you can find the sum of the items, as follows:

Example 3: A paper carrier's mean monthly income for the past year (12 months) was $49. What was the total income for the year?

mean monthly income → $49; number of months in year → 12; total income for the year → $588

$$\$49 \times 12 = \$588$$

Exercises

A **1.** To find the mean of 5, 5, 3, and 7, add the numbers and divide by ____.

2. The mean of 5, 5, 3, and 7 is ____.

3. If the mean of a set is 5 and there are 6 items in the set, what is the sum of the items?

4. The mean number of hours of sunlight the last 7 days was 9. What was the total number of hours of sunlight the last 7 days?

B Find the mean.

5. 3, 8, 4, 9

6. 7, 5, 6, 10

7. 2.1, 2.1, 3.2, 8.9, 1.2

8. 3.2, 1.6, 2.8, 1.5, 4.4

9. 12, 15, 21, 35, 6, 17, 10, 9, 11, 15, 0, 12

10. 9, 13, 16, 24, 8, 11, 19, 10, 5, 3, 13, 20

11. *The costs of 6 gasoline purchases:* \$9.70, \$11.25, \$12.60, \$16.60, \$10.50, \$14.70

12. *A basketball player's points per game for 7 games:* 15, 16, 25, 6, 18, 34, 21

13. *A football team's punt-return yardage for 6 returns:* 37, 19, 28, 17, 5, 12

14. *The speeds (miles per hour) recorded by 5 drivers in a qualifying trial for a stock-car race:* 156, 183, 147, 159, 164

Solve each problem.

15. For a 26-game season, a basketball team's mean score per game was 79 points. What was the total number of points scored?

De Wys, Inc./Rocky Weldon

Courtesy U. S. Navy

16. For a 29-game season, a hockey team's mean goals per game was 4. What was the total number of goals scored?

17. In 1846 a sailing ship sailed from Liverpool, England, to New York in 16 days. The mean nautical miles per day was 196.9. How many nautical miles was the trip?

18. In 1960 a submarine made an 84-day voyage around the world. The mean number of nautical miles per day was 494. How many nautical miles was the voyage?

19. Andrea scored a total of 112 points on 16 ten-point quizzes. Felicia scored a total of 96 points on 12 ten-point quizzes. Whose mean quiz score was higher?

20. Juan bowled 6 games and scored a total of 858 points. Ivan bowled 7 games and scored a total of 994 points. Whose mean score was higher?

C 21. After the first 6 games of the season, a soccer team's mean goals per game was 3. The team's record for the first 5 games was 2, 5, 0, 1, and 4. How many goals were scored in game 6? (*Hint:* Find the total goals for all 6 games and for the first 5 games.)

Use a frequency table to find the mean.

Example:

Number	Frequency	Multiply each number by its frequency.
5	1	$5 \times 1 = 5$
6	3	$6 \times 3 = 18$
7	4	$7 \times 4 = 28$
8	2	$8 \times 2 = 16$
Total	10	67 — Add the results.

$$\frac{67}{10} = 6.7$$

Divide by the total frequency.

↑ mean

22. *20 numbers:* 15, 16, 13, 13, 12, 13, 14, 15, 16, 14, 12, 13, 12, 13, 14, 14, 15, 15, 10, 15

23. *50 numbers:* 6, 6, 5, 4, 3, 8, 8, 7, 6, 5, 4, 2, 2, 1, 1, 7, 8, 7, 6, 6, 5, 5, 5, 4, 5, 3, 1, 1, 1, 7, 6, 5, 1, 2, 3, 4, 5, 5, 4, 7, 4, 4, 5, 6, 6, 7, 5, 6, 4, 7

24. *The life (in months) of 15 storage batteries of a certain make:* 39, 37, 37, 37, 36, 36, 35, 37, 39, 40, 37, 36, 37, 36, 36

25. *The strength (pounds per square inch) of 15 samples of a certain kind of wool fabric:* 132, 132, 135, 136, 135, 131, 129, 135, 132, 132, 131, 132, 133, 135, 135

Quick Quiz
Sections 15.1 to 15.4

Use the following set of numbers in Exercises 1–3.

6, 5, 1, 3, 1, 6, 8, 6

Find

1. the range **2.** the mode **3.** the median

4. Make a frequency table for the following set of numbers:

15, 10, 11, 12, 12, 13, 14, 13, 14, 15, 10, 12, 14, 14, 12, 13, 12, 10, 13, 14

5. Make a graph for the numbers in Exercise 4.

Use the following set of numbers in Exercises 6–7.

23, 38, 21, 20, 40, 36, 10, 21, 17, 31, 41, 21, 33, 44, 25

6. Find the mode. **7.** Find the median.

8. Find the mean for 8, 12, 13, 10, 7.

CONSUMER CORNER

WHAT'S AVERAGE?

In the last few sections you found the range, the mode, the median, and the mean. These four values are called *descriptive statistics.* Each helps describe a set of data (numbers).

The range gives an idea of how spread out the set of data is. And it is called *a measure of variability.*

The mode, the median, and the mean give an idea of the size of the numbers in a set of data. And these three descriptive statistics are called *measures of central tendency*. All three are also sometimes called "averages."

When studying this	A useful "average" is this	Why?
Clothing sizes	Mode	This gives the most-frequently-used sizes and therefore gives a better picture of typical sizes to manufacturers and storekeepers.
Salaries or home values	Median	This middle value is not affected by a few extreme values (like salaries of millionaires) and therefore gives a better picture of typical salaries or home values.
Sports performances	Mean	This value takes into account total performance (extreme scores as well as most-frequent scores) and therefore is a good way to compare teams or individuals.

Talk it over: Which "average" (mode, median, or mean) would probably be best to use in each case?

1. A food packager wants to know the "average" size of a certain product that people will buy.

2. A racehorse trainer wants to know the "average" time that a certain horse takes to run $1\frac{1}{8}$ miles.

3. A house builder wants to know the "average" income of families in a certain community.

4. A student wants to know the "average" score on a test.

5. A farmer wants to know the "average" yield per acre of a new corn plant.

Outcomes and Probabilities

15.5

If you roll a die (singular of *dice*), there are six possible outcomes—1, 2, 3, 4, 5, or 6 dots on the top face. If you toss a coin, there are two possible outcomes—heads or tails. What are the chances of heads on the toss of a coin? One way to find out is to toss a coin many times, say 100, and record the results.

COIN-TOSSING EXPERIMENT

Outcome	Tally	Number of times
heads	𝍸 𝍸 𝍸 𝍸 𝍸 𝍸 𝍸 𝍸 𝍸 II	47
tails	𝍸 𝍸 𝍸 𝍸 𝍸 𝍸 𝍸 𝍸 𝍸 𝍸 III	53
	Total	100

The table above shows that the outcome was heads 47 times out of 100 trials (tosses). So the **experimental probability** of the outcome being heads is $\frac{47}{100}$ or 0.47. A shorter way of writing this is

$$\text{ex pr (heads)} = \frac{47}{100} = 0.47.$$

$$\text{Similarly, ex pr (tails)} = \frac{53}{100} = 0.53.$$

Suppose an experiment *consisted of n* trials and a particular outcome *happened s* times by chance. Then the experimental probability of that outcome is $\frac{s}{n}$.

Sometimes a **theoretical probability,** pr, can be found without doing an experiment.

Suppose a trial in an experiment *can happen n* equally likely ways. If *s* of these ways *would result* in a particular outcome, then the **theoretical probability** of that outcome is $\frac{s}{n}$.

For the coin experiment, there are 2 ways the coin can land. So the number of ways a trial (toss) *can happen* is 2. (Assume the coin is fair and both ways of landing are equally likely.) The number of ways a trial *would result* in the outcome "heads" is 1. So,

$$\text{pr (heads)} = \frac{1}{2} = 0.5.$$

$$\text{Similarly, pr (tails)} = \frac{1}{2} = 0.5.$$

There are 10 marbles—7 orange and 3 black— of the same size in a paper bag. They are thoroughly mixed. An experiment was done to find the experimental probability of picking an orange marble from the bag by chance (without looking, and placing the picked marble back into the bag after each trial). The results are below.

MARBLE EXPERIMENT

Outcome	Number of times
picking an orange marble	53
picking a black marble	27
Total	80

Example 1: Using the table above, find the following *experimental probabilities* for the marble experiment: ex pr (orange) and ex pr (black).

$$\text{ex pr (orange)} = \tfrac{53}{80} \approx 0.66$$

$$\text{ex pr (black)} = \tfrac{27}{80} \approx 0.34$$

Example 2: Find the following *theoretical probabilities* for the marble experiment: pr (orange) and pr (black).

There are 10 equally likely ways a trial *can happen* (because there are 10 marbles in the bag).

There are 7 orange marbles, so the number of ways a trial could result in the outcome "picking an orange marble" is 7.

Therefore, $\text{pr (orange)} = \tfrac{7}{10} = 0.7.$

Similarly, because there are only 3 black marbles,

$$\text{pr (black)} = \tfrac{3}{10} = 0.3.$$

Notice that the experimental probabilities in Example 1 are close to the theoretical probabilities in Example 2. It has been proved that experimental probabilities get very close to theoretical probabilities when the number of trials is very large.

For both experimental and theoretical probabilities,

> Probabilities are never less than 0 or greater than 1.
> An impossible outcome has probability 0.
> An outcome that is sure to happen has probability 1.

Exercises

A **1.** A(n) (*experimental, theoretical*) probability is found without doing an experiment.

There are 10 marbles—5 red, 3 black, and 2 white—all the same size in a bag. One marble is picked from the bag as in Example 1.

2. Name all possible outcomes.

3. Find pr (red).

4. Find pr (black).

5. Find pr (white).

6. In 100 trials a red marble is picked from the bag 53 times. Find ex pr (red).

7. What is the probability of picking a blue marble from the bag?

8. Find pr (red) if all the marbles in the bag were red.

B The table at the right shows the results of rolling a fair die 100 times. Find **(a)** the experimental and **(b)** the theoretical probabilities for the following outcomes. Express each probability as a fraction reduced to lowest terms.

DIE-ROLLING EXPERIMENT

Outcome	Number of times
1 dot	17
2 dots	14
3 dots	15
4 dots	20
5 dots	16
6 dots	18
Total	100

9. 1 dot

10. 2 dots

11. 3 dots

12. 4 dots

13. 5 dots

14. 6 dots

15. 7 dots

16. less than 7 dots

A spinner like the one at the right has 8 regions—3 orange, 2 white, 2 brown, and 1 black—all the same size. The table at the right shows the results of 80 spins. (The pointer can't stop between regions.) Find **(a)** the experimental and **(b)** the theoretical probabilities for the following outcomes. Express each probability as a decimal.

SPINNER EXPERIMENT

Outcome	Number of times
orange	32
white	16
brown	20
black	12
Total	80

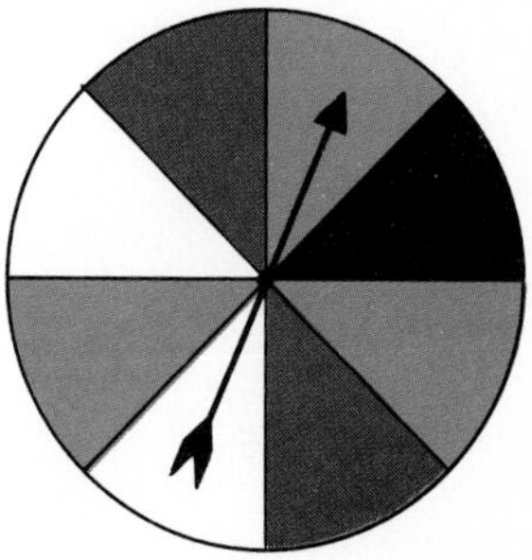

17. orange

18. white

19. brown

20. black

21. yellow

22. green

A regular deck of 52 playing cards is shown below. There are 13 cards in each of four suits—hearts, diamonds, clubs, and spades. For the experiment of drawing one card from a full, thoroughly shuffled deck, find each theoretical probability as a fraction.

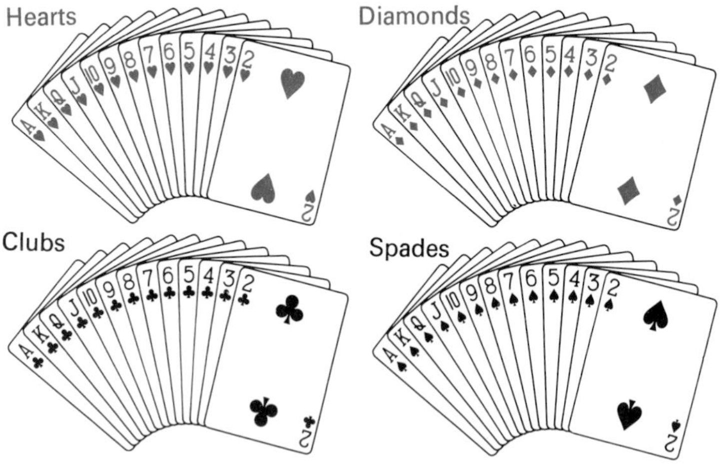

23. pr (the 10 of diamonds)

24. pr (the 6 of spades)

25. pr (a card in clubs)

26. pr (a card in hearts)

27. pr (a jack)

28. pr (a king)

29. pr (a black ace)

30. pr (a black queen)

C To **predict** how many times a particular outcome will happen, you *multiply* the number of trials by the probability of that outcome happening.

31. If you roll a die 240 times, how many times would you expect the outcome to be 4 dots?

32. If the experiment of drawing one card from a thoroughly shuffled deck is done 260 times, how many times would you expect to draw a card in diamonds?

33. The probability of recovering from a disease is 75% with treatment and 50% without treatment. If 12,000 people get the disease, how many more would you expect to recover if all had treatment than if none had treatment?

34. One baseball player's batting average is .250 (the probability of a hit is .250), and another player's average is .200. How many more hits would you expect the better batter to get if each had 540 official times at bat?

35. A supermarket is giving away tickets for cash prizes. There are 100 equal prizes, and the probability of winning a prize with one ticket is $\frac{1}{250,000}$. How many tickets will be given away? (*Hint:* Solve $\frac{1}{250,000} = \frac{100}{t}$.)

Tree Diagrams and Probability

You are a member of a group that is hosting a meeting. You must be on the setup committee or the cleanup committee and serve as a greeter, a guide, or a food server. Your committee and job are determined by two drawings.

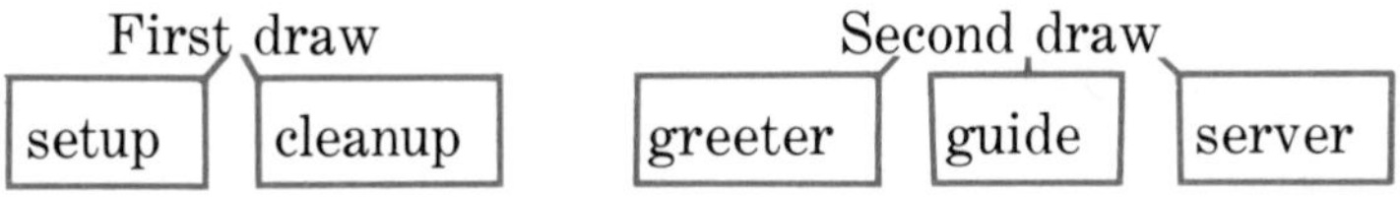

Example 1: To see the different possibilities of duties, you could make a *tree diagram.*

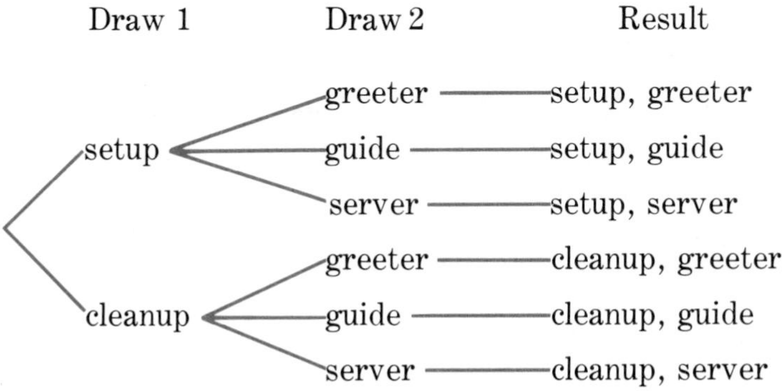

> A **tree diagram** is a drawing that shows the possible results of a series of events.

Example 2: The tree diagram can be used to determine the probability of your being on the cleanup committee and a greeter.

There are 6 possibilities. In only 1 of the possibilities are you on the cleanup committee and a greeter.

$\frac{\text{desired outcome} \rightarrow 1}{\text{possibilities} \rightarrow 6}$ The probability of being on the cleanup committee and a greeter is $\frac{1}{6}$.

pr (cleanup, greeter) $= \frac{1}{6}$

Example 3: Another way to find how many different ways you could work at the meeting is to use multiplication.

Number of possible results of Draw 1		Number of possible results of Draw 2		Number of results
↓		↓		↓
2	×	3	=	6

Exercises

[A] 1. What are the possible outcomes if you flip a coin?

2. What are the possible outcomes if you roll a die?

3. How many possible results are there if you flip a coin and roll a die?

[B] 4. Make a tree diagram that shows all the possible results of flipping a coin and rolling a die.

5. Make a tree diagram that shows all possible results of flipping two coins.

Use the tree diagrams in Exercises 4 and 5 to find each probability.

6. pr (6, heads)

7. pr (both heads)

8. pr (odd number, tails)

9. pr (one head, one tail)

[C] 10. If two dice are rolled, what is the probability that their sum is 7?

11. How many license plates that show 2 letters followed by 3 digits can be made?

12. The sports store has 3-speed, 5-speed, and 10-speed bicycles. They come in silver, blue, and black. The handlebars come in standard and racing styles. Make a tree diagram that shows all the possible bicycles.

Adding Probabilities

A bag contains 10 marbles—5 red, 3 white, and 2 blue. You pick one marble from the bag. What is the theoretical probability of picking "*either* a red marble *or* a blue marble"?

Since only one marble is picked at a time, both outcomes—(*1*) picking a red marble and (*2*) picking a blue marble—can't happen on the same trial. They are called **mutually exclusive events.** So we can reason as follows to find pr (red *or* blue):

> There are 5 ways to pick a red marble and 2 ways to pick a blue marble. So there are 5 + 2, or 7, ways to pick *either* a red *or* a blue marble. There are 10 ways a trial can happen, so pr (red *or* blue) $= \frac{7}{10}$. Notice that

$$\begin{aligned} \text{pr (red } \textit{or} \text{ blue)} &= \text{pr (red)} + \text{pr (blue)} \\ &= \tfrac{5}{10} + \tfrac{2}{10} \\ &= \tfrac{7}{10} \end{aligned}$$

> If *A* and *B* are *mutually exclusive events,* then the theoretical probability of outcome "*A or B*" can be found by adding pr (*A*) and pr (*B*).
>
> $$\text{pr }(A \textit{ or } B) = \text{pr }(A) + \text{pr }(B)$$

Example: Find the theoretical probability of picking *either* a red *or* a white marble in the experiment above.

$$\begin{aligned} \text{pr (red } \textit{or} \text{ white)} &= \text{pr (red)} + \text{pr (white)} \\ &= \tfrac{5}{10} + \tfrac{3}{10} \\ &= \tfrac{8}{10} \text{ or } \tfrac{4}{5} \end{aligned}$$

Exercises

A

1. If two outcomes are mutually exclusive events, then they (*can, cannot*) happen at the same time.

2. If *A* and *B* are mutually exclusive events, then pr (*A or B*) = ____.

3. A and B are mutually exclusive events and pr $(A) = \frac{1}{5}$ and pr $(B) = \frac{3}{5}$, so pr (A *or* B) = ____.

4. If a coin is tossed once, then pr (heads *or* tails) = ____.

A die is tossed once. Are the following mutually exclusive events?

5. A: throwing a 6; B: throwing a 3

6. A: throwing a 6; B: throwing an odd number

7. A: throwing a 6; B: throwing an even number

8. A: throwing an even number; B: throwing an odd number

B A and B are mutually exclusive events. Find pr (A *or* B) if

9. pr $(A) = \frac{1}{3}$, pr $(B) = \frac{1}{3}$

10. pr $(A) = \frac{1}{5}$, pr $(B) = \frac{2}{5}$

11. pr $(A) = \frac{1}{2}$, pr $(B) = \frac{1}{5}$

12. pr $(A) = \frac{2}{3}$, pr $(B) = \frac{1}{4}$

13. pr $(A) = 0.6$, pr $(B) = 0.2$

14. pr $(A) = 0.3$, pr $(B) = 0.25$

There are 12 marbles in a bag—6 red, 3 white, 2 blue, and 1 black. The marbles are thoroughly mixed, and one is picked from the bag. Find the following as fractions.

15. pr (red)

16. pr (white)

17. pr (blue)

18. pr (black)

19. pr (red *or* blue)

20. pr (white *or* black)

21. pr (red *or* white)

22. pr (white *or* blue)

23. pr (blue *or* black)

24. pr (red *or* black)

The integers from 1 to 10 are written on identical pieces of paper that are put into a bowl. They are thoroughly mixed, and one paper is picked from the bowl. Find the following as decimals.

25. pr (a multiple of 3)

26. pr (a multiple of 4)

27. pr (a multiple of 5)

28. pr (a prime number)

29. pr (a multiple of 3 *or* a multiple of 5)

30. pr (a multiple of 4 *or* a prime number)

31. pr (a multiple of 3 *or* a multiple of 4)

32. pr (a multiple of 4 *or* a multiple of 5)

One card is drawn from a thoroughly shuffled deck of 52 playing cards. (See page 498.) Find the following as fractions.

33. pr (a diamond *or* a club)

34. pr (a heart *or* a spade)

35. pr (a black 3 *or* a face card)

36. pr (a black jack *or* a 7)

37. pr (an ace *or* a face card)

38. pr (a heart *or* a black 5)

C To find the probability of an outcome **not** happening, you *subtract* from 1 the probability of that outcome happening.

Example: The probability of rain today is 0.7. What is the probability of no rain today?

$1 - 0.7 = 0.3$. So the probability of no rain today is 0.3.

39. In a particular city, the probability of being involved in an auto accident in a year is 0.2. What is the probability of not being involved in an auto accident in a year?

40. The probability of Rosemary hitting the bull's-eye of the archery target is 0.48. What is the probability of her not hitting the bull's-eye?

41. A person who enters a particular contest can win either a first, a second, or a third prize. (They are mutually exclusive events.) The probabilities of winning each prize are as follows: pr (first) = 0.001, pr (second) = 0.005, and pr (third) = 0.02. What is the probability of not winning a prize?

Photo Trends

15.8 Multiplying Probabilities

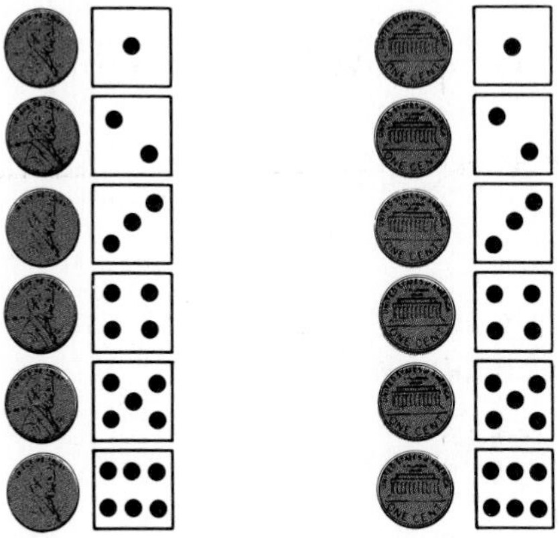

If you toss a coin *and* roll a die, there are 12 possible outcomes. There are two ways the coin can land and six ways the die can land. Notice that

$$2 \times 6 = 12$$

Tossing heads on a coin and rolling 2 dots on a die are called **independent events** because one outcome does not depend on the other outcome. Each can happen independently of the other.

Example 1: What is the theoretical probability of getting heads on the coin *and* 4 dots on the die in the experiment above?

By looking at the outcomes shown above, you can see that 1 of the 12 outcomes is heads *and* 4. So

$$\text{pr (heads } \textit{and} \text{ 4)} = \frac{1}{12}$$

Notice that

$$\begin{aligned} \text{pr (heads } \textit{and} \text{ 4)} &= \text{pr (heads)} \times \text{pr (4)} \\ &= \frac{1}{2} \times \frac{1}{6} \\ &= \frac{1}{12} \end{aligned}$$

If A and B are *independent events,* then the theoretical probability of the outcome "*A and B*" can be found by multiplying pr (A) and pr (B).

$$\text{pr } (A \textit{ and } B) = \text{pr } (A) \times \text{pr } (B)$$

Example 2: What is the theoretical probability of getting heads on the coin *and* a prime number of dots on the die in the experiment above?

$$\begin{aligned} \text{pr (heads } \textit{and} \text{ a prime)} &= \text{pr (heads)} \times \text{pr (a prime)} \\ &= \frac{1}{2} \times \frac{3}{6} \\ &= \frac{3}{12} \text{ or } \frac{1}{4} \end{aligned}$$

There are 3 primes—2, 3, and 5.

Exercises

A 1. If two outcomes are independent events, then one outcome (*does, does not*) depend on the other outcome.

2. If A and B are independent events, then you (*add, multiply*) pr (A) and pr (B) to find pr (A *and* B).

A coin is tossed *and* a die is rolled.

3. How many possible outcomes are there?

4. What is the theoretical probability of getting heads on the coin *and* 5 dots on the die?

5. What is the theoretical probability of getting tails on the coin *and* 1 dot on the die?

A penny is tossed *and* a nickel is tossed.

6. What is the theoretical probability of getting heads on the penny?

7. What is the theoretical probability of getting heads on the nickel?

8. What is the theoretical probability of getting heads on the penny *and* heads on the nickel?

B *A* and *B* are independent events. Find pr (*A and B*) if

9. pr $(A) = \frac{1}{3}$, pr $(B) = \frac{1}{3}$

10. pr $(A) = \frac{1}{5}$, pr $(B) = \frac{2}{5}$

11. pr $(A) = \frac{1}{2}$, pr $(B) = \frac{1}{4}$

12. pr $(A) = \frac{3}{8}$, pr $(B) = \frac{1}{4}$

13. pr $(A) = 0.8$, pr $(B) = 0.58$

14. pr $(A) = 0.3$, pr $(B) = 0.83$

A spinner has 6 regions of equal size—3 red, 2 white, and 1 blue. (The pointer can't stop between regions.) The spinner is spun once *and* a die is rolled. Find the following as fractions.

15. pr (red *and* 3)

16. pr (white *and* 4)

17. pr (white *and* an odd number)

18. pr (blue *and* an even number)

19. pr (blue *and* a prime number)

20. pr (red *and* a multiple of 3)

A red die and a white die are rolled. Find the following as fractions.

21. pr (red 4 *and* white 1)

22. pr (red 3 *and* white 6)

23. pr (red 2 *and* white even number)

24. pr (red 5 *and* white odd number)

25. pr (red odd number *and* white even number)

26. pr (red even number *and* white even number)

27. pr (red prime number *and* white multiple of 2)

28. pr (red multiple of 2 *and* white multiple of 3)

C 29. Suppose your probability of winning a car in contest A is $\frac{1}{100,000}$ and your probability of winning a TV set in contest B is $\frac{1}{50,000}$. (They are independent events.) What is your probability of winning the car *and* the TV set?

30. A basketball player who was fouled in the act of shooting is awarded two free throws. The player's free-throw average is 62% (the probability of making a free throw is 0.62). Find the probability (as a decimal) that the player will make *both* free throws. (They are independent events.)

Courtesy Parker Brothers

31. In Monopoly, two dice are rolled for each turn. The probability of rolling "doubles" is $\frac{1}{6}$. If doubles are rolled three times in a row, the player goes to "jail." What is the probability (as a fraction) of rolling doubles three times in a row? (They are independent events.)

CAREER CORNER

MATH IN PARAPROFESSIONS

You know that *paramedics* are specially trained helpers who work under a doctor's orders. There are other *paraprofessionals* too. These trained helpers work with some professional like an engineer, a lawyer, or a teacher. Here are just a few:

Agricultural Technician	Ecology Technician
Automotive Technician	Forestry Technician
Chemical Technician	Safety Technician
Child Health Associate	Social Work Aide
Community Aide	Teacher Aide
Dental Assistant	Urban Planning Technician

Most paraprofessions are very new. Some are just getting started. Others are jobs of the future. Probably the best way to become a paraprofessional is to finish high school and then take a special two-year course in a community college.

Some paraprofessions need no more math than you will get in this course. Others need more math in high school or in a community college. Here are some statistics and probability problems from the paraprofessions:

Courtesy E. P. A.

1. Forestry Technician: During the past 75 years a certain tree fungus that occurs in wet, hot summers appeared during 10 summers. A certain shrub blight that occurs in dry, cool summers appeared during 15 summers. What is the probability that either one or the other disease will appear during the next summer?

2. Chemical Technician: A certain chemical solution is used to control the growth of bacteria. During 30 tests the solution reduced the number of bacteria by the following per cents: 78, 79, 75, 80, 69, 73, 68, 73, 80, 65, 68, 68, 72, 71, 73, 73, 75, 76, 79, 76, 69, 69, 80, 67, 67, 65, 65, 66, 73, 76. Find the range of the solution's effectiveness.

3. Urban Planning Technician: The number of people per day that were in a park during the month of July are as follows: 135, 115, 145, 306, 215, 279, 25, 31, 95, 126, 161, 52, 226, 31, 16, 58, 152, 101, 175, 229, 176, 112, 92, 85, 20, 23, 37, 85, 139, 117, 99. Find the median and the mean.

Terms and Symbols Review

1. The ___ gives the low and the high numbers of a set of numbers.

2. The ___ is the most frequent number in a set of numbers.

3. The ___ is the number in the middle when the numbers in a set are listed in order.

4. To find the ___ of 3, 4, 4, 5, add the numbers and divide by 4.

5. Tossing heads and tossing tails are possible ___ for the experiment of tossing a coin.

6. A(n) ___ probability is found by doing an experiment.

Chapter 15 Review

15.1 Find the range.

1. 1, 5, 7, 8, 2, 10, 6

2. 125, 113, 104, 113, 184

Make a frequency table.

3. *25 numbers:* 8, 9, 9, 9, 10, 7, 6, 6, 6, 8, 10, 8, 9, 9, 6, 7, 6, 8, 9, 8, 10, 8, 10, 9, 9

4. *Number of students in 30 classrooms:* 26, 26, 26, 27, 27, 27, 25, 28, 26, 26, 26, 26, 28, 28, 29, 29, 25, 27, 27, 26, 29, 28, 26, 25, 27, 27, 26, 28, 26, 27

15.2 Use the graph at the right for Exercises 5–7.

5. What is the mode?

6. How many students received a score of 7?

7. How many students received a score of over 7?

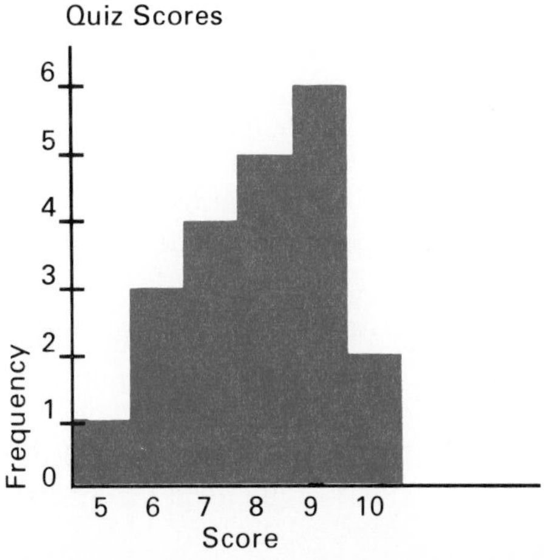

Find the median. 15.3

8. 6, 9, 11, 15, 21

9. 5, 12, 16, 24

Find the mean. 15.4

10. 12, 15, 16, 13, 10, 5

11. 1.8, 4.6, 3.9, 8.5, 1.7

12. For an 18-game season, a soccer team's mean goals per game was 3. Find the total number of goals scored during the season.

A spinner has 6 regions—3 red, 2 blue, and 1 green—all the same size. (The pointer can't stop between regions.) Find the following as fractions. 15.5

13. pr (red)

14. pr (blue)

15. pr (white)

16. If *all* the regions of the spinner above were red, find pr (red).

17. The pointer was spun 100 times and stopped on a blue region 35 times. Find ex pr (blue) as a decimal.

18. Draw a tree diagram to show the possible results of flipping a dime and then flipping a quarter. What is the probability that both coins will land showing heads? 15.6

19. If A and B are mutually exclusive events, you (*add, multiply*) pr (A) and pr (B) to find pr (A *or* B). 15.7

A and B are mutually exclusive events. Find pr (A *or* B) if

20. pr $(A) = \frac{1}{5}$, pr $(B) = \frac{3}{5}$

21. pr $(A) = \frac{1}{2}$, pr $(B) = \frac{1}{4}$

22. For the spinner described above, find pr (red *or* blue) as a fraction.

23. If A and B are independent events, you (*add, multiply*) pr (A) and pr (B) to find pr (A *and* B). 15.8

A and B are independent events. Find pr (A *and* B) if

24. pr $(A) = \frac{1}{2}$, pr $(B) = \frac{1}{3}$

25. pr $(A) = \frac{2}{3}$, pr $(B) = \frac{3}{5}$

The spinner for Exercises 15–17 is spun once, and a die is rolled once. Find the following as fractions.

26. pr (green *and* 5)

27. pr (blue *and* an odd number)

28. pr (red *and* a multiple of 3)

Chapter 15 Test

Use the following set of numbers in Exercises 1–3.

12, 15, 16, 11, 15, 14, 12, 12

Find

1. the range **2.** the mode **3.** the median

4. Make a frequency table for the following set of numbers: 17, 16, 18, 15, 18, 18, 18, 15, 15, 17, 18, 19, 17, 18, 15, 21, 15, 19, 16, 20.

5. Make a graph for the numbers in Exercise 4.

Use the following set of numbers in Exercises 6–7.

40, 23, 34, 10, 28, 11, 12, 31, 25, 29, 11, 34, 23, 47, 34

6. Find the mode. **7.** Find the median.

8. Find the mean for 8, 12, 10, 7, 3.

9. For a 25-game season, a basketball player's mean points per game was 12. What was the total number of points scored by the player?

There are 10 marbles in a bag—6 white, 3 red, and 1 blue—all the same size. The marbles are thoroughly mixed and one is picked by chance. Find the following as decimals.

RATE YOURSELF

Number Correct	
17	Superior
15–16	Excellent
13–14	Good
9–12	Fair
0–8	Poor

10. pr (white) **11.** pr (red) **12.** pr (blue)

13. pr (white *or* red) **14.** pr (red *or* blue)

One marble is picked from the bag in the experiment above, and a die is rolled. Find the following as fractions.

15. pr (white *and* 1) **16.** pr (red *and* an odd number)

17. Suppose the bag above contains only three marbles—red, blue, and white. A coin is tossed and a marble is picked. Draw a tree diagram to show the possible results.

Activity 1: Do each experiment below. Record the results of each experiment in a table like the one on page 495. Then find the experimental probability for each possible outcome.

a. Toss a coin 50 times.

b. Roll a die 60 times.

c. If a cork is tossed, it can land in one of the following ways:

large end up

small end up

on its side

Put five corks in a paper cup and shake the cup. Then turn the cup over quickly, spilling the corks onto your desk. Count the number of corks landing each way. (This is the same as doing five trials with one cork.) Do this 40 times for a total of 200 trials.

Activity 2: Make a top, following the steps below.

1. Cut a 3- by 3-inch square out of a piece of thin cardboard.

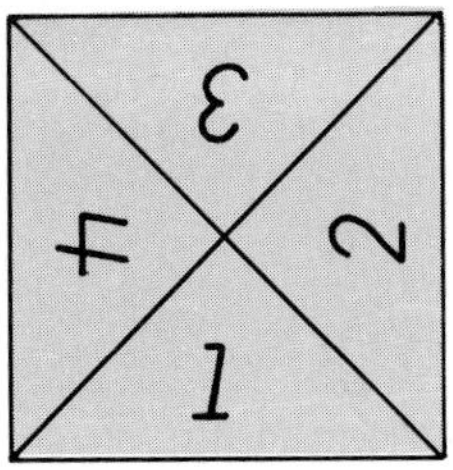

2. Draw a line between each pair of opposite corners. Number the 4 regions.

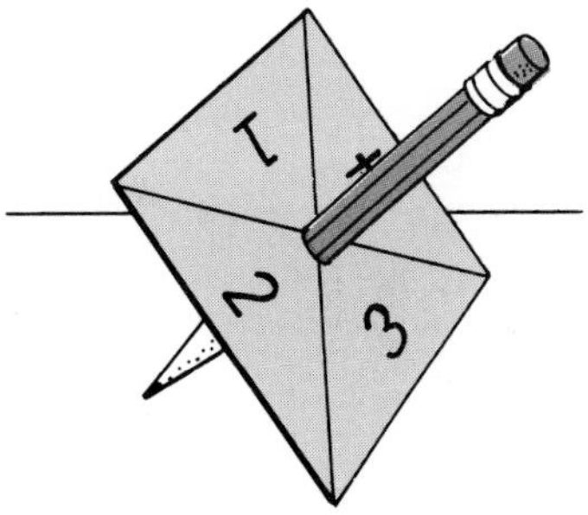

3. Make a small hole where the lines cross and push a short pencil through it.

To spin the top, hold the pencil straight up and down, and place the sharpened end on your desk top. The piece of cardboard should be "level" with your desk top. Then give the pencil a turn and let go. When the top stops, a side of one of the regions will be resting on the desk top (as shown in step 3 above). The number in that region is the outcome of the spin.

a. Spin the top 60 times, recording the outcomes as in Activity 1. Then find the experimental probability for each of the 4 possible outcomes.

b. Cut a 3- by 4-inch rectangle out of a piece of thin cardboard. Then follow steps 2 and 3 above to make a second top. Repeat part **a,** using the second top.

Terms and Symbols Review: Chapters 8–15

Which term or symbol in parentheses is the best choice?

Ch. 8

1. The x-axis is (*horizontal, vertical, a point*).

2. The negative direction on the y-axis is (*down, up, left*).

Ch. 9

3. The equation $\frac{5}{2} = \frac{10}{4}$ is a (*ratio, proportion, per cent*).

4. For $\frac{2}{3} = \frac{6}{9}$, 2 and 9 are the (*means, extremes, cross products*).

Ch. 10

5. In similar triangles, corresponding sides are always (*equal in length, proportional, overlapping*).

6. In similar triangles, corresponding angles have the same (*measure, name, sides*).

Ch. 11

7. The opposite of $\frac{3}{4}$ is ($\frac{4}{3}$, $-\frac{3}{4}$, $3 \div 4$).

8. Another way to name $^{-}3 \div {}^{-}4$ is ($\frac{3}{4}$, $\frac{4}{3}$, $-\frac{3}{4}$).

9. The sum of $-\frac{3}{4}$ and $-\frac{3}{4}$ is (*positive, negative, zero*).

Ch. 12

10. $^{-}1\frac{1}{2}$ is the (*reciprocal, opposite, product*) of $-\frac{2}{3}$.

11. 10^{-2} has a value of ($^{-}$*0.02*, *100*, *0.01*).

12. 1.34×10^2 is scientific notation for (*13.4*, *134*, *1340*).

Ch. 13

13. In a right triangle, the side opposite the right angle is the (*hypotenuse, square root, shortest side*).

14. The nonnegative square root of 9 is ($\sqrt{9}$, $^{-}\sqrt{9}$, 9^2).

15. Every positive number has (*0*, *1*, *2*) square root(s).

Ch. 14

16. A binomial has (*1*, *2*, *3*) term(s).

17. $2x^2$ and $^{-}3x^2$ are (*like, unlike, binomial*) terms.

Ch. 15

18. For 8, 5, 6, 7, 5, the (*range, mode, median*) is 6.

19. A(n) (*trial, experimental, theoretical*) probability is found without doing an experiment.

Ch. 8

1. Use the rule to complete the table below.

$y = 3x - 1$

x	1	2	3	4	5
y					

2. Draw a line graph for the table below.

x	0	1	2	3	4
y	$^-2$	0	2	4	6

Write the ordered pair for each point on the graph at the right.

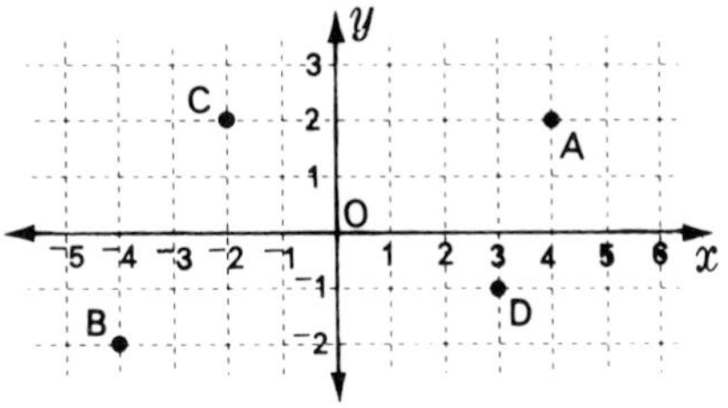

3. A 4. B

5. C 6. D

7. Is the graph for Exercises 3–6 the graph of a function?

8. Is the set of ordered pairs in Exercise 2 a function?

Copy and graph the following.

9. a slide 3 units up

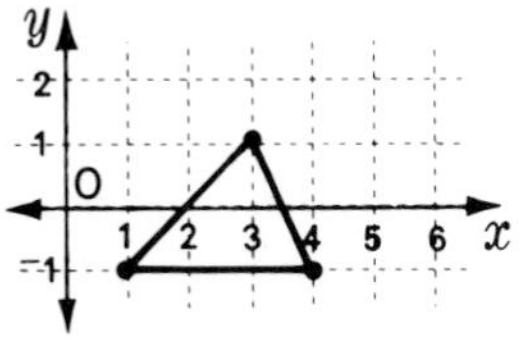

10. a 1-to-2 reduction

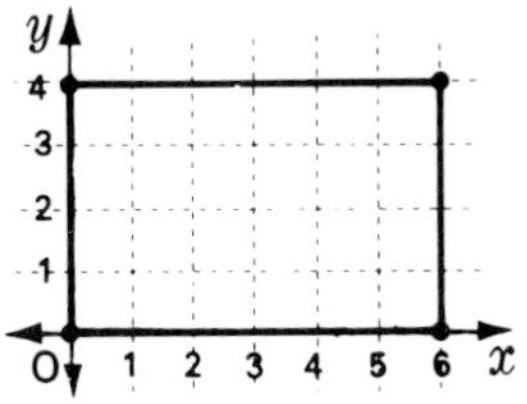

Copy and complete.

Ch. 9

	per cent	fraction	decimal
11.		$\frac{2}{5}$	
13.			0.48

	per cent	fraction or mixed number	decimal
12.	72%		
14.	130%		

Solve.

15. $\frac{7}{5} = \frac{n}{35}$ 16. $\frac{9}{2} = \frac{27}{x}$ 17. $\frac{6}{a} = \frac{18}{39}$

18. What is 26% of 75? 19. 17 is what per cent of 50?

20. 40% of what number is 10? 21. 15% of 22 is what number?

22. A basketball player attempted 15 free throws and made 6 of them. What per cent of attempted free throws did the player make?

Ch. 10

23. Name the corresponding sides and the corresponding angles for these similar triangles.

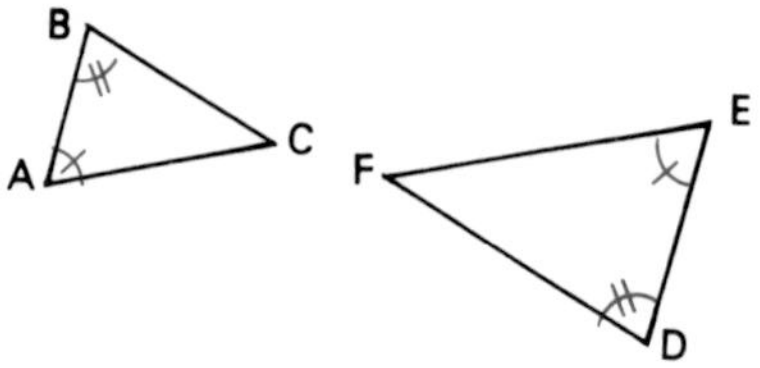

24. Which letter should replace each question mark?

a. $\frac{a}{e} = \frac{c}{?}$ **b.** $\frac{c}{f} = \frac{?}{d}$

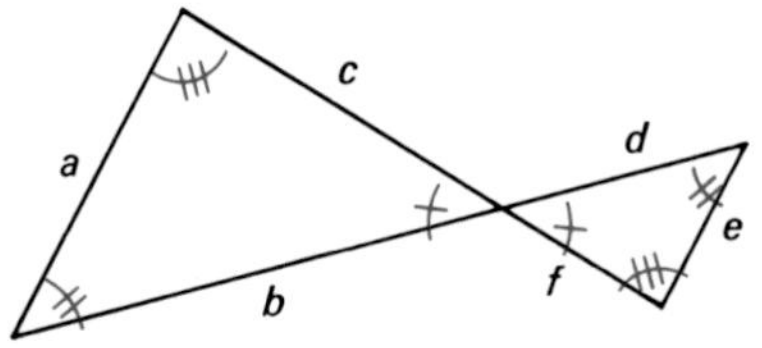

25. What is the actual distance between X and Y? Between Y and Z? Between X and Z?

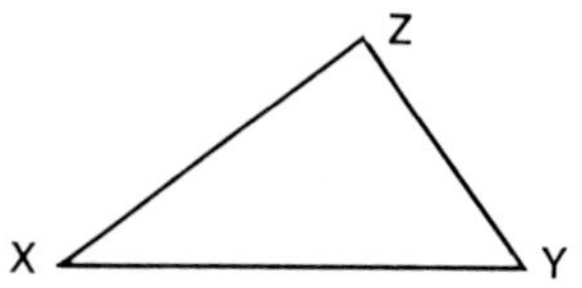

Scale: 1 in. = 40 ft

26. What is the height of the sign? (The triangles are similar.)

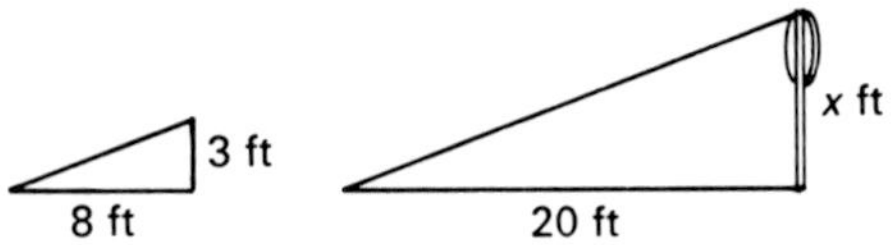

Ch. 11

Find each sum or difference.

27. $^{-}5.71 + 3.83$ **28.** $^{-}1.46 + {}^{-}3.57$ **29.** $^{-}3.47 - 8.16$

30. $2.86 - {}^{-}5.14$ **31.** $-\frac{1}{4} + (-\frac{3}{8})$ **32.** $\frac{3}{5} + (-\frac{1}{10})$

33. $\frac{1}{6} - (-\frac{2}{3})$ **34.** $-\frac{7}{10} - \frac{1}{4}$ **35.** $^{-}3\frac{1}{4} + {}^{-}4\frac{3}{4}$

36. $^{-}2\frac{1}{3} + 1\frac{2}{3}$ **37.** $(-\frac{7}{16}) + 2\frac{5}{8}$ **38.** $^{-}3\frac{3}{4} - 2\frac{1}{2}$

Solve.

39. $z - 5.7 = 7.2$ **40.** $y + {}^{-}3.6 = 1.2$

41. $c - 8.7 = {}^{-}11.4$ **42.** $\frac{7}{10} + a = -\frac{4}{5}$

43. $y - (-\frac{2}{3}) = -\frac{1}{6}$ **44.** $\frac{5}{12} = x - \frac{1}{2}$

45. $n + \frac{1}{4} = -\frac{3}{4}$ **46.** $\frac{1}{5} = y - \frac{1}{10}$

Solve this problem.

47. Yesterday Betty's body temperature was 101.2 °F. Today her temperature is 98.6 °F. What was the change in her temperature readings from yesterday to today?

Find each product or quotient. Ch. 12

48. $^{-}2.3 \times 4.5$ **49.** $0.0063 \div {}^{-}0.003$ **50.** $({}^{-}16.2)({}^{-}8.5)$

51. $-\frac{2}{5} \times \frac{3}{5}$ **52.** $\frac{7}{10} \div (-\frac{1}{2})$ **53.** $-\frac{9}{16} \div (-\frac{3}{4})$

54. $-\frac{3}{8} \div {}^{-}2\frac{1}{4}$ **55.** $19\frac{4}{10} \times {}^{-}2\frac{1}{10}$ **56.** $^{-}168 \div 5\frac{3}{5}$

Solve.

57. $\frac{x}{6.1} = {}^{-}3$ **58.** $^{-}25.9 = {}^{-}7.4n$ **59.** $-\frac{3}{10}y = \frac{3}{5}$

60. $\frac{t-5}{6} = -\frac{7}{18}$ **61.** $^{-}2.1r + 3.4 = 9.7$ **62.** $-\frac{5}{9} = \frac{2}{3}d$

63. Name the reciprocal, if any.

a. $\frac{4}{15}$ **b.** $^{-}1\frac{2}{3}$ **c.** $^{-}5$ **d.** 0

64. Express in scientific notation.

a. 7234.7 **b.** 0.000378 **c.** 42.1

65. From the formula $1000k = tw$, find the number (w) of watts required by a power tool that uses 21 kilowatt-hours (k) of electricity in 12 hours (t).

Find each square root as a whole number, fraction, or decimal, as given. Ch. 13

66. $\sqrt{25}$ **67.** $\sqrt{\frac{4}{49}}$ **68.** $\sqrt{0.36}$ **69.** $\sqrt{\frac{81}{100}}$

Find each square root by using the table on page 422.

70. $\sqrt{7}$ **71.** $\sqrt{41}$ **72.** $\sqrt{80}$ **73.** $\sqrt{200}$

Find the positive solution of each equation.

74. $x^2 = 64$ **75.** $x^2 = 31$ **76.** $x^2 + 3 = 52$

77. $x^2 - 5 = 76$ **78.** $x^2 - 4 = 18$ **79.** $x^2 + 20 = 70$

Use the Pythagorean Property to solve.

80. What is the distance from A to B?

81. What is the height of the kite?

Ex. 80

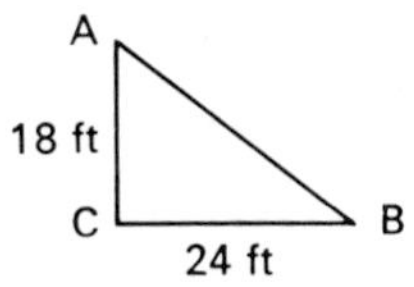

Ex. 81

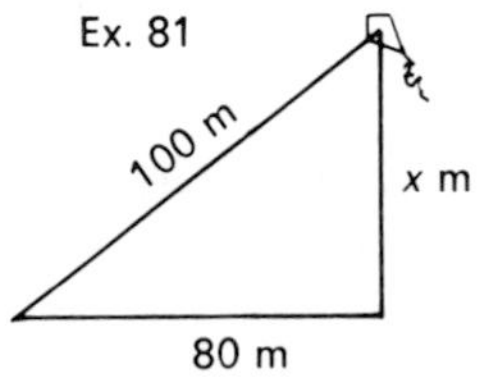

Ch. 14

Do the indicated operation.

82. $12x^2 + {}^-10x^2$

83. ${}^-8x + 3x + {}^-5x$

84. $(3y + {}^-1) + ({}^-5y + 7)$

85. $12y - {}^-9y$

86. $(2x^2 + 1) - ({}^-5x^2 + {}^-3)$

87. $a^3 \cdot a^4$

88. $4y^2({}^-5y)$

89. $(5y^2 + 3y)({}^-2y)$

90. $(x + 5)(x + 3)$

91. $({}^-5x + 4)({}^-3x + 1)$

92. $\dfrac{32x^4}{{}^-8x}$

93. $\dfrac{9y^3 + 15y^2 + {}^-3y}{3y}$

Give an equation for the problem. Then solve the problem.

94. Josh bought two bicycle parts costing a total of \$19. One part cost \$5 more than the other. How much did he pay for each part?

Ch. 15

Use the following set of numbers for Exercises 95–99.

3, 3, 5, 1, 4, 2, 1, 3, 2, 3

95. Find the range.

96. Find the mode.

97. Find the median.

98. Make a frequency table.

99. Make a graph.

100. Find the mean for 10, 15, 12, 10, 8.

There are 10 marbles in a bag—6 red, 3 black, and 1 white—all the same size. They are thoroughly mixed, and one marble is picked by chance.

101. In 100 trials (the picked marble was replaced after each trial), a black marble was picked 32 times. Find ex pr (black).

Find these theoretical probabilities for the marble situation above.

102. pr (red)

103. pr (red *or* white)

104. A coin is tossed and a marble is picked from the bag of marbles described above. Find pr (heads *and* black).

Complete each sentence.

1. There are ____ centimeters in one meter. 1.1

2. There are ____ millimeters in one meter.

3. There are ____ inches in one foot. 2.7

4. There are ____ inches in one yard.

5. There are ____ feet in one yard.

Use the formula to find each of the following:

6. Find the area of the parallelogram. 2.8

   $A = bh$

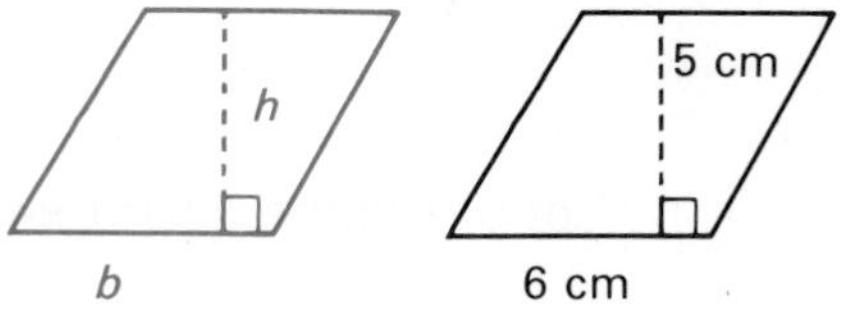

7. Find the area of the triangle.

   $A = bh \div 2$

8. Find the perimeter of the triangle. 3.2

   $p = a + b + c$

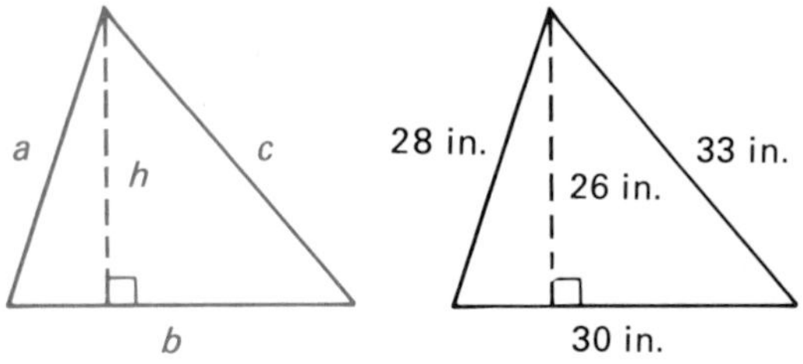

9. Find the area of the circle. Use 3.14 for π. 5.7

   $A = \pi r^2$

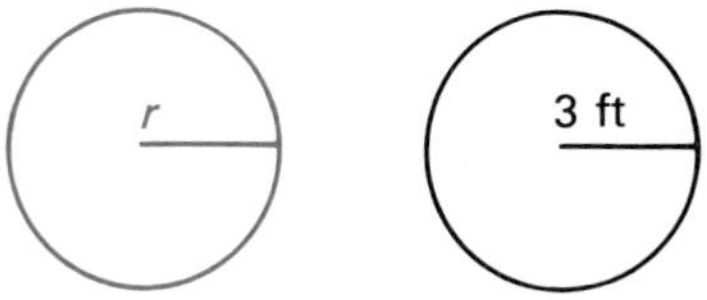

10. Find the volume of the prism. 2.8

    $V = \textit{area of base} \times h = Bh$

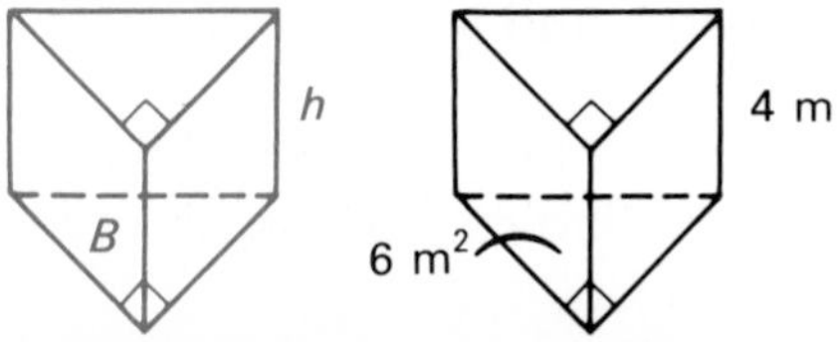

H. Armstrong Roberts

16 GEOMETRY

Geometry is a branch of mathematics that studies the size, shape, and location of objects in space.

Many occupations require a knowledge of geometric figures. They also require an ability to find perimeter, area, and volume.

Points, Lines, and Planes

16.1

A **point** is a location in space. It is named with a capital letter. A point has no dimensions.

point A

A **line** is a set of points that extends indefinitely in two opposite directions. A line is named by using two points on the line. Since only one line passes through two points, you could say that two points determine a line. A line has only one dimension, length.

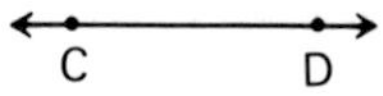

$\overleftrightarrow{CD}$

line CD

A **line segment** is part of a line with two *endpoints*. A line segment is named by using both endpoints.

$\overline{GH}$

segment GH

A **ray** is a part of a line that includes one endpoint and extends indefinitely in one direction. A ray is named by using the endpoint and one other point on the ray.

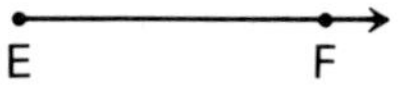

$\overrightarrow{EF}$

ray EF

An **angle** is formed by two rays with a common endpoint called a *vertex*. An angle is named by using the vertex or by using a point on one ray, then the vertex, and then a point on the other ray.

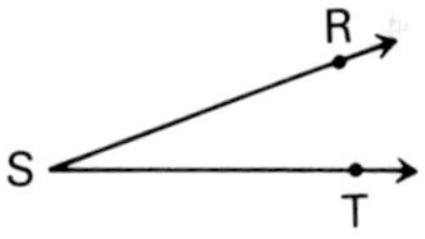

$\angle S$ or $\angle RST$

angle S

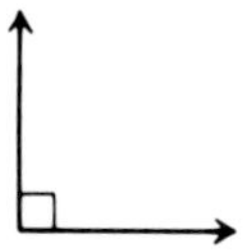

A **right angle** looks like a square corner.

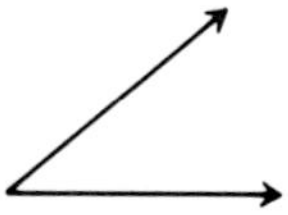

An **acute angle** is smaller than a right angle.

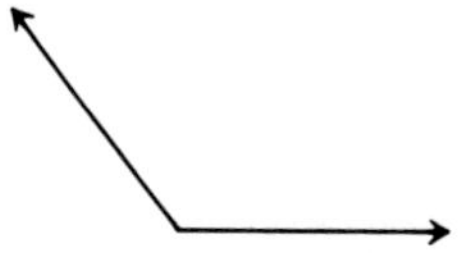

An **obtuse angle** is larger than a right angle.

Intersecting lines meet in a point. When two lines intersect, four angles are formed. If the angles are right angles, the lines are called *perpendicular lines*.

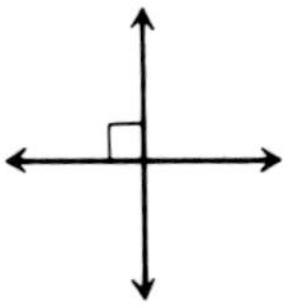

Parallel lines are lines in a plane that do not intersect.

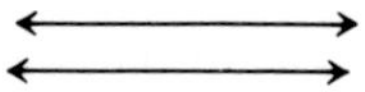

A **plane** is a set of points that is "flat" and extends without end in all directions. A plane is named by using any three *noncollinear* (not on the same line) points on the plane. Since only one plane passes through three noncollinear points, you could say that three noncollinear points determine a plane.

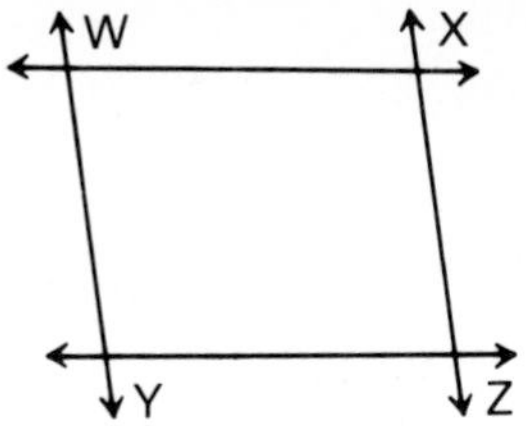

plane XYZ

A **half plane** is determined by one line in the plane and the part of the plane on only one side of that line.

Space is the set of all points and has three dimensions—length, width, and thickness.

Exercises

[A] Tell whether each of the following best describes a point, a line, or a plane.

1. a desk top
2. a corner of a box
3. a tip of a pencil
4. an edge of a box

Name a physical object that suggests each of the following:

5. a point
6. a line
7. a plane
8. a ray
9. a line segment
10. parallel lines
11. a right angle
12. space
13. perpendicular lines

Tell whether each of the following is acute, right, or obtuse.

14.

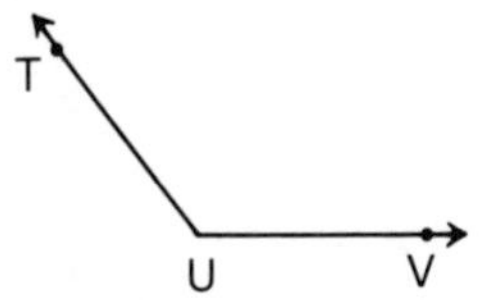

15.

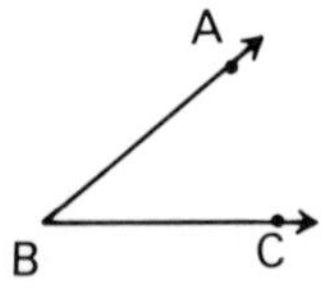

16.

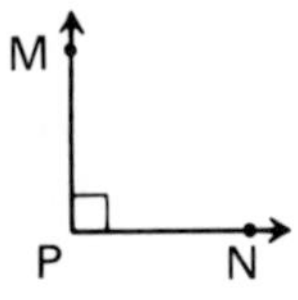

Using the angle in Exercise 14, give the

17. name.
18. vertex.
19. sides.

B Use the figure at the right for Exercises 20–26. (Remember, the lines can be extended.)

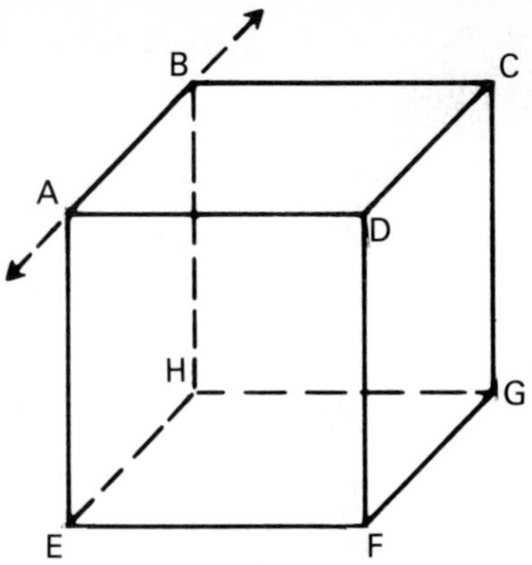

20. Are $\overleftrightarrow{AB}$ and $\overleftrightarrow{EH}$ parallel lines?

21. Are $\overleftrightarrow{BH}$ and $\overleftrightarrow{CG}$ perpendicular lines?

22. Name three lines that meet at point F.

23. Name a plane that is parallel to plane ABE.

24. Name two planes that intersect to form $\overleftrightarrow{DF}$.

25. Name three planes that contain point H.

26. Name a line that intersects plane ABC in only one point.

Draw each figure.

27. a line segment

28. a pair of perpendicular lines

29. a ray

30. a pair of parallel lines

C 31. two perpendicular rays with the same endpoint

32. two perpendicular rays that do not have the same endpoint

Skew lines are lines in different planes that are not parallel and that will never intersect. Use the figure above for Exercises 33–40.

33. Are $\overleftrightarrow{BH}$ and $\overleftrightarrow{EF}$ skew lines?

34. Are $\overleftrightarrow{DC}$ and $\overleftrightarrow{BH}$ skew lines?

Tell whether each pair of lines is parallel, perpendicular, or skew.

35. $\overleftrightarrow{HG}$ and $\overleftrightarrow{FG}$

36. $\overleftrightarrow{EA}$ and $\overleftrightarrow{BC}$

37. $\overleftrightarrow{AD}$ and $\overleftrightarrow{GH}$

38. $\overleftrightarrow{DF}$ and $\overleftrightarrow{EH}$

39. $\overleftrightarrow{EF}$ and $\overleftrightarrow{HE}$

40. $\overleftrightarrow{DF}$ and $\overleftrightarrow{BH}$

16.2 Polygons, Perimeter, and Circumference

Many figures are formed by joining the endpoints of line segments. If the line segments do not cross and the figure is closed, the figure is a **polygon.**

triangle

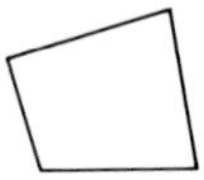

quadrilateral

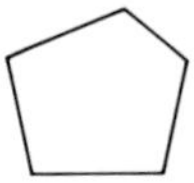

pentagon

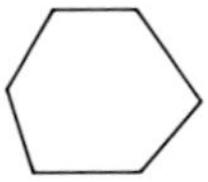

hexagon

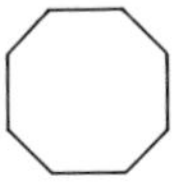

octagon

A regular polygon has all sides *congruent* (the same length) and all angles congruent (the same measure).

Triangles may be classified according to their sides.

scalene triangle
no sides congruent

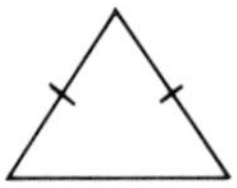

isosceles triangle
at least two congruent sides

equilateral triangle
all sides congruent

Triangles may also be classified according to their angles.

acute triangle
all acute angles

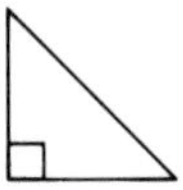

right triangle
one right angle

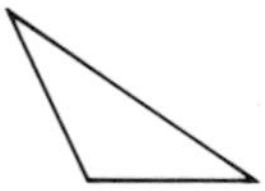

obtuse triangle
one obtuse angle

Some special quadrilaterals are shown.

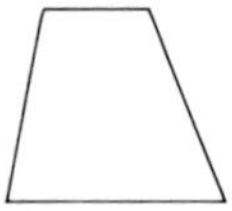

trapezoid
exactly one pair of parallel sides

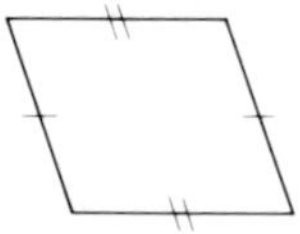

parallelogram
two pairs of parallel sides

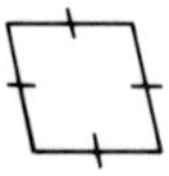

rhombus
parallelogram with four congruent sides

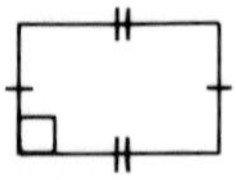

rectangle
parallelogram with four right angles

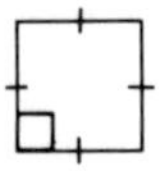

square
rectangle with four congruent sides

To find the perimeter of a polygon, add the lengths of the sides.

Example 1: Find the perimeter.

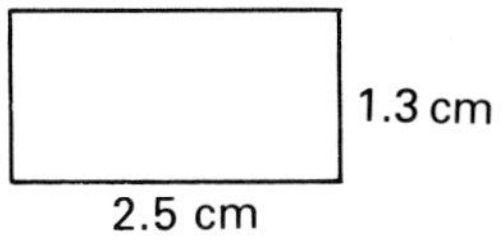

$2.5 + 1.3 + 2.5 + 1.3 = 7.6$

The perimeter is 7.6 cm.

Sometimes you may have to measure a side of a polygon.

Example 2: Find the length of $\overline{AB}$ to the nearest $\frac{1}{8}$ inch.

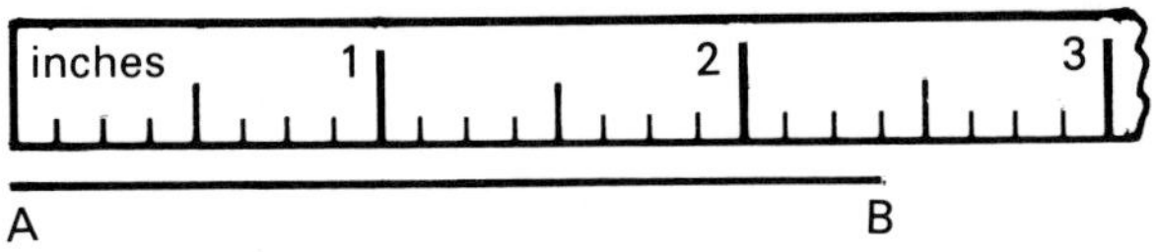

Read the measure to the nearest $\frac{1}{8}$ inch.

Be sure to align the end of the ruler or the zero mark with the endpoint of the segment.

$\overline{AB}$ is $2\frac{3}{8}$ in. long.

Example 3: Find the length of $\overline{CD}$ to the nearest centimeter.

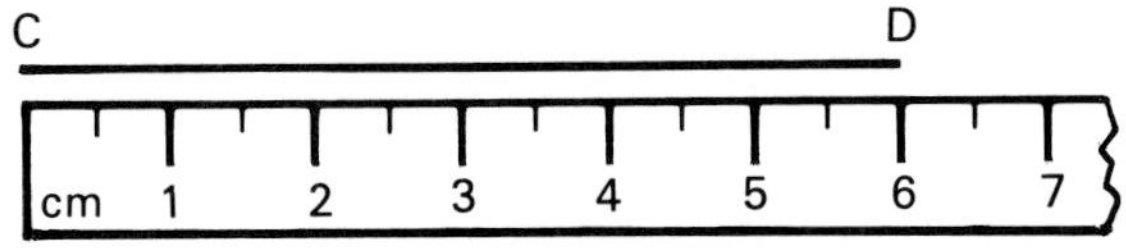

Read the measure to the nearest centimeter.

$\overline{CD}$ is 6 cm long.

The circumference of a circle is the distance around. You can use the following two formulas to find the circumference.

$C = \pi d$ The circumference is equal to π times the diameter.
$C = 2\pi r$ The circumference is equal to 2 times π times the radius.

Example 4: Find the circumference. Use 3.14 for π.

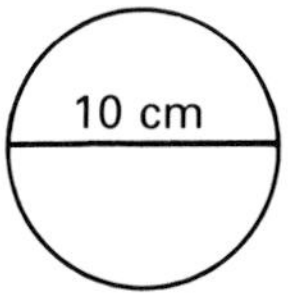

$$\begin{aligned} C &= \pi d \\ &= 3.14 \times 10 \\ &= 31.4 \end{aligned}$$

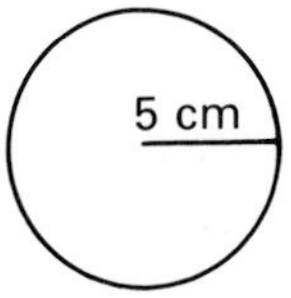

$$\begin{aligned} C &= 2\pi r \\ &= 2 \times 3.14 \times 5 \\ &= 31.4 \end{aligned}$$

The circumference is 31.4 cm.

Exercises

A Match each name with the letter of the figure.

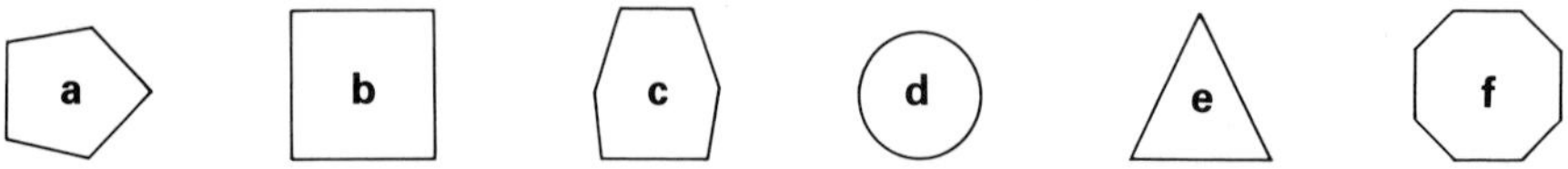

1. triangle 2. quadrilateral 3. hexagon 4. octagon

Classify each triangle according to its sides.

5. 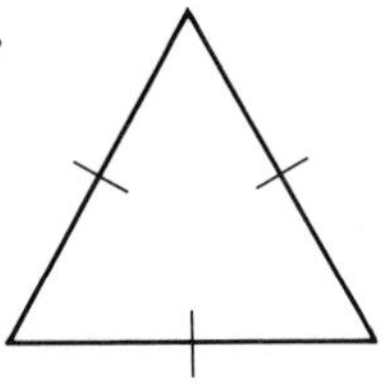

6. 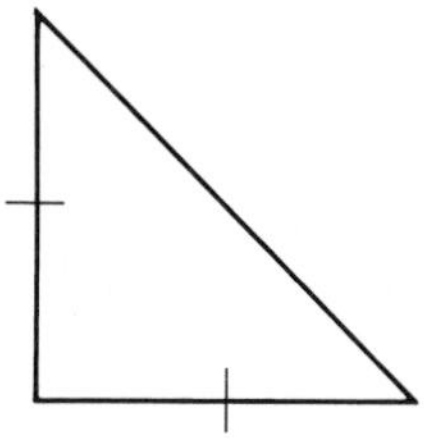

7. 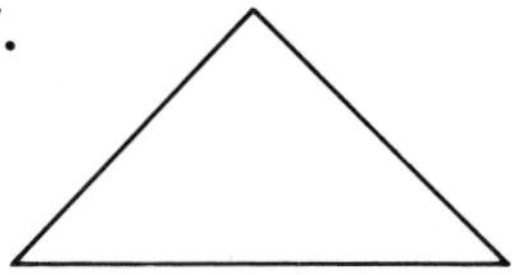

Classify each triangle according to its angles.

8. 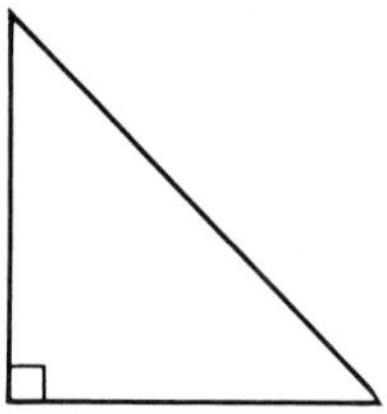

9. 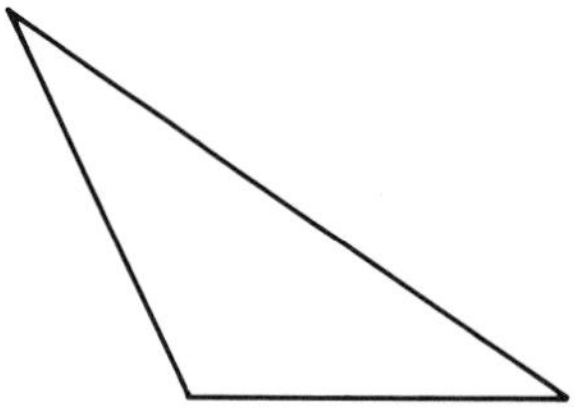

10. 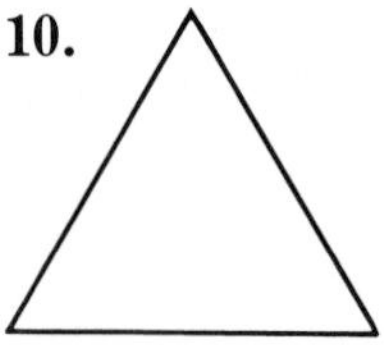

Measure each segment to the nearest $\frac{1}{8}$ inch.

11. —————— 12. ————— 13. ——

14. ———————————— 15. —————————

Measure each segment to the nearest centimeter.

16. —————— 17. —— 18. ————

19. —————————— 20. ————————

B Draw line segments with the following lengths.

21. $4\frac{3}{8}$ in. 22. $2\frac{5}{8}$ in. 23. 3 cm 24. 4 cm 25. $5\frac{1}{2}$ in.

26. $1\frac{1}{4}$ in. 27. 12 cm 28. 15 cm 29. $\frac{7}{8}$ in. 30. $\frac{3}{4}$ in.

Find each perimeter.

31.
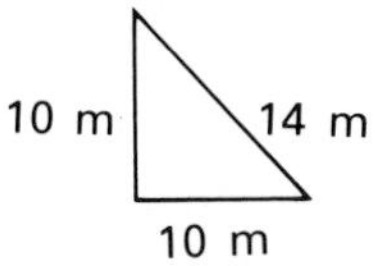

32.
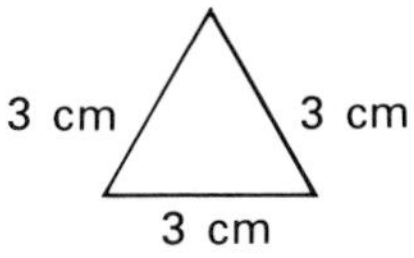

33.
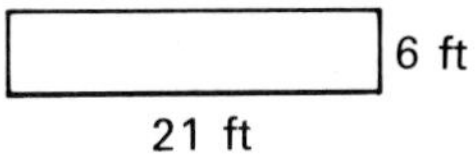

34.
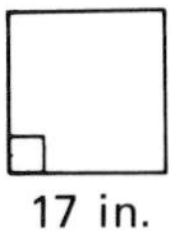

35.
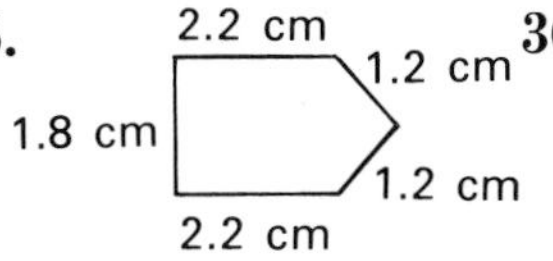

36.
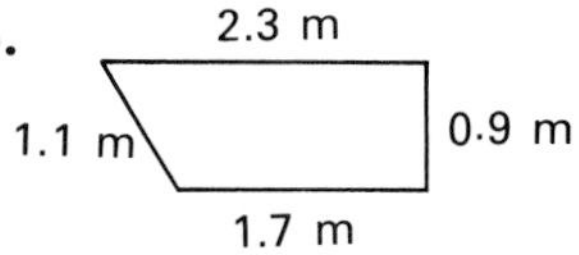

37. a regular hexagon, where each side is 24 cm

38. a rectangle with a length of 12 m and a width of 8 m

39. a square, where each side is $5\frac{3}{8}$ ft

40. a parallelogram with a length of $9\frac{1}{2}$ in. and a width of 6 in.

Find each circumference. Use 3.14 for π.

41.
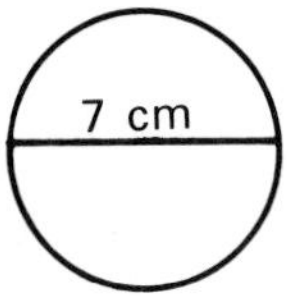

42.
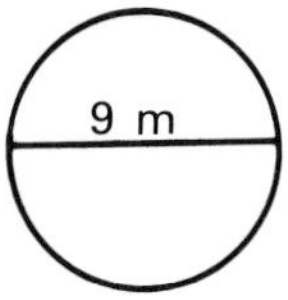

43.
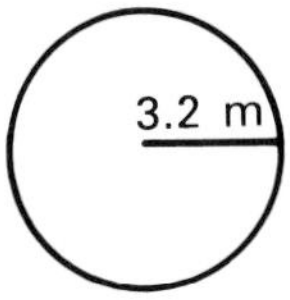

44.
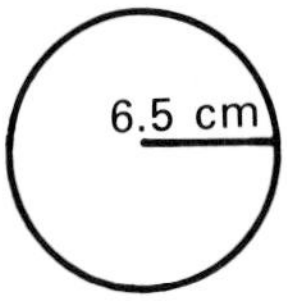

45. a diameter of 3.6 m

46. a radius of 15.6 cm

C Measure each side of the polygons to the nearest $\frac{1}{8}$ inch and give the perimeter for each polygon.

47.
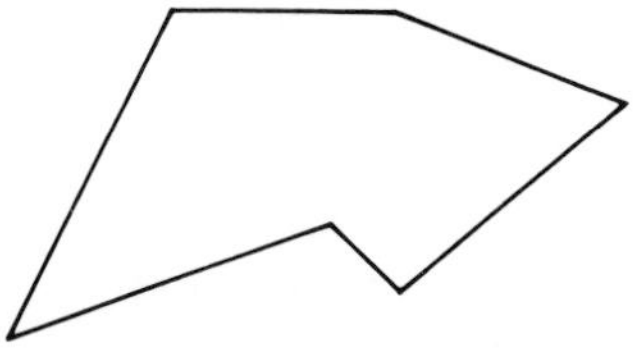

48.
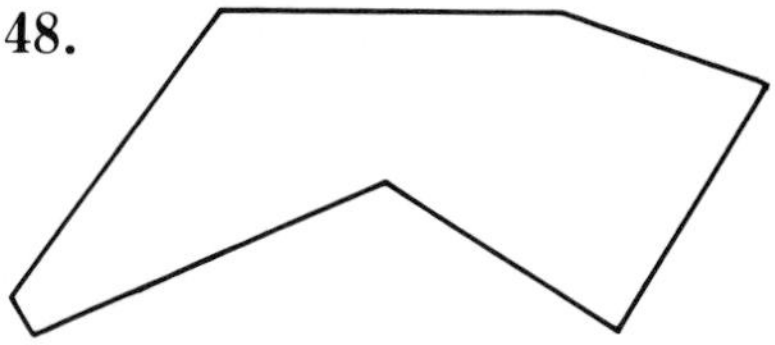

49. The distance between bases on a baseball diamond is 90 ft. How far does a batter run when he hits a home run?

50. What distance do you ride in one turn of a Ferris wheel when you sit 20 ft from the center?

51. Are all squares rectangles?

52. Are all rectangles squares?

53. Are all rhombuses squares?

54. Are all squares rhombuses?

Area

Example 1: Find the area of the rectangle.

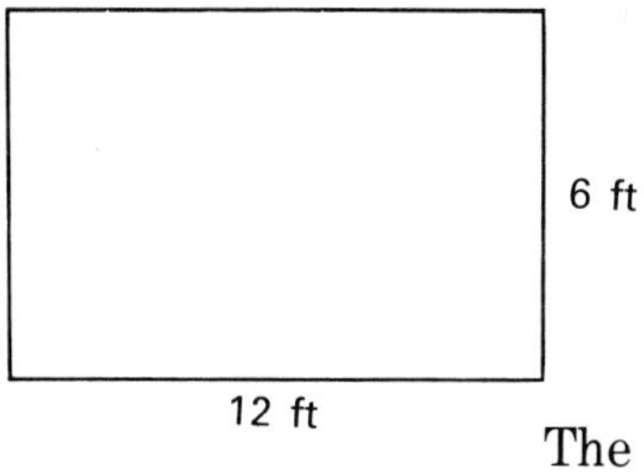

Area, length, width

$A = l \times w$

$= 12 \times 6$

$= 72$

The area is 72 sq. ft.

Example 2: Find the area of each triangle.

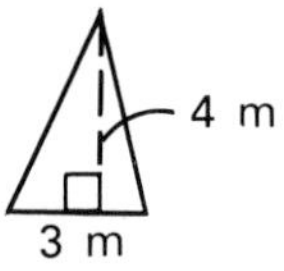

Area, base, height

$A = bh \div 2$

$= 3 \times 4 \div 2$

$= 6$

The area is 6 m^2.

Note that the height is perpendicular to the base. If the triangle is a right triangle, the sides of the right angle are the base and the height.

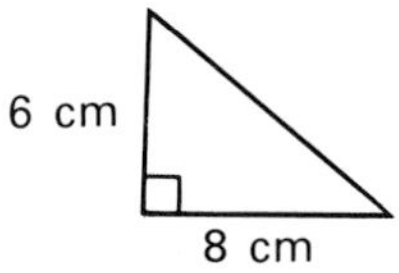

$A = bh \div 2$

$= 8 \times 6 \div 2$

$= 24$

The area is 24 cm^2.

Example 3: Find the area of the circle. Use 3.14 for π.

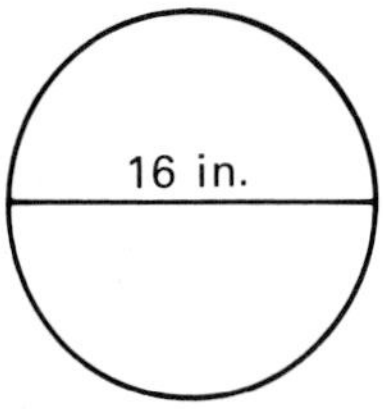

Area, radius

$A = \pi r^2$

$= 3.14(8)^2$

$= 200.96$

The diameter is given as 16 in. Divide by 2 to find the radius because the formula uses *r*.

The area is 200.96 sq in.

Exercises

A

1. How many square feet are in one square yard?
2. How many square centimeters are in one square meter?
3. How many square meters are in one square kilometer?
4. How many square inches are in one square foot?

B Find the area of each figure. Use 3.14 for π.

5. 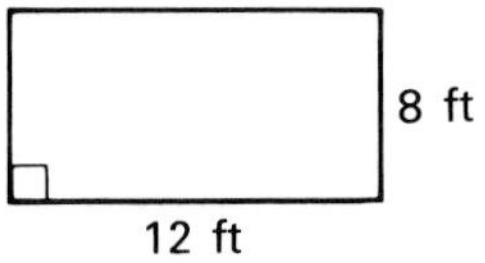

6. 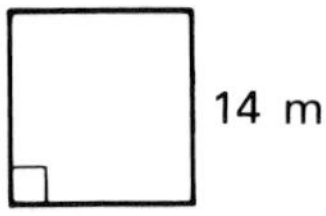

7. 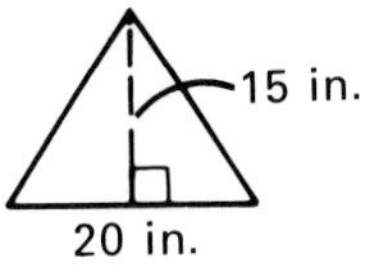

8. 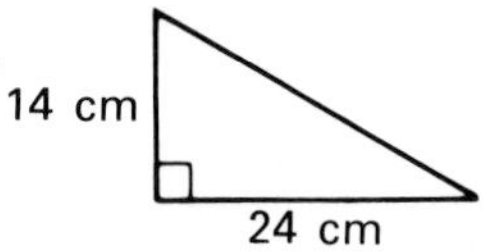

9. 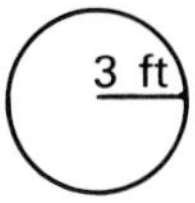

10. 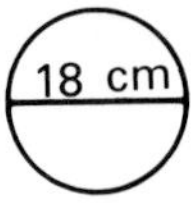

11. The official U.S. flag is 4 ft wide and $7\frac{1}{2}$ ft long. What is the area of the flag?

12. The screen of a television set is $18\frac{1}{2}$ in. wide and 14 in. high. What is the area of the screen?

13. What is the area of a circular skating rink that has a 140-ft diameter?

14. How much felt is used in a pennant with a base of 12 in. and a height of 30 in.?

C 15. Find the cost of carpeting a floor that is 15 ft by 12 ft at $24.95 per square yard.

16. To the nearest foot, what is the area of the floor space that remains uncovered if a rug with a 42-in. diameter is placed on a floor that is 14 ft by 10 ft?

Find the area of each figure.

17. 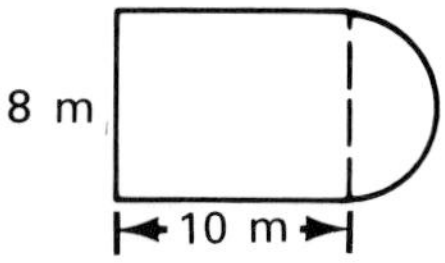

18. 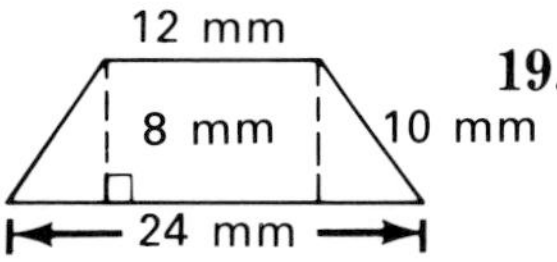

19. 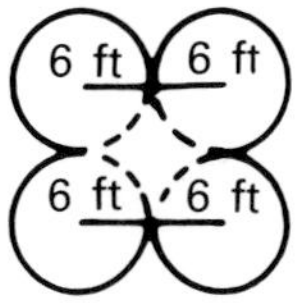

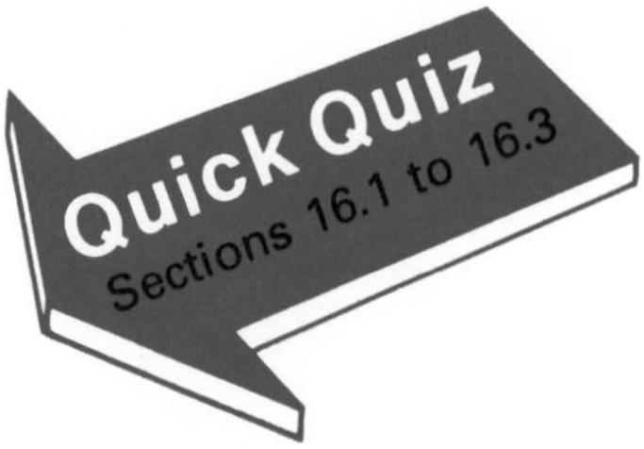

Draw each of the following:

1. $\overline{AB}$

2. $\overleftrightarrow{CD}$

3. $\overrightarrow{EF}$

Find the perimeter of each figure.

4. 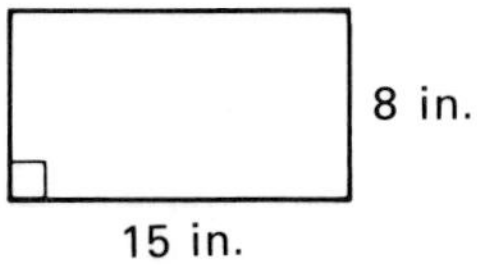

5. 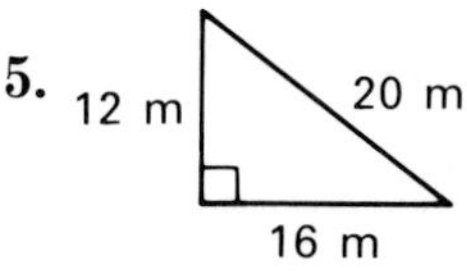

6. 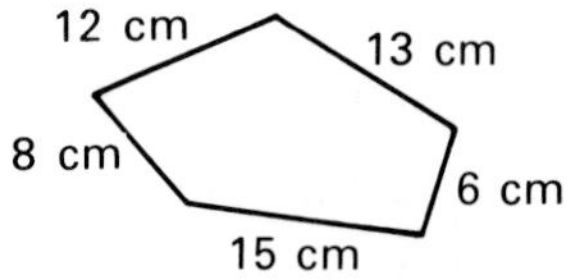

7. Find the area of the figure in Exercise 4.

8. Find the area of the figure in Exercise 5.

16.4

Surface Area

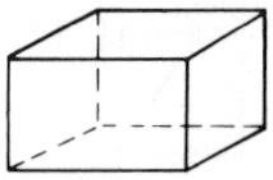

rectangular prism

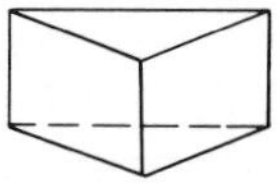

triangular prism

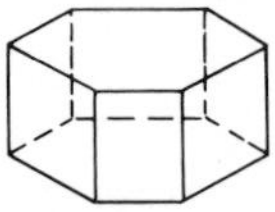

hexagonal prism

The solids shown above are **polyhedrons.** The faces (top, bottom, and sides) are all polygons.

> The surface area of a prism is the sum of the areas of the faces.

Example 1: Find the surface area of the following prism:

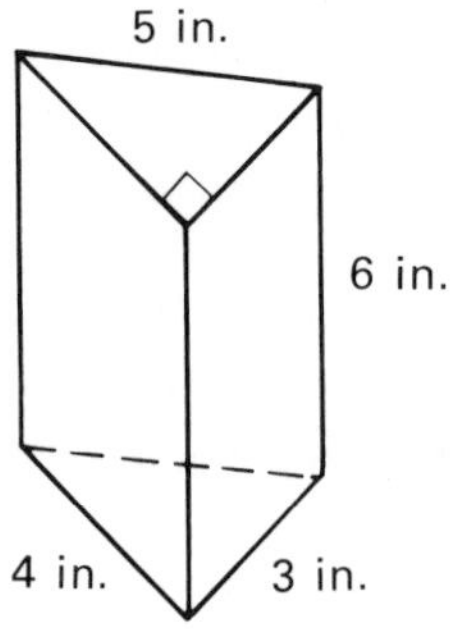

Face		Area
Top	$A = 3 \times 4 \div 2$	6
Bottom	$A = 3 \times 4 \div 2$	6
Right side	$A = 3 \times 6$	18
Left side	$A = 4 \times 6$	24
Back side	$A = 5 \times 6$	30
		84

The surface area is 84 sq in.

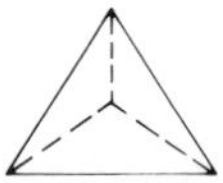

triangular pyramid

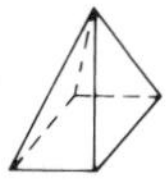

rectangular pyramid

cylinder

Other three-dimensional objects are pyramids and cylinders.

> The surface area of a pyramid is the sum of the areas of the faces.

If a cylinder were cut apart, you would see that the bases (top and bottom) are circles and the other surface is a rectangle. The length of the rectangle is the circumference of the base, and its width is the height of the cylinder.

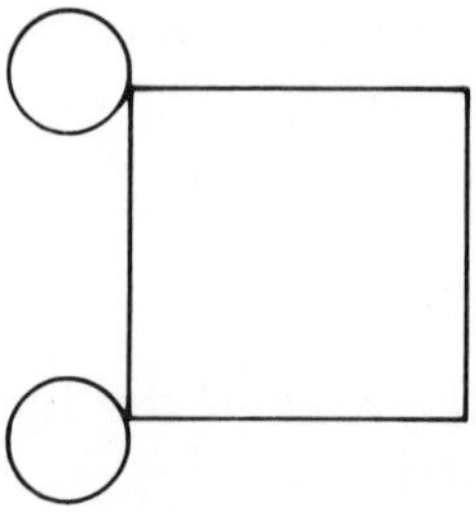

Example 2: Find the surface area of the cylinder.

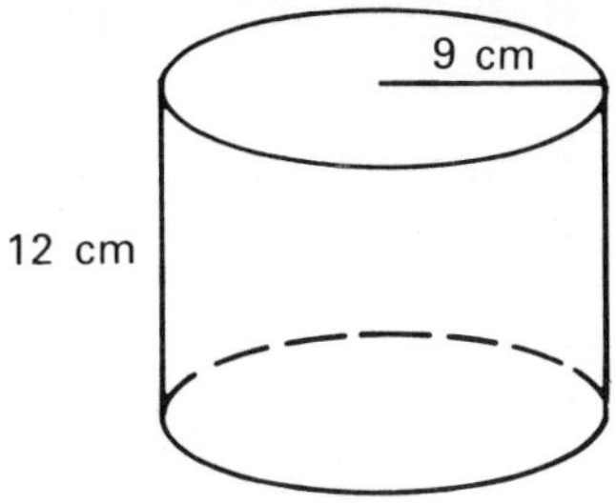

Area of each base

$A = \pi r^2$

$= 3.14(9)^2$

$= 254.34$

Area of the rectangle

$A = lw$

$= 2 \times 3.14 \times 9 \times 12$

$= 678.24$

Length of the rectangle
$l = 2\pi r$

Surface area $= 254.34 + 678.24 + 254.34$

$= 1186.92$

The surface area is $1186.92\ cm^2$.

Exercises

A Match each figure with its name.

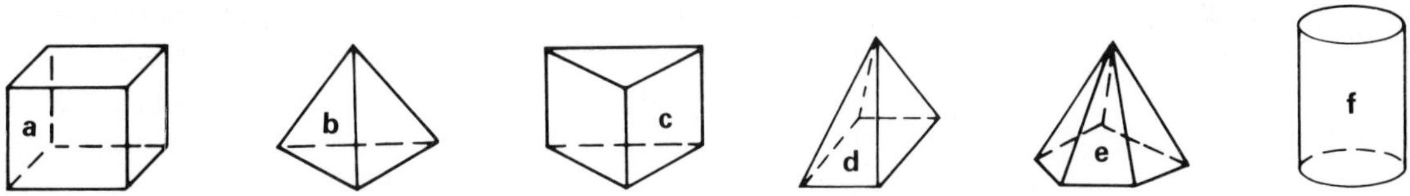

1. triangular prism
2. rectangular pyramid
3. cylinder
4. pentagonal pyramid

Tell the number of faces each of the following figures has:

5. rectangular prism
6. hexagonal prism
7. triangular pyramid
8. hexagonal pyramid
9. What is the shape of the sides of a prism?
10. What is the shape of the sides of a pyramid?

B Find the surface area of each figure. Use 3.14 for π.

11.
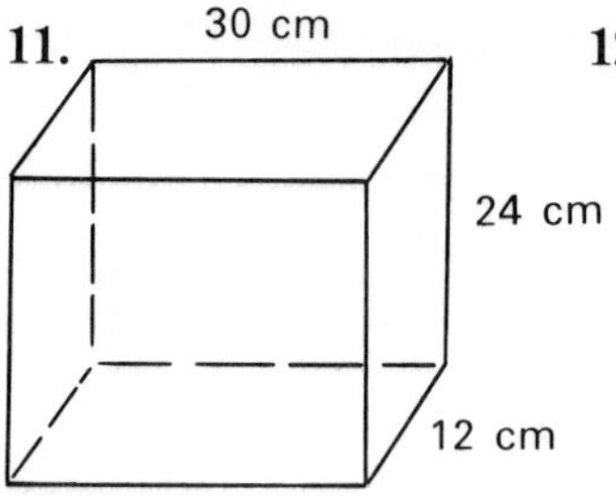

12.
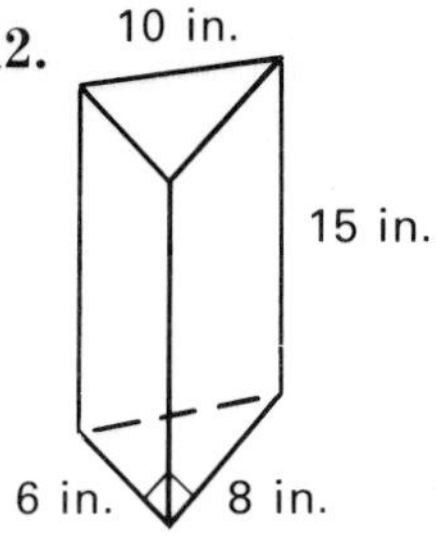

13.
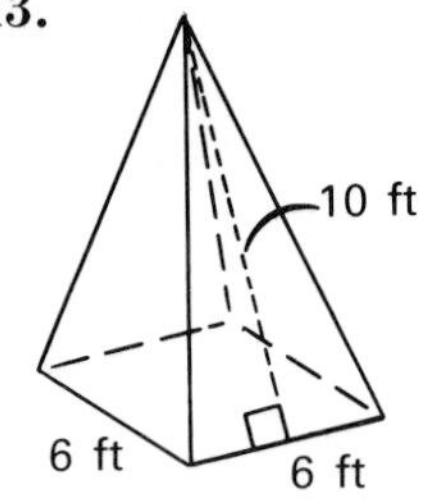

14.
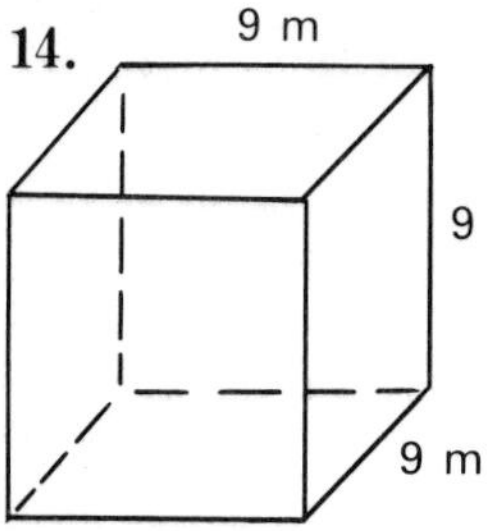

15.
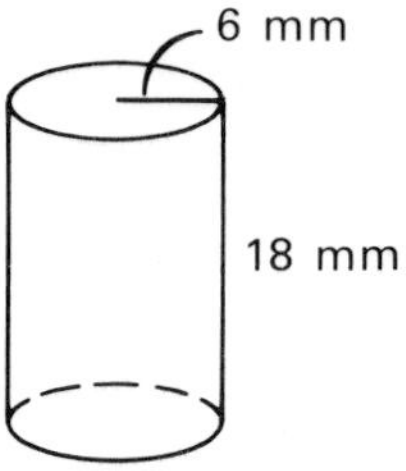

16.
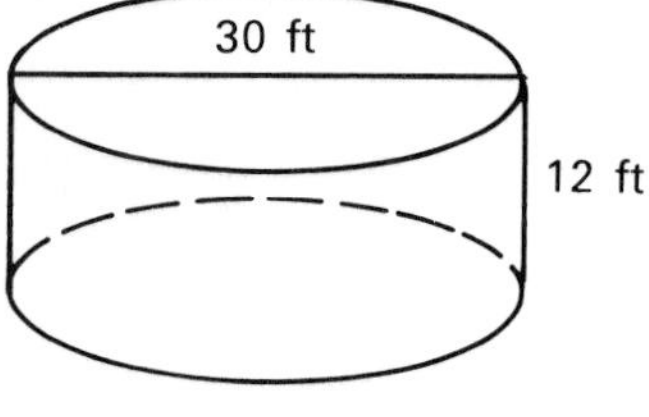

17. How much paper is needed to make a box 20 cm long, 12 cm wide, and 6 cm high?

18. A small can has a radius of 3 cm and a height of 7 cm. About how much metal was used to make the can?

19. How many square inches of wire mesh are needed to make a cage 36 in. long, 30 in. wide, and 15 in. high?

20. How many square feet of asbestos are needed to cover the curved surface and the ends of a water tank that is 4 ft in diameter and 6 ft high?

C **21.** How many square feet of paper are needed to make 1000 labels for cans, each 7 in. high and 4 in. in diameter? (Round your answer to the nearest square foot.)

The formula for the surface area of a sphere is $A = 4\pi r^2$. Find the surface areas of spheres with the following radii. Use 3.14 for π.

22. 5 in. **23.** 22 ft **24.** 4.5 m **25.** 6.2 cm **26.** 120 mm

27. The radius of the earth is about 4000 miles. Find its surface area. Use 3.14 for π.

28. The circumference of a basketball is about 30 in. Find its surface area. Use 3 for π.

Volume

> The volume (V) of a prism or a cylinder is equal to the area of the base (B) times the height (h).

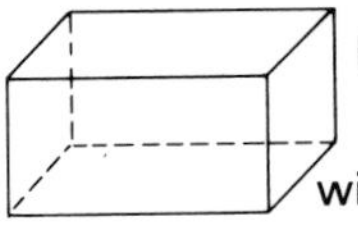

$V = Bh$ or

$V = lwh \quad (B = lw)$

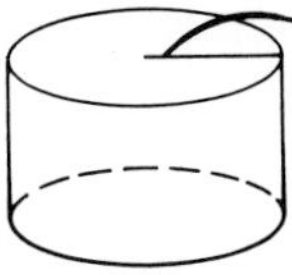

$V = Bh$ or

$V = \pi r^2 h \quad (B = \pi r^2)$

Example 1: Find the volume of this triangular prism.

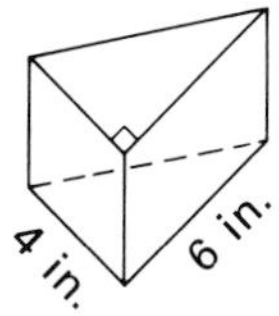

$$V = Bh$$
$$= (6 \times 4 \div 2) \times 4$$
$$= 48$$

The volume of the prism is 48 sq in.

Example 2: Find the volume of this cylinder. Use 3.14 for π.

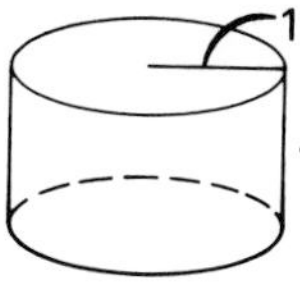

$$V = \pi r^2 h$$
$$= 3.14(10)^2 \times 12$$
$$= 3768$$

The volume of the cylinder is 3768 cm^3.

> The volume (V) of a pyramid is equal to one third of the area of the base (B) times the height (h).

Example 3: Find the volume of this pyramid.

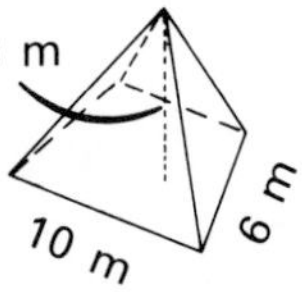

$$V = \tfrac{1}{3}Bh$$
$$= \tfrac{1}{3}(10 \times 6) \times 8$$
$$= 160$$

The volume of the pyramid is 160 m^3.

Exercises

A 1. How many cubic feet are in one cubic yard?

2. How many cubic inches are in one cubic foot?

3. How many cubic centimeters are in one cubic meter?

4. How many cubic millimeters are in one cubic centimeter?

5. How many cubic inches are in one cubic yard?

6. How many cubic meters are in one cubic kilometer?

B **Find the volume of each figure. Use 3.14 for π.**

7.

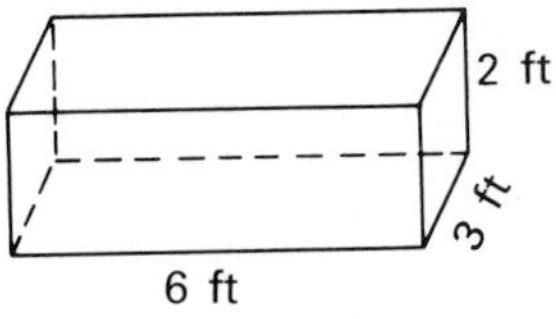

8.

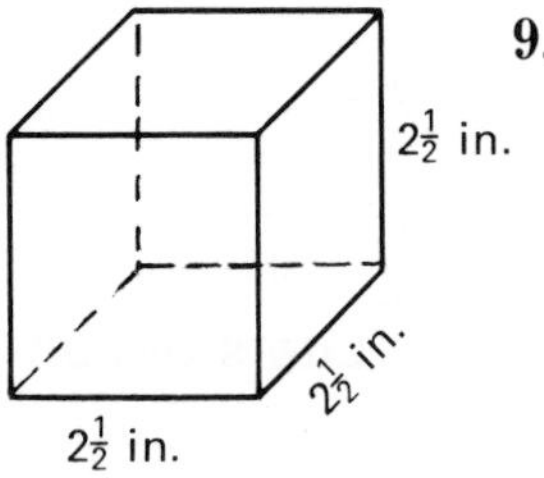

9.

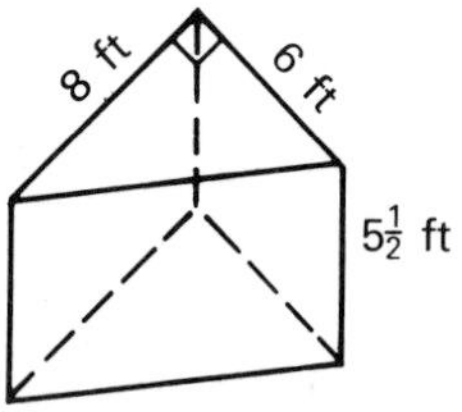

10.

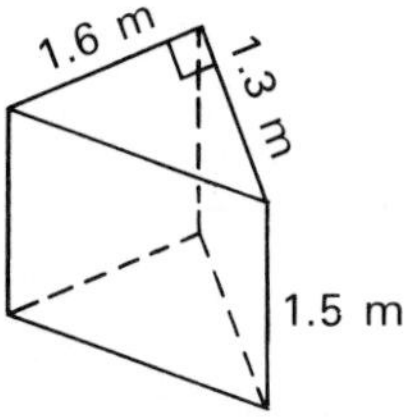

11.

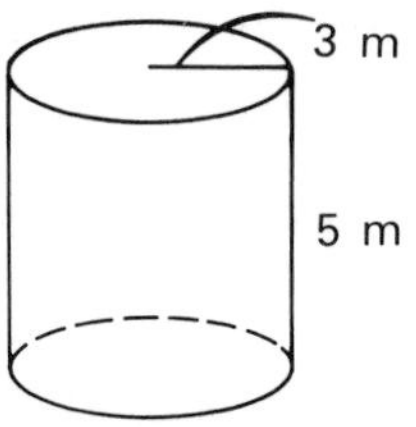

12.

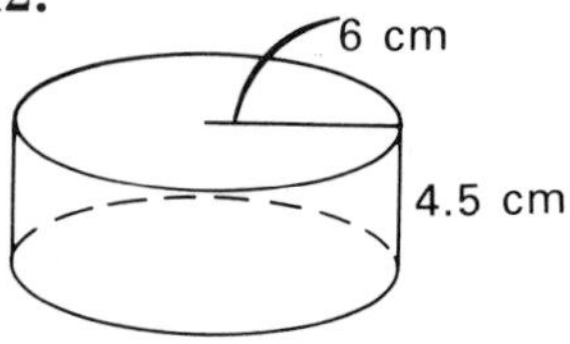

13.

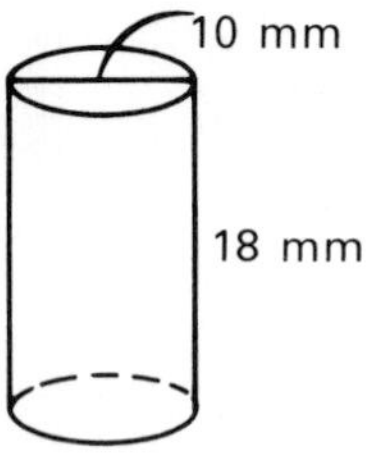

14.

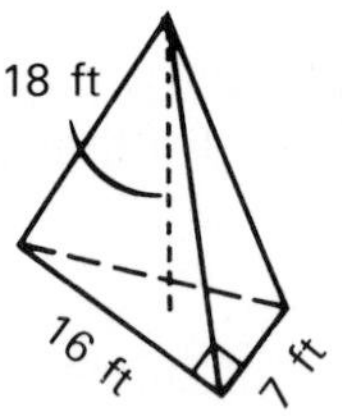

15.

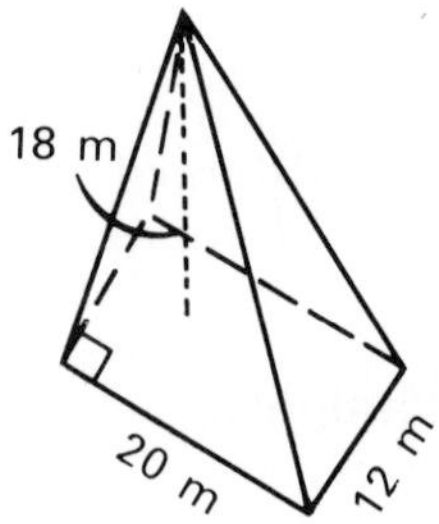

16. A pound of butter will fit into a container having the shape of a rectangular prism 8 in. long, 1 in. wide, and 4 in. high. Find the volume of this container.

17. A pound of cement will fit into a container having the shape of a rectangular prism 3 in. long, 1 in. wide, and 3 in. high. Find the volume of this container.

C 18. One cubic foot of water weighs about 62.4 lb. What is the weight of the water in a water bed that is 8 ft long, 6 ft wide, and 8 in. high?

19. Three hundred fourteen cubic feet of water was put into a cylindrical pool. If the pool had a radius of 5 ft, what was the height of the water?

20. What happens to the volume of a cylinder when you double its height?

21. What happens to the volume of a cylinder when you double its radius?

22. What happens to the volume of a cylinder when you double its height and its radius?

23. What happens to the volume of a rectangular prism when you double its length?

24. What happens to the volume of a rectangular prism when you double its length and its width?

25. What happens to the volume of a rectangular prism when you double all three of its dimensions?

Liters of Fun

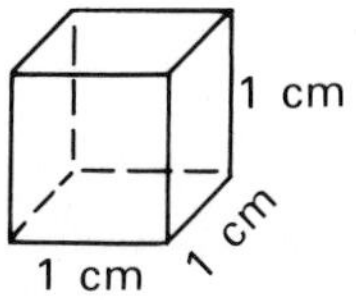

The box shown above has a capacity of 1 milliliter.

1. What is the capacity in milliliters of a box with a volume of 1000 cm^3?

2. What is the capacity in liters of a box with a volume of 1000 cm^3?

3. A liter of water has a mass of 1 kilogram. What is the volume of a container that holds 1 kilogram of water?

Tell how you could carry the following amounts of water, using only the containers shown above.

4. 5 liters

5. 2 liters

6. 4 liters

activities

TANGRAMS

An ancient Chinese puzzle called a **tangram** consists of 7 pieces that form a square.

Trace the tangram shown below.

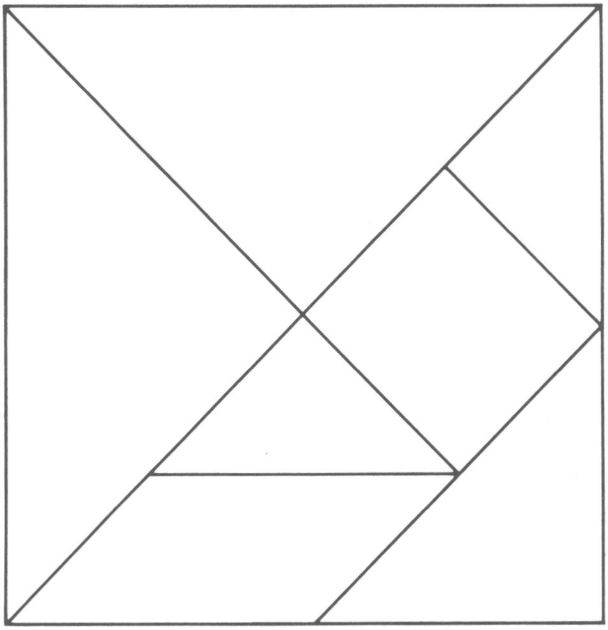

From these seven pieces you can make geometric figures and various pictures.

A. a right triangle

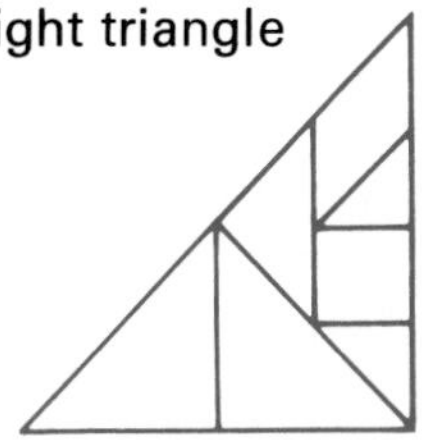

B. a rooster

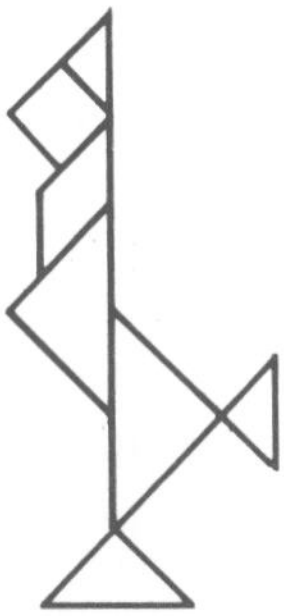

Can you make these figures? (Remember, you must use all seven pieces for each figure.)

1. a rectangle
2. a trapezoid
3. a parallelogram
4. a hexagon
5. a pentagon
6. an isosceles triangle
7. a cat
8. a dog
9. a whale

CAREER CORNER

H. Armstrong Roberts

MATH ON THE FARM

On page 478 there is a list of the numbers of years of high-school math recommended as preparation for various college programs. Notice that one of the longer lists of college programs can be found under Agriculture. Many farmers find a college education essential. Others do not have even a high-school education. Yet all find that math is required in operating a farm.

Farmers must know how to find perimeter, area, and volume. They also must use computation to figure yields, prices, income, and expenses.

In the United States the size (area) of a farm is measured in acres.

1 acre = 43,560 sq ft   1 sq mi = 640 acres

1. A farmer has a rectangular field that is 1980 feet long and 1100 feet wide. What is the area of the field in acres?

2. For irrigation in a field a farmer uses a center-pivot irrigation system. The pipeline carries water and rotates in a circle with a radius of 290 feet. To the nearest acre, how many acres does the irrigation system water?

3. If the farmer wants to fence the circular area irrigated in Exercise 2, how much fencing will be needed?

4. A bale of hay is 14 inches tall, 18 inches wide, and 38 inches long. What is the volume of a bale of hay?

5. The part of the loft shown in color will be filled with hay. What is the volume of that part of the loft?

6. When baled hay is stored, there must be "breathing room," or air space. If 80% of the space in Exercise 5 can be used for storing baled hay, how many bales (to the nearest whole bale) can be stored?

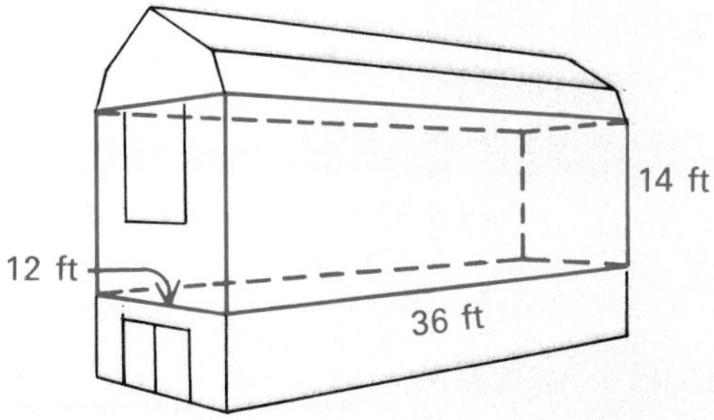

Terms and Symbols Review

Match each name with the letter of a symbol and with the letter of a figure.

1. angle MNP
2. line RS
3. line segment RS
4. ray RS

A. $\overleftrightarrow{RS}$

B. $\overrightarrow{RS}$

C. $\overline{RS}$

D. $\angle MNP$

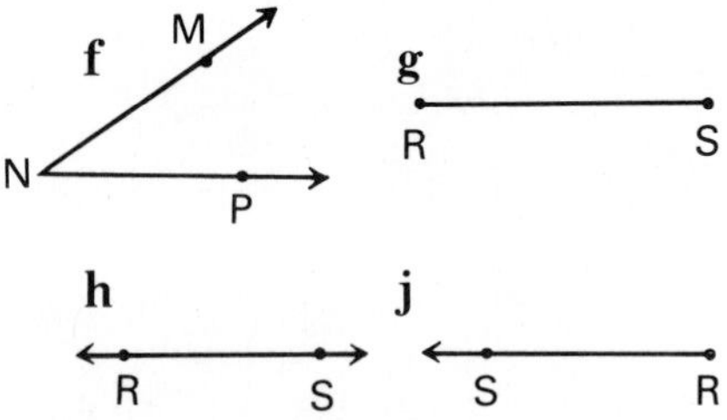

Match each name with the letter of a figure.

5. pentagon
6. square
7. prism
8. pyramid
9. hexagon
10. cylinder
11. trapezoid
12. right triangle
13. parallelogram
14. isosceles triangle

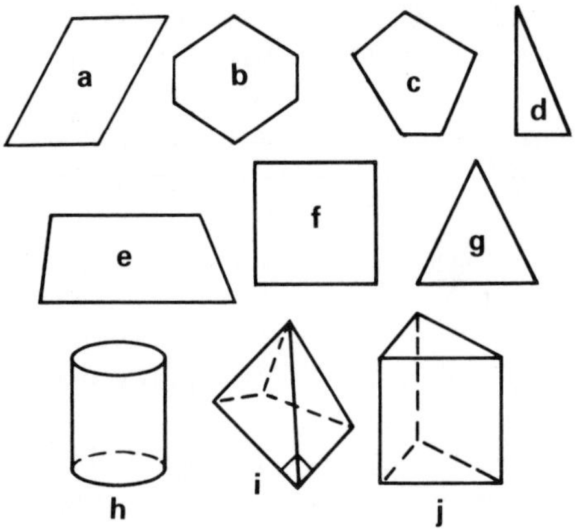

Chapter 16 Review

16.1 Tell whether each pair of lines is parallel, perpendicular, or neither.

1. 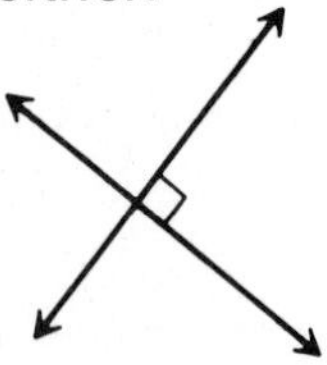

2. 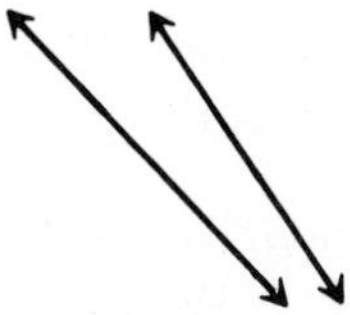

3. 

16.2 Find the measure of each line segment to the nearest $\frac{1}{8}$ inch and to the nearest centimeter.

4. ____

5. ____

Find the perimeter of each figure.

6. 

7. 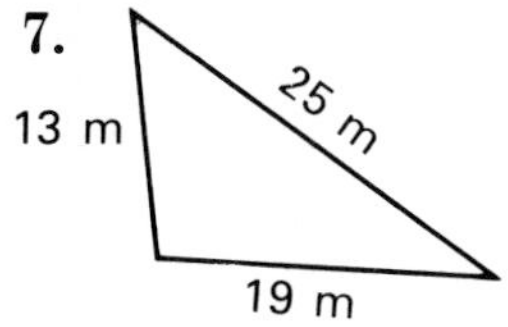

8. 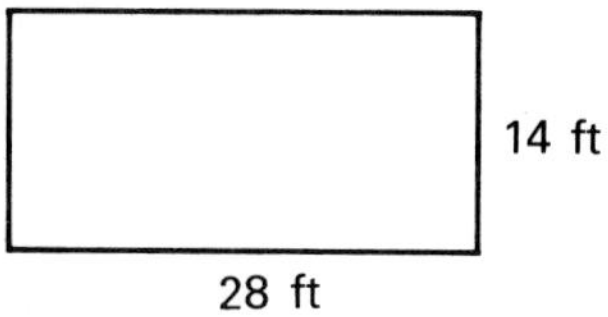

9. Find the circumference of a circle with a diameter of 4 m. Use 3.14 for π.

Find the area of each figure. Use 3.14 for π. 16.3

10. 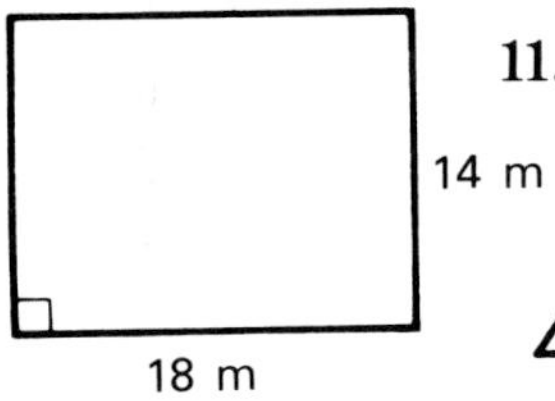

11. 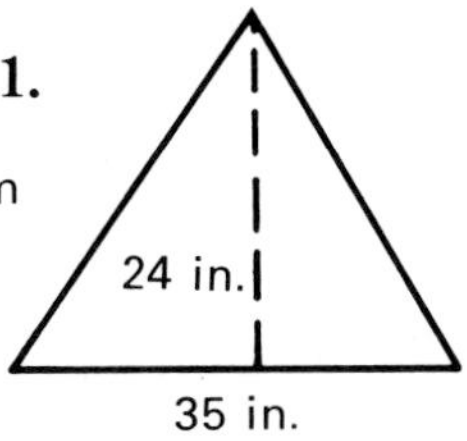

12. 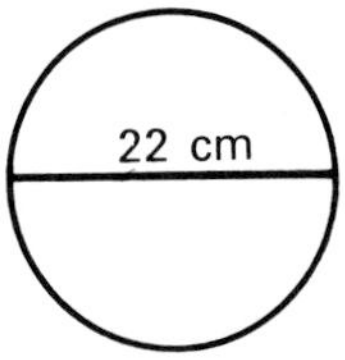

13. Bart mowed a rectangular lawn that was 60 ft long and 48 ft wide. What was the area of the lawn?

Find the surface area of each figure. Use 3.14 for π. 16.4

14. 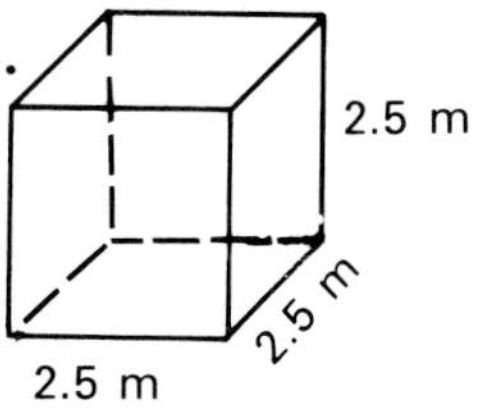

15. 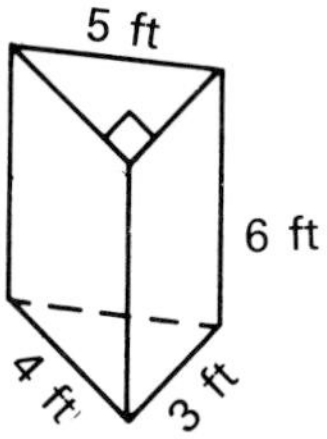

16. 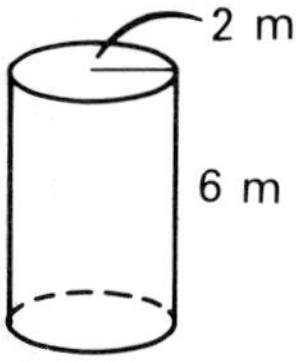

17. How much wood was used to make a crate that is 7 ft long, 3 ft wide, and 3 ft high?

Find the volume of each figure. Use 3.14 for π. 16.5

18. 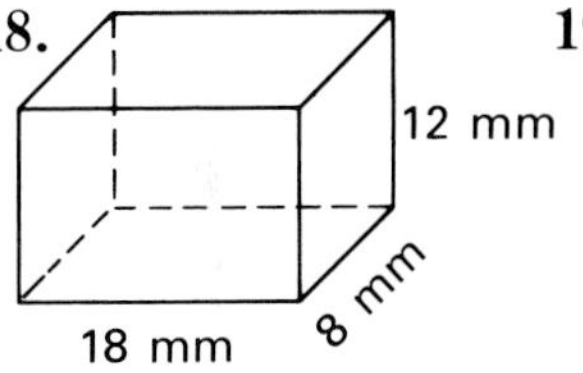

19. 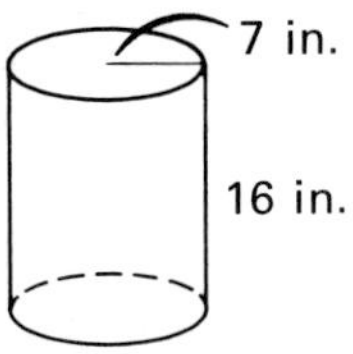

20. 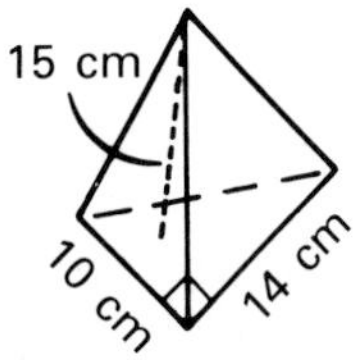

21. Ann rented a storage unit that was 12 ft long, 15 ft wide, and 10 ft high. What was the volume of the storage unit?

Chapter 16 Test

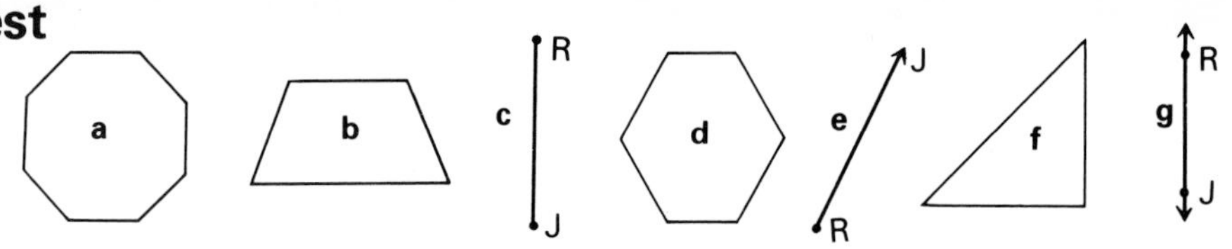

Match each name with the letter of a figure above.

1. $\overline{RJ}$ 2. $\overleftrightarrow{RJ}$ 3. $\overrightarrow{RJ}$

4. triangle 5. hexagon 6. trapezoid

Find the perimeter or circumference of each figure. Use 3.14 for π.

7.
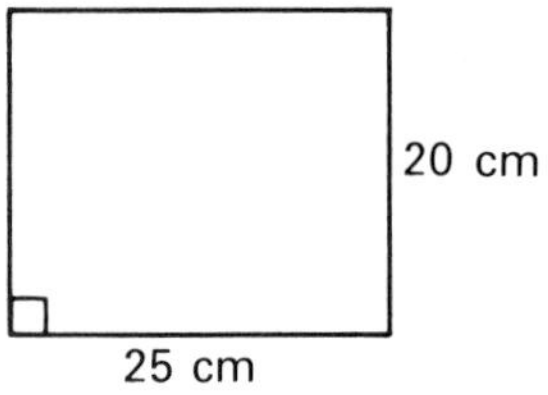

8.
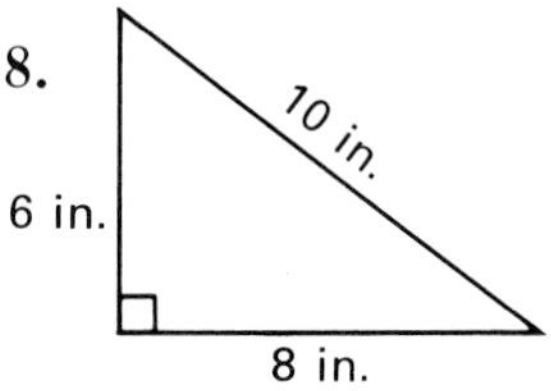

9.
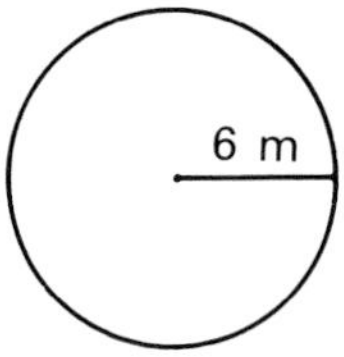

Find the area of the figure in

10. Exercise 7. 11. Exercise 8. 12. Exercise 9.

Find the surface area of each figure. Use 3.14 for π.

13.
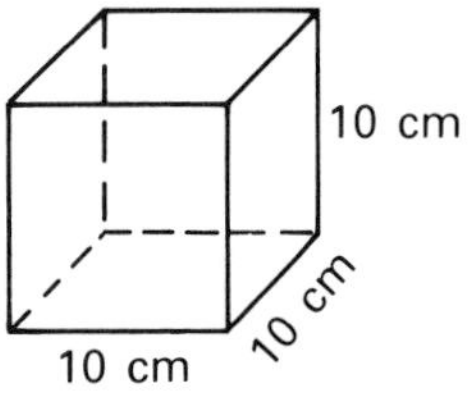

14.
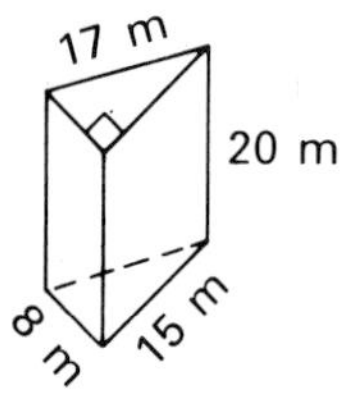

15.
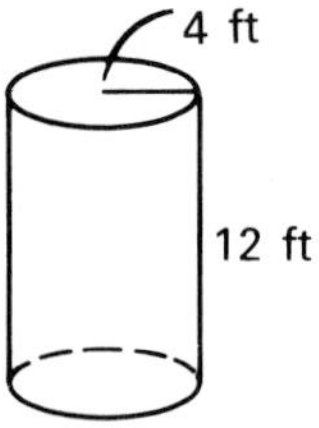

RATE YOURSELF

Number Correct	
20–21	Superior
18–19	Excellent
16–17	Good
11–15	Fair
0–10	Poor

Find the volume of the figure in

16. Exercise 13. 17. Exercise 14. 18. Exercise 15.

19. Nadia is refinishing a circular tabletop with a radius of 60 cm. What is the area of the tabletop? (Use 3.14 for π.)

20. How much cardboard is needed to make a box with a lid if the box is to be 12 in. long, 9 in. wide, and 6 in. high?

21. A pool is 12 ft long, 10 ft wide, and 5 ft deep. How many cubic feet of water is needed to fill the pool?

Solve and graph each inequality. 2.4

1. $n - 3 < 2$ **2.** $2x > 6$ **3.** $12 < 6 + m$

4. $\frac{s}{3} > 3$ **5.** $5 > r + 1$ **6.** $16 < 8p$

Solve each equation. 2.6

7. $2x - 3 = 81$ **8.** $21 = 3n + 6$ **9.** $52x + 5 = 109$

10. $6 + 10x = 86$ **11.** $4y - 30 = 130$ **12.** $16 = 12 + 4x$

Tell whether each of the following is a function. 8.5

13.

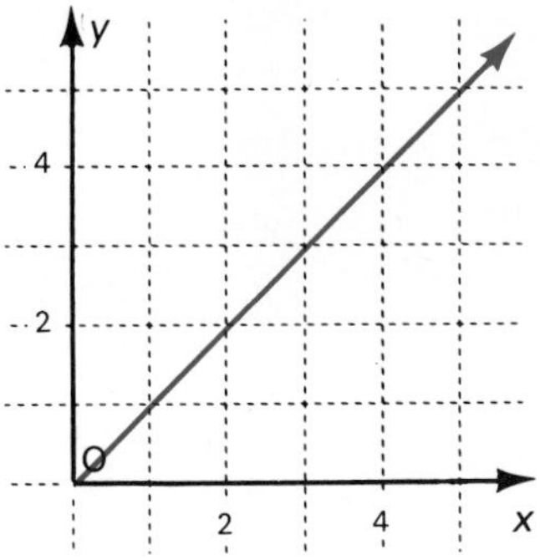

14.

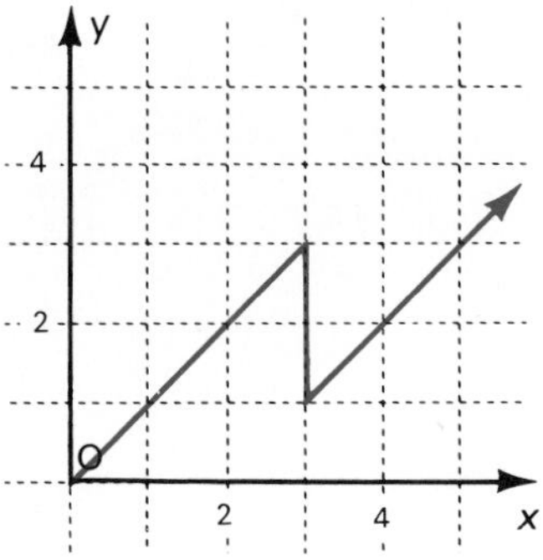

15.

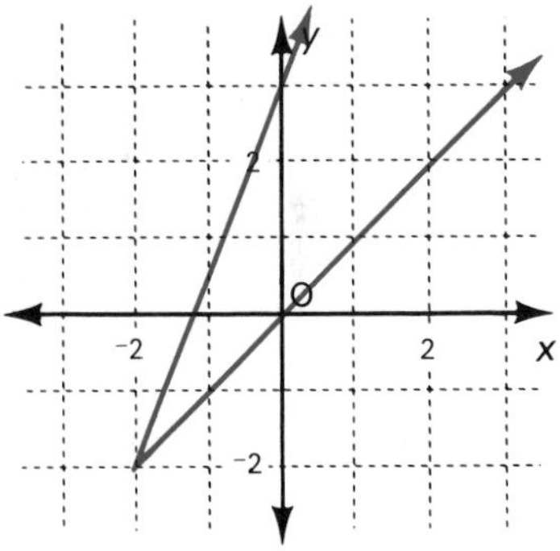

Draw a line graph for each table. 8.4

16.

x	0	1	2	3	4	5
y	3	4	5	6	7	8

17.

x	$^-4$	$^-3$	$^-2$	0	1
y	0	2	4	8	10

Historical Pictures Service, Chicago

17 More Algebra

In the seventeenth century René Descartes combined algebra and geometry to solve problems. In chapter 8 you studied the ideas of graphing and functions. In this chapter you will use those ideas in new ways to solve problems.

Graphing Equations in the Coordinate Plane

To draw the graph of an equation, make a table, plot enough points to determine the shape of the graph, and then sketch the graph. The graph of the equation shown at the right is a straight line.

$2x + y = 6$

x	0	${}^-2$	4
y	6	10	${}^-2$

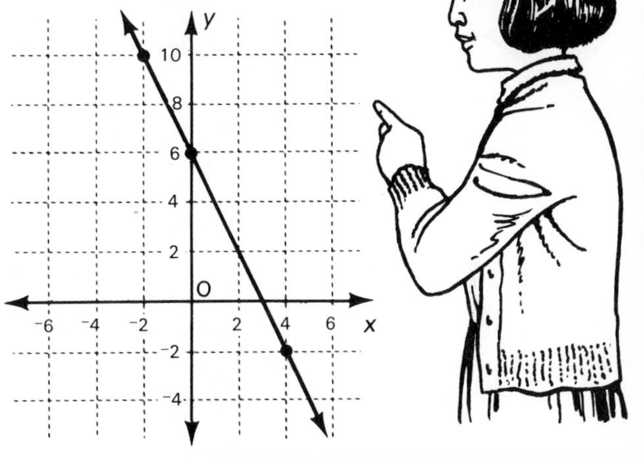

There are many forms of equations whose graphs are straight lines. One of the most common is the *standard form* of an equation, $ax + by = c$. The letter a is the *coefficient* of x. That is, a stands for a number that will be multiplied by the value of the variable x. In the same way, b is the coefficient of y. The letter c represents a number. Note that the values of a, b, and c can be positive, negative, or zero.

The **standard form** of an equation is $ax + by = c$.

Example 1: Sketch the graph of $3x + {}^-4y = 12$.

Make a table. Choose values of x that make it easy to compute y. Compute y.

x	0	2	4
y			

$$3x + {}^-4y = 12 \qquad 3x + {}^-4y = 12 \qquad 3x + {}^-4y = 12$$

$$3(0) + {}^-4y = 12 \qquad 3(2) + {}^-4y = 12 \qquad 3(4) + {}^-4y = 12$$

$$0 + {}^-4y = 12 \qquad 6 + {}^-4y = 12 \qquad 12 + {}^-4y = 12$$

$$^-4y = 12 \qquad {}^-4y = 6 \qquad {}^-4y = 0$$

$$y = {}^-3 \qquad y = {}^-1\tfrac{1}{2}, \text{ or } {}^-1.5 \qquad y = 0$$

Complete the table.
Plot the points.
Sketch the graph.

x	0	2	4
y	${}^-3$	${}^-1.5$	0

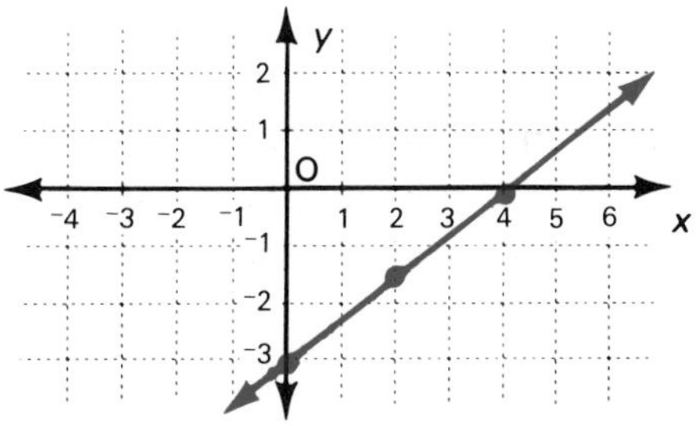

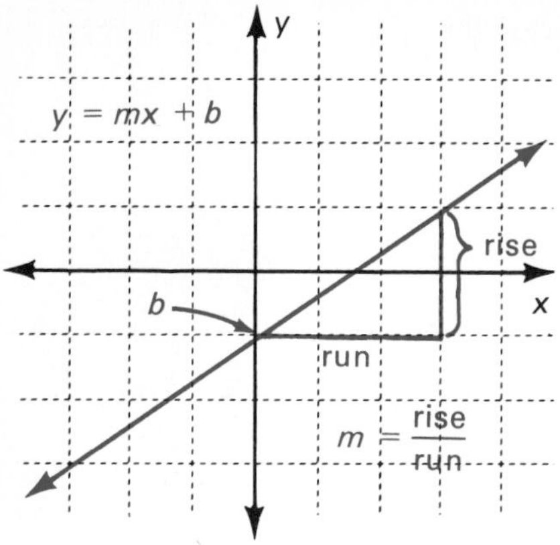

Another form of an equation is the *slope-intercept form*. The **slope** of a line is the ratio of its *rise* to its *run*. The coefficient m stands for the slope. The letter b stands for the number where the graph of the equation crosses the y-axis, called the y-intercept.

> The **slope-intercept form** of an equation is $y = mx + b$, where m is the slope and b is the y-intercept.

If the slope is negative, either the rise **or** the run will be in a negative direction—that is, to the left or down.

Example 2: Find the slope of the graph of each equation.

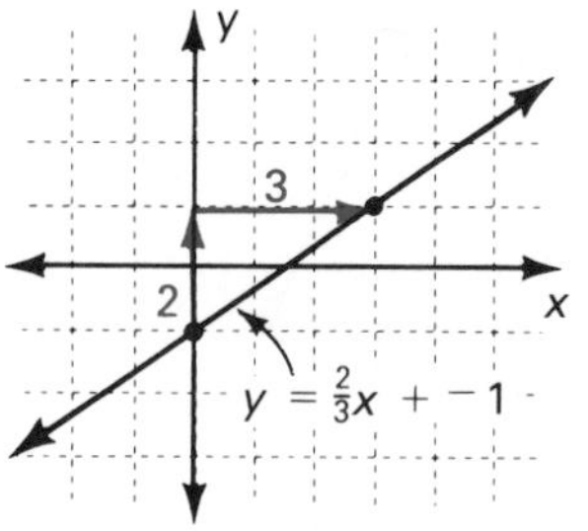

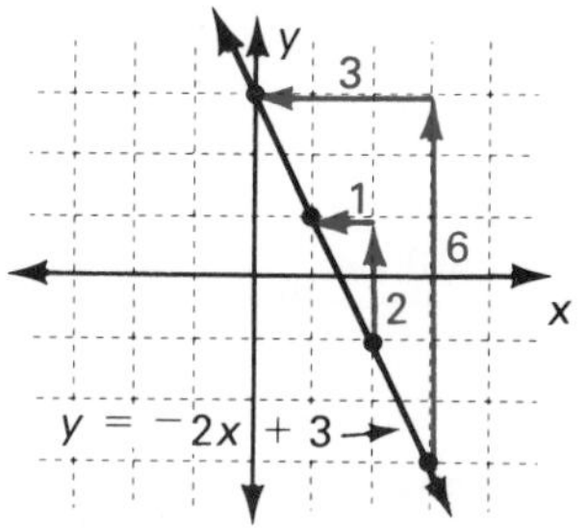

Notice that you can use any two points on the graph.

$$\frac{6 \text{ up}}{3 \text{ left}} \rightarrow \frac{6}{{}^{-}3} \qquad m = {}^{-}2$$

$$\frac{\text{rise}}{\text{run}} \rightarrow \frac{2 \text{ up}}{3 \text{ right}} \qquad m = \frac{2}{3}$$

$$\frac{\text{rise}}{\text{run}} \rightarrow \frac{2 \text{ up}}{1 \text{ left}} \quad \frac{2}{{}^{-}1} \qquad m = {}^{-}2$$

Example 3: Sketch the graph of $y = 0.5x - 3$.
Make a table. Compute y.
Complete the table.

x	$^{-}2$	0	6
y	$^{-}4$	$^{-}3$	0

Sketch the graph.

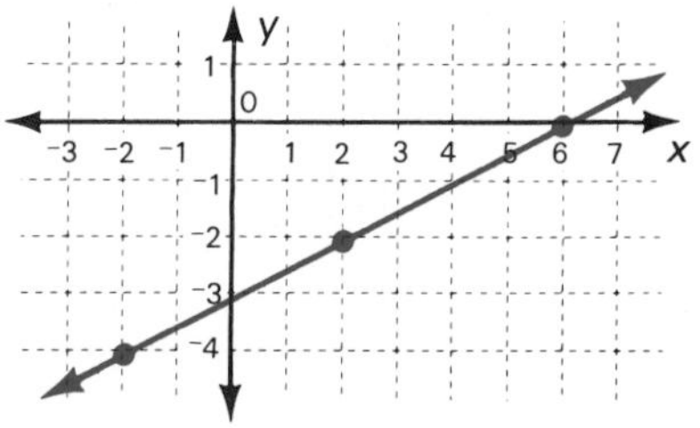

A standard-form equation can be changed to slope-intercept form.

Example 4: Change $2x + {}^{-}3y = 6$ to slope-intercept form.

Use the slope-intercept form to name the y-intercept and the slope.

$$2x + {}^{-}3y = 6$$

$${}^{-}3y = {}^{-}2x + 6$$

$$\frac{{}^{-}3y}{{}^{-}3} = \frac{{}^{-}2x}{{}^{-}3} + \frac{6}{{}^{-}3}$$

$$y = \tfrac{2}{3}x + {}^{-}2$$

Exercises

A Tell whether each equation is in standard form or in slope-intercept form. If it is in slope-intercept form, give the slope and the y-intercept.

1. $^{-}2x + y = 3$ **2.** $y = 9x - 3$ **3.** $2x + 9 = y$

4. $1 = \frac{^{-}2}{3}x + y$ **5.** $8 = 2x + {^{-}y}$ **6.** $y = {^{-}2}x + \frac{^{-}1}{2}$

B Graph each equation.

7. $3x + y = 6$ **8.** $y = {^{-}3}x + {^{-}1}$ **9.** $2x + 3 = y$

10. $x + {^{-}2}y = 3$ **11.** $9x + 2y = 12$ **12.** $y = {^{-}0.5}x + {^{-}2.5}$

Change each equation to slope-intercept form. Then name the slope and the y-intercept.

13. $2x + 5y = 10$ **14.** $^{-}8 = 3x + 4y$ **15.** $6x + {^{-}3}y = 4$

16. $3y + 2x = 0$ **17.** $0 = {^{-}2}x + y$ **18.** $3x = 2y$

C Equations like $y = 3$ and $x = -4$ have only one variable. You can think of these as being equations with two variables where one coefficient is zero. Notice how the equations are graphed.

$y = 3$
or
$0x + y = 3$

x	$^{-}2$	0	3
y	3	3	3

$x = {^{-}4}$
or
$x + 0y = {^{-}4}$

x	$^{-}4$	$^{-}4$	$^{-}4$
y	$^{-}1$	0	2

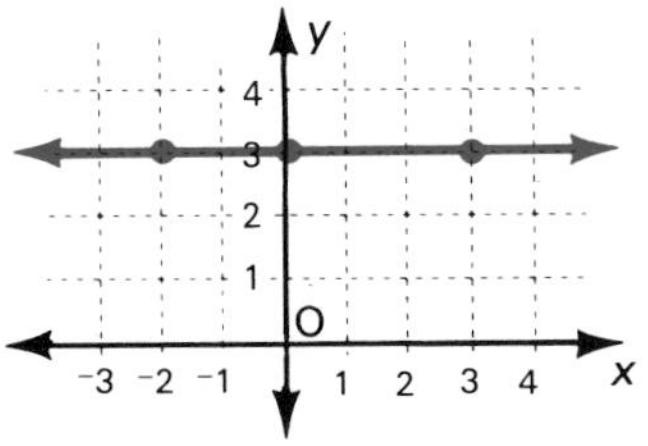

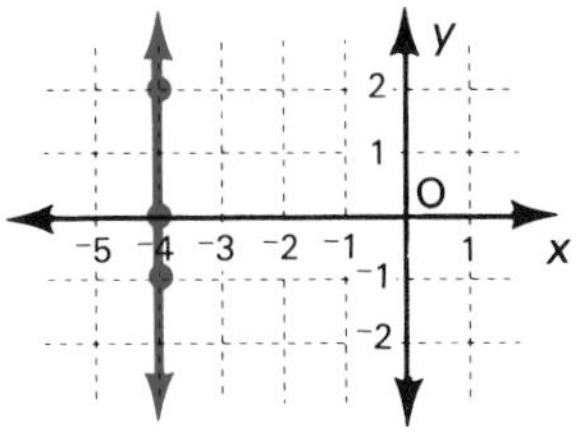

Draw the graph of each equation.

19. $y = {^{-}2}$ **20.** $x = 5$ **21.** $x = {^{-}7}$ **22.** $y = 8$

23. What equation describes the set of ordered pairs whose x-coordinates are zero? Draw the graph of that equation.

24. What equation describes the set of ordered pairs whose y-coordinates are zero? Draw the graph of that equation.

17.2 Graphing Inequalities in the Coordinate Plane

The graph of the $2x + y = {}^-4$ is shown by the solid line. The shaded part of the graph shows the solution for $2x + y > {}^-4$.

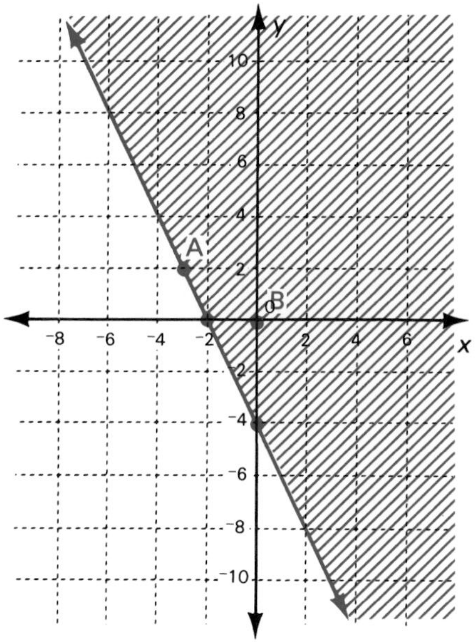

The entire graph (the solid line and the shaded area) shows the solution to $2x + y \geq {}^-4$. The symbol $\geq$ means "is greater than or equal to."

You can check the solution by choosing two or three points in the shaded area and substituting in the equation to see if the ordered pair for each point makes the inequality true. Suppose you choose points A and B.

Point	$A({}^-3, 2)$	$B(0, 0)$
Inequality	$2x + y \geq {}^-4$	$2x + y \geq {}^-4$
Substitute	$2(-3) + 2 \geq {}^-4$	$2(0) + 0 \geq {}^-4$
	This is true → $^-4 \geq {}^-4$ because $^-4 = {}^-4$. True	This is true → $0 \geq {}^-4$ because $0 > {}^-4$. True

Example 1: Show the graph of $x + {}^-2y \leq {}^-2$.
$\leq$ means "is less than or equal to."

Make a table for
$x + {}^-2y = {}^-2$

x	0	$^-2$	4
y	1	0	3

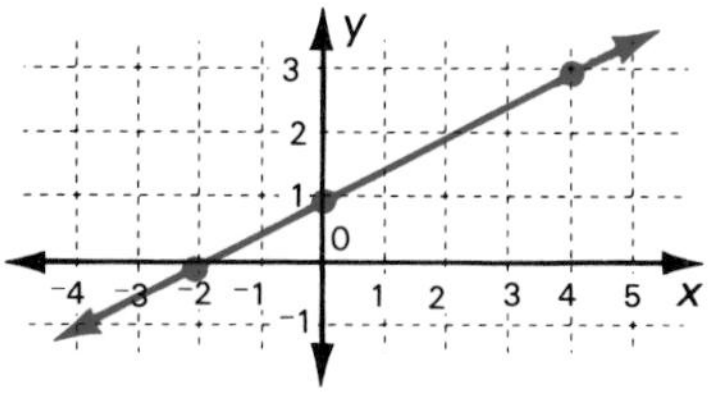

Graph the equation. Decide whether to shade above or below the line. An easy point to check is (0, 0).

$$x + {}^-2y \leq {}^-2$$
$$0 + {}^-2(0) \leq {}^-2$$
$$0 \leq {}^-2$$

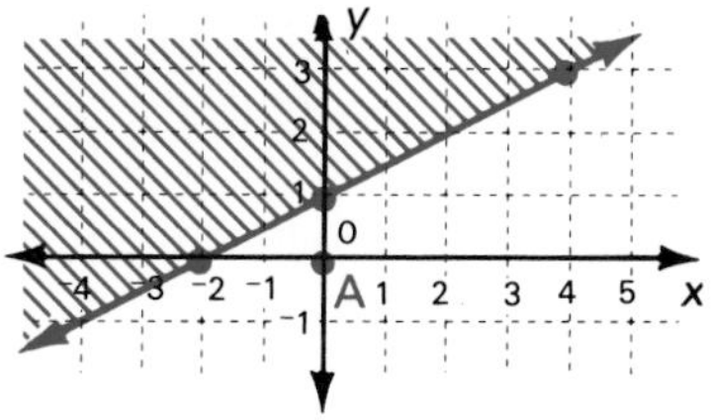

False. Shade the part that does not contain (0, 0)—above the line.

Example 2: Show the graph of $y > 0.5x - 1.5$.

Make a table for $y = 0.5x - 1.5$.

x	0	5	$^-3$
y	$^-1.5$	1	$^-3$

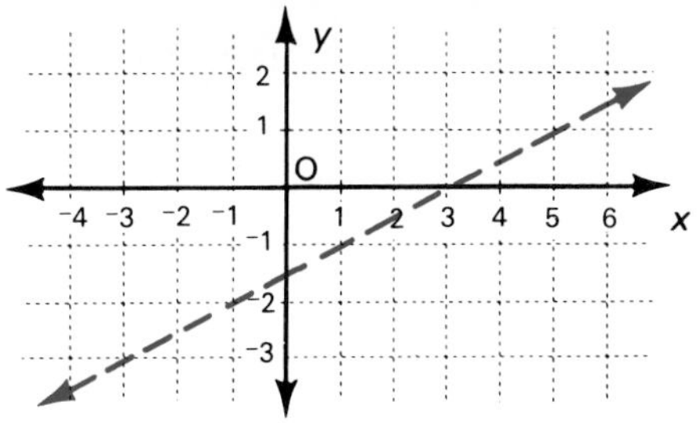

Use a dotted line for the graph of the equation. Notice that the inequality "is greater than" and does not include "is equal to." The dotted line shows that the equation is the boundary for the graph but is not included in the solution for the inequality.

Decide whether to shade above or below the dotted line. Use (0, 0) as the test point.

$y > 0.5x - 1.5$

$0 > 0.5(0) - 1.5$

$0 > {}^-1.5$

True. Shade the part containing (0, 0).

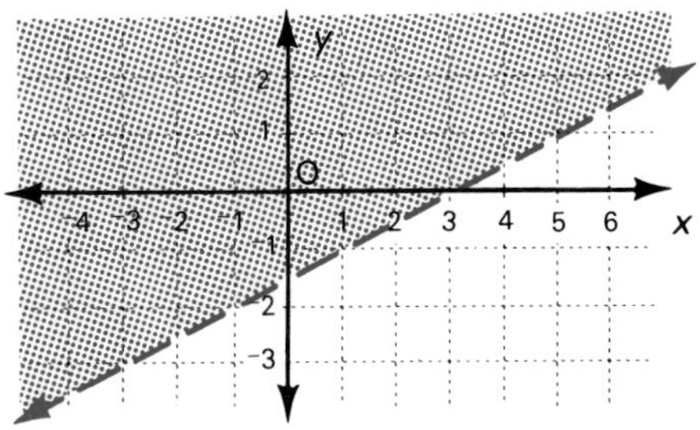

Exercises

A Tell whether each of the following would use a solid line or a dotted line on the completed graph.

1. $y < {}^-2x + 3$ **2.** $x + 2y \leq 0$

3. $5x + 2y \geq 0.5$ **4.** $x - y > 2$

Tell whether to shade above or below the line to complete each graph.

5. $y < {}^-2x + 3$ **6.** $x + 2y \leq 0$

7. $5x + 2y \geq 0.5$ **8.** $x - y > 2$

B Draw the graph of each inequality.

9. $y < x + 1$
10. $2x + y \geq 4$
11. $1.5x + {}^-2y > 0$
12. $2x + 3y \leq 6$
13. $2x + 3y \geq 6$
14. $2x + 3y > 6$
15. $2x + 3y < 6$
16. $3x - 4y \leq 12$
17. $4x - 3y \geq 12$
18. $y > 3x - 2$
19. $y \leq 4x + 2$
20. $y \geq {}^-x + {}^-2$

C

21. $y \leq 2$
22. $x > {}^-1$
23. $y > 5x$
24. $y \geq {}^-2x$
25. $x \geq 4$
26. $y \leq {}^-2$
27. On the same set of axes draw the graphs of $y \leq 3$ and $x \geq 2$. Shade the solution of $y \leq 3$ with lines like these: ////// . Shade the solution of $x \geq 2$ with lines like these: \\\\\\\\\\\\ . Completely shade in the area where the two graphs intersect (overlap).
28. Draw the graph of the intersection of the graphs of $x \leq 3$, $y \leq 3$, $y \geq 0$, and $x \geq {}^-2$. What is the shape of the intersection?

Write an inequality for each graph shown below.

29.

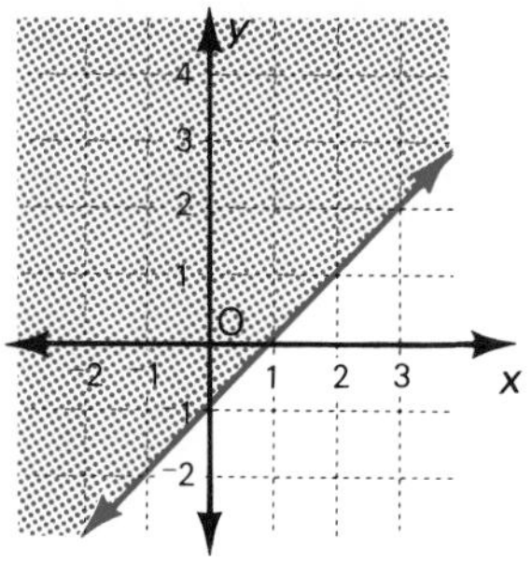

30.

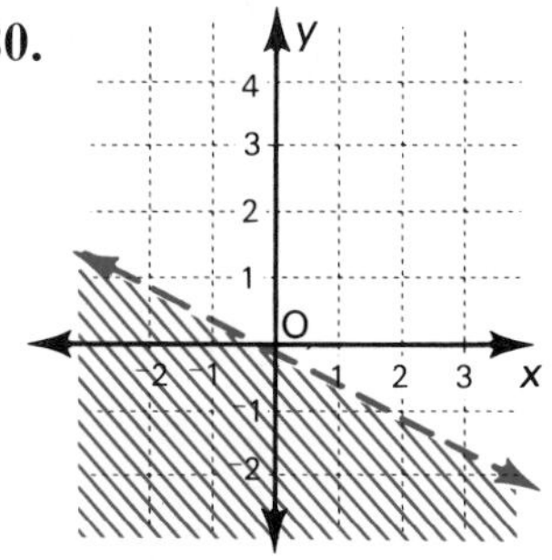

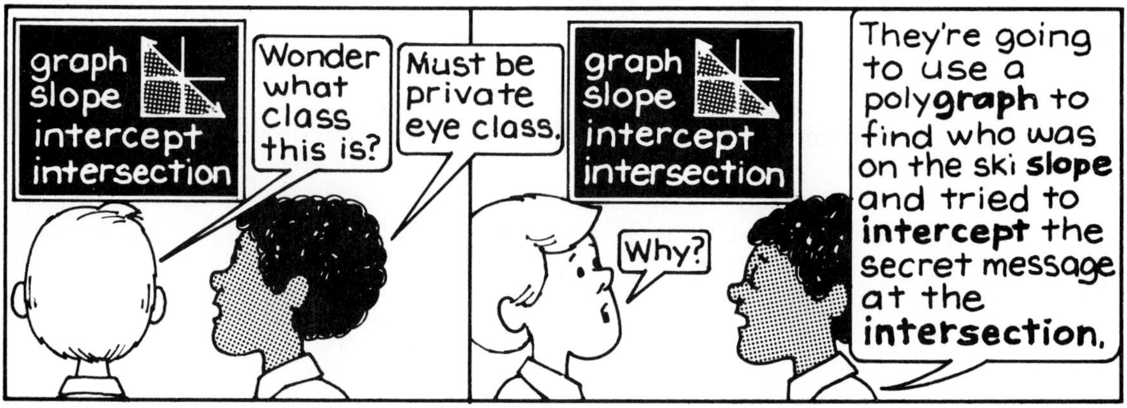

Quick Quiz
Sections 17.1 to 17.2

Tell whether each equation is in standard form or slope-intercept form.

1. $7x + 2 = y$
2. $x + 2y = {}^{-}2$
3. $y = 2x + 1$

Change each equation to slope-intercept form. Give the slope and the y-intercept.

4. $2x + y = 3$
5. $x + 2y = 3$
6. $12 = 4x + {}^{-}3y$

Draw the graph of each inequality.

7. $2x + y < 3$
8. $x + 2y \geq 3$
9. $12 \leq 4x + {}^{-}3y$

Hitting the Slopes

Mount Snow Ski Resort

1. On the same set of axes draw the graphs of $3x + 2y = 6$ and $3x + 2y = 2$.
2. Do you notice anything special about these lines?
3. What is the slope of each line?
4. Draw the graphs for $y = 3x + 4$ and $6x + {}^{-}2y = {}^{-}4$. Find the slope for each line.
5. If the slopes of two lines are the same, the lines are ____.
6. Draw the graphs for $2x + y = 3$ and $x + {}^{-}2y = {}^{-}2$.
7. Do you notice anything special about these lines?
8. What is the slope for each of these lines? Are the slopes the same? What product do you get if you multiply the slopes?
9. Draw the graphs for $y = {}^{-}3x + 1$ and $x - 3y = 3$. Find the slope for each line.
10. If the product of the slopes is ${}^{-}1$, the lines are ____.

17.3 Direct Variation

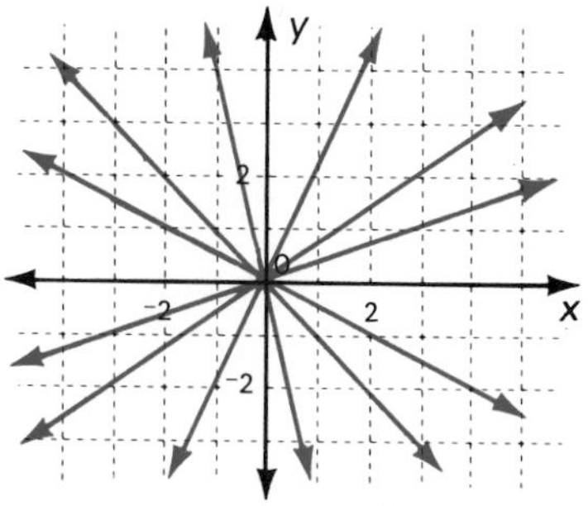

Each of the graphs shown at the right has a y-intercept of 0. Each line is a function—a set of ordered pairs whose first numbers are different.

The equation for each graph is of the form

$y = mx + b$, where $b = 0$ or $y = mx$

Since the slope of each line is constant, this equation is more often written $y = kx$. This function is called a *direct variation.*

> A **direct variation** is a function in which the ratio of two variables is constant.

The constant k is called the **constant of variation.** As either variable, x or y, changes in value, the value of the other variable also changes, so that the ratio between the variables remains the same. The relationship between the variables is stated, "y varies directly with x" or "y is directly proportional to x."

If you know the value of k and the value of one variable, you can find the value of the other variable.

$C = \pi d$ is a direct variation.

Example 1: Complete the table. Use 3.14 for π.

Circumference	diameter	$C = \pi d$
6.28	2	$\rightarrow 6.28 = 3.14d \rightarrow d = 2$
12.56	4	$\rightarrow C = 3.14(4) \rightarrow C = 12.56$
0	0	$\rightarrow 0 = 3.14d \rightarrow d = 0$

Example 2: Find the constant of variation for the graph at the right.

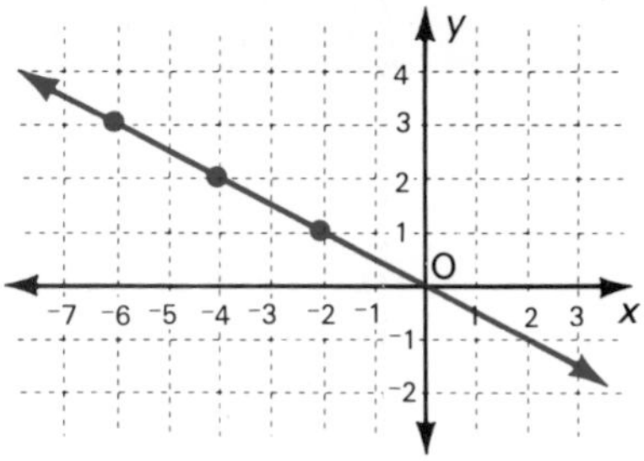

$$y = kx$$

Choose any points on the graph. Substitute the values in the equation and solve for k.

$(^-4, 2)$	$(2, ^-1)$	$(^-6, 3)$
$y = kx$	$y = kx$	$y = kx$
$2 = k(^-4)$	$^-1 = k(2)$	$3 = k(^-6)$
$^-\frac{1}{2} = k$	$^-\frac{1}{2} = k$	$^-\frac{1}{2} = k$

The constant of variation is $^-\frac{1}{2}$.

(0, 0) is also a point on the graph. Why is (0, 0) a poor choice for finding the value of k?

Example 3: The distance (d) a spring stretches varies directly with the force (f) applied. If 30 pounds of force stretches a spring 2 inches, how far will the spring be stretched by a 40-pound force?

Make a table.

f	30	40
d	2	?

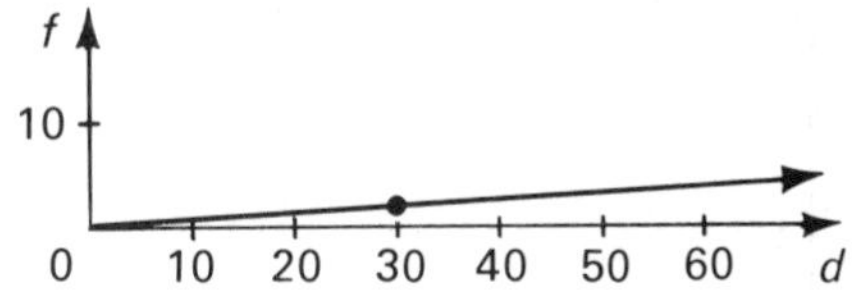

Find the value of k.

$d = kf$

$2 = k(30)$

$\frac{1}{15} = k$

$d = \frac{1}{15}f$ Write the formula.

$d = \frac{1}{15}(40)$ Substitute 40 for f.

$d = 2\frac{2}{3}$ Solve for d.

The spring will stretch $2\frac{2}{3}$ inches.

Barnes Group Inc.

Exercises

A Complete each sentence.

1. A direct variation is a function in which the ratio of two numbers is ___.

2. The constant k is called the ___.

3. In $y = kx$, if y increases in value, x will (increase, decrease) in value.

4. The perimeter (p) of a square varies directly with the length (s) of a side. The value of k is 4. The equation that expresses this direct variation is ___.

5. The total cost (c) of carpeting varies directly with the number of square yards (n) purchased. If $c = 200$ and $n = 10$, $k =$ ___.

B Each table shows a direct variation. For each table, find *k*, write the equation for the variation, and complete the table.

6.

x	2	3	4
y	60	90	?

7.

x	2	4	?
y	1	2	5

8.

x	10	100	200
y	1	10	?

9.

x	5	10	15
y	3	6	?

10.

x	2	4	5
y	$4n$	$8n$	?

11.

x	1	3	4	?
y	12	36	?	60

Draw a graph for each direct variation.

12. $p = 4s$ 13. $d = 5t$ 14. $m = \frac{1}{6}e$ 15. $C = 6.28r$

C Solve each problem.

16. The time (t) needed to cook a roast varies directly with the weight (w) of the roast. If a 3-pound roast requires 54 minutes to cook, how long should a 5-pound roast be cooked?

17. The number of bags (b) of cement needed varies directly with the number of cubic yards (n) of concrete to be made. If 25 bags of cement are needed to make 4 cubic yards of concrete, how many bags of cement are needed to make 18 cubic yards of concrete?

18. The amount (a) of simple interest earned varies directly with the amount saved (s). If \$13.75 in interest is earned on \$250, find the amount of interest earned on \$600.

Inverse Variation

Pete and Melissa would like to buy a stereo that costs \$360. They made a table to see how long it would take to save enough to buy the stereo. The amount saved per week is represented by r, and the number of weeks by t.

r	10	20	25	30	40	50
t	36	18	14.4	12	9	7.2

Notice that as r increases, t decreases. Furthermore, $r \times t = \$360$. The \$360 is the constant in the equation. This relationship is called an *inverse variation.*

> An **inverse variation** is a function in which the product of two variables is a constant.

The equation for an inverse variation is of the form $xy = k$, where k is the constant of variation.

Example 1: Sketch the graph of $rt = \$360$.

Use the table at the top of the page to locate points.

Notice that the points do not form a straight line. They form a curve.

What happens when $r = \$130$?

When $r = \$720$? When $t = 36$?

When $t = 72$? When $t = 720$?

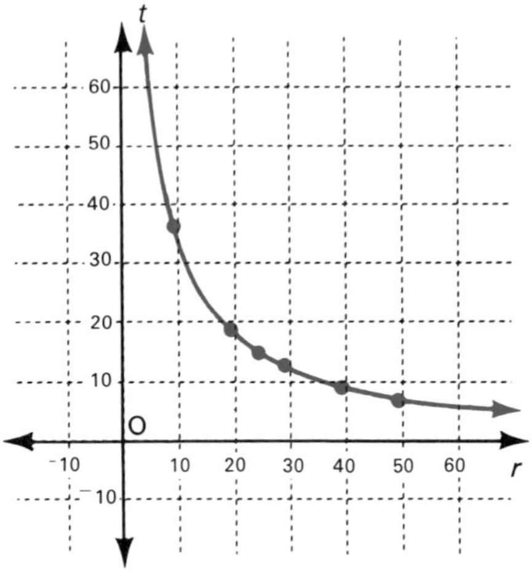

What happens if r or t has a negative value?

Generally, physical amounts can only be positive. Mathematics, however, deals with both positive and negative numbers. If Example 1 were extended to include negative numbers, the table and the graph would look like these.

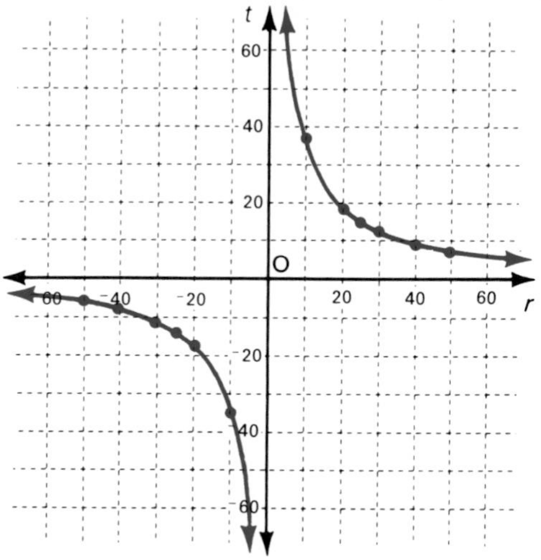

r	$^-10$	$^-20$	$^-25$	$^-30$
t	$^-36$	$^-18$	$^-14.4$	$^-12$

The graph has two sections and is called a hyperbola. As the negative values of r increase, the values of t decrease.

Example 2: The time (t) it takes to travel a certain distance varies inversely with the average rate (r). If it takes 6 hours to travel a certain distance at 50 miles per hour, how long will it take to travel the same distance at 75 miles per hour?

Make a table.

r	50	75
t	6	?

Find the constant of variation.

$$rt = k$$

$$(50)(6) = k$$

$$300 = k$$

$rt = 300$ Write the formula.

$75t = 300$ Substitute 75 for r.

$t = 4$ Solve for t.

It will take 4 hours.

Exercises

A Which of the following are inverse variations?

1. $ST = 300$ **2.** $y = 10x$ **3.** $y = \frac{x}{5}$ **4.** $y = \frac{16}{x}$

5.

x	2	4	6
y	1	2	3

6.

p	12	18	24
q	6	4	3

7.

I	10	20	40
W	100	50	25

8.

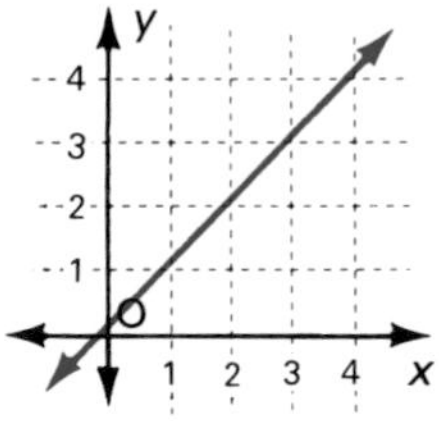

9.

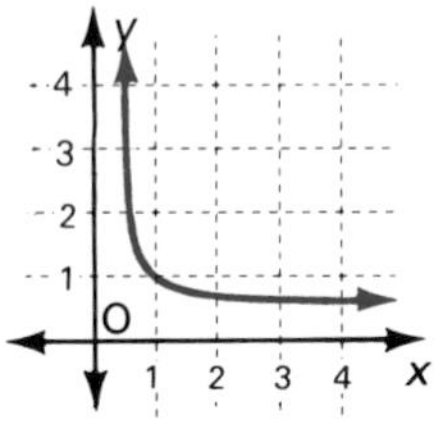

10.

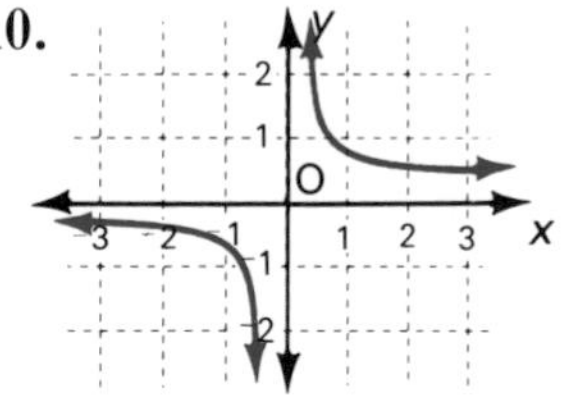

B Given the tables below, find each constant of variation *k*, and complete each table. Each table shows an inverse variation.

11.

x	9	?
y	2	3

12.

t	10	?
r	50	25

13.

x	$^{-}6$	9
y	$^{-}3$	?

14.

m	10	15
n	4.5	?

15.

t	2.5	20
r	100	?

16.

x	$^{-}18$	12
y	$^{-}18$	?

Write the inverse variation for each table. Complete each table and sketch the graph of the variation. ($x > 0$, $y > 0$)

17.

x	16	8	4	2
y	3	6	12	?

18.

x	16	8	4	2	1
y	0.25	0.5	?	2	?

C **19.**

x	$^{-}36$	$^{-}18$	$^{-}12$	$^{-}2$	2	6	24	72	144
y	$^{-}2$	$^{-}4$	$^{-}6$	?	36	12	?	?	?

Solve each problem.

The current (I) in an electrical circuit is inversely proportional to the resistance of the circuit (P). Suppose the current is 12 amperes when the resistance is 10 ohms.

20. Find the current when the resistance is 20 ohms.

21. Find the resistance when the current is 4 amperes.

22. Given the equation $xy = 30$, make a table and sketch the graph of the inverse variation. Use both positive and negative values for x and y.

17.5

Systems of Equations

Rolanda asked Chuck if he could guess the number of spots showing on the hidden dice. She gave him two clues: "The total number of spots showing is 7" and "Twice the number of spots on the first die minus the number of spots on the second die is 8."

Chuck said he could use algebra to solve the puzzle. He let x represent the number of spots showing on the first die and y represent the number of spots showing on the second die. He then wrote the following two equations:

$$x + y = 7 \text{ and } 2x - y = 8$$

To find an answer to the puzzle, find an ordered pair for which both equations are true.

Example 1: Find an answer to the dice puzzle.

Draw the graphs of the equations on the same set of axes.

$x + y = 7$

x	1	3	6
y	6	4	1

Label the graph for this equation "line *m*."

$2x - y = 8$

x	1	3	6
y	-6	-2	4

Label the graph for this equation "line *p*."

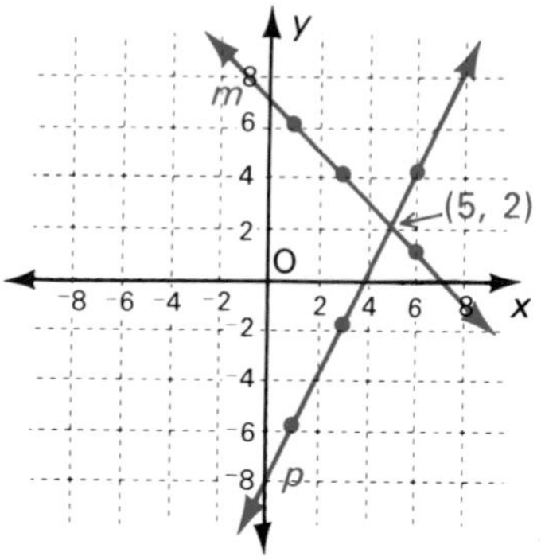

Lines m and p appear to intersect at (5, 2). Check to see if both equations are true for this ordered pair.

$x + y = 7$	$2x - y = 8$
$5 + 2 = 7$	$2(5) - 2 = 8$
$7 = 7$ ✓	$10 - 2 = 8$
	$8 = 8$ ✓

The answer is 5 spots and 2 spots.

A pair of equations like $x + y = 7$ and $2x - y = 8$ is called a **system of equations.**

A solution of a system of equations is an ordered pair (x, y) for which both equations are true.

The graphing method for solving a system of equations is useful, but not always exact. For that reason, it is necessary to check a solution. To check, substitute the ordered pair in each equation.

Example 2: Find the solution that satisfies both of these equations: $x - y = 2$ and $2x + y = 1$

Make a table for each equation.

$x - y = 2$

x	0	3	5
y	$^-2$	1	3

$2x + y = 1$

x	0	3	$^-2$
y	1	$^-5$	5

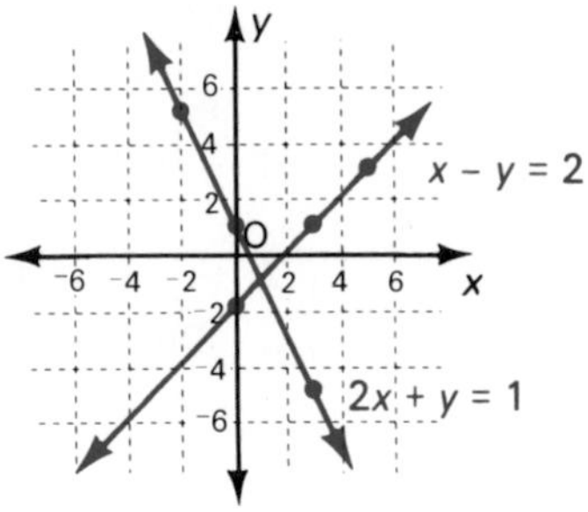

Draw the graphs and locate the point of intersection. Check that each equation is true for $(1, {}^-1)$.

$x - y = 2$	$2x + y = 1$
$1 - (^-1) = 2$	$2(1) + (^-1) = 1$
$1 + 1 = 2$	$2 + (^-1) = 1$
$2 = 2$ ✓	$1 = 1$ ✓

A system of equations that has one solution (the graphs intersect at one point) is **consistent.**

Example 3: Study the graphs of each system of equations.

Sometimes there are no solutions.

$x + y = 6$
$x + y = 2$

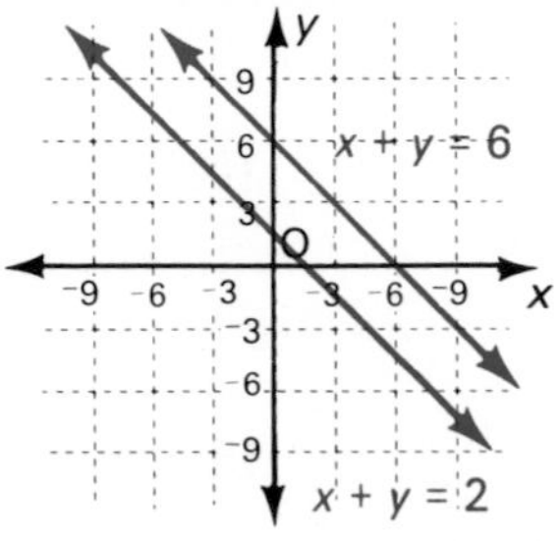

Since the lines are parallel, no ordered pair is the solution. This system is **inconsistent.**

Other times there are many solutions.

$x + y = 6$
$2x + 2y = 12$

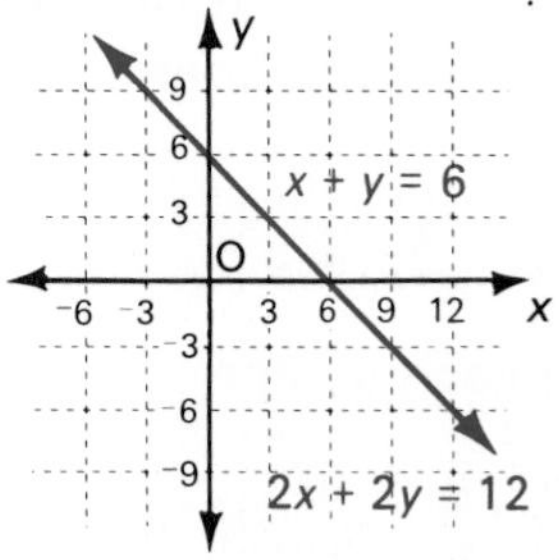

Since the equations have the same graph, there are many solutions. This system is **dependent** and consistent.

Exercises

A Pick the system that could be used to solve each problem.

1. The sum of two numbers is 8. Three times the first number minus twice the second number is 9. Find the numbers.

   a. $x - y = 8$, $3x - 2y = 9$ **b.** $x + y = 8$, $3x - 2y = 9$ **c.** $xy = 8$, $3x + 2y = 9$

2. April has \$0.55 in nickels and dimes. There are 8 coins. How many dimes does she have? (n = nickels, d = dimes)

   a. $0.05n + 0.10d = 0.55$, $n - d = 8$ **b.** $0.05n - 0.10d = 0.55$, $n + d = 8$

   c. $0.05n + 0.10d = 0.55$, $n + d = 8$ **d.** $0.05d - 0.10n = 0.55$, $n - d = 8$

3. The difference between Jo's house number and Ed's house number is 12. The sum of their house numbers is 86. Find the house numbers.

   a. $x - y = 12$, $x + y = 86$ **b.** $x + y = 12$, $x - y = 86$ **c.** $x - y = 12$, $x - y = 86$

B Determine whether the given ordered pair is a solution of the system of equations.

4. (3, ⁻2) $2x - y = 2$, $x + y = 1$
5. (⁻1, 0) $x - y = {}^-1$, $3x + 2y = {}^-3$
6. (1, ⁻4) $x + 2y = {}^-7$, $2x - y = 6$
7. (⁻5, ⁻3) ${}^-x + y = 2$, $x - 3y = 4$

Tell whether each of the following systems is consistent, inconsistent, or dependent.

8. $3x - y = {}^-1$, $6x - 2y = 4$
9. $2x + y = 3$, $4x + 2y = 6$
10. $x + 2y = 5$, $x + 3y = 6$

Solve each system by graphing.

11. $x + y = 10$, $x - y = 6$
12. ${}^-x + y = 3$, $x - 2y = 0$
13. $2x + y = 5$, $3x - y = 5$
14. $x + 3y = 4$, $x - 3y = {}^-2$
15. $3x - y = 7$, $x + y = 5$
16. $3x - y = 4$, $2x - y = 2$

Here is an algebraic method, called the substitution method, for solving a system of equations.

Solve this system by substitution: $3x - 4y = 8$ and $2x - 4y = 4$.

$2x - 4y = 4$ $2x = 4y + 4$ $x = 2y + 2$	Solve either equation for one variable in terms of the other. Solve the second equation for *x*.
$3x - 4y = 8$ $3(2y + 2) - 4y = 8$	Substitute $2y + 2$ for *x* in the first equation.
$6y + 6 - 4y = 8$ $2y = 2$ $y = 1$	Solve for *y*.
$3x - 4(1) = 8$ $3x = 12$ $x = 4$	Substitute *y* in either equation to find *x*.

Check:

$$\begin{aligned} 3x - 4y &= 8 \\ 3(4) - 4(1) &= 8 \\ 12 - 4 &= 8 \\ 8 &= 8 \checkmark \end{aligned} \qquad \begin{aligned} 2x - 4y &= 4 \\ 2(4) - 4(1) &= 4 \\ 8 - 4 &= 4 \\ 4 &= 4 \checkmark \end{aligned}$$

Solve each system by substitution.

17. $x - 2y = 5$
$2x - y = 10$

18. $4x + {}^-2y = 8$
${}^-2x + 5y = 20$

19. $2x - y = 30$
$6x + {}^-3y = 90$

Solve the following exercises on page 556.

20. Exercise 1

21. Exercise 2

22. Exercise 3

23. Change both equations in Exercise 8 to slope-intercept form. What is true about the slopes of the lines?

24. Change both equations in Exercise 9 to slope-intercept form. What is true about the slopes and the *y*-intercepts?

25. Rosa was thinking of two numbers. The sum of the numbers was 50. Twice the first number plus the second number was 90. What were the numbers?

26. Bill and Gloria have 95 cents between them. Bill has 7 cents more than Gloria. How much money does each one have?

CAREER CORNER

MATH AND SCIENCE

Pfizer Inc.

Many equations and formulas are used by scientists. Since it often is not safe or convenient to perform experiments under varying conditions, experiments are often carried out at room temperature and pressure. Results are then adjusted mathematically to different conditions.

There is a law that says that for gas confined in a container,

$PV = k$, where P is pressure, V is volume, and k is a constant

1. Is $PV = k$ an example of a direct variation or an inverse variation?

2. As the volume increases, what happens to the pressure?

3. Find the constant k for a gas that has a volume of 242 mL at a pressure of 657 mm Hg.

A given sample of gas has a pressure of P_1 and a volume of V_1. If the pressure exerted upon the gas sample is changed to P_2, the volume becomes V_2. According to Boyle's Law,

$$P_1V_1 = k$$
$$\text{and } P_2V_2 = k \text{ (the same constant);}$$
$$\text{therefore, } P_1V_1 = P_2V_2$$

4. A gas has a volume of 500 mL when a pressure of 760 mm Hg is exerted upon it. What is the volume if the pressure is reduced to 730 mm Hg? (Round to the nearest whole number.)

5. The pressure on 952 mL of gas is changed from 561 mm Hg to the standard pressure (760 mm Hg). What is the new volume of the gas? (Round to the nearest whole number.)

Terms and Symbols Review

Match each of the following.

1. standard form of an equation	**a.** $<$	**b.** $>$
2. slope-intercept form of an equation	**c.** $\geq$	**d.** $\leq$
3. is less than	**e.** $y = kx$	
4. is greater than or equal to	**f.** $xy = k$	
5. inverse variation	**g.** $y = mx + b$	
6. direct variation	**h.** $ax + by = c$	

Chapter 17 Review

Draw the graph of each equation. 17.1

1. $3x + y = 2$ **2.** $y = x - 2$ **3.** $7 = 2y + x$

4. $x = y + 3$ **5.** $2x + 3y = 6$ **6.** $^{-}2x + 4 = y$

Change each equation to slope-intercept form. Then name the slope and the *y*-intercept.

7. $6x + 3y = 10$ **8.** $2y - 4x = 8$ **9.** $7x - y = {}^{-}3$

10. $x - 2y = 4$ **11.** $3y + 4x = 12$ **12.** $^{-}2x + {}^{-}3y = 6$

Draw the graph of each inequality. 17.2

13. $y > x + 1$ **14.** $2x + y < 3$ **15.** $3x + 2y \geq 6$

16. $8 \leq 2x - y$ **17.** $4x > 2y + 2$ **18.** $y \leq {}^{-}2x - 3$

17.3 Each table shows a direct variation. For each table, find *k*, write the equation for the variation, and complete the table.

19.

x	4	6	12
y	2	3	?

20.

x	$^{-}2$	4	8
y	$^{-}8$	16	?

21.

x	$^{-}6$	2	?
y	30	$^{-}10$	$^{-}25$

Draw a graph for each direct variation.

22. $d = 6t$ **23.** $v = \frac{2}{3}x$ **24.** $a = {}^{-}0.5m$

17.4 Each table shows an inverse variation. For each table, find *k*, write the equation for the variation, and complete the table.

25.

x	6	8	?
y	4	3	2

26.

x	8	18	36
y	72	32	?

27.

x	$^{-}3$	6	?
y	12	$^{-}6$	$^{-}18$

Use each equation to complete the table. Then sketch the graph. $(x > 0,\ y > 0)$

28. $xy = 5$

x	20	10	?	1	0.5	?
y	0.25	0.5	1	?	10	20

29. $xy = 40$

x	0.5	1	4	8	10	?	40	80
y	80	40	10	?	4	2	1	?

17.5 Determine whether the given ordered pair is a solution of the system of equations.

30. (2, 0) $\quad 3x - y = 6$, $\quad x + 6y = 2$

31. ($^{-}5$, 2) $\quad 3x + y = {}^{-}12$, $\quad {}^{-}2x + y = 12$

Tell whether each of the following systems is consistent, inconsistent, or dependent.

32. $3x + y = 7$, $\quad x + 3y = 7$

33. $2x - 5y = 6$, $\quad 6x - 15y = 18$

34. $4x + 2y = 9$, $\quad 2x + y = {}^{-}9$

Solve each system by graphing.

35. $x + y = 3$, $\quad x - y = 5$

36. $3x - y = {}^{-}2$, $\quad x + 2y = 4$

37. $2x - 3y = 4$, $\quad 4x - y = {}^{-}2$

Chapter 17 Test

Draw the graph of each equation or inequality.

1. $2x + y = 3$
2. $x - 3y = {}^-1$
3. $y = 2x - 1$
4. $6x + 3y < 0$
5. $y \geq 4$
6. ${}^-3x + 2y \leq {}^-6$
7. $y = 4x$
8. $d = \frac{1}{5}x$
9. $r = {}^-3x$

Change each equation to slope-intercept form. Then name the slope and the *y*-intercept.

10. $4x + 3y = 6$
11. $3x - 5y = 10$
12. $6x + y = 2$

Use each equation to complete the table. Then sketch the graph. ($x > 0, y > 0$)

13. $xy = 8$

x	0.5	1	2	4	?	16
y	16	8	4	?	1	?

14. $xy = 20$

x	1	2	?	5	10	?
y	20	10	5	?	2	1

15. $xy = 15$

x	1	2	3	5	?	?
y	15	7.5	5	?	2	1

Tell whether each of the following systems is consistent, inconsistent, or dependent.

16. $x + 3y = 4$
    $3x + 9y = 12$
17. $2x + 4y = 5$
    $4x + 2y = 5$
18. $x + y = 3$
    $2x + 2y = 3$

Solve each system by graphing.

19. $x + y = 3$
    $x - 2y = 0$
20. $2x + y = 8$
    $2x - y = 4$
21. ${}^-x + y = 4$
    $x + 3y = 0$

RATE YOURSELF

Number Correct	
20–21	Superior
18–19	Excellent
16–17	Good
11–15	Fair
0–10	Poor

Terms and Symbols Review: Chapters 16–17

Ch. 16 Which term or symbol in parentheses is the best choice?

1. The symbol for line XY is ($\overline{XY}$, $\overrightarrow{XY}$, $\overleftrightarrow{XY}$).
2. The symbol for line segment RS is ($\overline{RS}$, $\overrightarrow{RS}$, $\overleftrightarrow{RS}$).
3. The symbol for ray AB is ($\overline{AB}$, $\overrightarrow{AB}$, $\overleftrightarrow{AB}$).
4. (*Intersecting*, *Parallel*, *Perpendicular*) lines never meet.
5. A(n) (*right*, *acute*, *obtuse*) angle is smaller than a right angle.
6. A triangle with three sides of different lengths is (*equilateral*, *scalene*, *isosceles*).
7. A polygon with five sides is a (*hexagon*, *trapezoid*, *pentagon*).
8. A (*trapezoid*, *parallelogram*, *rhombus*) has four congruent sides.
9. A (*square*, *trapezoid*, *rhombus*) is a rectangle with four congruent sides.
10. $V = lwh$ is the formula for the (*area*, *surface area*, *volume*) of a rectangular prism.

Ch. 17

11. The equation $ax + by = c$ is in (*standard form*, *slope-intercept form*).
12. The symbol that means "is less than or equal to" is ($\leq$, $<$, $\geq$).
13. In a direct variation, as x increases, y (*increases*, *decreases*).
14. The graph of an inverse variation is a (*straight line*, *curve*).
15. In the equation $y = 5x$, (y, *5*, x) is the constant of variation.
16. If the graphs of a system of equations are parallel, the system is (*consistent*, *inconsistent*, *dependent*).

Use the figure at the right for Exercises 1–6. Ch. 16

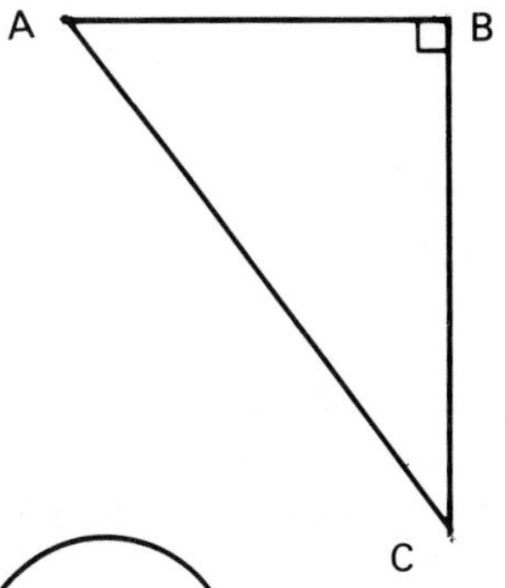

1. The length of $\overline{AB}$ is ____ cm.
2. The length of $\overline{BC}$ is ____ cm.
3. The length of $\overline{AC}$ is ____ cm.
4. The perimeter of triangle ABC is ____.
5. $\overline{AB}$ and $\overline{BC}$ are (*perpendicular, parallel*).
6. The area of triangle ABC is ____.
7. Find the circumference of the circle.
8. Find the area of the circle.

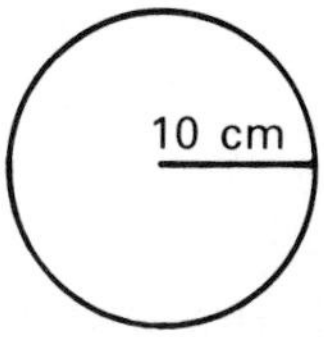

Find the surface area of each figure.

9.

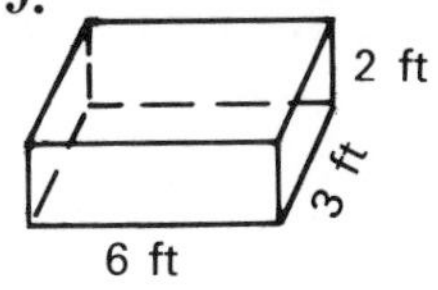

10.

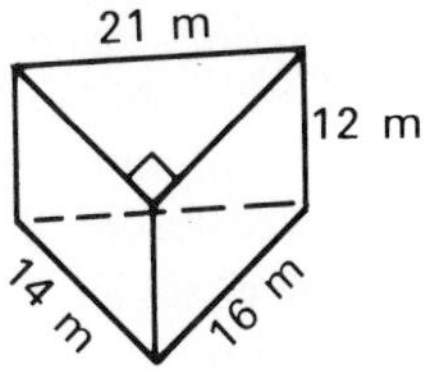

11.

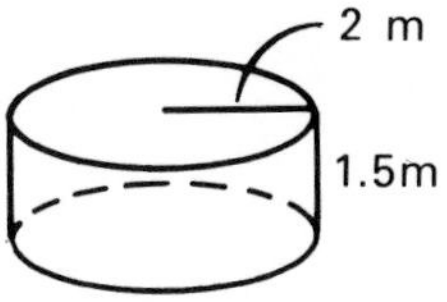

Find the volume of the figure in

12. Exercise 9. **13.** Exercise 10. **14.** Exercise 11.

Change each equation to slope-intercept form. Then give the slope and the *y*-intercept. Ch. 17

15. $2x + y = {}^{-}3$ **16.** $6x + {}^{-}2y = 15$ **17.** $3y - 2x = 12$

Graph each equation or inequality.

18. $2x + y = {}^{-}3$ **19.** $y = x + 2$ **20.** $3x - y \leq 3$

21. $y > x - 1$ **22.** $y = 2x$ **23.** $xy = 16\ (x > 0, y > 0)$

Solve each system by graphing.

24. $x - y = 4$ and $2x + y = 2$ **25.** $2x + 3y = 6$ and $3x + 2y = {}^{-}1$

INDEX

A

B

C

D

HOMEWORK HANDBOOK

This handbook contains model solutions and answers for selected exercises. Generally, the odd-numbered A and B exercises are answered, and a model solution is given for each major exercise type.

The model solutions and answers will be especially helpful when the student has had to miss some class time or when the teacher has had to shorten a class session for some unscheduled activity.

Pages 4–5 Section 1.1

1. Thousand **3.** Millimeter
5. Kilogram **7.** 37°
9. a. Gram **b.** Milligram **c.** Kilogram
d. Liter **11.** a, d **13.** c, d
15. b **17.** 41°C **19.** 1000

Page 8 Section 1.2

1. Add **3.** Subtract **5.** Multiply
7. Multiply **9.** Divide **11.** Add
***13.** 16 **15.** 27 **17.** 9 **19.** 10
***21.** 77 **23.** 3 **25.** 4 **27.** 6 **29.** 20

**Model solutions:*

13. $18 - 7 + 5$
$11 + 5$
16

21. $7 \times (6 + 5)$
7×11
77

Pages 10–11 Section 1.3

1. x **3.** n **5.** t **7.** c
9. y ***11.** 53 **13.** 17 **15.** 36
17. 16 **19.** 29 **21.** 80 **23.** 3
25. 35 **27.** 63 **29.** 41, 5, 77, 230
31. 15, 25, 5, 3 ***33.** 100 mm
35. 2300 mm **37.** 3 kg **39.** 92 kg

**Model solutions:*

11. $9n + 17 = 9(4) + 17$
$= 36 + 17$
$= 53$

33. $\square \times 10$
10×10
100 mm

Page 11 Quick Quiz

1. Weight or mass **2.** Capacity
3. Length **4.** 13 **5.** 11 **6.** 2
7. 5 **8.** 17 **9.** 25

Page 13 Section 1.4

1. Addition **3.** Multiplication
5. Division **7.** Division
9. Subtraction **11.** Multiplication
13. $52 - 20$ **15.** $12 \div 3$ or $3\overline{)12}$ or $\frac{12}{3}$
17. $x + 9$ **19.** $2B$ or $2(B)$ or $2 \times B$
21. $r - 6$ **23.** $n + 2$ **25.** $80 + 3$
27. $3c - 4$ **29.** $8 + 2b$

Page 15 Section 1.5

1. Thirteen equals twelve plus one.
3. Fifteen is greater than seven.
5. Two times seven is greater than thirteen.
7. Six divided by three equals two.
9. Four times x is greater than eight.
11. $2 < 9$
$9 > 2$
13. $82 + 5 < 91$
$91 > 82 + 5$
15. $12 \div 4 < 4$
$4 > 12 \div 4$
17. $13 - 4 < 10$
$10 > 13 - 4$
19. $92 < 12(8)$
$12(8) > 92$
21. $3(8) < 5(5)$
$5(5) > 3(8)$

23. $72 + 10 < 97 - 12$
$97 - 12 > 72 + 10$

25. $22 - 19 < 75 \div 15$ **27.** = **29.** >
$75 \div 15 > 22 - 19$

31. = **33.** $2x - 12 < 30$ **35.** $\frac{n}{2} > 40$

Model solution:

5. $\mathbf{0} + 8 = 12$ F $\mathbf{3} + 8 = 12$ F
$\mathbf{1} + 8 = 12$ F $\mathbf{4} + 8 = 12$ T
$\mathbf{2} + 8 = 12$ F $\mathbf{5} + 8 = 12$ F
So $n = 4$.

Pages 17–18 Section 1.6

1. T **3.** Can't dec. **5.** T **7.** F
9. T **11.** T **13.** O
15. T **17.** O **19.** T
21. Washington, D.C.; *any other city*
23. Alexander Graham Bell; *anyone else*
25. 12; *any other number*
27. *Any number less than 7; any other number*
29. *Any number greater than 6; any other number*

Page 18 Quick Quiz

1. $n + 1$ **2.** > **3.** < **4.** <
5. 5 **6.** *Any number less than 5*
7. *Any number greater than 3*

Pages 21–22 Section 1.7

1. a. $x + 4 = 13$
b. {8, 9, 10}
c. $\mathbf{8} + 4 = 13$
$\mathbf{9} + 4 = 13$
$\mathbf{10} + 4 = 13$

3. a. $t + 5 = 11$
b. {0, 1, 2, 3, 4}
c. $\mathbf{0} + 5 = 11$
$\mathbf{1} + 5 = 11$
$\mathbf{2} + 5 = 11$
$\mathbf{3} + 5 = 11$
$\mathbf{4} + 5 = 11$

***5.** 4 **7.** 0, 1, 2, 3, 4, 5 **9.** ∅
11. ∅ **13.** 2 **15.** 7 **17.** 6
19. 4 **21.** 5, 6, 7, 8 **23.** 2, 3, 4, 5
25. 51 **27.** 50, 51 **29.** 53

Pages 24–25 Section 1.8

1. 5 **3.** 2 ***5.** 8 **7.** 16
9. 10 **11.** 5 **13.** 13 **15.** 22
17. 35 **19.** 203 **21.** 35 **23.** 3
25. 479

Model solution:

5.
$$\begin{array}{rcl} n + 5 &=& 13 \\ -5 && -5 \\ \hline n &=& 8 \end{array}$$
Check:
$$\begin{array}{rcl} n + 5 &=& 13 \\ 8 + 5 &=& 13 \\ 13 &=& 13 \ \checkmark \end{array}$$

Pages 26–27 Section 1.9

1. Mathematical sentence
3. Multiplication ***5.** 12 m
7. 100 m **9.** 1000 m **11.** 13 202 m
***13.** 180 km **15.** 230 m **17.** 4680 m
19. 528 **21.** 66 **23.** 75

Model solutions:

5. $m = c \div 100$
$m = \mathbf{1200} \div 100$
$m = 12$
12 m

13. $d = rt$
$d = \mathbf{30} \times \mathbf{6}$
$d = 180$
180 km

Pages 28–29 Chapter Review

1. 1 meter **3.** 1 liter
5. Distance you could throw a ball
7. 3 **9.** 0 **11.** 48 **13.** 5
15. $n - 4$ **17.** $8 \div 3 < 1 + a$
19. T **21.** O **23.** F
25. 3 **27.** 6, 7, 8 **29.** 23

Page 30 Chapter Test

1. 19 **2.** 3 **3.** 81 **4.** 21
5. 2 **6.** 99 **7.** 29 **8.** 6
9. T **10.** O **11.** T **12.** F
13. 6 **14.** 3, 4 **15.** 7, 8, 9
16. 4 **17.** 3 **18.** $4x < 9 - 3$
19. a. Milligram(s) **b.** Kilometer(s) **c.** Liter(s)
20. a. Hundredths **b.** Thousandths **c.** Thousand
21. 198 km **22.** 351 cm

Page 36 Section 2.1

1. Subtracting 1 **3.** Dividing by 10
5. Adding 10 **7.** Subtracting 7
9. Adding 16

11. 52; $\begin{array}{r} 26 \\ +\ 52 \\ \hline 78 \end{array}$ **13.** 19; $\begin{array}{r} 19 \\ \times\ 4 \\ \hline 76 \end{array}$

15. 62; $\begin{array}{r} 62 \\ \times\ 15 \\ \hline 930 \end{array}$ **17.** 304; $\begin{array}{r} 48 \\ +\ 304 \\ \hline 352 \end{array}$ **19.** 19

21. n **23.** 15 **25.** Subtracting 25
27. Dividing by 5 **29.** Dividing by 23

Pages 37–39 Section 2.2

1. Subtract 5. **3.** Subtract 7.
5. Add 7. **7.** Add 8. **9.** Add 12.
11. Subtract 17. ***13.** 11 **15.** 26
17. 6 **19.** 14 **21.** 30 **23.** 33
25. 16 **27.** 26 **29.** 20 **31.** 8
33. 2 **35.** 92 **37.** 191 ***39.** 182
41. 168 **43.** 352 **45.** $177 **47.** $23

**Model solutions:*

13.
$$\begin{aligned} x + 7 &= 18 \\ x + 7 - 7 &= 18 - 7 \\ x &= 11 \end{aligned}$$

Check:
$$\begin{aligned} x + 7 &= 18 \\ \mathbf{11} + 7 &= 18 \\ 18 &= 18\ \checkmark \end{aligned}$$

39.
$$\begin{aligned} s + h &= f \\ s + \mathbf{39} &= \mathbf{221} \\ s + 39 - 39 &= 221 - 39 \\ s &= 182 \end{aligned}$$

Check:
$$\begin{aligned} s + h &= f \\ \mathbf{182} + \mathbf{39} &= 221 \\ 221 &= 221\ \checkmark \end{aligned}$$

Pages 40–41 Section 2.3

1. Divide by 3. **3.** Divide by 3.
5. Multiply by 5. **7.** Multiply by 5.
9. Multiply by 9. **11.** Multiply by 11.
***13.** 8 **15.** 35 **17.** 5 **19.** 4 **21.** 12
23. 3 **25.** 10 **27.** 110 **29.** 0 **31.** 210
33. 80 **35.** 51 **37.** 9 **39.** 5 **41.** 7
43. 16 **45.** 60 **47.** 39 hours

**Model solution:*

13.
$$\begin{aligned} 8y &= 64 \\ \frac{8y}{8} &= \frac{64}{8} \\ y &= 8 \end{aligned}$$

Check:
$$\begin{aligned} 8y &= 64 \\ 8(\mathbf{8}) &= 64 \\ 64 &= 64\ \checkmark \end{aligned}$$

Pages 43–44 Section 2.4

1. Subtract 4. **3.** Add 8. **5.** Divide by 7.
7. Dots at 4, 5, 6 **9.** Dot at 3
11. No dots **13.** Dots at 0, 1, 2, 3, 4, 5
***15.** $n < 26$ **17.** $10 > n$ **19.** $n < 0$
21. $n < 50$ **23.** $n > 4$ **25.** $n < 40$
27. $n < 12$ **29.** $n < 166$ **31.** $n > 1$
33. $25 < n$ **35.** $n > 1$ **37.** $n < 4$
39. a. Less than 99 °C
b. Less than 95 °C
c. Less than 98 °C

**Model solution:*

15.
$$\begin{aligned} n - 8 &< 18 \\ n - 8 + 8 &< 18 + 8 \\ n &< 26 \end{aligned}$$

Check:
$$\begin{aligned} n - 8 &< 18 \\ \mathbf{25} - 8 &< 18 \\ 17 &< 18\ \checkmark \end{aligned}$$

Pages 45–46 Section 2.5

1. b **3.** c ***5.** 16 **7.** 30
***9.** $x > 15$ **11.** 0 **13.** 4 **15.** $x < 1$
17. $x < 40$ **19.** $x > 6$ **21.** 3
23. $x < 48$ **25.** $x > 1$ **27.** 1

**Model solutions:*

5.
$$x - 4 = 12$$
$$x - 4 + 4 = 12 + 4$$
$$x = 16$$
Check:
$$x - 4 = 12$$
$$\mathbf{16} - 4 = 12$$
$$12 = 12 \checkmark$$

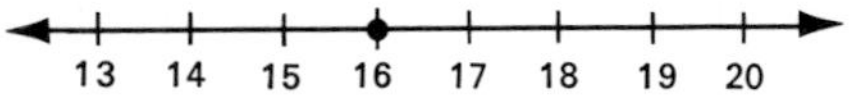

9.
$$\frac{x}{3} > 5$$
$$\frac{x}{3} \times 3 > 5 \times 3$$
$$x > 15$$
Check:
$$\frac{x}{3} > 5$$
$$\frac{\mathbf{18}}{3} > 5$$
$$6 > 5 \checkmark$$

Page 46 Quick Quiz

1. Addition **2.** Division **3.** 27
4. 102 **5.** 2 **6.** $n < 14$ **7.** $x > 2$
8. $a < 10$ **9.** 50 **10.** $32 > n$

Pages 48–49 Section 2.6

1. a. x mult. by 3; then 7 subtracted.
b. Add 7; then divide by 3.
3. a. n divided by 2; then 10 added.
b. Subtract 10; then multiply by 2.
5. a. 10 added to a; sum divided by 5.
b. Multiply by 5; then subtract 10.
7. a. x divided by 4; then 7 added.
b. Subtract 7; then multiply by 4.
9. a. y mult. by 9; then 17 subtracted.
b. Add 17; then divide by 9.
11. a. 7 added to n; sum divided by 3.
b. Multiply by 3; then subtract 7.
***13.** 7 ***15.** 108 **17.** 80 **19.** 40
21. 2 **23.** 3 **25.** 8 **27.** 30
29. 3 **31.** 24 **33.** 3 **35.** 40

**Model solutions:*

13.
$$6x - 3 = 39$$
$$6x - 3 + 3 = 39 + 3$$
$$6x = 42$$
$$\frac{6x}{6} = \frac{42}{6}$$
$$x = 7$$
Check:
$$6x - 3 = 39$$
$$6(\mathbf{7}) - 3 = 39$$
$$42 - 3 = 39$$
$$39 = 39 \checkmark$$

15.
$$\frac{x}{3} + 9 = 45$$
$$\frac{x}{3} + 9 - 9 = 45 - 9$$
$$\frac{x}{3} = 36$$
$$\frac{x}{3} \times 3 = 36 \times 3$$
$$x = 108$$
Check:
$$\frac{x}{3} + 9 = 45$$
$$\frac{\mathbf{108}}{3} + 9 = 45$$
$$36 + 9 = 45$$
$$45 = 45 \checkmark$$

Pages 51–52 Section 2.7

1. Multiply 3 by 5280. **3.** Divide 8 by 2.
5. Multiply **7.** 212 ***9.** 12 **11.** 28
13. 180 **15.** 81 **17.** 31 680 **19.** 16
***21.** 36 **23.** 120 **25.** 4 **27.** 15
29. 4 **31.** 19 **33.** 90 **35.** 21
37. 20 **39.** 9 **41.** 71
43. 30 yd per sec; 90 ft per sec
45. 158 **47.** 212

**Model solutions:*

9. $6 \times 2 = 12$
6 pt = <u>12</u> c

21. $108 \div 3 = 36$
108 ft = <u>36</u> yd

Pages 54–55 Section 2.8

1. 1 cm^2 **3.** 1 sq yd **5.** 1 cm^3
7. 1 cu ft **9.** 1 ft **11.** 1 mi
13. 1 yd **15.** 1 in. ***17.** 21 sq in.
19. 48 sq yd **21.** 273 sq ft ***23.** 120 m^3
25. 416 mm^3 **27.** 81 km^3 **29.** 5 yd
31. 5 mm **33.** 40 cm^2 **35.** 45 sq in.
37. 77 cm^3 **39.** 80 cu yd

**Model solutions:*

17.
$$A = lw$$
$$= \mathbf{7 \times 3}$$
$$= 21$$
21 sq in.

23.
$$V = lwh$$
$$= \mathbf{8 \times 5 \times 3}$$
$$= 120$$
120 m^3

Pages 57–58 Section 2.9

1. a. n b. $5n$ 3. a. P b. $P + 3$
5. Let n = the number; $21 = n + 6$
7. Let m = Mario's age; $12 = \frac{2m}{3}$
9. Let s = cost of 2nd shirt, $s + 2$ = cost of 1st shirt; $s + (s + 2) = 24$
11. Let n = 2nd number, $3n$ = 1st number; $3n + n = 20$
13. Let s = cost of student ticket, $s + 1$ = cost of adult ticket; $2(s + 1) + 3s = 12$
15. Let s = Stuart's wins, $s + 2$ = Evie's wins; $s + (s + 2) = 20$
17. Let b = Bulls' score, $b + 20$ = Pistons' score; $b + (b + 20) = 210$

Pages 59–60 Chapter Review

1. 59; $\begin{array}{r} 13 \\ +\ 59 \\ \hline 72 \end{array}$ 3. 43; $\begin{array}{r} 43 \\ \times\ 5 \\ \hline 215 \end{array}$ 5. 27

7. 3 9. 8 11. 49 13. 2 15. 7
17. $n < 5$ 19. $10 > y$ 21. $x > 7$
23. $x > 3$ 25. 9 27. 4 29. $n < 4$
31. $x > 5$ 33. 4 35. 14 37. 87
39. 156 41. 10 43. 6 45. 91 km^2
47. 1080 cu in. 49. Let n = the number; $35 = n + 7$

Page 61 Chapter Test

1. 12 2. 20 3. 8 4. 576
5. 6 6. 10 7. 24 8. 36
9. $x < 13$ 10. $n > 14$ 11. $n > 10$
12. $1 < y$ 13. 12 14. 5 15. $y < 4$
16. $n > 2$ 17. 20 18. 14 19. 144
20. 8 21. 60 cm^2 22. 210 cu in.
23. Let a = Angie's strikes, $2a + 3$ = Carolyn's strikes; $2a + 3 = 7$

Pages 67–68 Section 3.1

1. Yes 3. No 5. No *7. 8500
9. 12,840 11. 10,224 13. 251,800
*15. $x + 5 = 9$; 4 17. $14 = z + 8$; 6
19. $49 = 7t$; 7 21. $14 = t + 6$; 8
23. $m + 11 = 69$; 58
25. $n + 13 = 81$; 68
27. $c + 18 = 96$; 78
29. $91 = d + 17$; 74 31. 69 mph 33. $6

Model solutions:

7. $\begin{array}{r} 425 \\ \times\ 20 \\ \hline 8500 \end{array}$

15. $$\begin{aligned} x + 5 &= 9 \\ x + 5 - 5 &= 9 - 5 \\ x &= 4 \end{aligned}$$
Check: $$\begin{aligned} x + 5 &= 9 \\ 4 + 5 &= 9 \\ 9 &= 9 \checkmark \end{aligned}$$

Pages 71–72 Section 3.2

1. No 3. $(30 + 60) + 18$
5. $(54 + 6) + 27$ 7. $12 \times (4 \times 5)$
9. $(16 + 84) + 99$ 11. $(4 \times 250) \times 172$
*13. 1200 15. 900 17. 159 19. 1068
21. 34,000 23. 183 25. 172 *27. 10
29. 14 31. 6 33. 6 35. 12
37. 2 39. 5 in. 41. 6 ft

Model solutions:

13. $(5 \times 40) \times 6$ or $(5 \times 6) \times 40$
200×6 30×40
1200 1200

27. $$\begin{aligned} (n + 3) + 7 &= 20 \\ n + (3 + 7) &= 20 \\ n + 10 &= 20 \\ n + 10 - 10 &= 20 - 10 \\ n &= 10 \end{aligned}$$
Check: $$\begin{aligned} (n + 3) + 7 &= 20 \\ (10 + 3) + 7 &= 20 \\ 13 + 7 &= 20 \\ 20 &= 20 \checkmark \end{aligned}$$

Page 75 Section 3.3

1. 4 **3.** 42 **5.** 0 **7.** 0 **9.** 1
11. Any number **13.** 0 **15.** 1
17. 0 **19.** 79 **21.** Any number
23. 89 **25.** 296 **27.** 0 **29.** 197

3

Pages 77–79 Section 3.4

1. 2 **3.** 5 **5.** 1 **7.** x **9.** 3
***11.** **a.** 102 **13.** **a.** 182 **15.** **a.** 168
b. 102 **b.** 182 **b.** 168
***17.** 8 **19.** 22 **21.** 50 **23.** 6
25. 7 **27.** 2 **29.** 2 **31.** 4

**Model solutions:*

11. **a.** $6(8+9)$, $6(17)$, 102 **b.** $6(8+9)$, $6 \times 8 + 6 \times 9$, $48 + 54$, 102

17.
$$\begin{aligned} 7t + 2t &= 72 \\ (7+2)t &= 72 \\ 9t &= 72 \\ \frac{9t}{9} &= \frac{72}{9} \\ t &= 8 \end{aligned}$$

Check:
$$\begin{aligned} 7t + 2t &= 72 \\ 7(8) + 2(8) &= 72 \\ 56 + 16 &= 72 \\ 72 &= 72 \checkmark \end{aligned}$$

Page 79 Quick Quiz

1. c **2.** a **3.** b **4.** 9 **5.** 10
6. 2 **7.** 22 **8.** 0 **9.** 32 **10.** 1
11. 0 **12.** 10 **13.** 7

Page 81 Section 3.5

1. 1, 2, 3, 6 **3.** 1, 2, 4, 8
5. 1, 3, 7, 21 **7.** 1, 2, 3, 6, 9, 18
9. 1, 2, 4, 5, 10, 20 **11.** Yes **13.** No
***15.** No **17.** Yes **19.** No **21.** Yes
23. No

Ex. 25–33: Other answers possible

25. 2×6 **27.** 3×12 **29.** 4×7
31. 5×6 **33.** 4×12
35. 1, 2, 13, 26 **37.** 1, 3, 11, 33
39. 1, 2, 4, 8, 16, 32
41. 1, 5, 25 **43.** 1, 13

**Model solution:*

15. $3\overline{)38}$ = 12 R2 No

Page 84 Section 3.6

1. 2, 3 **3.** 2 **5.** 3, 5 **7.** 2, 5, 10
9. 2, 3, 5, 10 **11.** 2, 3, 5, 10
13. 2, 3 **15.** 3, 5 **17.** 2, 3, 5, 10
19. 1, 5, 11, 55
21. 1, 2, 3, 5, 6, 10, 15, 30
23. 1, 2, 5, 7, 10, 14, 35, 70

Page 87 Section 3.7

1. Comp. **3.** Comp. **5.** Comp.
7. Comp. **9.** Prime **11.** Comp.
13. Prime **15.** Comp. **17.** Comp.
19. Comp. **21.** 2×13 **23.** 2×11
25. 5×7 ***27.** $3 \times 3 \times 3$
29. $2 \times 2 \times 3 \times 3$ **31.** 7×7
33. $2 \times 2 \times 2 \times 2 \times 3 \times 3$
35. $3 \times 3 \times 5 \times 5$
37. $3 \times 3 \times 5 \times 13$

**Model solution:*

27.
$$\begin{aligned} 27 &= 3 \times 9 \\ &= 3 \times 3 \times 3 \end{aligned}$$

Pages 89–90 Section 3.8

1. Six to the first power; base 6; exp. 1
3. Four to the tenth power; base 4; exp. 10
5. Eleven squared or eleven to the second power; base 11; exp. 2

7. x^8 **9.** 5^5 **11.** 64 **13.** 100
15. No ***17.** 8 **19.** 1 **21.** 216
***23.** 16 **25.** 2 **27.** 1,000,000
***29.** 2×3^3 **31.** $2^3 \times 11$ **33.** $2^5 \times 3^2$
35. 2×5^4 **37.** $2^3 \times 5^2 \times 7$ **39.** No

**Model solutions:*

17. $2^3 = 2 \times 2 \times 2 = 8$

23. $2^4 = 2 \times 2 \times 2 \times 2 = 16$

29. $54 = 2 \times 27 = 2 \times (3 \times 9) = 2 \times (3 \times 3 \times 3) = 2 \times 3^3$

Page 92 Section 3.9

1. 3 **3.** 1 **5.** 6 **7.** 3 **9.** 4
***11.** 9 **13.** 6 **15.** 2 **17.** 25 **19.** 4
21. 18 **23.** 4

**Model solution:*

11. $36 = 4 \times 9 = 2^2 \times 3^2$
$45 = 5 \times 9 = 3^2 \times 5$
$3^2 = 9$

Pages 94–95 Section 3.10

1. 12 **3.** 60 **5.** 72 **7.** 32
9. 30 **11.** 35 ***13.** 80 **15.** 1225
17. 72 **19.** 210 **21.** 12 **23.** 150

**Model solution:*

13. $16 = 2^4$
$80 = 2^4 \times 5$
$2^4 \times 5 = 80$

Pages 96–98 Chapter Review

1. $x + 5 = 11$; 6 **3.** $6z = 96$; 16
5. 69 **7.** 210 **9.** 13 **11.** 16
13. 0 **15.** 0 **17.** 280 **19.** 11
21. 10 **23.** 1, 2, 17, 34
25. 1, 2, 3, 5, 6, 10, 15, 30 **27.** No
29. Yes **31.** 2, 3, 5, 10 **33.** 2, 3 **35.** 2
37. Prime **39.** Prime **41.** 2×23
43. $3 \times 3 \times 3 \times 3$ **45.** 5^6 **47.** $9^4 \times 2^2$
49. 729 **51.** 3 **53.** 21 **55.** 11 **57.** 2
59. When the numbers have no common prime factors
61. 192 **63.** 225 **65.** 340

Page 99 Chapter Test

1. c **2.** a **3.** b **4.** 295
5. 85 **6.** 0 **7.** 85 **8.** 0
9. 1 **10.** 89 **11.** 180 **12.** 6
13. 12 **14.** 2 **15.** 10 **16.** 1, 11
17. 1, 2, 3, 5, 10, 20 **18.** 1, 2, 11, 22
19. Yes; no; yes; yes **20.** Comp.
21. Prime **22.** Prime **23.** $2^2 \times 3 \times 5$
24. 2×3^3 **25.** $2^3 \times 3^2$ **26.** 16
27. 225 **28.** 6 **29.** 1
30. 12 **31.** 280 **32.** 18

Pages 109–110 Section 4.1

1. $2 \div 3$ **3.** $\frac{1}{4}$ **5.** $\frac{5}{6}$ **7.** $\frac{3}{1}$
9. $\frac{6}{1}$ **11.** 2 **13.** 4 **15.** 5 **17.** 10
19. 2; 8 **21.** 7 ***23.** $\frac{5}{2}$ **25.** $\frac{4}{5}$
27. $\frac{7}{6}$ **29.** $\frac{9}{7}$ **31.** $\frac{10}{9}$ **33.** $\frac{8}{3}$ **35.** 3

**Model solution:*

23. $\frac{1}{2} + \frac{4}{2} = \frac{1+4}{2} = \frac{5}{2}$

4

Page 112 Section 4.2

1. $\frac{1}{10}$ 3. $\frac{7}{16}$ 5. $\frac{1}{30}$ 7. $\frac{6}{25}$
9. $\frac{1}{27}$ *11. $\frac{7}{36}$ 13. $\frac{5}{24}$ 15. $\frac{3}{40}$
17. $\frac{11}{24}$ 19. $\frac{5}{6}$ 21. $\frac{27}{40}$ 23. $\frac{3}{20}$
25. $\frac{10}{5}$ or 2 27. $\frac{24}{3}$ or 8 29. $\frac{12}{11}$
31. $\frac{3}{4}$ yd 33. $\frac{5}{16}$ yd

**Model solution:*

11. $\frac{1}{4} \times \frac{7}{9} = \frac{1 \times 7}{4 \times 9} = \frac{7}{36}$

Pages 114–115 Section 4.3

1. 3 3. 5 5. 2 *7. $\frac{1}{4}$
9. $\frac{2}{3}$ 11. $\frac{7}{9}$ 13. $\frac{2}{3}$ 15. $\frac{1}{4}$
17. $\frac{1}{4}$ 19. $\frac{1}{2}$ 21. $\frac{3}{5}$ 23. $\frac{3}{4}$
25. $\frac{4}{5}$ 27. $\frac{3}{5}$ 29. $\frac{3}{8}$ 31. $\frac{2}{3}$
*33. $\frac{1}{4}$ 35. $\frac{1}{5}$ 37. $\frac{1}{3}$ 39. $\frac{1}{3}$
41. $\frac{1}{3}$ 43. $\frac{2}{9}$ 45. $\frac{1}{3}$ cup

**Model solutions:*

7. $\frac{3}{12} = \frac{3 \div 3}{12 \div 3} = \frac{1}{4}$ or $\frac{\cancel{3}^{1}}{\cancel{12}_{4}} = \frac{1}{4}$

33. $\frac{2}{1} \times \frac{1}{8} = \frac{\cancel{2}^{1}}{\cancel{8}_{4}} = \frac{1}{4}$ or $\frac{\cancel{2}^{1}}{1} \times \frac{1}{\cancel{8}_{4}} = \frac{1}{4}$

Pages 117–118 Section 4.4

1. $2 + \frac{1}{3}$ 3. $21 + \frac{5}{6}$ 5. $4\overline{)5}$
7. $5\overline{)14}$ *9. $\frac{7}{3}$ 11. $\frac{6}{5}$ 13. $\frac{5}{2}$
15. $\frac{29}{5}$ 17. $\frac{14}{3}$ *19. $2\frac{1}{2}$ 21. $1\frac{2}{3}$
23. $1\frac{2}{5}$ 25. $3\frac{1}{5}$ 27. $7\frac{3}{4}$ *29. $1\frac{1}{5}$
31. $3\frac{1}{3}$ 33. $1\frac{1}{8}$ 35. $3\frac{1}{2}$ 37. $1\frac{1}{4}$
39. $24\frac{1}{2}$ pounds; $1277\frac{1}{2}$ pounds

**Model solutions:*

9. $2\frac{1}{3} = \frac{2 \times 3 + 1}{3} = \frac{7}{3}$

19. $\begin{array}{r} 2 \text{ R}1 \\ 2\overline{)5} \end{array} = 2\frac{1}{2}$ 29. $\frac{1}{\cancel{2}_{1}} \times \frac{\cancel{12}^{6}}{5} = \frac{6}{5} = 1\frac{1}{5}$

Pages 120–121 Section 4.5

1. $\frac{3}{1}$; $\frac{9}{2}$ 3. $\frac{25}{6}$ 5. $\frac{10}{3}$ 7. $\frac{8}{1}$; $\frac{9}{8}$
9. $\frac{10}{7}$; $\frac{14}{5}$ 11. $6\frac{2}{3} \times 12$ 13. 1 *15. $1\frac{2}{3}$
17. $\frac{3}{4}$ 19. $7\frac{1}{2}$ 21. 8 23. $1\frac{9}{16}$
25. $9\frac{1}{3}$ 27. 4 29. $60\frac{1}{2}$ 31. 18
33. $12\frac{4}{5}$ *35. 80 37. $9\frac{1}{4}$ 39. $2\frac{3}{4}$

**Model solutions:*

15. $2\frac{1}{2} \times \frac{2}{3} = \frac{5}{\cancel{2}_{1}} \times \frac{\cancel{2}^{1}}{3} = \frac{5}{3} = 1\frac{2}{3}$

35. $6\frac{2}{3} \times 12 = \frac{20}{\cancel{3}_{1}} \times \frac{\cancel{12}^{4}}{1} = 80$;

$6\frac{2}{3}$ ft $= \underline{80}$ in.

Page 121 Quick Quiz

1. $\frac{3}{5}$ 2. $\frac{4}{7}$ 3. $\frac{5}{3}$ 4. Denominator
5. $3\frac{1}{2}$ 6. $\frac{3}{5}$ 7. $\frac{8}{11}$ 8. $\frac{14}{15}$ 9. $\frac{3}{35}$
10. $\frac{1}{6}$ 11. $3\frac{3}{5}$ 12. 5 13. 75 14. $2\frac{2}{3}$

Pages 124–125 Section 4.6

1. $\frac{2}{1}$ 3. $\frac{1}{6}$ 5. $7\frac{1}{2}$; 3 *7. $\frac{2}{5}$
9. 9 11. $\frac{1}{12}$ 13. $\frac{4}{5}$ 15. $1\frac{1}{3}$
17. $\frac{2}{5}$ 19. $\frac{5}{6}$ 21. $\frac{1}{4}$ 23. 39
25. 10 27. $\frac{2}{3}$ 29. $2\frac{2}{5}$ *31. $2\frac{1}{2}$
33. $\frac{7}{10}$ 35. $5\frac{1}{8}$ 37. $1\frac{3}{4}$ in. 39. 50 mph

**Model solutions:*

7. $\frac{1}{5} \div \frac{1}{2} = \frac{1}{5} \times \frac{2}{1} = \frac{2}{5}$

31. $7\frac{1}{2} \div 3 = \frac{\cancel{15}^{5}}{2} \times \frac{1}{\cancel{3}_{1}} = \frac{5}{2} = 2\frac{1}{2}$

$7\frac{1}{2}$ ft $= \underline{2\frac{1}{2}}$ yd

Pages 128–129 Section 4.7

1. 1 3. 1 5. 7 7. 1
9. $\frac{1}{2}$ 11. $2\frac{2}{3}$ *13. $\frac{2}{3}$ 15. $4\frac{1}{3}$
17. $1\frac{1}{2}$ 19. $\frac{3}{5}$ 21. $4\frac{2}{3}$ 23. $2\frac{1}{4}$

*25. $7\frac{1}{3}$ 27. $\frac{4}{5}$ 29. $4\frac{1}{3}$ yd 31. $\frac{1}{6}$
33. $1\frac{2}{3}$ 35. $12\frac{4}{9}$ 37. $2\frac{5}{7}$ 39. $\frac{11}{12}$
41. $4\frac{1}{4}$ qt *43. $\frac{2}{5}$ 45. $1\frac{1}{2}$ 47. $2\frac{5}{7}$

**Model solutions:*

13.
$$\begin{array}{rcr} 1\frac{1}{3} & = & \frac{4}{3} \\ -\ \frac{2}{3} & = & \frac{2}{3} \\ \hline & & \frac{2}{3} \end{array}$$

25.
$$\begin{array}{r} 5\frac{2}{3} \\ +\ 1\frac{2}{3} \\ \hline 6\frac{4}{3} = 7\frac{1}{3} \end{array}$$

43.
$$\begin{aligned} m + \tfrac{2}{5} &= \tfrac{4}{5} \\ m + \tfrac{2}{5} - \tfrac{2}{5} &= \tfrac{4}{5} - \tfrac{2}{5} \\ m &= \tfrac{2}{5} \end{aligned} \qquad \textit{Check: } \begin{aligned} m + \tfrac{2}{5} &= \tfrac{4}{5} \\ \tfrac{2}{5} + \tfrac{2}{5} &= \tfrac{4}{5} \\ \tfrac{4}{5} &= \tfrac{4}{5}\ \checkmark \end{aligned}$$

Pages 131–132 Section 4.8

1. 4 3. 5 5. 6 *7. $\frac{6}{16}$; $\frac{1}{16}$
9. $\frac{6}{30}$; $\frac{25}{30}$ *11. $\frac{3}{4}$ 13. $\frac{1}{8}$ 15. $\frac{1}{6}$
17. $\frac{11}{12}$ 19. $\frac{23}{24}$ 21. $\frac{1}{3}$ 23. $\frac{13}{24}$
25. $\frac{5}{16}$ *27. $\frac{1}{8}$ 29. $\frac{15}{28}$ 31. $\frac{19}{24}$

**Model solutions:*

7. $\frac{3}{8} \times \frac{2}{2} = \frac{6}{16}$
$\frac{6}{16}$; $\frac{1}{16}$

11.
$$\begin{array}{rcr} \frac{1}{2} \times \frac{2}{2} & = & \frac{2}{4} \\ +\ \frac{1}{4} & = & \frac{1}{4} \\ \hline & & \frac{3}{4} \end{array}$$

27.
$$\begin{aligned} u + \tfrac{3}{4} &= \tfrac{7}{8} \\ u + \tfrac{3}{4} - \tfrac{3}{4} &= \tfrac{7}{8} - \tfrac{3}{4} \\ u &= \tfrac{7}{8} - \tfrac{6}{8} \\ u &= \tfrac{1}{8} \end{aligned} \qquad \textit{Check: } \begin{aligned} u + \tfrac{3}{4} &= \tfrac{7}{8} \\ \tfrac{1}{8} + \tfrac{3}{4} &= \tfrac{7}{8} \\ \tfrac{1}{8} + \tfrac{6}{8} &= \tfrac{7}{8} \\ \tfrac{7}{8} &= \tfrac{7}{8}\ \checkmark \end{aligned}$$

Pages 133–134 Section 4.9

1. 2 3. 2 5. 6 *7. $11\frac{3}{4}$
*9. $\frac{7}{10}$ 11. $2\frac{3}{8}$ 13. $\frac{3}{4}$ 15. $2\frac{19}{20}$
17. $17\frac{17}{30}$ 19. $7\frac{13}{20}$ 21. $3\frac{17}{24}$
23. $1\frac{7}{8}$ yd 25. $8\frac{1}{6}$ hr

**Model solutions:*

7.
$$\begin{array}{rcr} 9\frac{1}{2} & = & 9\frac{2}{4} \\ +\ 2\frac{1}{4} & = & 2\frac{1}{4} \\ \hline & & 11\frac{3}{4} \end{array}$$

9.
$$\begin{array}{rcrcr} 2\frac{1}{10} & = & 2\frac{1}{10} & = & 1\frac{11}{10} \\ -\ 1\frac{2}{5} & = & 1\frac{4}{10} & = & 1\frac{4}{10} \\ \hline & & & & \frac{7}{10} \end{array}$$

Pages 137–138 Section 4.10

1. b 3. c 5. c *7. 4 times
9. 7 cans 11. 3 bottles 13. $9\frac{1}{3}$ in.

**Model solution:*

7. $2\frac{1}{4} \div \frac{1}{2} = \frac{9}{\cancel{4}_2} \times \frac{\cancel{2}^1}{1} = \frac{9}{2} = 4\frac{1}{2}$; 4 times

Pages 139–140 Chapter Review

1. $\frac{2}{5}$ 3. $\frac{8}{3}$ 5. $\frac{2}{5}$ 7. $\frac{7}{9}$ 9. $\frac{9}{16}$
11. $\frac{5}{32}$ 13. $\frac{1}{4}$ 15. 1 17. $\frac{5}{3}$ 19. $\frac{8}{5}$
21. $3\frac{1}{3}$ 23. $1\frac{3}{4}$ 25. $1\frac{1}{10}$ 27. $\frac{4}{9}$ 29. $\frac{1}{2}$
31. 8 33. $5\frac{3}{4}$ 35. $\frac{1}{15}$ 37. $5\frac{1}{3}$ 39. $\frac{3}{8}$
41. 2 43. 5 45. 8 47. $\frac{2}{3}$ 49. $2\frac{3}{8}$
51. 6 53. $\frac{5}{6}$ 55. $\frac{7}{8}$ 57. $3\frac{9}{10}$ 59. $14\frac{5}{12}$
61. 12 pieces 63. 14 packages

Page 141 Chapter Test

1. $\frac{6}{1}$ 2. $\frac{9}{2}$ 3. $\frac{3}{2}$ 4. $\frac{1}{3}$ 5. $2\frac{1}{2}$
6. $1\frac{2}{3}$ 7. $\frac{2}{15}$ 8. $\frac{1}{3}$ 9. $2\frac{1}{2}$ 10. 2
11. $\frac{3}{7}$ 12. $1\frac{1}{3}$ 13. $1\frac{1}{2}$ 14. 16 15. $2\frac{1}{2}$
16. 6 17. 4 18. 6 19. 1 20. 3
21. 3 22. 5 23. 7 24. 13 25. $\frac{1}{2}$
26. $1\frac{1}{3}$ 27. $\frac{2}{3}$ 28. $12\frac{1}{4}$ 29. $\frac{1}{6}$ 30. $\frac{3}{4}$
31. $9\frac{1}{3}$ 32. $\frac{7}{12}$ 33. 4 pieces 34. 6 cans

Page 146 Section 5.1

1. One tenth 3. Seven and nine tenths
5. Twelve hundredths
7. Six and fifty-five hundredths
9. One hundred twenty-three thousandths
11. Eight and sixty-three thousandths
13. $\frac{3}{10}$ 15. $68\frac{9}{10}$ 17. $\frac{17}{100}$ 19. $9\frac{7}{100}$
21. $\frac{321}{1000}$ 23. $18\frac{9}{1000}$ 25. $8\frac{3}{5}$ 27. $16\frac{17}{200}$
29. 0.5 31. 3.9 33. 0.16 35. 4.37
37. 0.225 39. 6.003 41. 6.9 43. 6.009

5

Pages 148–149 Section 5.2†

1. a. 1 **b.** 0 **c.** 8
3. a. 2 **b.** 4 **c.** 5
5. a. 2 **b.** 9 **c.** 5
7. a. 3 **b.** 1 **c.** 6
9. a. 0 **b.** 1 **c.** 2 **d.** 3
11. a. 9 **b.** 1 **c.** 5 **d.** 2
13. a. 5 **b.** 7 **c.** 2 **d.** 4
15. a. 6 **b.** 0 **c.** 5 **d.** 7
17. $30 \times 30 = 900$ **19.** $90 \times 10 = 900$
21. 0; 0.5; 0.45; 0.453
23. 9; 9.1; 9.08; 9.083
25. 133; 132.5; 132.52; 132.516
27. 9840; 9800; 10,000
29. 670, 700, 1000 ***31. a.** 63,000 **b.** 63,048 **33. a.** 370 **b.** 374

***Model solution:*

31. a.
$$\begin{array}{r} 900 \\ \times\ 70 \\ \hline 63{,}000 \end{array}$$
b.
$$\begin{array}{r} 888 \\ \times\ 71 \\ \hline 888 \\ 62\ 16 \\ \hline 63{,}048 \end{array}$$

Pages 151–152 Section 5.3†

1. Align the decimal points.
3. The same except for decimal points
5. Yes; in addition or subtraction if other numbers have thousandths
7. 17.39 **9.** 58.24 **11.** 1.68
13. 2.595 **15.** 63.1 **17.** 10.28
***19. a.** 52 **b.** 52.306 **21. a.** 12 **b.** 11.72
***23. a.** 5 **b.** 4.75 **25. a.** 14 **b.** 14.25

***Model solutions:*

19. a.
$$\begin{array}{r} 36 \\ 15 \\ +\ 1 \\ \hline 52 \end{array}$$
b.
$$\begin{array}{r} 36.2\mathit{00} \\ 14.85\mathit{0} \\ +\ 1.256 \\ \hline 52.306 \end{array}$$
23. a.
$$\begin{array}{r} 5 \\ -\ 0 \\ \hline 5 \end{array}$$
b.
$$\begin{array}{r} 5.\mathit{00} \\ -\ 0.25 \\ \hline 4.75 \end{array}$$

†Estimates may vary.

Pages 154–155 Section 5.4

1. 680.4 **3.** 6.804 **5.** 68.04
7. 0.6804 **9.** 3.24 **11.** 97,000
13. 1000 ***15. a.** 80 **b.** 90 **17. a.** 0.2 **b.** 0.189
19. a. 0.4 **b.** 0.5052 **21. a.** 155 **b.** 166.86 **23. a.** 24 **b.** 29.52
25. a. 0 **b.** 0.121 ***27.** 12.4372 **29.** 9.61
31. 5.625 **33.** 0.0632 **35.** 0.00079
37. 0.1 ***39.** 4520 **41.** 190
43. 476 **45.** $202.59 **47.** 18.75 in.

***Model solutions:*

15. a.
$$\begin{array}{r} 80 \\ \times\ 1 \\ \hline 80 \end{array}$$
b.
$$\begin{array}{r} 7 \\ \times\ 1.2 \\ \hline 150 \\ 75 \\ \hline 90.0 \end{array}$$
27.
$$\begin{array}{r} 4.012 \\ \times\ 3.1 \\ \hline 4012 \\ 12036 \\ \hline 12.4372 \end{array}$$
39. $4.52 \times 1000 = 4520$
4.52 km = <u>4520</u> m

Page 156 Quick Quiz†

1. $\frac{9}{10}$ **2.** $3\frac{71}{100}$ **3.** $\frac{1}{25}$ **4.** $7\frac{1}{4}$
5. 0.7 **6.** 0.03 **7.** 3.23 **8.** 4.007
9. a. 10 **b.** 7.05
10. a. 0 **b.** 3.98
11. a. 210 **b.** 206.42
12. a. 720 **b.** 723.58
13. a. 100 **b.** 100.552
14. a. 96 **b.** 92.7914

Pages 158–159 Section 5.5

1. 1.2 **3.** 0.012 **5.** 0.00123
7. 100 ***9.** 1.23 **11.** 0.035
13. 1.023 **15.** 0.0052 **17.** 0.42
19. 1.25 ***21.** 3.14 **23.** 9.12
25. 0.10302 **27.** 3.8 **29.** 0.0456

31. 0.03 **33.** 4.356 **35.** 0.56 ***37.** 0.625 **39.** 1.1875 **41.** 0.75 **43.** 0.4375 **45.** $2.\overline{6}$ **47.** $0.\overline{4}$ **49.** 5.6775 in.

***Model solutions:**

9.
```
   1.23
7)8.61
  7
  16
  14
    21
    21
```

21.
```
    3.14
9)28.26
  27
   12
    9
    36
    36
```

37.
```
   0.625
8)5.000
  48
   20
   16
    40
    40
```

Pages 160–162 Section 5.6

1. 0.2)8.4 **3.** 0.56)1400 **5.** 3.4)0.0068 **7.** 0.002)0.016 **9.** 0.09)0.225 **11.** 6.2 ***13.** 25.4 **15.** 0.025 **17.** 6.32 **19.** 0.32 **21.** 0.36 **23.** 0.42 **25.** 3.6 **27.** 65 ***29.** 27 **31.** 1.2 **33.** 21 **35.** 475 **37.** 395 **39.** 3.8 **41.** 76,410 ***43.** \$1.26 **45.** \$1.22 **47.** \$1.10 **49.** \$1.15 **51.** \$1.11

***Model solutions:**

13.
```
       25.4
0.6)15.24
    12
     32
     30
      24
      24
```

29.
```
          27
0.06)1.62
     12
      42
      42
```

43.
```
    1.26
8)10.08      $1.26
  8
  20
  16
   48
   48
```

Pages 165–166 Section 5.7

1. 156 **3.** 9470 ***5.** 148 993 m or 148.993 km **7.** 132.39 m or 13 239 cm ***9.** 198.6 mL **11. a.** 53.6 kg **b.** Under, by 6.4 kg ***13.** 25 434 m^2 **15.** 0.565 km; 0.8475 km; 1.27125 km **17.** \$23.25

***Model solutions:**

5.
```
  180 000 m    or    180.000 km
 − 31 007 m         − 31.007 km
  148 993 m          148.993 km
```

9.
```
  236.0
 − 37.4
  198.6
  198.6 mL
```

13. $A = \pi r^2$
$= 3.14 \times 90^2$
$= 25\,434$
25 434 m^2

Pages 167–168 Chapter Review†

1. $\frac{7}{10}$ **3.** $2\frac{9}{10}$ **5.** $1\frac{7}{200}$ **7.** $5\frac{21}{50}$ **9.** 0.5 **11.** 0.09 **13.** 2.16 **15.** 6.06 **17.** 50; 54; 54.1; 54.13 **19. a.** 18,000 **b.** 17,784 **21. a.** 200 **b.** 238 **23. a.** 40 **b.** 46.8 **25. a.** 9 **b.** 8.899 **27. a.** 80 **b.** 88.83 **29. a.** 2.4 **b.** 2.149 **31.** 5300 **33.** 3500 **35.** 3.54 **37.** 0.024 **39.** 0.00432 **41.** 0.425 **43.** 0.875 **45.** $0.\overline{5}$ **47.** 25.3 **49.** 3.12 **51.** 3.2 **53.** 441.13 m or 44 113 cm **55.** 154 330 m^2 or 0.154 33 km^2 **57.** 329.18 km

Page 169 Chapter Test†

1. $\frac{9}{10}$ **2.** $8\frac{1}{4}$ **3.** $\frac{7}{200}$ **4.** 0.019 **5.** 0.6 **6.** 5.75 **7.** 800; 765; 765.2 **8.** 400; 426; 425.9 **9. a.** 17 **b.** 17.02 **10. a.** 2 **b.** 2.624 **11. a.** 4 **b.** 2.88 **12. a.** 8 **b.** 7.65

5

13. **a.** 1.2 **b.** 1.22 **14.** **a.** 48 **b.** 45 **15.** 3.4 **16.** 36
17. 2.5 **18.** 2.25 **19.** 4800 **20.** 0.016
21. 9.2 **22.** 5800 **23.** 67,542 **24.** 78.32
25. 0.0855 **26.** 92.585 m or 92 585 mm
27. 10.4 kg or 10 400 g
28. 72 mm^2 or 0.72 cm^2
29. 27.83 m or 2783 cm **30.** 0.945 L

Pages 174–175 Section 6.1

1. $^{-}2$ **3.** 17 **5.** 2 **7.** $^{-}86$ **9.** 0
11. $^{+}3$ **13.** Five meters backward
15. 100 feet below sea level **17.** $^{+}8$
19. $^{-}70$ **21.** 10 **23.** 10 **25.** $^{-}7$
27. $^{-}3$, $^{-}1$, 3, 5
29. $^{-}25$, $^{-}20$, $^{-}10$, 0, 30
31. $^{-}8$, $^{-}5$, 0, 3, 7, 9
33. $^{-}5$, $^{-}4$, $^{-}3$, 0, 3, 4, 5

Page 177 Section 6.2

1. $3 + 4 = 7$ **3.** $5 + {^{-}2} = 3$ **5.** 11
7. $^{-}5$ **9.** $^{-}9$ **11.** 5 **13.** $^{-}4$ **15.** 10
17. $^{-}4$ **19.** 0 **21.** 1 **23.** 6 **25.** 5

Pages 179–180 Section 6.3

1. 16 **3.** 325 **5.** 0 **7.** Pos.
9. 0 **11.** Neg. **13.** 28 **15.** 0
17. $^{-}57$ **19.** 85 **21.** 16 ***23.** $^{-}8$
25. $^{-}1451$ **27.** 0 **29.** $^{-}581$ **31.** 276
33. 1568 **35.** 2357 ***37.** 9 **39.** 6
41. $^{-}5$ **43.** $^{-}9$ **45.** $^{-}9$

**Model solutions:*

23. $103 + {^{-}111} = {^{-}8}$

$$\begin{array}{r} 111 \\ -103 \\ \hline 8 \end{array}$$

37. $(2 + 4) + 3 = 6 + 3$
$= 9$

Page 182 Section 6.4

1. $6 + {^{-}7}$ **3.** $9 + 12$ **5.** $^{-}4 + 2$
***7.** $^{-}4$ **9.** $^{-}29$ **11.** $^{-}14$ **13.** 4
15. 22 **17.** $^{-}12$ ***19.** $^{-}34$ **21.** $^{-}92$
23. 337 **25.** 3641 **27.** $^{-}161$

**Model solutions:*

7. $15 - 19 = 15 + {^{-}19}$
$= {^{-}4}$

19. ${^{-}18} - 16 = {^{-}18} + {^{-}16}$
$= {^{-}34}$

Page 182 Quick Quiz

1. $^{-}1$ **2.** $^{-}11$ **3.** $^{-}15$ **4.** 0
5. 17 **6.** 112 **7.** 25 **8.** $^{-}98$
9. $^{-}3$ **10.** $^{-}9$ **11.** 0 **12.** 102

Page 184 Section 6.5

1. $^{-}7$ **3.** $^{-}9$ **5.** $^{-}8$ ***7.** 6
9. 17 **11.** $^{-}7$ **13.** 23 **15.** $^{-}21$
17. $^{-}41$ **19.** 11 **21.** 14 **23.** 18

**Model solution:*

7.
$n + 3 = 9$
$n + 3 + {^{-}3} = 9 + {^{-}3}$
$n = 6$

Check:
$n + 3 = 9$
$6 + 3 = 9$
$9 = 9$ ✓

Page 187 Section 6.6

1. **a.** $n + {^{-}7} = {^{-}6}$ **b.** 7
3. **a.** $14 = k + {^{-}7}$ **b.** 7
5. **a.** $x + {^{-}8} = 0$ **b.** 8
***7.** 16 **9.** 5 **11.** 22 **13.** $^{-}12$
15. 32 **17.** $^{-}50$ **19.** 13 **21.** $^{-}11$

**Model solution:*

7.
$x - 9 = 7$
$x + {^{-}9} = 7$
$x + {^{-}9} + 9 = 7 + 9$
$x = 16$

Check:
$x - 9 = 7$
$16 - 9 = 7$
$7 = 7$ ✓

Page 189 **Section 6.7**

1. Add 5. **3.** Add 7.
5. Add 6. **7. a.** $t + {}^-6 > {}^-9$ **b.** 6
***7.** $x > {}^-1$ **9.** $a > 13$ **11.** $z > 2$
13. $b > 22$ **15.** $n < {}^-2$ **17.** $c < 12$
19. $k < 8$ **21.** $t < {}^-3$ **23.** $j < 20$
25. $r < 2$ **27.** $m > 8$ **29.** $s > 12$

**Model solution:*

7. $x + 5 > 4$
$x + 5 + {}^-5 > 4 + {}^-5$
$x > {}^-1$

Check:
$x + 5 > 4$
$0 + 5 > 4$
$5 > 4$ ✓

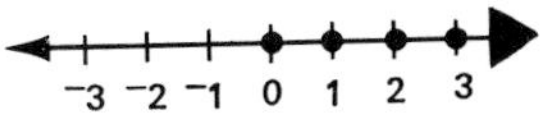

Pages 191–192 **Section 6.8**

1. c **3.** b **5.** a ***7.** $^-20$ **9.** $^-$\$17
11. $^-4621$ ft **13.** 30,324 ft **15.** $^-$\$60

**Model solution:*

7. Let n = number.
Then $n + {}^-10 = {}^-30$.
$n + {}^-10 + 10 = {}^-30 + 10$
$n = {}^-20$
So the number is $^-20$.

Check: Does the sum of $^-20$ and $^-10$ equal $^-30$? ✓

Pages 196–197 **Chapter Review**

1. $^-6$ **3.** 0 **5.** 3 **7.** $^-2$ **9.** 56
11. 19 **13.** 0 **15.** $^-11$ **17.** $^-47$
19. $^-114$ **21.** $^-5$ **23.** $^-5$ **25.** 29
27. 19 **29.** 9 **31.** 40 **33.** $y < {}^-7$
35. $t > 10$ **37.** $x < 35$ **39.** 11 °C

Page 198 **Chapter Test**

1. 2 **2.** 1 **3.** $^-39$ **4.** $^-8$
5. $^-71$ **6.** $^-76$ **7.** $^-26$ **8.** $^-34$
9. 108 **10.** $^-36$ **11.** 36 **12.** $^-88$
13. 21 **14.** $^-6$ **15.** $^-5$ **16.** 11
17. $x < {}^-3$ **18.** $x > 5$ **19.** $n < 13$
20. $x > 1$ **21.** $^-1925$ feet

Page 202 **Section 7.1**

1. Pos. **3.** Neg. **5.** Neg. **7.** Neg.
9. Neg. ***11.** $^-18$ **13.** $^-21$ **15.** $^-40$
17. $^-40$ **19.** $^-80$ **21.** 0 **23.** $^-156$
25. $^-252$ **27.** $^-456$ **29.** $^-714$ **31.** $^-952$
33. 33,216

**Model solution:*

11. $3 \times {}^-6 = {}^-(3 \times 6)$
$= {}^-18$

Page 204 **Section 7.2**

1. Pos. **3.** Neg. **5.** Neg. **7.** 42
9. 32 **11.** 255 **13.** 380 **15.** 324
***17.** 220 **19.** $^-336$ **21.** 152 **23.** 226,008
25. 7182

**Model solution:*

17. $11 \times {}^-4 \times {}^-5 = {}^-(11 \times 4) \times {}^-5$
$= {}^-44 \times {}^-5$
$= 220$

Page 206 **Section 7.3**

1. Pos. **3.** Neg. **5.** Neg. **7.** Pos.
9. Neg. ***11.** $^-4$ **13.** 9 **15.** $^-6$
17. $^-9$ **19.** $^-11$ **21.** 7 **23.** $^-13$
25. $^-3$ **27.** 5 **29.** $^-15$ **31.** 9
33. $^-18$ ***35.** 42 **37.** 72 **39.** $^-29$
41. $^-20$ **43.** $^-14$

**Model solutions:*

11. $16 \div {}^-4 = {}^-(16 \div 4)$
$= {}^-4$

35. ${}^-6 \times 14 \div {}^-2 = {}^-(6 \times 14) \div {}^-2$
$= {}^-84 \div {}^-2$
$= 42$

Page 209 Section 7.4

1. Divide by 7 **3.** Divide by $^{-}9$ **5.** Divide by 12 **7.** 2 **9.** $^{-}2$ **11.** $^{-}5$ ***13.** 6 **15.** $^{-}4$ **17.** $^{-}16$ **19.** $^{-}12$ **21.** $^{-}14$ **23.** $^{-}18$ **25.** $^{-}9$ **27.** 6 **29.** 12 **31.** 50 seconds **33.** $^{-}\$400$

***Model solution:*

13. $9x = 54$, $\frac{9x}{9} = \frac{54}{9}$, $x = 6$

Check: $9x = 54$, $9(\mathbf{6}) = 54$, $54 = 54$ ✓

Page 210 Quick Quiz

1. $^{-}56$ **2.** $^{-}54$ **3.** 42 **4.** $^{-}50$ **5.** $^{-}270$ **6.** $^{-}364$ **7.** 48 **8.** $^{-}60$ **9.** $^{-}9$ **10.** 5 **11.** $^{-}7$ **12.** $^{-}8$ **13.** $^{-}8$ **14.** 4

Page 212 Section 7.5

1. Mult. by 3 **3.** Mult. by $^{-}5$ **5.** Mult. by $^{-}6$ **7.** $^{-}56$ **9.** $^{-}56$ **11.** $^{-}100$ ***13.** 27 **15.** $^{-}15$ **17.** 72 **19.** $^{-}78$ **21.** $^{-}22$ **23.** $^{-}18$ **25.** 492 **27.** $^{-}192$ **29.** $^{-}78$ **31.** $^{-}42$

***Model solution:*

13. $\frac{n}{3} = 9$, $\frac{n}{3} \times 3 = 9 \times 3$, $n = 27$

Check: $\frac{n}{3} = 9$, $\frac{\mathbf{27}}{3} = 9$, $9 = 9$ ✓

Pages 215–216 Section 7.6

1. No **3.** No **5.** Yes ***7.** $18 > 12$ **9.** $^{-}56 < 14$ **11.** $^{-}30 < 0$ **13.** $x < {}^{-}32$ **15.** $x > {}^{-}70$ ***17.** $x < {}^{-}36$ **19.** $48 < k$ **21.** $x < {}^{-}6$ **23.** $t < 132$ **25.** $^{-}56 > n$ **27.** $x > 24$ **29.** $a < 60$ **31.** $^{-}288 > d$ **33.** $c > {}^{-}245$

***Model solutions:*

7. $6 > 4$, $6 \times 3 > 4 \times 3$, $18 > 12$

17. $\frac{x}{4} < {}^{-}9$, $\frac{x}{4} \times 4 < {}^{-}9 \times 4$, $x < {}^{-}36$

Check: $\frac{x}{4} < {}^{-}9$, $\frac{\mathbf{^{-}40}}{4} < {}^{-}9$, $^{-}10 < {}^{-}9$ ✓

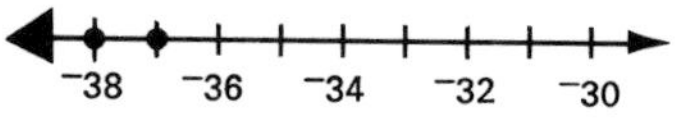

Pages 218–219 Section 7.7

1. No **3.** Yes **5.** No ***7.** $4 > 2$ **9.** $^{-}9 > {}^{-}16$ **11.** $^{-}7 > {}^{-}8$ **13.** $x > 5$ **15.** $x > {}^{-}4$ ***17.** $x < 8$ **19.** $^{-}9 < x$ **21.** $x > 2$ **23.** $x < 10$ **25.** $^{-}16 > x$ **27.** $x > {}^{-}6$ **29.** $x > 16$ **31.** $^{-}49 < x$ **33.** $x > {}^{-}3$

***Model solutions:*

7. $8 > 4$, $\frac{8}{2} > \frac{4}{2}$, $4 > 2$

17. $6x < 48$, $\frac{6x}{6} < \frac{48}{6}$, $x < 8$

Check: $6x < 48$, $6(\mathbf{7}) < 48$, $42 < 48$ ✓

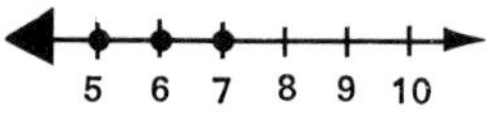

Page 219 Quick Quiz

1. $^{-}30$ **2.** 50 **3.** $^{-}24$ **4.** 28 **5.** 60 **6.** $^{-}60$ **7.** $n < {}^{-}6$ **8.** $^{-}4 < a$ **9.** $x > 16$ **10.** $^{-}2 > x$ **11.** $3 < x$ **12.** $t > 3$

Page 221 Section 7.8

1. Add 7 to each side. Divide each side by 2. **3.** Mult. each side by $^{-}4$. Add 9 to each side. **5.** Add $^{-}5$ to each side. Mult. each side by $^{-}7$.

*7. $^-2$ **9.** 29 **11.** 5 **13.** $^-69$ **15.** 3
17. 26 **19.** $^-35$ **21.** $^-72$ **23.** 22

Model solution:

7. $2k + {}^-5 = {}^-9$	*Check:*
$2k + {}^-5 + 5 = {}^-9 + 5$	$2k + {}^-5 = {}^-9$
$2k = {}^-4$	$2({}^-2) + {}^-5 = {}^-9$
$\frac{2k}{2} = \frac{{}^-4}{2}$	${}^-4 + {}^-5 = {}^-9$
$k = {}^-2$	${}^-9 = {}^-9$ ✓

Pages 223–224 Section 7.9

1. d = distance, r = rate, t = time
***3.** $^-11$ ft/min **5.** $^-715$ people
7. $^-125$ mm **9.** $^-120$ m **11.** $^-8$ ft/min

Model solution:

3. Let r = rate of change.	*Check:* Does a rate of $^-11$ ft/min for 5 min give a change of $^-55$ ft? ✓
$d = rt$	
${}^-55 = r(5)$	
${}^-55 = 5r$	
$\frac{{}^-55}{5} = \frac{5r}{5}$	
${}^-11 = r$	

Pages 226–227 Chapter Review

1. 63 **3.** $^-48$ **5.** $^-143$ **7.** 24 **9.** 182
11. $^-4$ **13.** 4 **15.** $^-5$ **17.** 16 **19.** 9
21. $^-12$ **23.** 18 **25.** $^-28$ **27.** $x < {}^-24$
29. ${}^-24 > m$ **31.** $x > 9$ **33.** ${}^-12 < x$
35. 5 **37.** 20 **39.** $^-2000$ ft/min

Page 228 Chapter Test

1. $^-9$ **2.** 40 **3.** 399
4. $^-768$ **5.** $^-15$ **6.** 14
7. $^-4$ **8.** $^-8$ **9.** $^-9$
10. $^-4$ **11.** 9 **12.** 162
13. $^-21$ **14.** 60 **15.** $r < {}^-32$
16. ${}^-90 > w$ **17.** $20 > c$ **18.** $m > {}^-4$
19. $5 < x$ **20.** $r < {}^-5$ **21.** $^-10$
22. 4 **23.** 32 **24.** 23 **25.** $^-\$240$

Pages 238–239 Section 8.1

1. $y = x + 7$ **3.** $y = 8x$
5. $y = 3x - 2$ **7.** $y = \frac{x}{3} + 2$
9. 1.8; Chapter 1, Section 8
11. 6–11; Serving team has 6; other team has 11.
13. *1, 5, 9, 13, 17, 21, 25
15. 0, 7, 14, 21, 28, 35, 42
17. 30, 50, 70, 90, 110, 130

Model solution:

13. (For $x = 1$)
$y = 4x - 3$
$= 4(1) - 3$
$= 1$

Pages 241–242 Section 8.2

1. 3 right, 4 up **3.** 0 right, 5 up
5. 6 right, 2 up **7.** 10 right, 7 up
9. (0, 4) **11.** (8, 3) **13.** (9, 9)
15. (7, 7) **17.** (5, 3)

19.
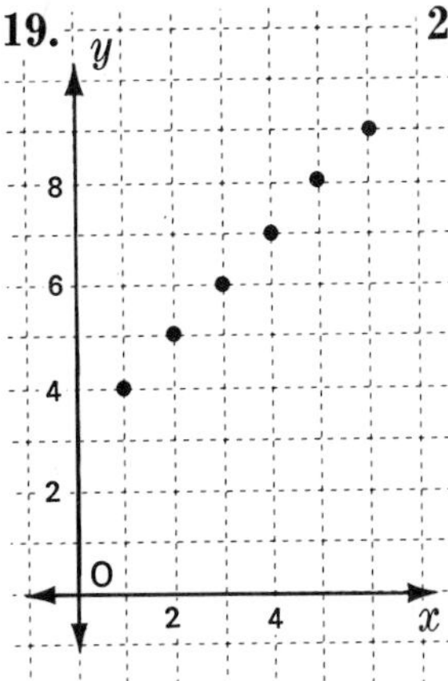

21.
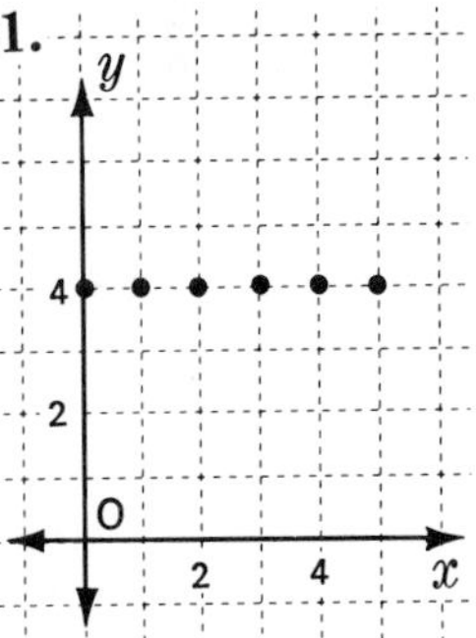

23.
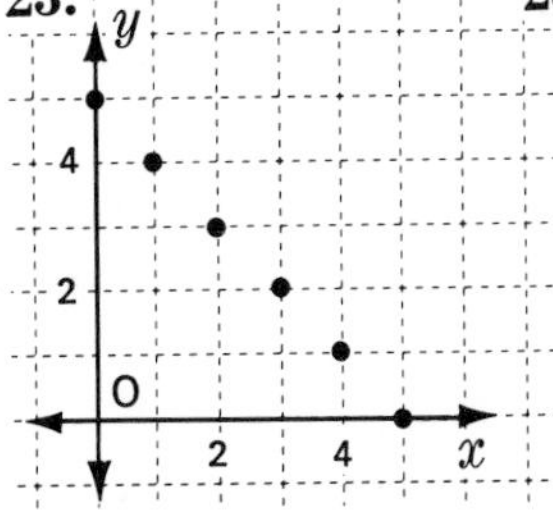

25.
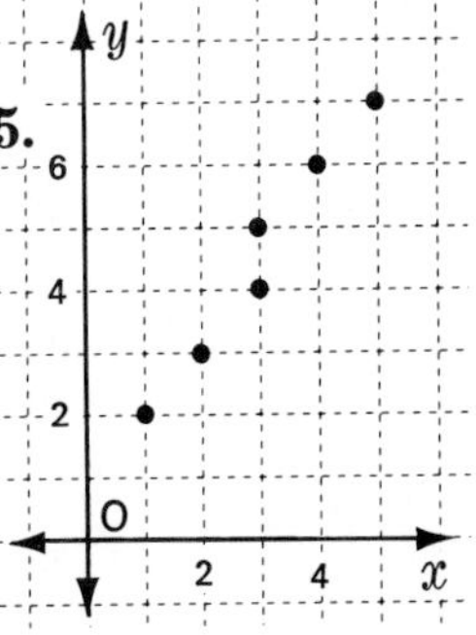

Pages 244–245 Section 8.3

1. Right **3.** (0, 0) **5.** 1 right, 2 down
7. 1 right, 4 up **9.** 3 left, 8 up
11. 18 left, 25 down **13.** (2, 1) **15.** (⁻3, 4)
17. (5, 0) **19.** (⁻2, ⁻4) **21.** (2, ⁻4)
23. (⁻2, 2)
25–35. (odd)

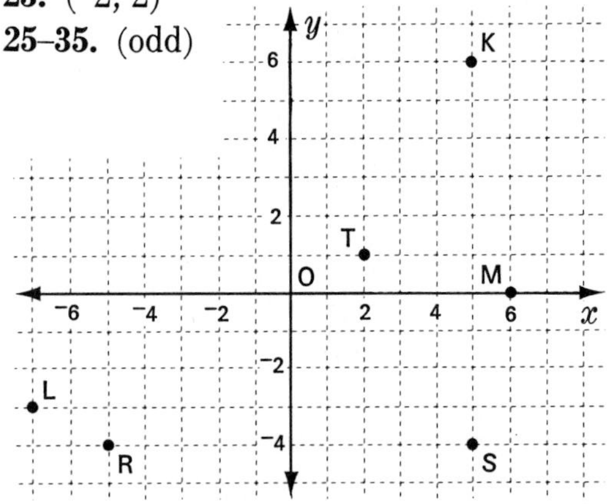

Pages 247–248 Section 8.4

1. Line **3.** 2 miles

5.

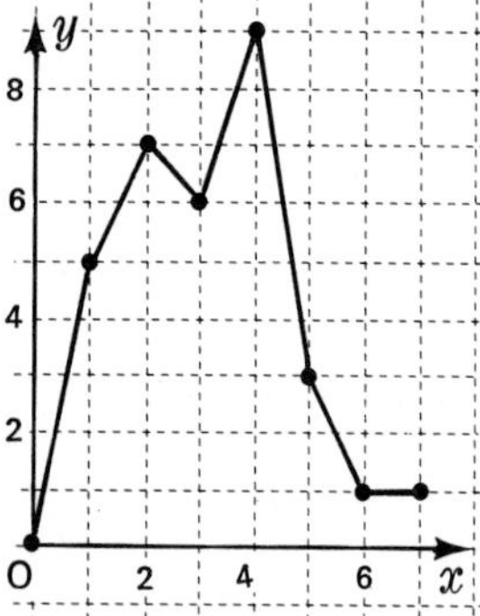

7.

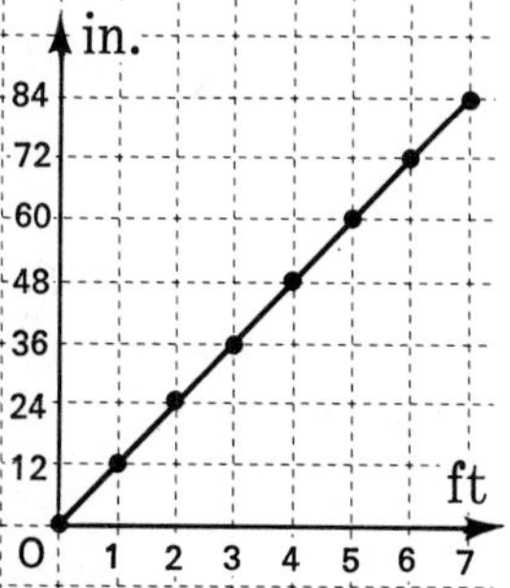

9.

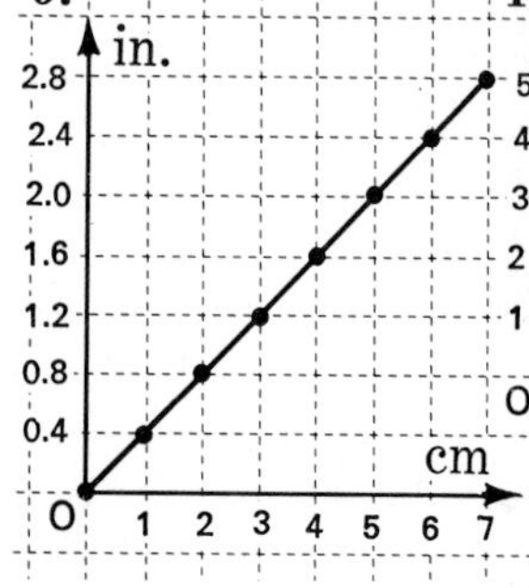

11.

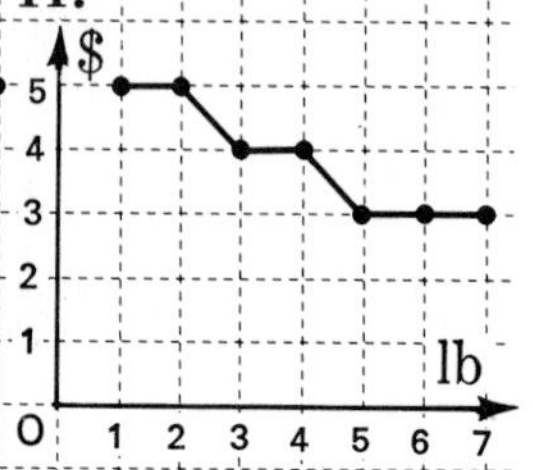

13.

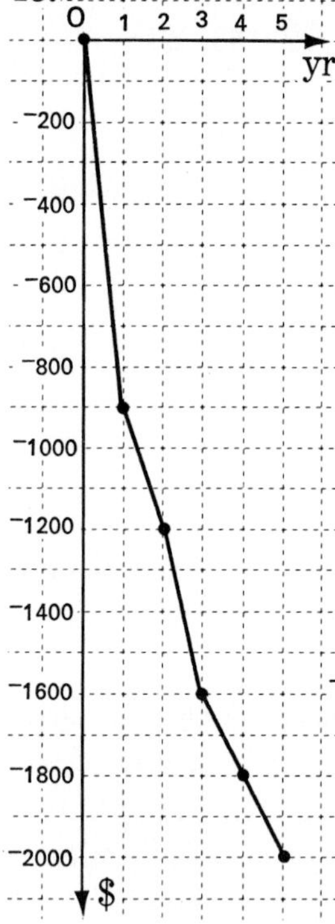

15.

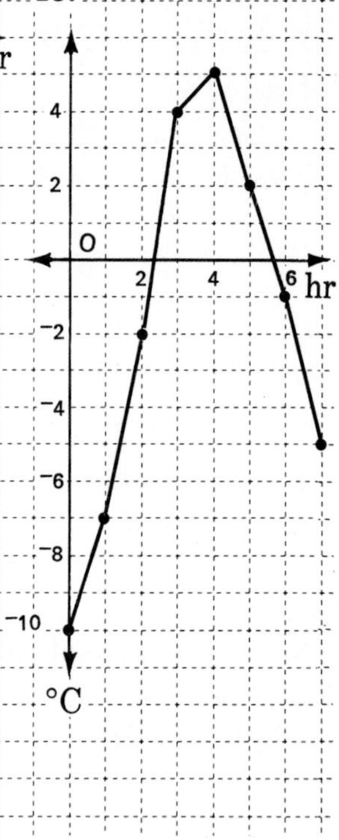

Pages 252–253 Section 8.5

1. Yes **3.** Yes **5.** Yes
7. Yes **9.** No **11.** Yes
13. No **15.** Yes **17.** No

Page 253 Quick Quiz

1. 1, 4, 7, 10, 13, 16, 19
2. **a.** (1, 2)
b. (⁻3, 0)
c. (4, ⁻5)
d. (⁻5, 4)
3. *See graph at right.*
4. Yes

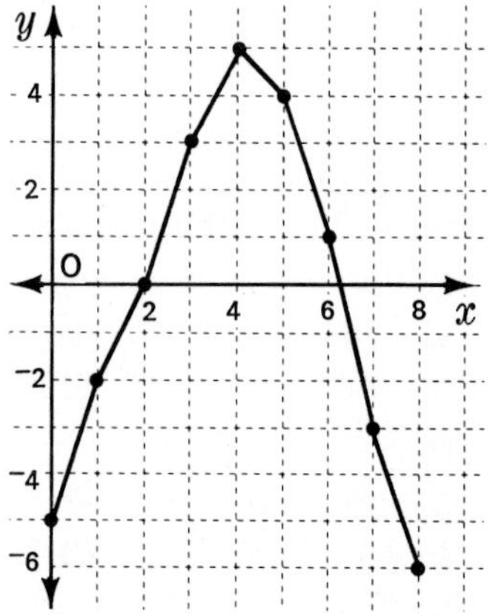

Pages 255–257 Section 8.6

1. 5 sec **3.** Solve 93,000,000 = 186,000t.
***5.** 160 mph **7.** 510 mph **9.** 1600 ft
11. 30,000 lb **13.** $^{-}40$ °F

**Model solution:*

5.
$$
\begin{aligned}
g &= a - 34 \\
126 &= a - 34 \\
126 + 34 &= a - 34 + 34 \\
160 &= a
\end{aligned}
$$

Check:
$$
\begin{aligned}
126 &= a - 34 \\
126 &= \mathbf{160} - 34 \\
126 &= 126 \checkmark
\end{aligned}
$$

Pages 259–260 Section 8.7

1. Mult. each by 4. **3.** Divide each by 2.

5.

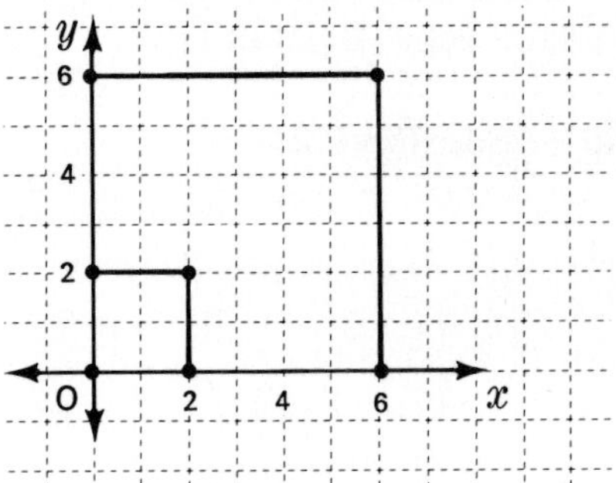

7.

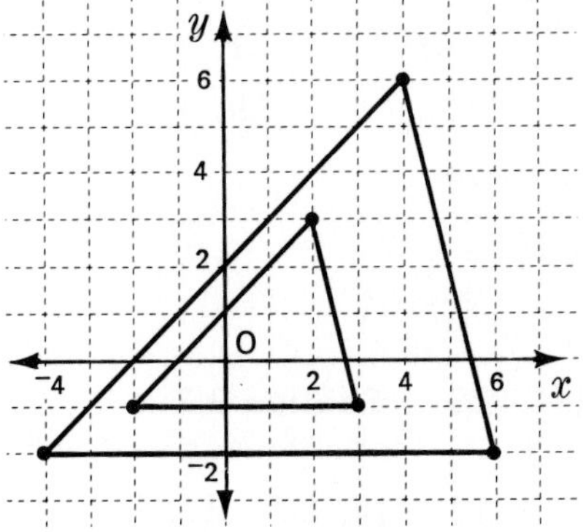

Pages 263–264 Section 8.8

1. Add 6 to 1st number.
3. Subtract 3 from 1st number.
5. Add 2 to 1st number.
Add 5 to 2nd number.

7.

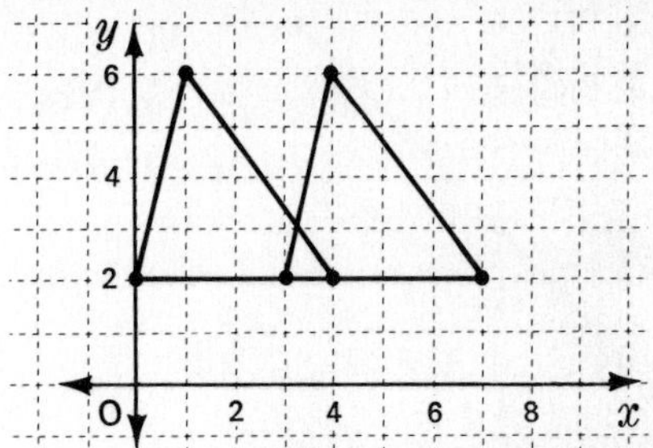

9.

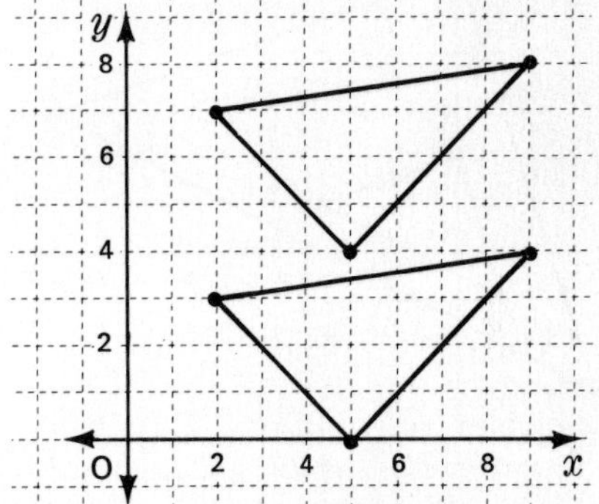

11.

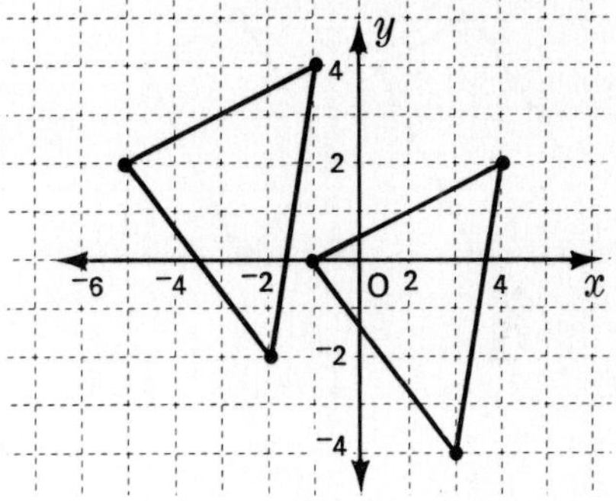

Pages 265–267 Chapter Review

1. 5, 7, 9, 11, 13, 15

3.

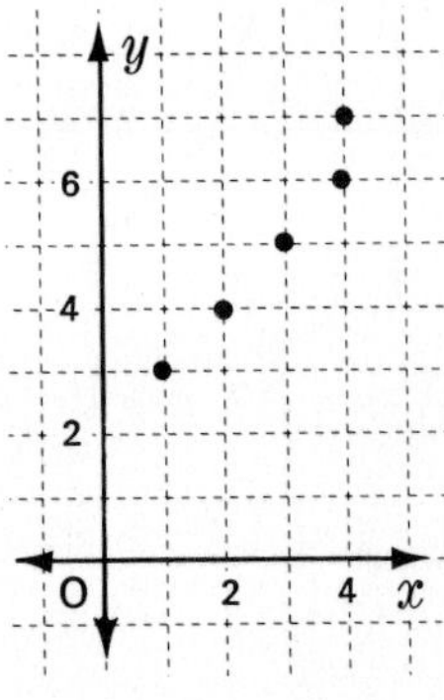

5. 5 right, 6 down

7.

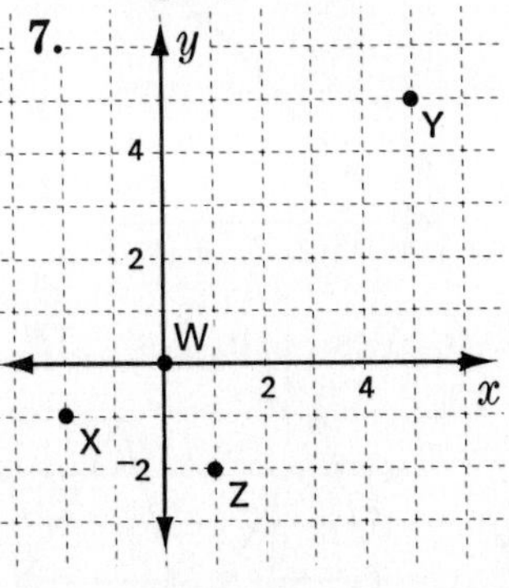

9.

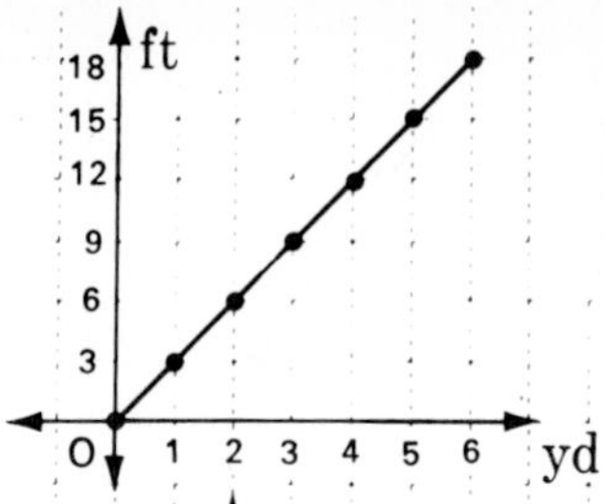

11. No
13. Yes
15. 470 mph

17.

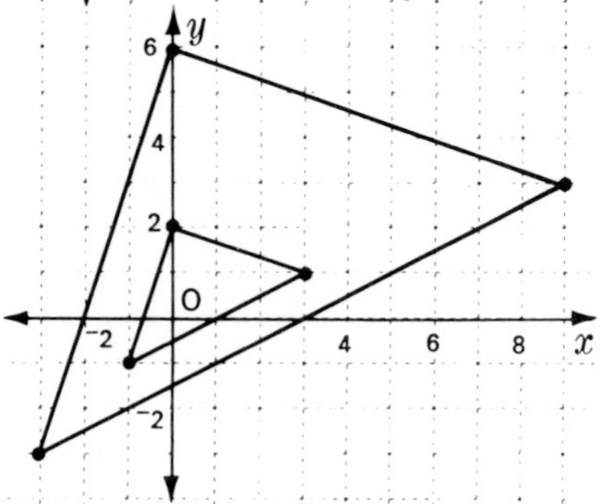

19.

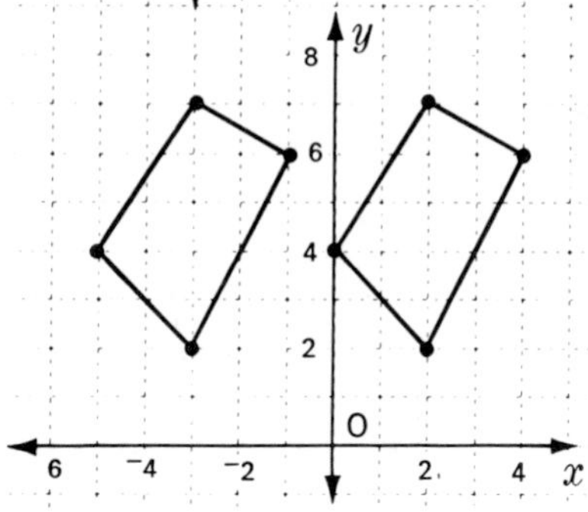

14.

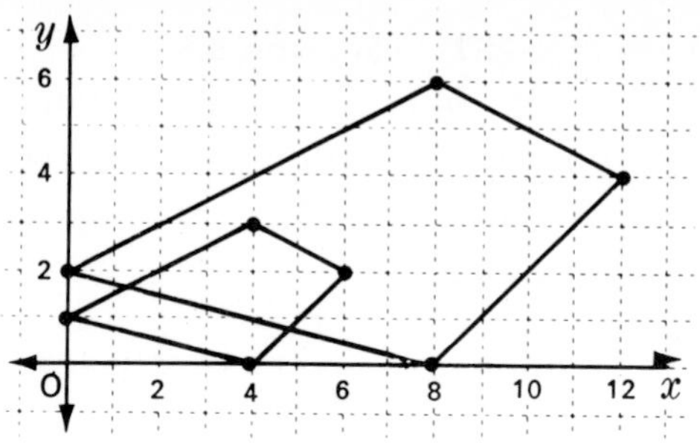

Pages 276–277 Section 9.1

1\. a. $\frac{3}{5}$ b. $\frac{5}{3}$ 3. a. $\frac{13}{8}$ b. $\frac{8}{21}$ c. $\frac{13}{21}$ 5. $\frac{2400}{100}$

7\. $\frac{65}{2}$ 9. $\frac{7}{12}$ or 7:12 or 7 to 12 11. $\frac{1}{6}$

13\. $\frac{1}{4}$ 15. $\frac{2}{5}$ *17. $\frac{4}{3}$ 19. $\frac{4}{5}$ 21. $\frac{6}{5}$

**Model solution:*

17\. $\frac{\text{number sides of top figure}}{\text{number sides of bottom figure}} = \frac{4}{3}$

Page 280 Section 9.2

1\. $\frac{1}{3}$; $\frac{2}{6}$; $\frac{4}{12}$; Yes 3. 20 5. 5; 2 7. 24

Ex. 9–25: Other answers possible.

*9\. $\frac{2}{8}$; $\frac{3}{12}$ 11. $\frac{12}{14}$; $\frac{18}{21}$ 13. $\frac{20}{26}$; $\frac{30}{39}$

15\. $\frac{2}{10}$; $\frac{3}{15}$ 17. $\frac{28}{34}$; $\frac{42}{51}$ 19. $\frac{40}{62}$; $\frac{60}{93}$

21\. $\frac{10}{16}$; $\frac{15}{24}$ 23. $\frac{10}{18}$; $\frac{15}{27}$ 25. $\frac{14}{24}$; $\frac{21}{36}$

*27\. $\frac{1}{3}$ 29. $\frac{1}{2}$ 31. $\frac{3}{7}$ 33. $\frac{2}{9}$

35\. $\frac{4}{9}$ 37. $\frac{5}{2}$ 39. $\frac{7}{3}$ 41. $\frac{1}{3}$

**Model solutions:*

9\. $\frac{1}{4} = \frac{1 \times 2}{4 \times 2} = \frac{2}{8}$
$\frac{1}{4} = \frac{1 \times 3}{4 \times 3} = \frac{3}{12}$

27\. $\frac{2}{6} = \frac{2 \div 2}{6 \div 2} = \frac{1}{3}$

Pages 284–285 Section 9.3

1\. T 3. F 5. T 7. F 9. T

*11\. 9 13. 12 15. 30 17. 5 19. 12

21\. 2 23. 6 25. 9 27. 180

29\. 4.2 31. 0.75 33. 10

35\. $\frac{12}{2} = \frac{18}{3}$, $\frac{3}{18} = \frac{2}{12}$, $\frac{18}{12} = \frac{3}{2}$;
all cross products = 36

37\. $\frac{1.2}{3} = \frac{1.6}{4}$, $\frac{4}{1.6} = \frac{3}{1.2}$, $\frac{1.6}{1.2} = \frac{4}{3}$;
all cross products = 4.8

Page 268 Chapter Test

1\. 5, 9, 13, 17, 21, 25

2\. 6, 7, 9, 10 3. (−4, 0)

4\. (−2, 3) 5. (4, 4) 6. (3, −2)

7.

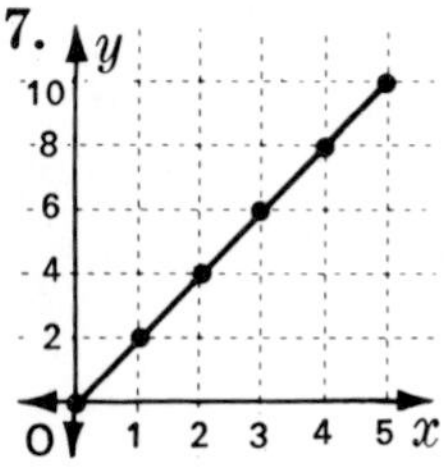

8.

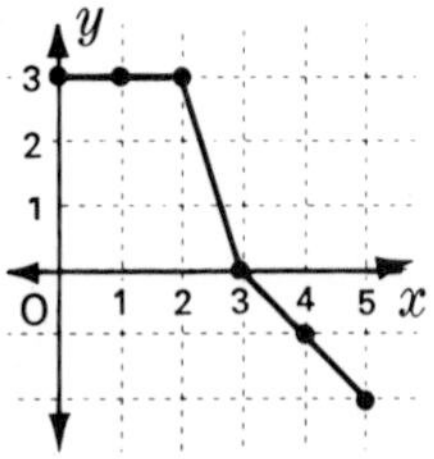

9\. Yes 10. No 11. Yes 12. 9900 ft

13.

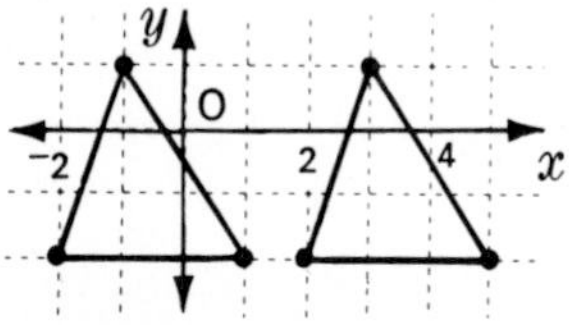

39. $\frac{2.6}{7.8} = \frac{5.\bar{6}}{15.6}, \frac{15.6}{5.2} = \frac{7.8}{2.6}, \frac{5.2}{2.6} = \frac{15.6}{7.8}$; all cross products = 40.56

Model solution:

11. $\frac{2}{3} = \frac{6}{n}$
$2n = 18$
$\frac{2n}{2} = \frac{18}{2}$
$n = 9$

Check: $\frac{2}{3} = \frac{6}{n}$
$\frac{2}{3} = \frac{6}{9}$
$2 \times 9 = 3 \times 6$
$18 = 18$ ✓

Pages 286–287 Section 9.4

1. $x = 15$ 3. $12 = 0.3x$ 5. $1.8x = 36$
*7. 602 more voters 9. 18 in.
11. 20 watts 13. 22 ft/sec
15. 7000 votes 17. 40 oz
19. 54¢ a month

Model solution:

7. $\frac{3514}{502} = \frac{x}{86}$
$3514 \times 86 = 502x$
$302{,}204 = 502x$
$\frac{302{,}204}{502} = \frac{502x}{502}$
$602 = x$

Check: Is 602 voters for 86 jurors equivalent to 3514 voters for 502 jurors? ✓

602 more voters are needed.

Page 289 Quick Quiz

1. 6:5, $\frac{6}{5}$ *Ex. 2–4: Answers may vary.*
2. $\frac{8}{14}, \frac{12}{21}, \frac{16}{28}$ 3. $\frac{12}{24}, \frac{1}{2}, \frac{3}{6}$ 4. $\frac{3}{10}, \frac{6}{20}, \frac{60}{200}$
5. 12 6. 12 7. 5 8. 132 cups

Pages 291–292 Section 9.5

1. 50% 3. 9% 5. 59% 7. 64%
9. 135% 11. 0.0375 13. Less than
15. 68 17. 135 19. $\frac{21}{100}$, 0.21
21. $\frac{61}{100}$, 0.61 23. $\frac{7}{10}$, 0.7 *25. $\frac{1}{2}$, 0.5
27. $\frac{7}{20}$, 0.35 29. $\frac{1}{8}$, 0.125
31. $\frac{63}{1000}$, 0.063 33. $\frac{333}{1000}$, 0.333
35. $\frac{7}{80}$, 0.0875 37. $1\frac{1}{100}$, 1.01
39. $1\frac{27}{100}$, 1.27 41. $2\frac{1}{2}$, 2.5 43. $\frac{1}{10}$
45. $\frac{3}{5}$ 47. 4 49. 10 51. 60 53. $\frac{a+3}{100}$

Model solution:

25. $50\% = \frac{50}{100} = \frac{1}{2} = 0.5$

Page 295 Section 9.6

1. 28% 3. 460% 5. 100% 7. 31%
9. 53% 11. 70% 13. 112% 15. 400%
17. 12.5% 19. 137.5% *21. 30%
23. 50% 25. 20% 27. 37.5%
29. 25% 31. 60% 33. 12.5%
35. 62.5% 37. 87.5% 39. 16%
41. 90% 43. 35% *45. $133\frac{1}{3}\%$
47. 150% 49. 262.5% 51. $383\frac{1}{3}\%$
53. 15% alcohol solution

Model solutions:

21. $\frac{3}{10}$
$10\overline{)3.0}$ = 0.3 = 30%

45. $1\frac{1}{3} = \frac{4}{3}$
$3\overline{)4.00}$ = $1.33\frac{1}{3} = 133\frac{1}{3}\%$

Page 297 Section 9.7

1. c 3. a 5. d *7. 60%
9. 60% 11. 30% 13. 13.6 15. 48
17. 7 19. 80 21. 40 23. 160

Model solution:

7. $\frac{45}{75} = \frac{p}{100}$
$45 \times 100 = 75p$
$4500 = 75p$
$\frac{4500}{75} = \frac{75p}{75}$
$60 = p$

Check: $\frac{45}{75} = \frac{p}{100}$
$\frac{45}{75} = \frac{60}{100}$
$45 \times 100 = 75 \times 60$
$4500 = 4500$
So 45 is 60% of 75. ✓

Pages 299–301 Section 9.8

1. 28 out of 200 is what per cent?
3. 150 out of what whole is 3%?
*5. 80% 7. 75% 9. 92.5%
11. 87.5% 13. \$40 15. 150 men
17. \$2100 19. 0.288 g 21. \$5000
23. 18 games 25. 72 in.

Model solution:

5. $\frac{32}{40} = \frac{p}{100}$
$32 \times 100 = 40p$
$3200 = 40p$
$\frac{3200}{40} = \frac{40p}{40}$
$80 = p$

Check: Is 80% of 40 equal to 32? ✓

So Rona answered 80% correctly.

Pages 302–303 Section 9.9

1. 0.23 **3.** 0.645 **5.** 1.22 **7.** 0.43 **9.** 0.015 *Ex. 11–17: Answers may vary.*
11. 0.8×20 **13.** 1.2×60
15. 0.7×50 **17.** 0.7×90
19. 3×0.1 **21.** 5×0.1
23. 57×0.1
Ex. 25–35: Estimates may vary.
***25.** 44, 41.81 **27.** 74, 70.11
29. 72, 64.26 **31.** 133, 137.24
33. 1.4 oz **35.** $63

**Model solution:*

25. $x = 0.37 \times 113 = 0.4 \times 110 = 4 \times 0.1 \times 110 = 4 \times 11.0 = 44$

$$\begin{array}{r} 113 \\ \times 0.37 \\ \hline 791 \\ 339 \\ \hline 41.81 \end{array}$$

Pages 305–306 Section 9.10

1. Subtr. 20% from 100%
3. Subtr. $0.90 from $1.08
***5.** $5 **7.** 20% **9.** $10.70
11. $60.90 **13.** $250 **15.** $8
17. $500 **19.** $20 **21.** 25%
23. 50% **25.** 40% **27.** 20%
29. 25% **31.** $12\frac{1}{2}\%$

**Model solution:*

5. $100\% - 20\% = 80\%$

$\frac{4}{x} = \frac{80}{100}$

$4 \times 100 = 80x$

$400 = 80x$

$\frac{400}{80} = \frac{80x}{80}$

$5 = x$

So the regular price was $5.

Check: Is $5 minus 20% of $5 equal to $4? ✓

Pages 307–308 Chapter Review

Ex. 5–9: Answers may vary.

1. $\frac{3}{4}$ **3.** $\frac{4}{9}$ **5.** $\frac{2}{4}, \frac{3}{6}$ **7.** $\frac{20}{32}, \frac{30}{48}$
9. $\frac{16}{12}, \frac{24}{18}$ **11.** 5 **13.** 5 **15.** 8
17. 225 cal **19.** $\frac{18}{25}$, 0.72 **21.** $\frac{13}{200}$, 0.065
23. 47% **25.** 42.6% **27.** 25% **29.** 150%
31. 200% **33.** 325% **35.** 37.5 **37.** 45
39. 75% **41.** $21 **43.** $0.5 \times 280 = 140$

Page 309 Chapter Test

1. $\frac{3}{5}$ **2.** $\frac{3}{4}$ **3.** $\frac{2}{3}$ **4.** $\frac{1}{3}$ **5.** $\frac{7}{4}$
6. $\frac{1}{3}$ **7.** 16 **8.** 24 **9.** 14 **10.** 12
11. 5 **12.** 24 **13.** 12 **14.** 1 **15.** 48%
16. 45% **17.** 32 **18.** 120 **19.** 0.2, 20%
20. $\frac{7}{8}$, 87.5% **21.** $\frac{9}{10}$, 90%
22. 0.375, 37.5% **23.** $\frac{63}{100}$, 0.63
24. $1\frac{1}{2}$, 1.5 **25.** $0.5 \times 680 = 340$
26. 67.5 min **27.** $3000 **28.** $5

Pages 315–317 Section 10.1

1. *c* **3.** *c* **5.** Yes **7.** No **9.** Yes
11. No **13.** Yes **15.** No **17.** Yes
19. △ABC, △JKL; △DEF, △GTH

Pages 319–321 Section 10.2

1. ∠C, ∠N; ∠M, ∠P; ∠A, ∠D
3. TX, WV; TR, WZ; RX, ZV
5. ∠R, ∠H; ∠D, ∠V; ∠G, ∠W; GD, WV; RD, HV; RG, HW
7. XT, DA; XM, DZ; MT, ZA
9. ∠R, ∠X; ∠A, ∠V; ∠C, ∠W
11. ∠WFC, ∠RFG; ∠FWC, ∠R; ∠FCW, ∠G; FW, FR; FC, FG; WC, RG
13. ∠XZY, ∠QZP; ∠X, ∠Q; ∠Y, ∠P; XZ, QZ; XY, QP; YZ, PZ

Pages 323–325 Section 10.3

1. *t* **3.** *q* **5.** *t* **7.** *c* **9.** *d* **11.** *a*
***13.** $x = 10, z = 8$ **15.** $x = 2\frac{1}{2}, z = 3\frac{3}{4}$
17. $x = 3, z = 2$ **19.** $x = 45, z = 60$

9

*Model solutions:

13. $\frac{3}{6} = \frac{5}{x}$ | $\frac{3}{6} = \frac{4}{z}$
$3x = 30$ | $2z = 24$
$\frac{3x}{3} = \frac{30}{3}$ | $\frac{3z}{3} = \frac{24}{3}$
$x = 10$ | $z = 8$
Check: Are the ratios 3 to 6 and 5 to 10 equivalent? ✓ | *Check:* Are the ratios 3 to 6 and 4 to 8 equivalent? ✓

Page 325 Quick Quiz

1. No
2. Yes
3. ∠R, ∠T; ∠G, ∠S; ∠E, ∠A; RE, TA; EG, AS; RG, TS
4. ∠L, ∠A; ∠M, ∠B; ∠V, ∠C; VL, CA; VM, CB; LM, AB
5. $x = 11\frac{1}{4}$, $z = 12\frac{3}{4}$

Pages 327–329 Section 10.4

1. The ratios are equivalent.
3. d 5. c 7. a' 9. $\frac{1}{2}$
11. $\frac{2}{1}$ *13. 63 ft 15. 200 m 17. 29 ft

*Model solution:

13. $\frac{6}{42} = \frac{9}{h}$
$6h = 378$
$\frac{6h}{6} = \frac{378}{6}$
$h = 63$
So the height is 63 ft.
Check: Are the ratios 6 to 42 and 9 to 63 equivalent? ✓

Pages 333–334 Section 10.5

1. Between C and D
3. △ACB and △DEB must be similar.
*5. AB = 20 in., BD = 60 in.
7. △GAB and △HCB must be similar.
9. AB = 4 yd, BC = 2 yd

*Model solution:

5. $\frac{AC}{DE} = \frac{10}{30} = \frac{1}{3}$
$1x + 3x = 80$
$4x = 80$
$x = 20$
So $AB = 1x = 1 \times 20 = 20$.
$BD = 3x = 3 \times 20 = 60$.

Pages 337–338 Section 10.6

1. Measure the map distance. Then use the proportion $\frac{1}{50} = \frac{2\frac{1}{2}}{x}$.
*3. $62\frac{1}{2}$ mi
5. $43\frac{3}{4}$ mi
7. 3 in., 24 mi
9. 2 in., 16 mi
11. 48 min

*Model solution:

3. $\frac{1 \text{ in.}}{50 \text{ mi}} = \frac{1\frac{1}{4} \text{ in.}}{d \text{ mi}}$
$\frac{1}{50} = \frac{1\frac{1}{4}}{d}$
$d = 50 \times 1\frac{1}{4}$
$d = 62\frac{1}{2}$
So the distance is $62\frac{1}{2}$ mi.
Check:
$\frac{1}{50} = \frac{1\frac{1}{4}}{\mathbf{62\frac{1}{2}}}$
$62\frac{1}{2} = 62\frac{1}{2}$ ✓

Pages 340–341 Section 10.7

1. $\frac{1}{3} = \frac{5}{x}$ *3. 1.5 cm, 4.5 m
5. 2.5 cm, 1.5 m 7. 1.0 cm, 0.6 m
9. 1.0 cm, 0.6 m 11. 18 in. 13. $4\frac{1}{2}$ in.

*Model solution:

3. $\frac{1 \text{ cm}}{3 \text{ m}} = \frac{1.5 \text{ cm}}{d \text{ m}}$
$\frac{1}{3} = \frac{1.5}{d}$
$d = 4.5$ So the distance is 4.5 m.
Check:
$\frac{1}{3} = \frac{1.5}{\mathbf{4.5}}$
$4.5 = 4.5$ ✓

10

Pages 344–346 Chapter Review

1. Yes 3. No 5. Yes
7. ∠R, ∠A; ∠X, ∠T; ∠W, ∠Z;
9. VW, TR; VB, TZ; WB, RZ
11. n 13. w 15. 36 ft 17. 2 in., 24 mi
19. $1\frac{1}{2}$ in., 18 mi 21. $1\frac{1}{2}$ ft

Page 347 Chapter Test

1. ∠D, ∠A; ∠X, ∠Z; ∠B, ∠W; XD, ZA; XB, ZW; BD, WA
2. ∠N, ∠V; ∠E, ∠F; ∠T, ∠I; NE, VF; NT, VI; TE, IF
3. w 4. x 5. w
6. $x = 4$, $z = 8$ 7. $x = 20$, $z = 17.5$
8. 8 mi, 12 mi, 6 mi 9. 12 m

Pages 355–356 Section 11.1

1. Fraction 3. Absolute value
5. Negative 7. Negative
9. $-\frac{3}{4}$ 11. 0.57 13. $^-3\frac{1}{2}$ 15. 4.795
17. $\frac{3}{8}$ 19. 0.34 21. $4\frac{1}{6}$ 23. 3.159

25.
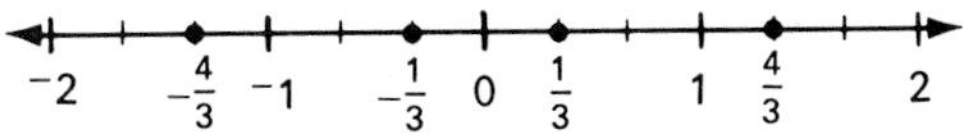

27.
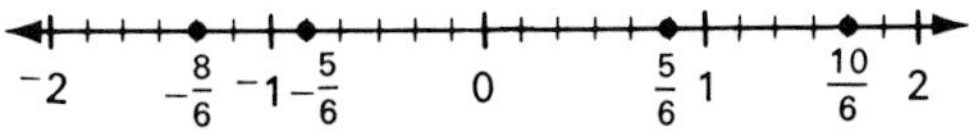

29.
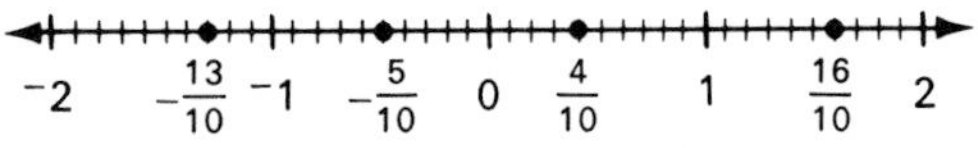

Page 358 Section 11.2

1. $\frac{7}{12}$ 3. $-\frac{5}{12}$ 5. $\frac{1}{2}$ 7. $<$
9. $>$ *11. $<$ *13. $>$ 15. $=$
17. $>$ 19. $>$ 21. $<$

Model solutions:

11. $\frac{5}{2} = \frac{10}{4}$ and $\frac{3}{4} < \frac{10}{4}$, so $\frac{3}{4} < \frac{5}{2}$.

13. $-\frac{3}{8} = -\frac{9}{24}$ and $-\frac{7}{24} > -\frac{9}{24}$, so $-\frac{7}{24} > -\frac{3}{8}$.

Pages 360–361 Section 11.3

1. Positive 3. Negative
5. Positive 7. $1.6 + {}^-1.9$
9. $8.27 + 6.28$ 11. $0.632 + 9.568$
13. 5.7 *15. $^-3.841$ 17. 0
19. 3.3 *21. $^-8.43$ 23. 11.3
25. 1.345 27. $^-1.8$ 29. $^-0.751$
31. $^-0.59$ 33. $^-38.7$ 35. 4.6
37. $^-14.31$ 39. $^-0.351$ 41. 35.8

Model solutions:

15. $0.834 + {}^-4.675 = {}^-3.841$ $\quad 4.675 - 0.834 = 3.841$

21. $^-4.65 - 3.78 = {}^-4.65 + {}^-3.78 = {}^-8.43$ $\quad 4.65 + 3.78 = 8.43$

Page 364 Section 11.4

1. Add $^-6.7$ to each side.
3. Add 3.7 to each side.
5. Add 9.1 to each side.
7. Change $d - 1.5$ to $d + {}^-1.5$. Add 1.5 to each side.
9. Change $f - {}^-5.9$ to $f + 5.9$. Add $^-5.9$ to each side.
11. Change $g - {}^-0.3$ to $g + 0.3$. Add $^-0.3$ to each side.

*13. 15.8 15. 9.3 17. 3.3
19. $^-2.1$ 21. 3.56 23. $^-1.01$
25. 6.8 27. 5.98 29. 10.1

Model solution:

13.
$$\begin{aligned} n - 6.3 &= 9.5 \\ n + {}^-6.3 &= 9.5 \\ n + {}^-6.3 + 6.3 &= 9.5 + 6.3 \\ n &= 15.8 \end{aligned}$$

Check:
$$\begin{aligned} n - 6.3 &= 9.5 \\ \mathbf{15.8} - 6.3 &= 9.5 \\ 9.5 &= 9.5 \checkmark \end{aligned}$$

Page 365 Quick Quiz

1. Rational 2. $\frac{3}{4}$ 3. 0.73 4. $<$
5. $<$ 6. $=$ 7. $^-1.7$ 8. 0.55
9. $^-4.13$ 10. 0.7 11. $^-16.77$

Page 367 Section 11.5

1. Pos. 3. Neg. 5. Neg.
7. $\frac{1}{8} + (-\frac{7}{8})$ 9. $\frac{1}{2} + \frac{3}{8}$ 11. $-\frac{2}{3} + \frac{1}{2}$
13. $\frac{5}{6}$ *15. $-\frac{3}{5}$ 17. 0 19. $-\frac{17}{24}$
21. $-\frac{7}{8}$ 23. $-\frac{1}{4}$ 25. $\frac{1}{2}$ *27. $-\frac{2}{3}$
29. $-\frac{2}{5}$ 31. $\frac{3}{8}$ 33. $-\frac{2}{5}$ 35. $-\frac{3}{8}$

Model solutions:

15. $-\frac{7}{10} + \frac{1}{10} = -\frac{\cancel{6}^{\,3}}{\cancel{10}_{\,5}} = -\frac{3}{5}$

27.
$$\begin{aligned} -\tfrac{1}{6} - \tfrac{1}{2} &= -\tfrac{1}{6} + (-\tfrac{1}{2}) \\ &= -\tfrac{1}{6} + (-\tfrac{3}{6}) \\ &= -\frac{\cancel{4}^{\,2}}{\cancel{6}_{\,3}} = -\tfrac{2}{3} \end{aligned}$$

Page 369 Section 11.6

1. Pos. 3. Neg. 5. Zero

7. $1\frac{1}{3} + {}^-2\frac{2}{3}$ 9. $-\frac{1}{3} + 1\frac{5}{6}$ 11. $\frac{3}{4} + 2\frac{1}{8}$

*13. $\frac{1}{2}$ 15. $1\frac{2}{5}$ *17. $4\frac{1}{2}$ *19. ${}^-3\frac{5}{8}$

21. ${}^-1\frac{7}{8}$ 23. ${}^-1\frac{2}{5}$ 25. $1\frac{1}{8}$ 27. $-\frac{1}{4}$

29. ${}^-4\frac{1}{4}$ 31. ${}^-2\frac{7}{12}$ 33. $11\frac{3}{4}$

**Model solutions:*

13. $1\frac{3}{4} + {}^-1\frac{1}{4} = \frac{\cancel{2}^{1}}{\cancel{4}_{2}}$

$= \frac{1}{2}$

17. $3\frac{1}{8} - {}^-1\frac{3}{8} = 3\frac{1}{8} + 1\frac{3}{8}$

$= 4\frac{\cancel{4}^{1}}{\cancel{8}_{2}} = 4\frac{1}{2}$

19. ${}^-5\frac{1}{2} + 1\frac{7}{8} = {}^-5\frac{4}{8} + 1\frac{7}{8}$

$= {}^-4\frac{12}{8} + 1\frac{7}{8}$

$= {}^-3\frac{5}{8}$

Pages 371–372 Section 11.7

1. a. $\frac{1}{5}$ b. $-\frac{1}{5}$ c. 0 d. $\frac{3}{5}$

3. Add $-\frac{3}{4}$ to each side.

5. Add $\frac{1}{2}$ to each side.

7. Add $-\frac{3}{7}$ to each side.

9. Change $b - \frac{1}{4}$ to $b + (-\frac{1}{4})$.
Add $\frac{1}{4}$ to each side.

11. Change $d - (-\frac{4}{7})$ to $d + \frac{4}{7}$.
Add $-\frac{4}{7}$ to each side.

13. Change $g - \frac{3}{8}$ to $g + (-\frac{3}{8})$.
Add $\frac{3}{8}$ to each side.

*15. $\frac{2}{3}$ 17. $\frac{3}{4}$ 19. $\frac{1}{4}$ 21. $-\frac{1}{10}$

23. $-\frac{7}{8}$ 25. $-\frac{9}{10}$ 27. $-\frac{8}{9}$ 29. $-\frac{3}{10}$

31. $-\frac{2}{9}$ *33. ${}^-10\frac{2}{3}$ 35. ${}^-1\frac{3}{5}$ 37. $8\frac{3}{4}$

**Model solutions:*

15.
$a - \frac{1}{3} = \frac{1}{3}$
$a + (-\frac{1}{3}) = \frac{1}{3}$
$a + (-\frac{1}{3}) + \frac{1}{3} = \frac{1}{3} + \frac{1}{3}$
$a = \frac{2}{3}$

Check:
$a - \frac{1}{3} = \frac{1}{3}$
$\frac{2}{3} - \frac{1}{3} = \frac{1}{3}$
$\frac{1}{3} = \frac{1}{3}$ ✓

33.
$a + 3\frac{1}{3} = {}^-7\frac{1}{3}$
$a + 3\frac{1}{3} + {}^-3\frac{1}{3} = {}^-7\frac{1}{3} + {}^-3\frac{1}{3}$
$a = {}^-10\frac{2}{3}$

Check:
$a + 3\frac{1}{3} = {}^-7\frac{1}{3}$
${}^-10\frac{2}{3} + 3\frac{1}{3} = {}^-7\frac{1}{3}$
${}^-7\frac{1}{3} = {}^-7\frac{1}{3}$ ✓

Pages 374–376 Section 11.8

1. c 3. a *5. ${}^-0.14$ in.

7. ${}^-2.7$ °F 9. ${}^-1\frac{1}{4}$ lb 11. $1\frac{1}{6}$ ft

13. \$5.97 15. $1\frac{1}{6}$ ft

**Model solution:*

5. Let c = change in reading.
$29.96 + c = 29.82$
$c + 29.96 = 29.82$
$c + 29.96 + {}^-29.96 = 29.82 + {}^-29.96$
$c = {}^-0.14$

Check: Does a reading of 29.96 followed by a ${}^-0.14$ change give a reading of 29.82? ✓

The change was ${}^-0.14$ inches.

Pages 380–381 Chapter Review

1. $-\frac{1}{3}$ 3. $-1\frac{2}{5}$ 5. 10.49 7. $\frac{4}{9}$

9. $<$ 11. $>$ 13. $<$ 15. ${}^-2.2$

17. 3.69 19. ${}^-0.5$ 21. 4 23. ${}^-4.7$

25. ${}^-1.9$ 27. $\frac{1}{4}$ 29. $-\frac{5}{6}$ 31. $-\frac{3}{4}$

33. $\frac{1}{4}$ 35. ${}^-4\frac{5}{12}$ 37. $1\frac{7}{8}$ 39. $-\frac{1}{2}$

41. $1\frac{1}{4}$ 43. $-\frac{5}{8}$ 45. $\frac{5}{8}$ gal.

Page 382 Chapter Test

1. $5\frac{1}{3}$ 2. 7.03 3. $-\frac{5}{8}$ 4. $\frac{3}{8}$

5. $\frac{7}{8}$ 6. ${}^-8$ 7. 0.54 8. ${}^-15.54$

9. $-\frac{9}{10}$ 10. $\frac{7}{8}$ 11. $\frac{14}{15}$ 12. ${}^-2.9$

13. ${}^-14.1$ 14. 8.17 15. $2\frac{1}{3}$ 16. $-\frac{7}{10}$

17. $-\frac{1}{8}$ 18. $-\frac{4}{5}$ 19. 12.5 20. ${}^-2.5$

21. ${}^-1\frac{3}{8}$ 22. $\frac{7}{8}$ 23. 3.1 24. ${}^-1\frac{1}{3}$

25. $1\frac{3}{8}$ 26. 15.2 27. $\frac{3}{4}$

28. \$32.2 million 29. $-\frac{3}{4}$ mph

Pages 386–387 Section 12.1

1. Pos. **3.** Neg. **5.** Neg.
7. Pos. **9.** Neg. **11.** Neg.
13. 7.82 ***15.** $^{-}6.1125$ **17.** $^{-}0.4875$
19. 12.39 **21.** $^{-}8.484$ **23.** $^{-}59.4$ **25.** 1.1
***27.** $^{-}3.7$ **29.** $^{-}0.69$ **31.** $^{-}90$ **33.** 4.5
35. 17 **37.** $^{-}67.5$ ft **39.** $^{-}8.75$ ft
***41.** $^{-}39.508$ **43.** $^{-}23$ **45.** $^{-}4$
47. $^{-}13.896$ **49.** $^{-}43.43$ **51.** $^{-}14.9$
53. 5.64 **55.** $^{-}12.6$ **57.** $^{-}17.4$

**Model solutions:*

15.
$$\begin{array}{r} 0.125 \\ \times\, ^{-}48.9 \\ \hline 1125 \\ 1000 \\ 500 \\ \hline ^{-}6.1125 \end{array}$$

27.
$$\begin{array}{r} ^{-}3.7 \\ ^{-}2.7\overline{)9.9\,9} \\ 8\,1 \\ \hline 1\,8\,9 \\ 1\,8\,9 \\ \hline 0 \end{array}$$

41. $1.7 \times {}^{-}2.8 \times 8.3 = {}^{-}4.76 \times 8.3$
$= {}^{-}39.508$

Pages 388–389 Section 12.2

1. Divide by 4.1. **3.** Multiply by 6.
5. Multiply by $^{-}3.7$. **7.** Multiply by $^{-}4$.
***9.** 31.5 **11.** $^{-}57.6$ **13.** 0.6 **15.** $^{-}4$
17. $^{-}28.14$ **19.** 2.7 **21.** 20.21 **23.** 9
***25.** $\frac{n}{^{-}0.05} = 10$; $^{-}0.5$
27. $0.9x = 64.8$; 72 capsules
29. $\frac{^{-}2169.15}{3} = a$; $^{-}\$723.05$

**Model solutions:*

9. $\frac{x}{6.3} = 5$ *Check:* $\frac{x}{6.3} = 5$
$\frac{x}{6.3} \times 6.3 = 5 \times 6.3$ $\frac{31.5}{6.3} = 5$
$x = 31.5$ $5 = 5$ ✓

25. Let n = the number.
$\frac{n}{^{-}0.05} = 10$
$\frac{n}{^{-}0.05} \times {}^{-}0.05 = 10 \times {}^{-}0.05$
$n = {}^{-}0.5$
Check: Is $^{-}0.5 \div {}^{-}0.05 = 10$? ✓
The number is $^{-}0.5$.

Pages 390–391 Section 12.3

1. Pos. **3.** Neg. **5.** Neg. **7.** Pos.
9. Neg. **11.** Neg. **13.** Neg. **15.** Neg.
***17.** $-\frac{7}{12}$ **19.** $^{-}3\frac{1}{3}$ **21.** 7 **23.** $^{-}21$
25. 75 **27.** $^{-}21$ **29.** $^{-}1\frac{5}{16}$ **31.** $\frac{1}{3}$
33. $-\frac{7}{10}$ **35.** $\frac{1}{4}$ **37.** $-\frac{1}{15}$ **39.** $\frac{1}{5}$
***41.** $^{-}4\frac{4}{5}$ **43.** $\frac{1}{12}$ **45.** $\frac{3}{64}$

**Model solutions:*

17. $-\frac{\overset{1}{\cancel{2}}}{3} \times \frac{7}{\underset{4}{\cancel{8}}} = -\frac{7}{12}$

41. $-\frac{8}{3} + (-\frac{4}{5}) \div \frac{3}{8} = -\frac{8}{3} + (-\frac{4}{5}) \times \frac{8}{3}$
$= -\frac{8}{3} + (-\frac{32}{15})$
$= -\frac{40}{15} + (-\frac{32}{15})$
$= -\frac{\overset{24}{\cancel{72}}}{\underset{5}{\cancel{15}}} = {}^{-}4\frac{4}{5}$

Pages 392–393 Section 12.4

1. Pos. **3.** Neg. **5.** Neg. **7.** Neg.
9. Neg. **11.** Neg. **13.** Neg. **15.** Pos.
***17.** $^{-}9$ **19.** $2\frac{1}{3}$ **21.** $^{-}1\frac{4}{5}$ **23.** $^{-}1\frac{5}{13}$
25. $1\frac{4}{7}$ **27.** $^{-}5\frac{5}{8}$ **29.** $^{-}2\frac{3}{4}$ **31.** $-\frac{21}{88}$
33. $^{-}1\frac{7}{8}$ **35.** $^{-}1\frac{5}{9}$ **37.** $^{-}8\frac{1}{8}$ **39.** $23\frac{1}{2}$
41. $^{-}90\frac{17}{30}$ ***43.** $^{-}9\frac{3}{5}$

**Model solutions:*

17. $4\frac{1}{2} \div (-\frac{1}{2}) = \frac{9}{\underset{1}{\cancel{2}}} \times (-\frac{\overset{1}{\cancel{2}}}{1})$
$= -\frac{9}{1} = {}^{-}9$

43. $6\frac{2}{5} \div 3\frac{2}{3} \times {}^{-}5\frac{1}{2} = 6\frac{2}{5} \div \frac{11}{3} \times {}^{-}5\frac{1}{2}$
$= \frac{\overset{16}{\cancel{32}}}{5} \times \frac{3}{\underset{1}{\cancel{11}}} \times (-\frac{\overset{1}{\cancel{11}}}{\underset{1}{\cancel{2}}})$
$= -\frac{48}{5} = {}^{-}9\frac{3}{5}$

Page 394 Quick Quiz

1. $^{-}3.91$ **2.** $8\frac{1}{2}$ **3.** $^{-}20.52$ **4.** $^{-}250$
5. 2.13 **6.** 207 **7.** $^{-}8$ **8.** $\frac{8}{15}$
9. $^{-}9$ **10.** $^{-}3\frac{1}{2}$ **11.** $16\frac{7}{8}$ **12.** $^{-}1\frac{3}{4}$
13. $^{-}3\frac{1}{3}$ **14.** $^{-}5$ **15.** $^{-}3\frac{1}{6}$ **16.** $^{-}8.1$
17. $^{-}32$ **18.** 0.25

Page 396 Section 12.5

1. $\frac{5}{3}$ **3.** $-\frac{7}{4}$ or ${}^-1\frac{3}{4}$ **5.** $\frac{1}{7}$
7. $-\frac{1}{9}$ **9.** 1 **11.** 1 **13.** 1 **15.** 2
17. $-\frac{13}{4}$ or ${}^-3\frac{1}{4}$ **19.** $\frac{1}{17}$ **21.** $-\frac{3}{13}$
23. $\frac{2}{11}$ **25.** $-\frac{10}{63}$ **27.** $\frac{4}{51}$ **29.** 1

Pages 398-399 Section 12.6

1. Divide by $\frac{2}{3}$ or multiply by $\frac{3}{2}$.
3. Divide by $-\frac{3}{10}$ or multiply by $-\frac{10}{3}$.
5. Divide by $-\frac{5}{6}$ or multiply by $-\frac{6}{5}$.
7. Multiply by 3. **9.** Multiply by ${}^-6$.
***11.** $\frac{3}{4}$ **13.** 7 **15.** ${}^-8\frac{3}{4}$ **17.** $-\frac{3}{10}$
19. ${}^-54$ **21.** $-\frac{10}{31}$ **23.** ${}^-18$ **25.** $\frac{1}{15}$
27. $\frac{9}{40}$ **29.** ${}^-1\frac{1}{5}$ **31.** ${}^-12\frac{2}{3}$ **33.** ${}^-72$
35. 0 **37.** $-\frac{4}{5}n = -12; 15$
39. $\frac{n}{6} = -\frac{2}{3}; {}^-4$

**Model solution:*

11.
$$-\frac{2}{5} = -\frac{8}{15}t$$
$$-\frac{2}{5} \div \left(-\frac{8}{15}\right) = -\frac{8}{15}t \div \left(-\frac{8}{15}\right)$$
$$-\frac{\cancel{2}^{1}}{\cancel{5}_{1}} \times \left(-\frac{\cancel{15}^{3}}{\cancel{8}_{4}}\right) = t$$
$$\frac{3}{4} = t$$

Check:
$$-\frac{2}{5} = -\frac{8}{15}t$$
$$-\frac{2}{5} = -\frac{\cancel{8}^{2}}{\cancel{15}_{5}}\left(\frac{\cancel{3}^{1}}{\cancel{4}_{1}}\right)$$
$$-\frac{2}{5} = -\frac{2}{5}\ \checkmark$$

Page 402 Section 12.7

1. Add ${}^-0.4$ to each side; divide each side by 2.6.
3. Change $3.6t - 2.4$ to $3.6t + {}^-2.4$; add 2.4 to each side; divide each side by 3.6.
5. Add $-\frac{6}{5}$ to each side; divide each side by $-\frac{2}{5}$.
***7.** 2 **9.** ${}^-6$ **11.** ${}^-2.4$ **13.** $-\frac{11}{24}$ **15.** $\frac{25}{36}$
17. ${}^-16.8$ **19.** ${}^-34.2$ **21.** ${}^-6.232$ **23.** 0
25. 1.26 **27.** $4\frac{1}{14}$ **29.** ${}^-1$ **31.** $\frac{1}{6}$ **33.** $-\frac{3}{4}$

**Model solution:*

7.
$$2.7m + 0.4 = 5.8$$
$$2.7m + 0.4 + {}^-0.4 = 5.8 + {}^-0.4$$
$$2.7m = 5.4$$
$$\frac{2.7m}{2.7} = \frac{5.4}{2.7}$$
$$m = \frac{\cancel{54}^{2}}{\cancel{27}_{1}}$$
$$m = 2$$

Check:
$$2.7m + 0.4 = 5.8$$
$$2.7(2) + 0.4 = 5.8$$
$$5.4 + 0.4 = 5.8$$
$$5.8 = 5.8\ \checkmark$$

Page 403 Quick Quiz

1. $\frac{5}{2}$ or $2\frac{1}{2}$ **2.** $-\frac{8}{7}$ or ${}^-1\frac{1}{7}$ **3.** $\frac{1}{17}$
4. $-\frac{2}{9}$ **5.** $-\frac{15}{16}$ **6.** $1\frac{5}{7}$ **7.** $-\frac{3}{13}$
8. $2\frac{2}{3}$ **9.** ${}^-3.4$ **10.** $9\frac{1}{2}$

Page 405–407 Section 12.8

1. Multiply \$0.045 by 2.
3. Solve $1000(8.5) = 50w$.
5. $h = 0.4 \times n \times d^2$ ***7.** 13.2 **9.** 28
11. 100 **13.** 750 **15.** 12.5 hr **17.** 2
19. $1\frac{1}{3}$ **21.** 150 **23.** 38.4 **25.** 45 **27.** 8

**Model solution:*

7.
$$1000k = tw$$
$$1000k = 12 \times 1100$$
$$k = \frac{13200}{1000}$$
$$k = 13.2$$

Check: Is 1000×13.2 equal to 12×1100? ✓

Pages 409–410 Section 12.9

1. 1 **3.** 3 **5.** 1 **7.** ${}^-1$ **9.** ${}^-3$ **11.** ${}^-1$
13. 2 **15.** 1 **17.** Right **19.** 3.421×10^1
21. 5.9603×10^4 **23.** 6.08×10^2
25. 1.42×10^{-3} **27.** 2.5×10^{-1}
29. 3.04×10^{-2} **31.** 1.2×10^{18} kg
33. 2.76×10^9 mi; 4.6×10^9 mi

Pages 411–412 Chapter Review

1. ${}^-7.686$ **3.** ${}^-36.4$ **5.** 12.3 **7.** ${}^-8.6$
9. ${}^-22.4$ **11.** ${}^-0.6$ **13.** $-\frac{12}{35}$ **15.** $-\frac{1}{3}$

17. $-\frac{3}{4}$ **19.** $2\frac{5}{14}$ **21.** $^-10\frac{1}{8}$ **23.** $1\frac{1}{3}$
25. $\frac{11}{7}$ or $1\frac{4}{7}$ **27.** $\frac{3}{17}$ **29.** None **31.** $^-1\frac{1}{2}$
33. $^-1\frac{1}{5}$ **35.** $-\frac{5}{8}$ **37.** 1 **39.** $^-5$
41. $^-0.95$ **43.** 320 hr **45.** 3.002×10^2
47. 9.34×10^5 **49.** 9.842×10^{-3}

Page 413 Chapter Test

1. $-\frac{1}{2}$ **2.** $-\frac{21}{64}$ **3.** $^-3\frac{1}{8}$ **4.** $5\frac{5}{32}$
5. 36.585 **6.** 59.86 **7.** $\frac{16}{21}$ **8.** $-\frac{5}{18}$
9. $-\frac{4}{5}$ **10.** $-\frac{9}{17}$ **11.** $^-3.3$ **12.** 14
13. $-\frac{1}{2}$ **14.** $^-26$ **15.** $-\frac{7}{32}$ **16.** 1
17. 1 **18.** 1 **19.** $\frac{2}{27}$ **20.** $^-1.5$
21. $^-45.26$ **22.** $5\frac{1}{3}$ **23.** $-\frac{1}{18}$ **24.** $-\frac{8}{9}$
25. $^-33.85$ **26.** 5.3 **27.** 1500 watts
28. $4\frac{2}{5}$ horsepower **29.** 6.73×10^4
30. 9.804×10^2 **31.** 3.6×10^{-4}

Page 418 Section 13.1

1. 1, $^-1$ **3.** 5, $^-5$ **5.** 2, $^-2$
7. 4, $^-4$ **9.** 8, $^-8$ **11.** 9, $^-9$
13. 2 **15.** $^-2$ **17.** 6 **19.** $^-7$
21. 8 **23.** $^-5$ **25.** 9 **27.** 12

Page 421 Section 13.2

1. Find 7 in the n-column. Read $\sqrt{7}$ in the $\sqrt{n}$-column.
3. Find 142 in the n-column. Read $\sqrt{142}$ in the $\sqrt{n}$-column.
5. Find 87 in the n-column. Read 87^2 in the n^2-column.
7. 4.24 **9.** 9.70 **11.** 11.31 **13.** 196
15. 4,761 **17.** 11,664 **19.** 5.39 **21.** 7.94
23. 11.05 **25. a.** 1.41 **b.** 1.9881
27. a. 3.87 **b.** 14.9769
29. a. 7.48 **b.** 55.9504

Pages 424–425 Section 13.3

1. 13 **3.** 24 **5.** 29 **7.** 51
9. $\sqrt{9} \times \sqrt{2}$ **11.** $\sqrt{25} \times \sqrt{3}$
13. $\sqrt{100} \times \sqrt{3}$ **15.** $\sqrt{9} \times \sqrt{11}$
17. $\sqrt{81} \times \sqrt{10}$ **19.** $\sqrt{36} \times \sqrt{10}$
21. $3 \times \sqrt{2}$ **23.** $5 \times \sqrt{3}$ **25.** $10 \times \sqrt{3}$
27. $3 \times \sqrt{11}$ **29.** $9 \times \sqrt{10}$ **31.** $6 \times \sqrt{10}$
***33.** 25.28 **35.** 31.6 **37.** 38.7
39. 13.74 **41.** 26.5 **43.** 12.96
45. 22.12 **47.** 25.11

**Model solution:*

33.
$$\sqrt{640} = \sqrt{64 \times 10} = \sqrt{64} \times \sqrt{10} \approx 8 \times 3.16 \approx 25.28$$

Page 425 Quick Quiz

1. 5 **2.** 7 **3.** 9 **4.** 6, $^-6$ **5.** 10, $^-10$
6. 3, $^-3$ **7.** 3.32 **8.** 529 **9.** 11.79
10. 17.3 **11.** 18.96 **12.** 12.69

Page 426–427 Section 13.4

1. $(\frac{4}{10})^2$ **3.** $(\frac{1}{2})^2$ **5.** $(\frac{8}{9})^2$ **7.** $(\frac{7}{8})^2$
9. $\frac{9}{100}$ **11.** $\frac{16}{100}$ **13.** $\frac{25}{100}$ **15.** $\frac{1}{100}$
***17.** $\frac{3}{5}$ **19.** $\frac{5}{8}$ **21.** $\frac{1}{2}$ **23.** $\frac{3}{4}$
***25.** 0.3 **27.** 0.2 **29.** 0.6 **31.** 0.06

**Model solutions:*

17. $$\sqrt{\frac{9}{25}} = \frac{\sqrt{9}}{\sqrt{25}} = \frac{3}{5}$$

25. $$\sqrt{0.09} = \sqrt{\frac{9}{100}} = \frac{\sqrt{9}}{\sqrt{100}} = \frac{3}{10} = 0.3$$

Page 429 Section 13.5

1. Take the square root of each side.
3. Add $^-9$ to each side. Take the square root of each side.
5. Add $^-2$ to each side. Take the square root of each side.
***7.** $x = 3$ **9.** $x \approx 6.48$ **11.** $x \approx 5.74$
13. $x = 8$ **15.** $x = 13$ **17.** 100 mi
19. 141 mi **21.** 160 mi

**Model solution:*

7. $x^2 = 9$, $\sqrt{x^2} = \sqrt{9}$, $x = 3$

Check: $x^2 = 9$, $3^2 = 9$, $9 = 9$ ✓

Page 433–434 Section 13.6

1. $c^2 = 3^2 + 4^2$

3. Add $^-9$ to each side. Take the square root of each side.
5. Add 144 and 25. Take the square root of each side.
7. Find 10^2 and 8^2. Add $^-64$ to each side. Take the square root of each side.

*9. 5 11. 17 13. 7 15. 9
17. 16 19. 20 21. Yes 23. Yes

Model solution:

9.
$$c^2 = a^2 + b^2 \qquad \textit{Check:}$$
$$c^2 = 3^2 + 4^2 \qquad c^2 = a^2 + b^2$$
$$c^2 = 9 + 16 \qquad 5^2 = 3^2 + 4^2$$
$$\sqrt{c^2} = \sqrt{25} \qquad 25 = 9 + 16$$
$$c = 5 \qquad 25 = 25 \checkmark$$

Page 435 Quick Quiz

1. $\frac{2}{7}$ 2. $\frac{5}{9}$ 3. $\frac{1}{10}$ 4. 0.4
5. 0.7 6. 0.3 7. 5 8. 6
9. 9 10. 15 11. 5 12. 6

Pages 437–438 Section 13.7

1. $c^2 = 28^2 + 45^2$ 3. $85^2 = 77^2 + b^2$
*5. 60 yd 7. 84.6 ft 9. 11.62 ft
11. 10.77 ft

Model solution:

5.
$$c^2 = a^2 + b^2$$
$$100^2 = a^2 + 80^2$$
$$10{,}000 = a^2 + 6400$$
$$10{,}000 + {}^-6400 = a^2 + 6400 + {}^-6400$$
$$\sqrt{3600} = \sqrt{a^2}$$
$$\sqrt{36} \times \sqrt{100} = a$$
$$60 = a$$

Check: Is $100^2 = 60^2 + 80^2$? ✓
The kite is 60 yd high.

Page 441 Section 13.8

1. t = time storm will last in hours.
d = diameter of storm in miles.
3. 5.20 hr *5. 8 sec 7. 10 cm
9. 12.64 ft

Model solution:

5.
$$s = 16t^2 \qquad \textit{Check: } \text{Is}$$
$$1024 = 16t^2 \qquad 1024 = 16 \times 8^2? \checkmark$$
$$\frac{1024}{16} = \frac{16t^2}{16}$$
$$\sqrt{64} = \sqrt{t^2}$$
$$8 = t$$

It took 8 sec to hit the water.

Pages 443–444 Chapter Review

1. 3, $^-3$ 3. 4, $^-4$ 5. 7, $^-7$
7. 1.41 9. 2.65 11. 5.10 13. 4.58
15. 9.80 17. 2,704 19. 14.1 21. 24.5
23. 18.96 25. $\frac{1}{2}$ 27. $\frac{7}{10}$ 29. 0.6
31. 7 33. 5.83 35. 17 37. 7
39. 85 m 41. 2 sec

Page 445 Chapter Test

1. 6 2. 9 3. $\frac{2}{3}$ 4. $\frac{4}{5}$ 5. 0.8
6. 0.9 7. 2.24 8. 2.83 9. 3.46
10. 16.92 11. 15.8 12. 26.5 13. 5
14. 6.08 15. 6 16. 7 17. 4.80
18. 5.66 19. 24 ft 20. 4100 m 21. 3 m

Pages 450–451 Section 14.1

1. $n + 1, n + 2$ 3. $n + 2, n + 4$
*5. $n + n + 1 = 65$; 32, 33
7. $x + 5x = 18$; 3 qt yellow, 15 qt red
9. $n + n + 1 + n + 2 = {}^-57$;
$^-20, {}^-19, {}^-18$
11. $x + x + x + 3 = 24$;
7 in., 7 in., 10 in.
13. $x + x + 3 = 15$; \$6, \$9
15. $x + x + x + 5.5 = 124$;
39.5 cm, 39.5 cm, 45 cm

Model solution:

5. Let n = one integer and
$n + 1$ = the next integer.
$$n + n + 1 = 65$$
$$2n + 1 = 65$$
$$2n = 64$$
$$n = 32 \text{ and } n + 1 = 33$$

Check: Are 32 and 33 consecutive integers? ✓ Is $32 + 33 = 65$? ✓
The integers are 32 and 33.

Pages 452–453 Section 14.2

1. a. How much he earned last month

13

b. Too little

3. a. The cost of both the camera and the lens **b.** Just enough

5. Not pos. **7.** \$267 ***9.** $^-\$340$

11. $18\frac{1}{4}$ in. **13.** \$410 **15.** \$15.80

******Model solution:*

9. Let c = the change in balance.

$$270 + c = {}^-70$$
$$c + 270 + {}^-270 = {}^-70 + {}^-270$$
$$c = {}^-340$$

Check: Does the balance of \$270 followed by a $^-\$340$ change give a balance of $^-\$70$? ✓

The change in balance was $^-\$340$.

Page 455 Section 14.3

1. Yes **3.** Yes **5.** Yes **7.** Yes
9. Yes **11.** Binomial **13.** Trinomial
15. Binomial **17.** Like **19.** Like
21. Unlike **23.** Unlike **25.** Unlike
27. Like **29.** Unlike **31.** Unlike
33. Like **35.** $2x + {}^-5$
37. $x^2 + {}^-3x + 2$ **39.** $8y^3 + {}^-y$

Pages 457–458 Section 14.4

1. 6 **3.** 6 **5.** $^-2$ **7.** 2.9
9. b, c ***11.** *2, 7, 12; *0, 7, 14; no
13. 0, 4, 16; 0, 4, 64; no
15. 0, $^-4$, $^-8$; 0, $^-4$, $^-8$; yes
17. 0, $^-2$, $^-4$; 0, $^-2$, $^-4$; yes
***19.** $11x$ **21.** ^-3y **23.** $^-12y^2$
25. $8m^2n$ **27.** $^-4y^2 + 8y$ **29.** $12n + 10$
31. ^-4y **33.** $8x^2$ **35.** $8.2x$
37. $\frac{1}{2}m^2$ **39.** $7x$ **41.** ^-3ab

******Model solutions:*

11. For $x = 0$

$5x + 2$	$7x$
$5(\mathbf{0}) + 2$	$7(\mathbf{0})$
$0 + 2$	0
2	

19. $8x + 3x$
$(8 + 3)x$
$11x$

Page 460 Section 14.5

1. b **3.** 6 **5.** 7 **7.** 6 **9.** 6 **11.** 2
***13.** a^7 **15.** y^{14} ***17.** $6x$ **19.** $^-30x^2$
21. $^-4x^4$ **23.** $200x^2$ **25.** $^-12m^4$
27. $^-z^6$ **29.** $^-18x^6$ **31.** $0.02c^3d^4$

******Model solutions:*

13. $a^5 \cdot a^2 = a^{5+2} = a^7$

17. $(2x)3 = (2 \cdot 3) \cdot x = 6x$

Page 461 Quick Quiz

1. \$4 and \$6 **2.** Unlike **3.** Like
4. Unlike **5.** $11y$ **6.** ^-20a **7.** ^-3n
8. $14ab$ **9.** $^-12y^2$ **10.** m^6 **11.** x^5
12. $15m^2$ **13.** $^-16n^3$ **14.** $16x^7$ **15.** $^-32x^2$

Page 463 Section 14.6

1. d **3.** a **5.** a, b **7.** 8 **9.** 2
***11.** $9ab^4 + a^2b^3$ **13.** $^-9x^2 + 15xy$
15. $^-15a^2 - 21ab$ or $^-15a^2 + {}^-21ab$ (*Note:* Either answer is acceptable; only the first form will be given from now on.)
17. $18x^3y + 6xy^2$ **19.** $110rs^3 - 80s^2$
21. $4m^2 + 2\frac{1}{2}m$ **23.** $0.68x^2 + 0.3x$

******Model solution:*

11. $b^3(9ab + a^2) = b^3 \cdot 9ab + b^3 \cdot a^2 = 9ab^4 + a^2b^3$

Pages 466–467 Section 14.7

1. x **3.** 41
5. A: x^2, B: $5x$, C: $2x$, D: 10; $x^2 + 7x + 10$
***7.** $x^2 + 7x + 10$ **9.** $x^3 + 4x^2 + x + 4$
11. $2y^2 + 13y + 6$
13. $x^2y - 3xy + x - 3$
15. $6x^2 + 8xy - 30y^2$
17. $10x^4 + 11x^2y - 6y^2$
19. $16m^4 - 8m^2 + 1$ **21.** $\frac{1}{4}x^2 + 3x + 8$
23. $0.33m^2 + 7.5m + 18$

******Model solution:*

7. $(x + 2)(x + 5)$
$= (x + 2)x + (x + 2)5$
$= x^2 + 2x + 5x + 10$
$= x^2 + 7x + 10$

Page 469 Section 14.8

1. 12 **3.** 11 **5.** $5x + 9$ **7.** $3y - 1$
9. $13a + 16b$ ***11.** $4a + 2b + 7c$
13. $2m - 2n + 2p$ **15.** $7x^2y - 9xy + 24$
17. $a + 1$ **19.** $-\frac{4}{5}x + \frac{2}{5}$
21. $2.1m - 3.1$ **23.** $18x^2 + 17x + 3$

**Model solution:*

11.
$$\begin{array}{r} 2a + 3b + 3c \\ 2a + {}^{-}1b + 4c \\ \hline 4a + 2b + 7c \end{array}$$

Pages 471–472 Section 14.9

1. $^{-}7x$ **3.** $^{-}2x - 1$
5. $^{-}9y^2 - 2y - 3$ **7.** $2x$ **9.** $^{-}2a$
11. $19a$ **13.** $^{-}6a$ ***15.** $8x - 1$
17. $10a - 1$ **19.** $7y - 5$
21. $^{-}7z^2 + 7$ **23.** $2m^2 + 16m + 3$
25. $6x^2 + 11x + 12$
27. $^{-}7a^2 + 22a - 17$

**Model solution:*

15.
$$\begin{array}{r} 3x + 1 \\ -({}^{-}5x + 2) \\ \hline \end{array} \qquad \begin{array}{r} 3x + 1 \\ +(5x - 2) \\ \hline 8x - 1 \end{array}$$

Page 474 Section 14.10

1. 3 **3.** 4 **5.** 4 **7.** $4x$
***9.** y^2 **11.** 1 **13.** $2x^2$ **15.** $4x^3$
17. $9y^2$ **19.** $^{-}3abc$ ***21.** $4a^2 + 2a$
23. $c^4 + c$ **25.** $9x^2 - 8x - 12$
27. $^{-}6x^2y - 3xy + 4$

**Model solutions:*

9. $\frac{y^6}{y^4} = y^{6-4} = y^2$ *Check:* $y^2 \cdot y^4 = y^6$ ✓

Pages 475–476 Chapter Review

1. $x + x + 12 = 40$; \$14 and \$26
3. No **5.** No **7.** $7y$ **9.** $^{-}2xy^2$
11. x^8 **13.** $^{-}6x^4$ **15.** $^{-}10x^2 + 2x$
17. $15x^3 - 20x^2$ **19.** $6x^2 + 16x + 8$
21. $24z^2 - 47z + 20$ **23.** $11x + 10$
25. $5x^2 - x + 11$ **27.** $^{-}17y^2 - 3y + 9$
29. $^{-}18y$ **31.** $m^2 - 6m + 4$
33. $^{-}3$ **35.** $9x^2 + 4x + 7$

Page 477 Chapter Test

1. $x + x + 20 = 120$; \$70 and \$50
2. $^{-}9y^2$ **3.** $^{-}17a$ **4.** $7y - 4$
5. $19x^2 + 3x - 1$ **6.** a^8 **7.** $21m^5$
8. $20x^2 - 35x$ **9.** $18y^3 - 6y^2$
10. $y^2 + 9y + 14$ **11.** $6x^2 - 5x - 4$
12. $17y$ **13.** $^{-}12x + 9$ **14.** $5x^2$
15. $9m^3$ **16.** $6a^2 - 4a + 5$

Pages 481–483 Section 15.1

1. T **3.** 3 **5.** 7 **7.** 5 9 **9.** 17 21

Ex. 11–17: Tally columns are omitted.

11.

No.	Freq.
5	1
6	1
7	3
8	5
9	1
Total	11

13.

No.	Freq.
17	3
18	2
19	1
20	1
21	3
Total	10

15.

Rating	Freq.
$^{-}2$	3
$^{-}1$	5
0	17
1	17
2	8
Total	50

17.

Mi gal.	Freq.
20	10
21	6
22	7
23	5
24	9
25	4
26	5
27	0
28	4
Total	50

Pages 485–486 Section 15.2

1. Buses 35 and 42 **3.** Bus 15
5. Buses 35 and 42
7. Buses 22, 35, and 42 **9.** 2 hours
11. 5 students **13.** 9 students
15.

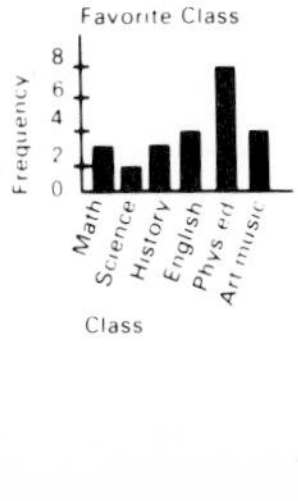

14

Pages 488–489 Section 15.3

1. Median 3. 4 5. 7 7. 12
9. 27 11. 85 13. 6 15. 3.8
17. 247.5 19. 18.5 21. 2:33

Pages 491–492 Section 15.4

1. 4 3. 30 *5. 6 7. 3.5
9. 13.6 or 14 11. $12.558 or $12.56
13. 19.7 yd or 20 yd *15. 2054 points
17. 3150.4 naut. mi 19. Felicia's (8 to 7)

Page 493 Quick Quiz

1. 1–8 2. 6 3. 5.5

4.

No.	Freq.
10	3
11	1
12	5
13	4
14	5
15	2
Total	20

5.

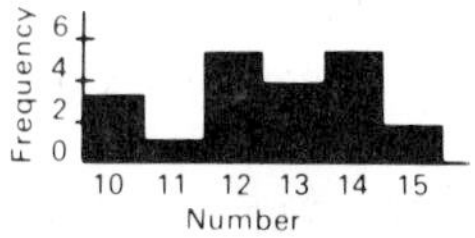

6. 21
7. 25
8. 10

Pages 497–498 Section 15.5

1. Theoretical 3. $\frac{1}{2}$ or 0.5 5. $\frac{1}{5}$ or 0.2
7. 0 9. a. $\frac{17}{100}$ b. $\frac{1}{6}$
11. a. $\frac{3}{20}$ b. $\frac{1}{6}$ 13. a. $\frac{4}{25}$ b. $\frac{1}{6}$
15. a. 0 b. 0 *17. a. 0.4 b. 0.375
19. a. 0.25 b. 0.25 21. a. 0 b. 0
23. $\frac{1}{52}$ 25. $\frac{1}{4}$ 27. $\frac{1}{13}$ 29. $\frac{1}{26}$

**Model solution:*

17. a. $\frac{32}{80} = 0.4$ b. $\frac{3}{8} = 0.375$

Page 500 Section 15.6

1. heads, tails 3. 12

5.

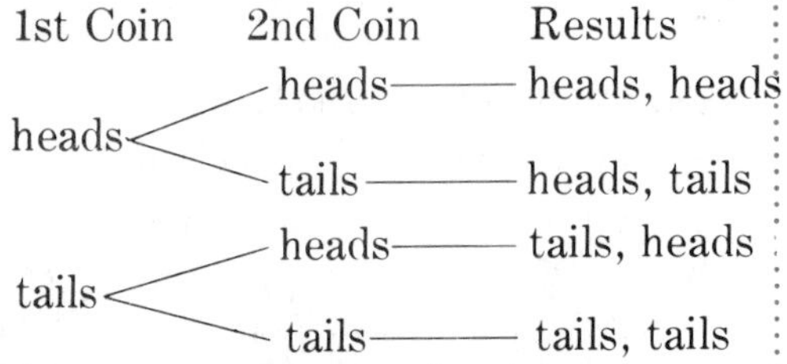

7. $\frac{1}{4}$ 9. $\frac{2}{4}$ or $\frac{1}{2}$

Pages 501–503 Section 15.7

1. Cannot 3. $\frac{4}{5}$ 5. Yes 7. No
*9. $\frac{2}{3}$ 11. $\frac{7}{10}$ 13. 0.8 15. $\frac{1}{2}$ 17. $\frac{1}{6}$
*19. $\frac{2}{3}$ 21. $\frac{3}{4}$ 23. $\frac{1}{4}$ 25. 0.3 27. 0.2
29. 0.5 31. 0.5 33. $\frac{1}{2}$ 35. $\frac{7}{26}$ 37. $\frac{4}{13}$

**Model solutions:*

9. $\frac{1}{3} + \frac{1}{3} = \frac{2}{3}$

19. $\frac{6}{12} + \frac{2}{12} = \frac{\cancel{8}^{2}}{\cancel{12}_{3}} = \frac{2}{3}$

Pages 505–506 Section 15.8

1. Does not 3. 12 5. $\frac{1}{12}$ 7. $\frac{1}{2}$
*9. $\frac{1}{9}$ 11. $\frac{1}{8}$ 13. 0.464 *15. $\frac{1}{12}$ 17. $\frac{1}{6}$
19. $\frac{1}{12}$ 21. $\frac{1}{36}$ 23. $\frac{1}{12}$ 25. $\frac{1}{4}$ 27. $\frac{1}{4}$

**Model solutions:*

9. $\frac{1}{3} \times \frac{1}{3} = \frac{1}{9}$

15. $\frac{\cancel{3}^{1}}{\cancel{6}_{2}} \times \frac{1}{6} = \frac{1}{12}$

Pages 508–509 Chapter Review

1. 1–10

3.

No.	Freq.
6	5
7	2
8	6
9	8
10	4
Total	25

5. 9 7. 13
9. 14 11. 4.1
13. $\frac{1}{2}$ 15. 0
17. 0.35 19. add
21. $\frac{3}{4}$ 23. multiply 25. $\frac{2}{5}$ 27. $\frac{1}{6}$

Page 510 Chapter Test

1. 11–16 2. 12 3. 13

4.

No.	Freq.
15	5
16	2
17	3
18	6
19	2
20	1
21	1
Total	20

5.

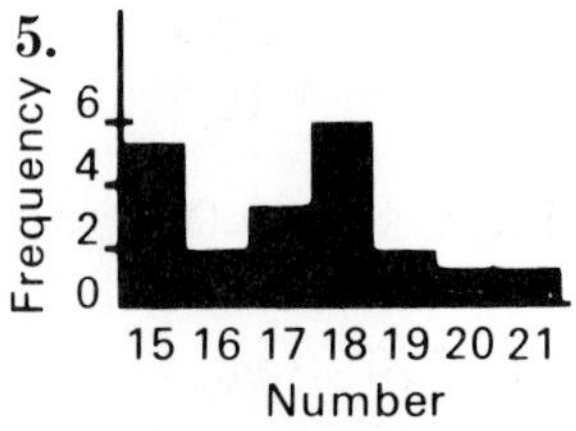

6. 34 7. 28
8. 8
9. 300 points
10. 0.6 11. 0.3 12. 0.1 13. 0.9

15